FREDERICK W. BYRON, JR., *University of Massachusetts*
ROBERT W. FULLER, *Trinity College, Hartford*

MATHEMATICS OF CLASSICAL AND QUANTUM PHYSICS

VOLUME TWO

ADDISON-WESLEY PUBLISHING COMPANY
Reading, Massachusetts
Menlo Park, California · London · Amsterdam · Don Mills, Ontario · Sydney

This book is in the
ADDISON-WESLEY SERIES IN ADVANCED PHYSICS

Consulting Editor: Morton Hamermesh

ISBN 0-201-00746-0
DEFGHIJKLM-HA-79876

To Edith and Ann

PREFACE

This book is designed as a companion to the graduate level physics texts on classical mechanics, electricity, magnetism, and quantum mechanics. It grows out of a course given at Columbia University and taken by virtually all first year graduate students as a fourth basic course, thereby eliminating the need to cover this mathematical material in a piecemeal fashion within the physics courses. The two volumes into which the book is divided correspond roughly to the two semesters of the full-year course. The consolidation of the mathematics needed for graduate physics into a single course permits a unified treatment applicable to many branches of physics. At the same time the fragments of mathematical knowledge possesed by the student can be pulled together and organized in a way that is especially relevant to physics. The central unifying theme about which this book is organized is the concept of a *vector space*. To demonstrate the role of mathematics in physics, we have included numerous physical applications in the body of the text, as well as many problems of a physical nature.

Although the book is designed as a textbook to complement the basic physics courses, it aims at something more than just equipping the physicist with the mathematical techniques he needs in courses. The mathematics used in physics has changed greatly in the last forty years. It is certain to change even more rapidly during the working lifetime of physicists being educated today. Thus, the physicist must have an acquaintance with abstract mathematics if he is to keep up with his own field as the mathematical language in which it is expressed changes. It is one of the purposes of this book to introduce the physicist to the language and the style of mathematics as well as the content of those particular subjects which have contemporary relevance in physics.

The book is essentially self-contained, assuming only the standard under-graduate preparation in physics and mathematics; that is, intermediate mechanics, electricity and magnetism, introductory quantum mechanics, advanced calculus and differential equations. The level of mathematical rigor is generally comparable to that typical of mathematical texts, but not uniformly so. The degree of rigor and abstraction varies with the subject. The topics treated are of varied subtlety and mathematical sophistication, and a logical completeness that is illuminating in one topic would be tedious in another.

While it is certainly true that one does not need to be able to follow the proof of Weierstrass's theorem or the Cauchy–Goursat theorem in order to be able to compute Fourier coefficients or perform residue integrals, we feel that the student who has studied these proofs will stand a better chance of growing mathematically *after* his formal coursework has ended. No reference work, let alone a text, can cover all the mathematical results that a student will need. What *is* perhaps possible, is to generate in the student the confidence that he can find what he needs in the mathematical literature, and that he can understand it and use it. It is our aim to treat the limited number of subjects we do treat in enough detail so that after reading this book physics students will not hesitate to make direct use of the mathematical literature in their research.

The backbone of the book—the theory of vector spaces—is in Chapters 3, 4, and 5. Our presentation of this material has been greatly influenced by P. R. Halmos's text, *Finite-Dimensional Vector Spaces.* A generation of theoretical physicists has learned its vector space theory from this book. Halmos's organization of the theory of vector spaces has become so second-nature that it is impossible to acknowledge adequately his influence.

Chapters 1 and 2 are devoted primarily to the mathematics of classical physics. Chapter 1 is designed both as a review of well-known things and as an introduction of things to come. Vectors are treated in their familiar three-dimensional setting, while notation and terminology are introduced, preparing the way for subsequent generalization to abstract vectors in a vector space. In Chapter 2 we detour slightly in order to cover the mathematics of classical mechanics and develop the variational concepts which we shall use later. Chapters 3 and 4 cover the theory of finite dimensional vector spaces and operators in a way that leads, without need for subsequent revision, to infinite dimensional vector spaces (Hilbert space)—the mathematical setting of quantum mechanics. Hilbert space, the subject of Chapter 5, also provides a very convenient and unifying framework for the discussion of many of the special functions of mathematical physics. Chapter 6 on analytic function theory marks an interlude in which we establish techniques and results that are required in all branches of mathematical physics. The theme of vector spaces is interrupted in this chapter, but the relevance to physics does not diminish. Then in Chapters 7, 8, and 9 we introduce the student to several of the most important techniques of theoretical physics—the Green's function method of solving differential and partial differential equations and the theory of integral equations. Finally, in Chapter 10 we give an introduction to a subject of ever increasing importance in physics—the theory of groups.

A special effort has been made to make the problems a useful adjunct to the text. We believe that only through a concerted attack on interesting problems can a student really "learn" any subject, so we have tried to provide a large selection of problems at the end of each chapter, some illustrating or extending mathematical points, others stressing physical applications of techniques developed in the text. In the later chapters of the book, some rather significant results are left as problems or even as a programmed series of problems, on the theory that as the student develops confidence and sophistication in the early chapters he will be able, with a few hints, to obtain some nontrivial results for himself.

The text may easily be adapted for a one-semester course at the graduate (or advanced undergraduate) level by omitting certain chapters of the instructor's choosing. For example, a one-semester course could be based on Volume 1. Another possibility, and one essentially used by one of the authors at the University of California at Berkeley, is to give a semester course based on the material in Chapters 3, 4, 5, and 10. On the other hand, a one-semester course in advanced mathematical methods in physics could be constructed from Volume II.

Certain sections within a chapter which are difficult and inessential to most of the rest of the book are marked with an asterisk.

In writing a book of this kind one's debts proliferate in all directions. In addition to the book of Halmos, we have been influenced by Courant–Hilbert's treatment of, and T. D. Lee's lecture notes on, Hilbert space, Riesz and Nagy's treatment of integral equations, and M. Hamermesh's book, *Group Theory*.

A special debt of gratitude is owed to R. Friedberg whose comments on the material have been extremely helpful. In particular, the presentation of Section 5.10 is based on his lecture notes.

Parts of the manuscript have also been read and taught by Ann L. Fuller, and her comments have improved it greatly. Richard Haglund and Steven Lundeen read and commented on the manuscript. Their painstaking work has removed many blemishes, and we thank them most sincerely.

Much of this book appeared in the form of lecture notes at Columbia University. Thanks are owed to the many students there, and elsewhere, who pointed out errors, or otherwise helped to improve the manuscript. Also, the enthusiasm of the students studying this material at Berkeley provided important encouragement.

While all the above named people have helped us to improve the manuscript, we alone are responsible for the errors and inadequacies that remain. We will be grateful if readers will bring errors to our attention so corrections can be made in subsequent printings.

One of us (FWB) held an Alfred P. Sloan Fellowship during much of the period of the writing; he gratefully thanks Professors M. Demeur and C. J. Joachain for their hospitality at the Université Libre de Bruxelles. The other author (RWF) would like to thank R. A. Rosenbaum of Wesleyan University, the University's Center for Advanced Studies, and its director, Paul Horgan, for their hospitality during the course of much of the work. We would also like to thank F. J. Milford and Battelle Memorial Institute's Seattle Research Center for providing support that facilitated the completion of the work.

Many of the practical problems of producing the manuscript were alleviated by the valued assistance of Rae Figliolina, Cheryl Gruger, Barbara Hollisi, and Barbara Satton.

Amherst, Mass.   F.W.B., Jr.
Hartford, Conn.   R.W.F.
January 1969

CONTENTS

CHAPTER 6

ELEMENTS AND APPLICATIONS OF THE THEORY OF ANALYTIC FUNCTIONS

INTRODUCTION

The role played by the theory of analytic functions in physics has changed considerably over the past few decades. It no longer suffices to be able to work out residue integrals; a deeper understanding of the mathematical ideas has become essential if one wants to follow current applications to physical theory. Therefore the emphasis here will be on introducing the mathematical concepts and the logical structure of the theory of analytic functions. Assuming only that the reader is familiar with the properties of complex numbers, we aim to present a self-contained account of this theory in a way that prepares one to cope with modern applications of the theory as well as those of the past.

"Imaginary" numbers were discovered in the Middle Ages in the search for a general solution of quadratic equations. It is clear from the name given them that they were regarded with suspicion. Gauss, in his doctoral thesis of 1799, gave the now familiar geometrical representation of complex numbers, and thus helped to dispel some of the mystery about them. In this century, the trend has been toward defining complex numbers as abstract symbols subject to certain formal rules of manipulation. Thus complex numbers never have taken on the "earthy" qualities of real numbers. In fact, more nearly the opposite has occurred: we have come to view real numbers abstractly as symbols obeying their own set of axioms, just like complex numbers. We now speak of *number fields*: the real field and the complex field. The axioms which define a field were stated in Chapter 3 on vector spaces.

The theory of complex numbers can be developed by viewing them as ordered pairs of real numbers, written (x, y). Let (a, b) and (c, d) be two different complex numbers, and let K be a real number. Then we define addition, multiplication of a real and a complex number, and multiplication of two complex numbers by the following rules:

1. $(a, b) + (c, d) = (a + b, c + d)$,
2. $K \cdot (a, b) = (Ka, Kb)$,
3. $(a, b) \cdot (c, d) = (ac - bd, bc + ad)$.

From these definitions, we see that the set of all complex numbers—the complex plane—has the same mathematical structure as the set of all vectors in a plane.

This approach is followed in Landau's *Foundations of Analysis,* in which the various number systems are built up logically from Peano's five axioms; the imaginary number i is never mentioned. However, if we write the ordered pair (a, b) as $a + ib$, where $i^2 = -1$, then the above rule of complex-number multiplication is obeyed if we simply multiply out the product $(a + ib)(c + id)$ according to the usual rules of multiplication of reals. The introduction of the symbol i subsumes the ordering aspect of the ordered pair of real numbers, while extending the formal rules of arithmetic from real to complex numbers.

From the complex numbers constructed as ordered pairs of reals, where $(a, b) = a + ib$, it is possible to generalize to hypercomplex numbers of three or more components, for example $(a, b, c) = a + ib + kc$. The four-component quaternions, a type of hypercomplex number which satisfies all the rules of arithmetic except the commutative law of multiplication, are useful in dealing with rotations of a rigid body. The four 4×4 Dirac matrices, $\gamma_i (i = 1, 2, 3, 4)$, form a set of hypercomplex numbers which satisfy the anticommutative relations

$$\gamma_i \gamma_j + \gamma_j \gamma_i = 2\delta_{ij} .$$

It can be shown that no matter how we define addition and multiplication for these hypercomplex numbers, it is impossible to retain all the usual rules of arithmetic. As Weyl points out, the complex numbers form a natural boundary for the extension of the number concept in this respect.

6.1 ANALYTIC FUNCTIONS—THE CAUCHY-RIEMANN CONDITIONS

If to each complex number z in a certain domain there corresponds another complex number w, then w is a function of the complex variable z: $w = f(z)$. If the correspondence is one to one, we can view this as a mapping from one plane (or part of it), the z-plane, to another, the w-plane. The complex functions thus defined are equivalent to ordered pairs of real functions of two variables, because w is a complex number depending on $z = x + iy$ and therefore can be written in the form

$$w(z) = u(x, y) + iv(x, y) .$$

However, this class of functions is too general for our purposes. We are interested only in functions which are differentiable with respect to the complex variable z—a restriction which is much stronger than the condition that u and v be differentiable with respect to x and y. Therefore one of our first tasks in the study of complex function theory will be to determine the necessary and sufficient conditions for a complex function to have a derivative with respect to the complex variable z. Single-valued functions of a complex variable which have derivatives throughout a region of the complex plane are called *analytic* functions. We shall restrict our attention to this special class of complex functions.

Two examples of complex functions (both written in the form $w = u + iv$) are

1. $w = z^* = x - iy$,
2. $w = z^2 = (x + iy)^2 = x^2 - y^2 + i2xy$.

Presently, we shall show that (1) is not an analytic function, but that (2) is analytic everywhere in the complex plane; i.e., its derivative exists at all points.

Before stating exactly what is meant by the derivative of a function of a complex variable, we must have a notion of *continuity* for these functions.

In the definition that follows, mention is made of the *absolute value* of a complex number, denoted by $|z|$. The reader will recall that $|z| \equiv (zz^*)^{1/2} = (x^2 + y^2)^{1/2}$. The absolute value is sometimes called the *modulus*.

Definition. A complex function $w = f(z)$ is continuous at the point z_0 if, given any $\epsilon > 0$, there exists a δ such that $|f(z) - f(z_0)| < \epsilon$, when $|z - z_0| < \delta$, or $f(z)$ is continuous at z_0 if

$$\lim_{z \to z_0} f(z) = f(z_0) .$$

This definition is formally exactly like the definition of continuity for real functions of a real variable. However, here the absolute value signs mean that whenever z lies within a *circle* of radius δ centered at z_0 in the complex z-plane, then $f(z)$ lies within a *circle* of radius ϵ centered at $f(z_0)$ in the complex w-plane. If $f(z) = u(x, y) + iv(x, y)$, then $f(z)$ is continuous at $z_0 = x_0 + iy_0$ if u and v are continuous at (x_0, y_0).

From the class of single-valued, continuous complex functions, we now want to select those that can be differentiated. Patterning the definition of a derivative after that of real analysis, we have

Definition. $f(z)$ is differentiable at the point z_0 if the limit

$$\lim_{z \to z_0} \frac{f(z) - f(z_0)}{z - z_0} = \lim_{\Delta z \to 0} \frac{\Delta f}{\Delta z}$$

exists. We shall denote this limit, the derivative of $f(z)$ at z_0, by $f'(z_0)$.

A very important feature of the limits that occur in the definitions of continuity and the derivative is that z may approach z_0 from *any direction* on the plane. When we say the limit exists, we therefore mean that the same number must result from the limiting process regardless of how the limit is taken. This is also true in real analysis, but in that case there are only two possible directions of approach in taking the limit: from the left or the right on the real line. In real analysis, the limiting process is one-dimensional; in complex analysis, it is two-dimensional.

The equation that defines the derivative means that given any $\epsilon > 0$, there exists a δ such that

$$\left| f'(z) - \frac{f(z) - f(z_0)}{z - z_0} \right| < \epsilon$$

provided $|z - z_0| < \delta$. The requirement that the ratio $[f(z) - f(z_0)]/(z - z_0)$ always tends to the same limiting value, no matter along what path z approaches z_0, is an extremely exacting condition. The theory of analytic functions contains a number of amazing theorems, and they all result from this stringent initial requirement that the functions possess "isotropic" derivatives.

A single-valued function of z is said to be *analytic* (or *regular*) at a point z_0 if it has a derivative at z_0 and at all points in some neighborhood z_0. Thus a slight distinction is drawn between differentiability and analyticity. It pays to do this, because although there exist functions which have derivatives at certain points, or even along certain curves, no interesting results can be obtained unless functions are differentiable throughout a region, i.e., unless they are analytic. Thus if we say a function is analytic on a curve, we mean that it has a derivative at all points in a two-dimensional strip containing the curve. If a function is not analytic at a point or on a curve, we say it is *singular* there.

We shall now examine the two complex functions mentioned earlier for differentiability and analyticity. We write the derivative at z_0 in the form

$$f'(z_0) = \lim_{\Delta z \to 0} \frac{f(z_0 + \Delta z) - f(z_0)}{\Delta z} ,$$

by letting $z = z_0 + \Delta z$ in the original definition. For $f(z) = z^2$, we have

$$f'(z_0) = \lim_{\Delta z \to 0} \frac{(z_0 + \Delta z)^2 - z_0^2}{\Delta z} = \lim_{\Delta z \to 0} (2z_0 + \Delta z) = 2z_0 ,$$

a result which is clearly independent of the path along which $\Delta z \to 0$, so $f(z) = z^2$ is differentiable and analytic everywhere. The result parallels exactly the result for the derivative of the real function $f(x) = x^2$.

On the other hand, if $f(z) = z^*$, we have

$$f'(z_0) = \lim_{\Delta z \to 0} \frac{z_0^* + \Delta z^* - z_0^*}{\Delta z} = \lim_{\Delta z \to 0} \frac{\Delta z^*}{\Delta z} .$$

Now if $\Delta z \to 0$ along the real x-axis, then $\Delta z = \Delta x$ and $\Delta z^* = \Delta x^* = \Delta x$, so $f'(z_0) = +1$. However, if Δz approaches zero along the imaginary y-axis, then $\Delta z = i\Delta y$ so $\Delta z^* = -i\Delta y = -\Delta z$, so $f'(z_0) = -1$. Since at any point z_0 the limit as $z \to z_0$ depends on the direction of approach, the function is not differentiable or analytic anywhere. [As a general rule, $\Delta z^*/\Delta z = e^{-2i\theta}$, where $\theta = \tan^{-1}(\Delta y/\Delta x)$, which manifestly involves the direction of approach (θ) in taking the limit.]

Many of the theorems on differentiability in real analysis have analogs in complex analysis. For example:

1. A constant function is analytic.
2. $f(z) = z^n$ $(n = 1, 2, \cdots)$ is analytic.
3. The sum, product, or quotient of two analytic functions is analytic, provided, in the case of the quotient, that the denominator does not vanish anywhere in the region under consideration.
4. An analytic function of an analytic function is analytic.

The proofs go through exactly as in the real case.

We now determine the necessary and sufficient conditions for a function $w(z) = u(x, y) + iv(x, y)$ to be differentiable at a point. First, we assume that

$w(z)$ is in fact differentiable for some $z = z_0$. Then

$$w'(z_0) = \lim_{\Delta z \to 0} \frac{\Delta w}{\Delta z} = \lim_{\Delta z \to 0} \left(\frac{\Delta u}{\Delta z} + i \frac{\Delta v}{\Delta z} \right).$$

Since $w'(z_0)$ exists, it is independent of how $\Delta z \to 0$; that is, it is independent of the ratio $\Delta y/\Delta x$. If the limit is taken along the real axis, $\Delta y = 0$, and $\Delta z = \Delta x$. Then

$$w'(z_0) = \lim_{\Delta x \to 0} \left(\frac{\Delta u}{\Delta x} + i \frac{\Delta v}{\Delta x} \right) = \frac{\partial u}{\partial x} + i \frac{\partial v}{\partial x}.$$

On the other hand, if we approach the origin along the imaginary axis, $\Delta x = 0$ and $\Delta z = i\Delta y$. Now

$$w'(z_0) = \lim_{\Delta y \to 0} \left(\frac{\Delta v}{\Delta y} - i \frac{\Delta u}{\Delta y} \right) = \frac{\partial v}{\partial y} - i \frac{\partial u}{\partial y}.$$

But by the assumption of differentiability, these two limits must be equal. Therefore, equating real and imaginary parts, we have

$$\frac{\partial u}{\partial x} = \frac{\partial v}{\partial y} \quad \text{and} \quad \frac{\partial v}{\partial x} = -\frac{\partial u}{\partial y}. \tag{6.1}$$

Equations (6.1) are known as the Cauchy-Riemann equations. They give a *necessary* condition for differentiability. We have determined this condition from special cases of the requirement of differentiability; therefore it is not surprising that these conditions alone are not sufficient.

The sufficient conditions for the differentiability of $w(z)$ at z_0 are, first, that the Cauchy-Riemann equations hold there, and second, that the first partial derivatives of $u(x, y)$ and $v(x, y)$ exist and be continuous at z_0.

The proof is straightforward. To begin, u is continuous at (x_0, y_0) because it is differentiable there; the partial derivatives of u are continuous by hypothesis. Under these assumptions, it follows from the calculus of functions of several variables* that

$$\Delta u = u(x_0 + \Delta x, y_0 + \Delta y) - u(x_0, y_0)$$

$$= \frac{\partial u}{\partial x} \Delta x + \frac{\partial u}{\partial y} \Delta y + \epsilon_1 \Delta x + \epsilon_2 \Delta y,$$

where $\partial u/\partial x$ and $\partial u/\partial y$ are the partial derivatives evaluated at the point (x_0, y_0) and where ϵ_1 and ϵ_2 go to zero as both Δx and Δy go to zero. Using a similar formula for $v(x, y)$, we have

$$\Delta w = w(z_0 + \Delta z) - w(z_0) = \Delta u + i\Delta v$$

$$= \frac{\partial u}{\partial x} \Delta x + \frac{\partial u}{\partial y} \Delta y + \epsilon_1 \Delta x + \epsilon_2 \Delta y + i \left(\frac{\partial v}{\partial x} \Delta x + \frac{\partial v}{\partial y} \Delta y + \epsilon_3 \Delta x + \epsilon_4 \Delta y \right).$$

---

* See, for example, G. B. Thomas, Jr. *Calculus and Analytic Geometry*, 4th Ed., Addison-Wesley Publishing Co., 1968, Section 15-4, p. 503 Eq. 4, or W. Kaplan, *Advanced Calculus*, Addison-Wesley Publishing Co., 1953, Section 2-6, p. 84.

Now using the Cauchy-Riemann equations, which by assumption hold at the point (x_0, y_0), we have

$$\Delta w = \frac{\partial u}{\partial x}(\Delta x + i\Delta y) + i\frac{\partial v}{\partial x}(\Delta x + i\Delta y) + \Delta x(\epsilon_1 + i\epsilon_3) + \Delta y(\epsilon_2 + i\epsilon_4) .$$

Therefore

$$\frac{\Delta w}{\Delta z} = \frac{\partial u}{\partial x} + i\frac{\partial v}{\partial x} + (\epsilon_1 + i\epsilon_3)\frac{\Delta x}{\Delta z} + (\epsilon_2 + i\epsilon_4)\frac{\Delta y}{\Delta z} .$$

Since $|\Delta z| = [(\Delta x)^2 + (\Delta y)^2]^{1/2}$, $|\Delta x| \le |\Delta z|$ and $|\Delta y| \le |\Delta z|$, and so $|\Delta x/\Delta z| \le 1$ and $|\Delta y/\Delta z| \le 1$. Since these factors are bounded, the last two terms in the above equation tend to zero with Δz because ϵ_1, ϵ_2, ϵ_3, and ϵ_4 go to zero as Δz goes to zero. Therefore at z_0

$$w'(z_0) = \frac{\partial u}{\partial x} + i\frac{\partial v}{\partial x} ; \tag{6.2}$$

the limit is independent of the path followed, so the derivative exists. Using the Cauchy-Riemann conditions, we also have

$$w'(z_0) = \frac{\partial v}{\partial y} - i\frac{\partial u}{\partial y} . \tag{6.3}$$

Example. Consider the function z^3. We have

$$z^3 = (x^3 - 3xy^2) + i(3x^2y - y^3) = u + iv .$$

Thus

$$\frac{\partial u}{\partial x} = 3x^2 - 3y^2 = \frac{\partial v}{\partial y} , \qquad \text{and} \qquad \frac{\partial v}{\partial x} = 6xy = -\frac{\partial u}{\partial y} .$$

Thus the Cauchy-Riemann equations hold everywhere. Since the partial derivatives are continuous, the function z^3 is, in fact, analytic everywhere. A function which is analytic in the entire complex plane is said to be an *entire* function. The derivative of z^3 may be found using Eq. (6.2) or (6.3). We obtain

$$\frac{\partial z^3}{\partial z} = \frac{\partial u}{\partial x} + i\frac{\partial v}{\partial x} = 3[(x^2 - y^2) + 2ixy] = 3z^2 ,$$

a satisfying result. As a second example, we leave it to the reader to show that the function $|z|^2 \equiv zz^*$ is differentiable only at the origin, and therefore is analytic nowhere.

One remarkable result which points to connections with physics follows immediately from the Cauchy-Riemann equations. Assuming that they hold in a region, we have

$$\frac{\partial^2 u}{\partial x^2} = \frac{\partial^2 v}{\partial x\,\partial y} = \frac{\partial^2 v}{\partial y\,\partial x} = -\frac{\partial^2 u}{\partial y^2} \implies \frac{\partial^2 u}{\partial x^2} + \frac{\partial^2 u}{\partial y^2} = \nabla^2 u = 0 \tag{6.4}$$

if the second partial derivatives are continuous, so we can interchange the orders of differentiation in the mixed partial derivative. It follows in the same way that the function v also satisfies the two-dimensional Laplace equation. Thus both the real and imaginary parts of an analytic function with continuous second partial derivatives satisfy the two-dimensional Laplace equation. We shall later prove, using integration theory, that the second partial derivatives of an analytic function are necessarily continuous, so this qualification can be dropped. (It is interesting that these theorems about derivatives can be proved only by integration.) Any function ϕ satisfying $\nabla^2\phi = 0$ is called a *harmonic function*. If $f = u + iv$ is an analytic function, then $\nabla^2 u = \nabla^2 v = 0$, and u and v are called *conjugate* harmonic functions.

Given one of two conjugate harmonic functions, the Cauchy-Riemann equations can be used to find the other, up to a constant. For example, the function $u(x, y) = 2x - x^3 + 3xy^2$ is easily seen to be harmonic. To find its harmonic conjugate, we proceed as follows:

$$\frac{\partial u}{\partial x} = \frac{\partial v}{\partial y} = 2 - 3x^2 + 3y^2 \Longrightarrow v = 2y - 3x^2y + y^3 + \phi(x) \, ,$$

where $\phi(x)$ is some function of x. Now, using the other Cauchy-Riemann equation, we obtain

$$\frac{\partial v}{\partial x} = -\frac{\partial u}{\partial y} \Longrightarrow -6xy + \phi'(x) = -6xy \Longrightarrow \phi' = 0 \, .$$

Thus $\phi(x)$ must be a constant, and the harmonic conjugate of u is

$$v = 2y - 3x^2y + y^3 + \text{const.}$$

Note that the function $w = u + iv = 2z - z^3 + C$ is an analytic function, as we know it must be.

Before leaving the Cauchy-Riemann conditions, let us take advantage of being physicists to present another, shorter derivation of these conditions, based on the use of infinitesimals. Let $w = u + iv$ and $w' = p + iq$. Then $\delta w = w'\delta z$, or, taking real and imaginary parts,

$$\delta u = p\delta x - q\delta y \, , \qquad \delta v = p\delta y + q\delta x \, .$$

It follows immediately that

$$\frac{\partial u}{\partial x} = \frac{\partial v}{\partial y} = p \, , \qquad \frac{\partial v}{\partial x} = -\frac{\partial u}{\partial y} = q \, .$$

These equations are identical to the Cauchy-Riemann equations (6.1).

Continuing in this informal spirit, we may derive another closely related result which provides some insight into the meaning of analyticity. Again, let $w(z) = w(x, y) = u(x, y) + iv(x, y)$. We now show that $\partial w/\partial z^* = 0$ if and only if the Cauchy-Riemann equations hold. We shall not worry about the meaning of this derivative with respect to z^*, but just differentiate formally, treating the derivative as symbolic. Using the expressions

$$x = (z + z^*)/2 \qquad \text{and} \qquad y = (z - z^*)/2i$$

we have

$$\frac{\partial w}{\partial z^*} = \frac{\partial w}{\partial x}\frac{\partial x}{\partial z^*} + \frac{\partial w}{\partial y}\frac{\partial y}{\partial z^*}$$

$$= \left(\frac{\partial u}{\partial x} + i\frac{\partial v}{\partial x}\right)\tfrac{1}{2} + \left(\frac{\partial u}{\partial y} + i\frac{\partial v}{\partial y}\right)\left(-\frac{1}{2i}\right)$$

$$= \tfrac{1}{2}\left(\frac{\partial u}{\partial x} - \frac{\partial v}{\partial y}\right) + \frac{i}{2}\left(\frac{\partial v}{\partial x} + \frac{\partial u}{\partial y}\right).$$

If the Cauchy-Riemann equations hold, this last expression vanishes. If, on the other hand, $\partial w/\partial z^* = 0$, then both the real and imaginary parts of the last expression must vanish, so the Cauchy-Riemann equations hold.

This purely formal result, which can be made rigorous, is trying to tell us that analytic functions are independent of z^*: they are functions of z alone. Thus analytic functions are true functions of a *complex* variable, not just complex functions of two real variables (see, for example, Problem 1), which will in general depend on z^* as well as z according to

$$f(x, y) = f\left(\frac{z + z^*}{2}, \frac{z - z^*}{2i}\right).$$

6.2 SOME BASIC ANALYTIC FUNCTIONS

One of the most useful functions in the complex domain is the exponential function which we define for $z = x + iy$ by

$$e^z \equiv e^x (\cos y + i \sin y) . \tag{6.5}$$

It follows easily from this definition and our earlier work that e^z is an entire function and that

$$\frac{d}{dz} e^z = e^z .$$

The other familiar properties of exponentials, in particular, $e^{z_1 + z_2} = e^{z_1} e^{z_2}$, follow readily from Eq. (6.5). We note that e^z is a periodic function of period $2\pi i$:

$$e^{z + 2\pi i} = e^z e^{2\pi i} = e^z (\cos 2\pi + i \sin 2\pi) = e^z .$$

From Eq. (6.5) we see that

$$e^{iy} = \cos y + i \sin y ,$$

so it follows that

$$\cos y = \frac{e^{iy} + e^{-iy}}{2} , \qquad \sin y = \frac{e^{iy} - e^{-iy}}{2i} .$$

These relations suggest that for an arbitrary complex z we define

$$\cos z \equiv \frac{e^{iz} + e^{-iz}}{2} , \qquad (6.6)$$

$$\sin z \equiv \frac{e^{iz} - e^{-iz}}{2i} . \qquad (6.7)$$

Since

$$\frac{d}{dz} e^z = e^z ,$$

it is a simple matter to calculate the derivatives of $\cos z$ and $\sin z$. We find that

$$\frac{d}{dz} \cos z = \frac{ie^{iz} - ie^{-iz}}{2} = -\sin z ,$$

$$\frac{d}{dz} \sin z = \frac{ie^{iz} + ie^{-iz}}{2i} = \cos z ,$$

as we might expect from experience with the real variable case. Using Eqs. (6.6) and (6.7), it is a simple matter to verify that all the familiar trigonometric identities, such as

$$\cos (z_1 + z_2) = \cos z_1 \cos z_2 - \sin z_1 \sin z_2 ,$$

continue to be valid for complex variables.

The complex functions sine and cosine may, of course, be put in the form $u(x, y) + iv(x, y)$. For example,

$$\sin z = \frac{1}{2i} [e^{i(x+iy)} - e^{-i(x+iy)}]$$

$$= \frac{1}{2i} e^{-y}(\cos x + i \sin x) - \frac{1}{2i} e^{y}(\cos x - i \sin x)$$

$$= \sin x(e^y + e^{-y})/2 + i \cos x(e^y - e^{-y})/2 .$$

Therefore

$$\sin z = \cosh y \sin x + i \sinh y \cos x . \qquad (6.8)$$

Similarly,

$$\cos z = \cosh y \cos x - i \sinh y \sin x . \qquad (6.9)$$

Setting $x = 0$, we obtain the useful relations $\sin (iy) = i \sinh y$ and $\cos (iy) = \cosh y$. We also see that the Cauchy-Riemann conditions are satisfied everywhere, as we know they must be. Other properties which follow directly from Eqs. (6.8) and (6.9) are

$$(\sin z)^* = \sin (z^*) ,$$

$$\sin (-z) = -\sin (z) ,$$

$$\sin (z + 2\pi) = \sin (z) .$$

Using the sine and cosine functions, we can define the other familiar trigonometric functions. For example,

$$\tan z = \sin z / \cos z \; ;$$

similar extensions of the real case are defined for the cotangent, secant, and cosecant. These functions differ from the sine and cosine in that they are *not* analytic everywhere. The tangent, being the ratio of two analytic functions, will be analytic everywhere *except* at points where $\cos z = 0$. Using the real and imaginary parts of the cosine, we can rewrite this condition as

$$\cosh y \cos x = 0 \; , \qquad \sinh y \sin x = 0 \; .$$

Now $\cosh y \geq 1$ for all real y, so the first equation has a solution whenever $\cos x = 0$, or $x = (2n + 1)\pi/2, n = 0, \pm 1, \pm 2, \cdots$. At these points, $\sin x = \pm 1$, so the second equation requires that $\sinh y = 0$, that is, $y = 0$. Thus the tangent function is singular at the points $(2n + 1)\pi/2, (n = 0, \pm 1, \cdots)$ on the real axis, and only at these points. Therefore $\tan z$ becomes infinite at precisely those points where $\tan x$ (real x) becomes infinite and *only* at those points.

On the basis of the above discussion, one might be tempted to think that the complex trigonometric functions are "just the same thing" as their real counterparts. However, the reader can easily show that

$$|\sin z|^2 = \sin^2 x + \sinh^2 y \; ,$$

and this expression increases *without limit* as y tends to infinity. This is in marked contrast with the real case, where $|\sin x| \leq 1$ for all real x.

The functions which we have discussed thus far all have the property that if we pick any point z_0 in the complex plane and follow any path from z_0 through the plane back to z_0, then the value of the function changes continuously along the path, returning to its original value at z_0. For example, suppose that we consider the function $w(z) = e^z$ and start at the point $z_0 = 1$, encircling the origin in the z-plane counterclockwise along the unit circle. Figure 6.1(a) shows the circular path in the z-plane, and Fig. 6.1(b) shows the corresponding path in the w-plane. [The use of two complex planes to "graph" the function $w(z)$ is often employed in complex variable theory.] We note that both paths are closed, which is just the geometrical statement of the fact that if we start at a point z_0, where the function has the value $w(z_0)$, then when we move along a closed curve back to z_0, the functional values also follow a smooth path back to $w(z_0)$.

Now for e^z this result is hardly surprising since we have *defined* e^z in such a way as to ensure this behavior, letting ourselves be guided by the properties of the real exponential function. Now if we look at another simple function, namely, the square root, we see that things do not always go so smoothly. Let us write formally

$$w(z) \equiv \sqrt{z} \equiv \sqrt{x + iy} \; .$$

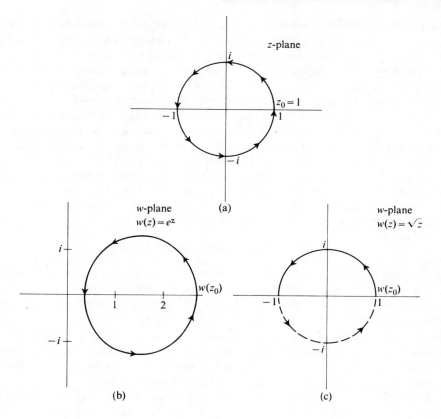

Fig. 6.1(a) A circular contour in the z-plane about the origin.   **6.1(b)** The mapping of the contour of Figure 6.1(a) by the function e^z.   **Fig. 1(c)** The mapping of the contour of Figure 6.1(a) by the function $\sqrt{z}$.

We observe that this definition is empty, since there is no set of operations presently at our disposal which will enable us to find $w(z)$ for some given x and y (unless $y = 0$). This is in contrast with the situation in Eq. (6.5) where all problems of evaluation can be handled by familiar real-variable operations.

Fortunately, in the case of the square root there is another possibility, namely, we can write z in polar form[†] as $z = re^{i\theta}$. In this form, a logical extension of the square root to the complex domain is contained in the definition

$$w(z) \equiv \sqrt{z} \equiv \sqrt{r}\, e^{i\theta/2} = \sqrt{r}\,[\cos{(\theta/2)} + i\sin{(\theta/2)}\,]\,.$$

[†] If we write $z = x + iy$ and make the familiar change to polar coordinates ($x = r\cos\theta$, $y = r\sin\theta$) we obtain $z = r(\cos\theta + i\sin\theta) = re^{i\theta}$, where $r = (x^2 + y^2)^{1/2}$ and $\theta = \tan^{-1}(y/x)$.

Clearly, this function satisfies $w^2 = z$, which is certainly a minimum requirement for any sensible square root. Using this definition, let us vary z along the
same path chosen in Fig. 6.1(a), starting at $r = 1$, $\theta = 0$. Figure 6.1(c) shows the
corresponding path in the w-plane. Note that it is *not* a closed path; after making
a complete circle around the origin in the z-plane, we arrive at the point $w = -1$
in the w-plane, not at $w = +1$. In order to get back to $w = +1$, we must let
θ go from 2π to 4π; that is, make the circular trip in the z-plane one more time
[see the dotted curve in Fig. 6.1(c)]. Actually this is not quite the best way to
describe the situation; we do not want to think of tracing the circular path in
the original z-plane a second time, but rather of tracing an identical circular path
in a *different* z-plane. This corresponds to the fact that in the first circuit, θ went
from 0 to 2π, whereas in the second circuit, it went from 2π to 4π.

This is not so different from the case of functions like e^z as one might
imagine at first glance. We can write in polar variables

$$e^z = e^{r \cos \theta} \left[\cos \left(r \sin \theta \right) + i \sin \left(r \sin \theta \right) \right],$$

and then trace out a circular path as many times as we please ($\theta = 0 \to \theta = 2\pi$,
$\theta = 2\pi \to \theta = 4\pi$, etc.). In this case we get the same values of e^z for each
circuit. Therefore no information about e^z is lost if we identify the z-planes
corresponding to $\theta = 0 \to \theta = 2\pi$, $\theta = 2\pi \to \theta = 4\pi$, etc., with each other.
However, in the case of $w(z) = \sqrt{z}$ we need two planes, usually referred to as
Riemann sheets, to characterize the values of $w(z)$ in a single-valued manner.
Two planes are clearly sufficient: when we let θ range from 4π to 6π we obtain
the same values as we did when we let θ range from 0 to 2π.

It is important to remember that the path of Fig. 6.1(a) encloses the origin.
If we choose a closed path which neither encloses the origin nor intersects the
positive real axis, then we also obtain a closed path in the w-plane. Fig. 6.2(a)
and (b) illustrates the situation for $w(z) = \sqrt{z}$, starting from the $z_0 = \sqrt{5} \, e^{i\phi_0}$,
where $\phi_0 = \tan^{-1} 2$ (we adopt the usual trigonometric convention that $\tan^{-1} x$
takes on values between 0 and $\pi/2$). In Fig. 6.2(a) we may say that we start at
$z_0 = 1 + 2i$ on the *first Riemann sheet* and return to that point without encircling the origin. If we do the same thing for $z_0 = 1 + 2i$ on the *second Riemann
sheet* (that is, $\phi_0 = \tan^{-1} 2 + 2\pi$), we obtain the corresponding closed curve
traced out in the w-plane (Fig. 6.2(c)).

It is readily seen that the difficulties described above for $w(z) = \sqrt{z}$ will
persist for any path beginning on the positive real axis and returning to the
original point along a path enclosing the origin. Thus if we wish to consider
$w(z) = \sqrt{z}$ in the simple fashion that we used for e^z, then we conclude that $\sqrt{z}$
is not continuous along the positive real axis and is not analytic there. However,
to avoid this dilemma, we can say that when we come back to the real axis after
a circuit of 2π radians, we transfer continuously onto the *second* Riemann sheet.
If we go around $z = 0$ once more on the second sheet, when we return toward
the positive real axis, we transfer continuously back to the *first* Riemann sheet.
Thus the two sheets can be imagined to be *cut* along the positive real axis and

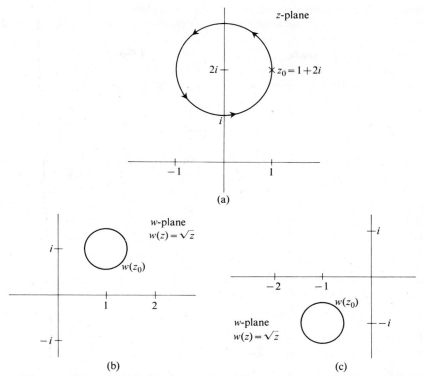

Fig. 6.2(a) A closed contour in the z-plane which does not enclose the origin. 6.2(b).
The mapping of the contour of Figure 6.2(a) by the function $\sqrt{z}$, if the contour of
Figure 6.2(a) is imagined to lie on the *first* Riemann sheet. 6.2(c) The mapping of
the contour of Figure 6.2(a) by the function $\sqrt{z}$, if the contour of Figure 6.2(a) is
imagined to lie on the *second* Riemann sheet.

joined in the manner illustrated in Fig. 6.3. With this construction, the function
$w(z) = \sqrt{z}$ is seen to be single valued everywhere [on both sheets we set $w(0) = 0$]
and analytic everywhere except at the origin, where $\sqrt{z}$ suffers from the same
difficulty as does $\sqrt{x}$ in the real variable case. Thus the origin is a singular
point for $w(z) = \sqrt{z}$.

In general, suppose that we have a singular point, z_0, of some function $w(z)$,
and a path starting at z_1, which encircles z_0. If we must sweep through an angle

Fig. 6.3 A side view of the two Riemann sheets, looking down the real axis towards
the origin, for the function $w(z) = \sqrt{z}$.

greater than 2π in order to return to the original value at z_1, then z_0 is called a *branch point* of $w(z)$. The cut which emanates from this point is called a *branch cut*. In the simple case discussed above [$w(z) = \sqrt{z}$], the value of $w(z_1)$ with z_1 on the *second* sheet is just the negative of $w(z_1)$ with z_1 on the *first* sheet. Note that it is possible for a point z_1 on the *first* sheet to be a point at which some function $w(z)$ is analytic, whereas the point z_1 on the *second* sheet is a singular point. The function

$$w(z) = \frac{1}{i + \sqrt{z}}$$

is an example of such a function; $w(z)$ is a single-valued function over a two-sheeted Riemann surface cut along the positive real axis and joined as in Fig. 6.3. It is analytic at $z = -1(\phi = \pi)$ on the first Riemann sheet and is singular at $z = -1(\phi = 3\pi)$ on the second Riemann sheet.

In the above discussions we could, of course, have insisted that θ, the argument of z, range only through 2π radians. Then we could say that

$$w_1(z) = \sqrt{r}\, e^{i\theta/2}, \qquad 0 \le \theta < 2\pi,$$

defines a single-valued function, analytic everywhere in the complex z-plane *except along the positive real axis* (including $z = 0$), and that

$$w_2(z) = \sqrt{r}\, e^{i(\theta + 2\pi)/2} = -\sqrt{r}\, e^{i\theta/2}, \qquad 0 \le \theta < 2\pi,$$

also defines such a function. Both $w_1(z)$ and $w_2(z)$ satisfy $w_1^2 = w_2^2 = z$ and are referred to as *single-valued branches* of $\sqrt{z}$. Clearly, if we defined

$$w_3(z) = \sqrt{r}\, e^{i(\theta + 4\pi)/2}, \qquad 0 \le \theta < 2\pi,$$

we would find $w_3(z) = w_1(z)$, so we do not obtain a new branch in this manner. We leave it as an exercise to show that one can define *three* single-valued branches of $w(z) = \sqrt[3]{z}$ and that, in this case, if one wants to define $w(z)$ as a single-valued function, analytic everywhere except at $z = 0$, a three-sheeted Riemann surface is necessary.

It should be noted that the choice of the real axis as the branch cut for $w(z) = \sqrt{z}$ was entirely arbitrary. Any other ray, say $\theta = \theta_0$, will serve equally well. The only thing which is *not* arbitrary is the choice of $z = 0$ as a branch point; $z = 0$ is a bona fide singular point for $w(z) = \sqrt{z}$, and this cannot be changed. However, in the functions $w_1(z)$ and $w_2(z)$ defined above, the singular line $\theta = 0$ is, apart from $z = 0$, a line of "man-made" singularities; we could equally well choose the line $\theta = \theta_0$ to be the singular line. For example, we could define

$$w_1(z) = \sqrt{r}\, e^{i\theta/2}, \qquad \theta_0 \le \theta < \theta_0 + 2\pi,$$

and, similarly,

$$w_2(z) = \sqrt{r}\, e^{i(\theta + 2\pi)/2} = -\sqrt{r}\, e^{i\theta/2}, \qquad \theta_0 \le \theta < \theta_0 + 2\pi.$$

If we want a single-valued function which is analytic everywhere except at $z = 0$, then we can construct a two-sheeted Riemann surface, cut and joined along the line $\theta = \theta_0$. On the counterclockwise edge of the cut, $\sqrt{z} = \sqrt{r}\, e^{i\theta_0/2}$. After going through a circuit of 2π radians, we do not return to this value, but to $-\sqrt{r}\, e^{i\theta_0/2}$, and we pass onto the second sheet. Note that, in this case, some of the values of $w(z) = \sqrt{z}$ which were on the *first* Riemann sheet when the cut was made along $\theta = 0$ now find themselves on the *second* Riemann sheet and vice versa. This brings home the fact that the Riemann construction is merely a way to write a collection of values of a function in a single-valued manner. Distinctions between the first sheet and the second sheet are purely matters of convention. In fact, it should not be difficult for the reader to imagine that any reasonable curve from the origin to infinity could serve as an acceptable cut along which the two Riemann sheets of $w(z) = \sqrt{z}$ can be joined.

Before leaving this example, let us first propose an argument which might appear at first sight to contradict what we have been saying. Consider any point $x_0 \neq 0$ on the positive real axis. We should imagine that there exists a neighborhood of x_0 in which we can write $z = x_0 + \rho$, where ρ is some complex number, and then define $\sqrt{z}$ by the power series

$$\sqrt{z} \equiv \sqrt{x_0}\left(1 + \tfrac{1}{2}\frac{\rho}{x_0} - \tfrac{1}{8}\frac{\rho^2}{x_0^2} + \cdots\right),$$

whenever the series converges (we will see later that the series converges whenever $|\rho| < x_0$). This is a single-valued function which defines $\sqrt{z}$ continuously across a part of the positive real axis. However, this definition does not apply to the whole complex plane since the series does not converge everywhere. It turns out that it is impossible to extend (or "continue") this function to all points of the z-plane in such a way that $\sqrt{z}$ is single-valued and analytic. We will return to this point when we discuss the principle of analytic continuation later in this chapter. The continuity of the series definition across the positive real axis does not contradict our original positioning of a cut along the positive real axis, because, as we have seen above, the cut could be positioned anywhere so long as it begins at $z = 0$. In particular, the cut can be chosen so that it lies completely outside the domain of convergence of the series used to define $\sqrt{z}$ (for example, the cut could be chosen to lie along the negative real axis). We may remark in passing that we *could* successfully define e^z in this manner. The function e^x possesses an everywhere convergent power series for real x, and it is not hard to believe that a complex power series with the same coefficients $(1/n!)$ will converge *everywhere* in the complex plane.

As another example of a multivalued function, we consider the logarithm. Again using $z = re^{i\theta}$, we define

$$\log z \equiv \ln r + i\theta ,$$

where ln denotes the usual natural logarithm of a positive real number. Note that

$$e^{\log z} = e^{\ln r + i\theta} = e^{\ln r}e^{i\theta} = re^{i\theta} = z$$

and also that

$$\log(z_1 z_2) = \ln(r_1 r_2) + i(\theta_1 + \theta_2) = \ln r_1 + i\theta_1 + \ln r_2 + i\theta_2 = \log z_1 + \log z_2,$$

so the logarithm has the main properties that one would expect by analogy with the real variable case. With the logarithm, the multivaluedness difficulties described above are more striking, since no matter how many times one encircles the origin, starting, say, at some point on the positive real axis, one *never* returns to the original value of the logarithm. The logarithm increases by $2\pi i$ on each circuit (or decreases by $2\pi i$ if one moves in the direction of decreasing θ). Thus an infinite number of Riemann sheets, each one joined to the one below it via a cut along the positive real axis, is necessary to turn $\log z$ into a single-valued function. When this is done, $\log z$ is analytic everywhere except at $z = 0$, where we assign the value $\log(z = 0) = -\infty$ on all sheets. We can also form an infinite number of single-valued branches of the logarithm:

$$w_n(z) = \ln r + i\theta + 2\pi n i, \qquad 0 \le \theta < 2\pi,$$

where $n = 0, \pm 1, \pm 2, \cdots$, and $w_n(z)$ is a single-valued function, analytic everywhere except at $z = 0$ and along the positive real axis. Just as before,

$$e^{w_n(z)} = z,$$

but

$$w_n(z_1 z_2) = w_n(z_1) + w_n(z_2) - 2\pi n i.$$

The branch

$$w_0(z) = \ln r + i\theta, \qquad 0 \le \theta < 2\pi,$$

is called the principal value or principal branch of the logarithm and is usually denoted by $\text{Log } z$. We have

$$e^{\text{Log } z} = z,$$

$$\text{Log}(z_1 z_2) = \text{Log } z_1 + \text{Log } z_2.$$

As before, the choice of the ray $\theta = 0$ as the line of singularities is entirely arbitrary.

From the preceding examples, it is a simple matter to build up to more complicated cases. For example, the function

$$w(z) = \sqrt{z - a}$$

is a single-valued function on the two-sheeted Riemann surface cut from a to infinity. The point $z = a$ is a branch point singularity; if we choose the branch cut to lie parallel to the real axis, we obtain the picture of Fig. 6.4. We thus may define, using the notation of Fig. 6.4,

$$w(z) \equiv |z - a|^{1/2} e^{i\theta/2}.$$

A more challenging problem is provided by the function

$$w(z) = \sqrt{(z - a)(z - b)}.$$

Fig. 6.4 The appropriate cut for the function $w(z) = \sqrt{z - a}$.

Fig. 6.5 The appropriate cuts for the function $w(z) = \sqrt{(z - a)(z - b)}$.

To simplify the geometry, we will consider the special case when a and b are real. The most obvious way to proceed is simply to put in two cuts from the branch points $z = a$ and $z = b$ as shown in Fig. 6.5. We have chosen these two simple directions for the cuts because of pictorial convenience. The left-hand cut corresponds to what we would have for the function $\sqrt{z - a}$, the right-hand cut to what we would have for $\sqrt{z - b}$. Here we take θ_1 to begin on the "bottom" of the left-hand cut at $-\pi$ and go to $+\pi$ on the "top" of the cut. At π we transfer to the second sheet and θ_1 continues to 3π, where we return to the first sheet. As we look down the negative real axis toward the origin, the two sheets are joined as shown in Fig. 6.3. Similarly, for the right-hand cut, we start at the "top" of the cut at $\theta_2 = 0$ and move counterclockwise, passing to the second sheet at $\theta_2 = 2\pi$, and finally return to the first sheet when $\theta_2 = 4\pi$. Along the positive real axis, the two sheets are joined as shown in Fig. 6.3. Using the above conventions, we define

$$w(z) \equiv |z - a|^{1/2}|z - b|^{1/2}e^{i\theta_1/2}e^{i\theta_2/2} .$$

As shown in Fig. 6.6, any point z_0 on the second sheet can be reached from the point z_0 on the first sheet either by going via the left-hand cut or the right-hand cut. These two options differ only in the sense that in the first case θ_1 increases by 2π, whereas in the second case θ_2 increases by 2π. In both cases, the value

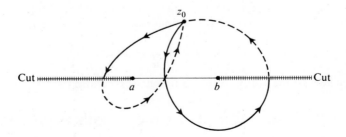

Fig. 6.6 Two different paths by which one can go from $z = z_0$ on the first sheet to $z = z_0$ on the second sheet. The function in question is $w(z) = \sqrt{(z - a)(z - b)}$.

of $w(z)$ is the same (the negative of what it would be for the corresponding point on the first sheet), as it must be if we are to have a single-valued function. With this construction, $w(z) = \sqrt{(z - a)(z - b)}$ becomes a single-valued function, analytic everywhere except at $z = a$ and $z = b$.

Note that in the above example, if we go through 2π radians in both θ_1 and θ_2, starting for example on the "top" of the right-hand cut, then we go down to the second sheet via the left-hand cut and return to our starting point on the first sheet via the right-hand cut. This suggests that it should equally well be possible to cut and join the two sheets along the real axis from -1 to $+1$. The reader may find it interesting to show that this is indeed the case.

Using the above ideas, we can also obtain sensible expressions for the inverse trigonometric functions. For example, consider

$$w = \tan^{-1} z .$$

Writing this as

$$z = \tan w = \frac{1}{i} \frac{e^{iw} - e^{-iw}}{e^{iw} + e^{-iw}} ,$$

we obtain readily

$$(1 - iz)e^{iw} = (1 + iz)e^{-iw} ,$$

and hence

$$e^{2iw} = \frac{1 + iz}{1 - iz} .$$

Taking the logarithms of both sides, we find that

$$w = \frac{1}{2i} \log \left(\frac{1 + iz}{1 - iz} \right) = \frac{1}{2i} \log \left(\frac{i - z}{i + z} \right) .$$

Thus

$$\tan^{-1} z = \frac{i}{2} \log \left(\frac{i + z}{i - z} \right) .$$

Just as we did in discussing the logarithm, we can speak of single-valued branches of $\tan^{-1} z$ corresponding to single-valued branches of $\log z$. The principal branch of the inverse tangent is defined in the obvious manner:

$$\text{Tan}^{-1} z = \frac{i}{2} \left[\text{Log} \, (i + z) - \text{Log} \, (i - z) \, \right] .$$

Similar considerations apply to the functions $\sin^{-1} z$ and $\cos^{-1} z$.

6.3 COMPLEX INTEGRATION—THE CAUCHY-GOURSAT THEOREM

We now come to integration of complex functions, the part of the theory that makes the subject really interesting to both mathematicians and physicists. Because of the correspondence between complex numbers and two-dimensional vectors, we might expect to be able to define the line integral of a complex function along a curve in the z-plane.

Let t be a real parameter ranging from t_A to t_B, and let $z = z(t)$ be a curve, or *contour* C, in the complex plane, with endpoints $A = z(t_A)$ and $B = z(t_B)$. (See Fig. 6.7.) Now we mark off a number of points t_i between t_A and t_B, and approximate the curve by a series of straight lines drawn from each $z(t_i)$ to $z(t_{i+1})$.

Fig. 6.7

To define the integral of a function w of a complex variable, we form the quantity

$$\lim_{|\Delta z_i| \to 0} \sum_{i=0}^{n} w(z_i)\Delta z_i \equiv \int_C w(z)\,dz \, ,$$

where $\Delta z_i = z(t_{i+1}) - z(t_i)$, and $w(z_i)$ is the function evaluated at a point z_i on C between $z(t_{i+1})$ and $z(t_i)$. The sum is evaluated in the limit of an arbitrarily fine partition of the range through which the real parameter t moves as it generates the contour from A to B; that is, as $n \to \infty$, or, what is the same thing, in the limit of arbitrarily small $|\Delta z_i|$ for all i.

Writing $w(z) = u(x, y) + iv(x, y)$ and $dz = dx + i\,dy$, we have

$$\int_C w(z)\,dz = \int_C (u\,dx - v\,dy) + i\int_C (u\,dy + v\,dx) \, . \qquad (6.10)$$

We can also write this in parametric form. Then

$$dx = \frac{dx}{dt}\,dt \, , \qquad dy = \frac{dy}{dt}\,dt$$

and so

$$\int_C w(z)\,dz = \int_{t_A}^{t_B}\left(u\frac{dx}{dt} - v\frac{dy}{dt}\right)dt + i\int_{t_A}^{t_B}\left(u\frac{dy}{dt} + v\frac{dx}{dt}\right)dt \, .$$

For a given contour C running from A to B we define the opposite contour, written as $-C$, to be the same curve but traversed from B to A. The integral of $w(z)$ along $-C$ is clearly given by the above equation but with t_A and t_B interchanged. Thus,

$$\int_C = -\int_{-C} \, . \qquad (6.11)$$

Also it follows that

$$\int_{C_1} + \int_{C_2} = \int_{C_1 + C_2} . \tag{6.12}$$

If C is a closed curve that does not intersect itself, we shall always interpret $\oint_C$ to mean the integral taken counterclockwise along the closed contour C.

Another property of the integral that we shall need very often is

$$\left| \int_C f(z)\, dz \right| \leq \int_C |f(z)|\, |dz| \leq ML , \tag{6.13}$$

where M is the maximum value of $|f(z)|$ on C, and the length of C is L. The first inequality in Eq. (6.13) is a generalization of $|z_1 + z_2| \leq |z_1| + |z_2|$, the triangle inequality; both inequalities are derived exactly as in the real case.

Fig. 6.8

Before presenting the general theorems on the integration of functions of a complex variable, we work out two examples of such integrals using only the results obtained so far. First, we evaluate the integral

$$I = \int_C \sin z \, dz$$

over the two paths shown in Fig. 6.8: (1) $C_1 = OB$, (2) $C_2 = OA + AB$. Since

$$\sin z = \cosh y \sin x + i \sinh y \cos x ,$$

we have, using Eq. (6.10),

$$I \equiv \int_C \sin z \, dz = \int_C [\cosh y \sin x \, dx - \sinh y \cos x \, dy]$$
$$+ i \int_C [\cosh y \sin x \, dy + \sinh y \cos x \, dx] .$$

Along the curve C_1, $x = y$. Therefore

$$I_1 = (1 + i) \int_0^1 \cosh x \sin x \, dx - (1 - i) \int_0^1 \sinh x \cos x \, dx$$
$$= (1 - \cosh 1 \cos 1) + i(\sinh 1 \sin 1) .$$

Now we compute I along C_2. Along the path from O to A, $x = 0$ and $dx = 0$, and along the path from A to B, $y = 1$ and $dy = 0$. Therefore

$$I_2 = \int_{C_2} \sin z \, dz = -\int_0^1 \sinh y \, dy + \int_0^1 \cosh 1 \sin x \, dx + i \int_0^1 \sinh 1 \cos x \, dx$$

$$= 1 - \cosh 1 \cos 1 + i \sinh 1 \sin 1 = I_1 .$$

The integral from O to B is the same for both paths. In fact, we shall prove later that it is the same for any path whatsoever—it depends only on the two endpoints. Also, the definite integral around the closed contour consisting of C_1 and $-C_2$ (that is, C_2 traveled backward) is zero. We shall show that this result holds for any function which is analytic on and inside the closed contour.

Note that if we evaluate formally, according to the rule of real calculus,

$$I_1 = I_2 = \int_0^{1+i} \sin z \, dz = -\cos z \Big]_0^{1+i}$$

$$= 1 - \cosh 1 \cos 1 + i \sinh 1 \sin 1 ,$$

where we have used Eq. (6.9). We shall also prove this "fundamental theorem of complex calculus," which holds in any region in which the integrand is analytic.

As a second example, let us integrate the function $f(z) = z^*$ counterclockwise around the unit circle centered at the origin. The values of z on this curve are given by $z = e^{i\theta}$, $\theta = 0$ to 2π. Therefore

$$I = \oint_C z^* \, dz = \int_0^{2\pi} e^{-i\theta} i e^{i\theta} \, d\theta = 2\pi i .$$

Since $zz^* = 1$ on C, we also obtain the result

$$\oint_C \frac{1}{z} \, dz = 2\pi i .$$

Neither integral around the closed contour is zero. The reason, as we shall see, is that z^* is not analytic anywhere, and therefore not within and on C, and z^{-1} is not analytic at $z = 0$, which is within C.

Both these examples are explained by

Cauchy's Theorem. If a function $f(z)$ is analytic within and on a closed contour C, *and $f'(z)$ is continuous throughout this region*, then

$$\oint_C f(z) \, dz = 0 .$$

We shall give two proofs of this theorem.

Proof 1.

$$\oint_C f(z) \, dz = \oint_C (u \, dx - v \, dy) + i \oint_C (u \, dy + v \, dx) .$$

To evaluate the two line integrals on the right, we use Green's theorem for line integrals. It states that if the derivatives of P and Q are continuous functions within and on a closed contour C, then

$$\oint_C (P\,dx + Q\,dy) = \int_R \int \left(\frac{\partial Q}{\partial x} - \frac{\partial P}{\partial y}\right) dx\,dy,$$

where R is the surface bounded by C. By hypothesis, $f'(z)$ is continuous, so the first partial derivatives of u and v are also continuous; then Green's theorem yields

$$\oint_C (u\,dx - v\,dy) + i\oint_C (u\,dy + v\,dx)$$
$$= \int_R \int \left(\frac{\partial u}{\partial y} + \frac{\partial v}{\partial x}\right) dx\,dy + i\int_R \int \left(\frac{\partial u}{\partial x} - \frac{\partial v}{\partial y}\right) dx\,dy.$$

But since the Cauchy-Riemann equations hold, the integrands above all vanish. Therefore

$$\oint_C f(z)\,dz = 0. \qquad \text{QED}$$

Proof 2. Cauchy's theorem may also be proved if we use Stokes's theorem, which is closely related to Green's theorem and is perhaps more familiar. We write

$$\oint_C f(z)\,dz = \oint_C \mathbf{F}\cdot d\mathbf{l} + i\oint_C \mathbf{G}\cdot d\mathbf{l},$$

where

$$\mathbf{F} = u\mathbf{i} - v\mathbf{j}, \qquad \mathbf{G} = v\mathbf{i} + u\mathbf{j}, \qquad \text{and} \qquad d\mathbf{l} = dx\mathbf{i} + dy\mathbf{j}.$$

Let S be the region interior to and including C. Since the Cauchy-Riemann conditions hold throughout S, it follows that $(\nabla \times \mathbf{F})_z = 0$ and $(\nabla \times \mathbf{G})_z = 0$ throughout S, where the subscript z identifies the $\mathbf{k}$ component of the curl; for example,

$$(\nabla \times \mathbf{F})_z = \frac{\partial(-v)}{\partial x} - \frac{\partial u}{\partial y} = 0,$$

by virtue of the Cauchy-Riemann equations. Now, using Stokes's theorem, the validity of which depends on the continuity of the four first partials of u and v,

$$\oint_C f(z)\,dz = \oint_C \mathbf{F}\cdot d\mathbf{l} + i\oint_C \mathbf{G}\cdot d\mathbf{l} = \int_S (\nabla \times \mathbf{F})\cdot d\mathbf{S} + i\int_S (\nabla \times \mathbf{G})\cdot d\mathbf{S}$$
$$= \int_S (\nabla \times \mathbf{F})_z\,dS + i\int_S (\nabla \times \mathbf{G})_z\,dS = 0,$$

where $d\mathbf{S} = \mathbf{k}\,dS$. \qquad QED

It is possible to prove Cauchy's theorem without assuming the continuity of $f'(z)$. This is because any function which is analytic in a region *necessarily* has a continuous derivative. In fact, we shall prove that an analytic function has derivatives of all orders, and therefore all its derivatives are continuous, the continuity of the nth derivative being a consequence of the existence of the derivative of order $n + 1$. But we shall only be able to establish this result on higher derivatives *after* we have shown that the continuity of $f'(z)$ is not needed in the proof of Cauchy's theorem.

This relaxation or weakening of the hypotheses under which

$$\oint_C f(z)\, dz = 0$$

is therefore of the utmost importance—it is, in fact, the centerpiece of the theory of analytic functions. Some authors (never mathematicians) define an analytic function as a differentiable function *with a continuous derivative*. Then the central result of the theory follows trivially, as we have seen in the previous theorem. But this is a mathematical fraud of cosmic proportions. It was Goursat who first proved that the condition that $f'(z)$ be continuous is superfluous. It is Goursat's result that really distinguishes the theory of integration of a function of a complex variable from the theory of line integrals in the real plane. Although the theorem is often simply called Cauchy's theorem, it is the "-Goursat" half that gives it real mathematical power. In our proof we follow the presentations of Franklin and of Knopp.

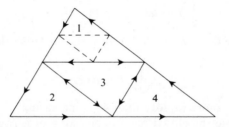

Fig. 6.9

Cauchy-Goursat Theorem. If a function $f(z)$ is analytic within and on a closed contour C, then $\oint_C f(z)\, dz = 0$.

Proof. We shall first prove the theorem for a triangular region; then it is very easily extended to an arbitrary region. Let R denote the closed region consisting of the points interior to and on the triangle bounded by the closed contour T of total length L. Since $f(z)$ is analytic in R, $f'(z)$ exists throughout R, and therefore, $f(z)$ is continuous in R. We now begin subdividing R into smaller triangles as shown in Fig. 6.9. Each subtriangle is similar to the original triangle but its sides (and perimeter) are only one-half as long. The boundaries of the subtriangles are denoted by T_i $(i = 1, 2, 3, 4)$. Clearly

$$\oint_T f(z)\, dz = \sum_{i=1}^{4} \oint_{T_i} f(z)\, dz \,,$$

where all contours are traversed in a counterclockwise direction. All three of the boundaries of triangle 3 in Fig. 6.9 are traversed in both directions and therefore cancel out. Applying the triangle inequality to this equation, we obtain

$$\left| \oint_T f(z) \, dz \right| \leq \sum_{i=1}^{4} \left| \oint_{T_i} f(z) \, dz \right| .$$

The object of the proof is to show that the quantity on the left is arbitrarily small.

Now let C_1 denote the triangle which contributes the largest term to the above sum. Then we have

$$\left| \oint_T f(z) \, dz \right| \leq 4 \left| \oint_{C_1} f(z) \, dz \right| ,$$

where the length of $C_1 \equiv L_1 = L/2$. We now repeat this process on the subtriangle bounded by C_1. That is, we find a contour C_2, bounding a "sub-subtriangle," such that

$$\left| \oint_{C_1} f(z) \, dz \right| \leq 4 \left| \oint_{C_2} f(z) \, dz \right| ,$$

where the length of $C_2 \equiv L_2 = L_1/2 = L/2^2$. If the subdivision is repeated n times, we obtain a nested sequence of triangular contours C_n, such that

$$\left| \oint_T f(z) \, dz \right| \leq 4^n \left| \oint_{C_n} f(z) \, dz \right| , \qquad (6.14)$$

where the length of $C_n \equiv L_n = L/2^n$. In order to finish the proof, we have to show that

$$\left| \oint_{C_n} f(z) \, dz \right|$$

is decreasing with n more rapidly than 4^n is increasing.

We let R_n denote the closed region consisting of C_n and the interior points of the (sub)[nth]-triangle bounded by C_n. Clearly, each point of the region R_{n+1} is a point of R_n, and as n goes to infinity this nested sequence of closed sets closes down on a single point z_0 which is in each R_n, and R itself. (If R is the continent of Africa and we select R_n as that subregion which contains the biggest lion in Africa, we have an algorithm for capturing a big lion—we simply build a cage about the point z_0.)

Since $f'(z)$ exists, it follows by definition that for any $\epsilon > 0$, there exists a δ, such that when $0 < |z - z_0| < \delta$,

$$\left| \frac{f(z) - f(z_0)}{z - z_0} - f'(z_0) \right| \leq \epsilon .$$

Now consider the function $g(z)$ defined by

$$g(z) = \begin{cases} \dfrac{f(z) - f(z_0)}{z - z_0} - f'(z_0) & \text{for } z \neq z_0 , \\ 0 & \text{for } z = z_0 . \end{cases}$$

Note that $|g(z)| \leq \epsilon$ if $|z - z_0| < \delta$; $g(z)$ is therefore continuous at $z = z_0$.

Now $f(z)$ is given for all z in R by

$$f(z) = f(z_0) + (z - z_0)f'(z_0) + (z - z_0)g(z) ;$$

we use this relation to evaluate $\oint_{C_n} f(z)\,dz$. The first two terms are entire functions of z (z_0 is constant) with *derivatives* that are *continuous* everywhere. Therefore we may apply the earlier version of Cauchy's theorem to deduce that

$$\oint_{C_i} [f(z_0) + (z - z_0)f'(z_0)]\,dz = 0 , \qquad \text{for all } i .$$

Therefore

$$\oint_{C_n} f(z)\,dz = \oint_{C_n} (z - z_0)g(z)\,dz .$$

We now subdivide enough times (i.e., we choose n large enough) so that $2^n > L/\delta$. Then $L_n = L/2^n < \delta$. Furthermore, for any point z on C_n, $|z - z_0| < L_n < \delta$, since z_0 is inside R_n, and the distance from any interior point to any point on the boundary of a triangle is clearly less than the perimeter of the triangle. Therefore, since $|z - z_0| < \delta, |g(z)| < \epsilon$, and $|(z - z_0)g(z)| \le L_n\epsilon$. Consequently,

$$\left| \oint_{C_n} f(z)\,dz \right| = \left| \oint_{C_n} (z - z_0)g(z)\,dz \right| \le L_n^2\epsilon = \epsilon(L/2^n)^2 = \epsilon L^2/4^n ,$$

where we have used Eq. (6.13). It now follows from Eq. (6.14) that

$$\left| \oint_T f(z)\,dz \right| \le \epsilon L^2 .$$

Since L is the fixed finite perimeter of the triangular region R, and ϵ is arbitrary, we can make the quantity ϵL^2 smaller than any preassigned number ϵ'. Thus

$$\left| \oint_T f(z)\,dz \right| = 0 , \qquad \text{and hence} \qquad \oint_T f(z)\,dz = 0 .$$

This proves the Cauchy-Goursat theorem for triangular contours.

We shall not give a formal proof of the extension of this result to arbitrary regions, because the method and result are simple and clear. Given an arbitrary C, we inscribe a polygon in C. Any polygon may be decomposed into a sum of triangles, so we know the theorem holds for polygons of any number of sides. It is clear that the difference

$$\left| \oint_C f(z)\,dz - \oint_P f(z)\,dz \right| ,$$

where P is the perimeter of the polygon inscribed in C, can be made arbitrarily small by simply choosing a polygon with a sufficiently large number of sides. This establishes the Cauchy-Goursat theorem for a region of arbitrary shape.

Throughout the proof we have tacitly assumed that the region R is a *simply-connected* region. This means that any closed contour in R encloses only points belonging to R. Suppose, however, that R were a region with one or more subregions "punched out." Then it would be possible to construct curves around these holes in such a way that the curves would lie entirely in R, but enclose points *not* belonging to R. Such regions are called *multiply-connected*. Cauchy's theorem does not hold for arbitrary contours in multiply-connected regions.

6.4 CONSEQUENCES OF CAUCHY'S THEOREM

The hardest work is behind us; we turn now to an examination of some of the main consequences of Cauchy's theorem.

Path Independence

We first prove that if $f(z)$ is analytic in the region R and C_1 and C_2 lie in R and have the same endpoints, then

$$\int_{C_1} f \, dz = \int_{C_2} f \, dz .$$

The proof follows immediately by applying Cauchy's theorem to the closed contour consisting of C_2 and $-C_1$ as shown in Fig. 6.10;

$$\int_{C_2} + \int_{-C_1} = 0 \Longrightarrow \int_{C_2} = -\int_{-C_1} = \int_{C_1}$$

by Eq. (6.11).

Fundamental Theorem of Calculus

From our discussion of path independence it follows that the equation

$$F(z) \equiv \int_{z_0}^{z} f(z') \, dz'$$

defines a unique function of z if $f(z')$ is analytic throughout the region containing the path between z_0 and z.

Theorem. $F(z)$ is analytic and $F'(z) = f(z)$.

Proof.

$$F(z + \Delta z) - F(z) = \int_{z}^{z+\Delta z} f(z') \, dz' ,$$

where the path from z to $(z + \Delta z)$ may be taken to be a straight line. We can write

$$f(z) = \frac{f(z)}{\Delta z} \int_{z}^{z+\Delta z} dz' = \frac{1}{\Delta z} \int_{z}^{z+\Delta z} f(z) \, dz' ,$$

and it follows that

$$\frac{F(z + \Delta z) - F(z)}{\Delta z} - f(z) = \frac{1}{\Delta z} \int_{z}^{z+\Delta z} [f(z') - f(z)] \, dz' .$$

Now $f(z)$ is continuous because it is analytic; therefore, for all $\epsilon > 0$, there exists a $\delta > 0$ such that if $|z' - z| < \delta$, then $|f(z') - f(z)| < \epsilon$. Now take $0 < |\Delta z| < \delta$. Then

$$\left| \frac{F(z + \Delta z) - F(z)}{\Delta z} - f(z) \right| < \epsilon \frac{1}{|\Delta z|} \int_{z}^{z+\Delta z} |dz'| = \epsilon .$$

That is,

$$F'(z) \equiv \lim_{\Delta z \to 0} \frac{F(z + \Delta z) - F(z)}{\Delta z} = f(z) ,$$

so $F(z)$ is analytic and its derivative is $f(z)$.

Thus the integral $F(z)$ of an analytic function $f(z)$ is an analytic function of its upper limit, provided the path of integration is confined to a region R within which the integrand is analytic. The fundamental theorem of calculus follows immediately from this result.

$$\int_a^b f(z) \, dz = \int_{z_0}^b f(z) \, dz - \int_{z_0}^a f(z) \, dz = F(b) - F(a) ,$$

where a and b are points in R, and $F'(z) = f(z)$, that is, $F(z)$ is an antiderivative of $f(z)$. We have already noticed that this method of evaluating integrals worked in a special case: the integral of $\sin z$ from $a = 0$ to $b = 1 + i$ (Section 6.3).

Fig. 6.10

Fig. 6.11

Cauchy's Integral Formula

We now prove one of the most useful results in all mathematical physics.

Theorem. If $f(z)$ is analytic within and on a closed contour C, then for *any* point z_0, interior to C,

$$f(z_0) = \frac{1}{2\pi i} \oint_C \frac{f(z)}{z - z_0} \, dz . \tag{6.15}$$

Proof. Inside the contour C, draw a circle $\tilde{C}_0$ of radius r about z_0, and consider the contour shown in Fig. 6.11. It consists of the circle $\tilde{C}_0$ and the contour C joined by two straight line segments, L_1 and L_2, which lie arbitrarily close to each other. Let us call this entire contour C'. Now consider

$$\oint_{C'} \frac{f(z)}{z - z_0} \, dz = \oint_C \frac{f(z)}{z - z_0} \, dz + \int_{L_1} \frac{f(z)}{z - z_0} \, dz + \oint_{\tilde{C}_0} \frac{f(z)}{z - z_0} \, dz + \int_{L_2} \frac{f(z)}{z - z_0} \, dz .$$

Inside C', $f(z)/(z - z_0)$ is analytic, so by the Cauchy-Goursat theorem,

$$\oint_{C'} \frac{f(z)}{z - z_0} \, dz = 0 .$$

Now, as we bring the line segments L_1 and L_2 arbitrarily close together,

$$\int_{L_1} \frac{f(z)}{z - z_0} \, dz \to -\int_{L_2} \frac{f(z)}{z - z_0} \, dz ,$$

since the lines are traversed in opposite directions. Thus in this limit we have

$$\oint_{C'} \frac{f(z)}{z - z_0} \, dz = 0 = \oint_C \frac{f(z)}{z - z_0} \, dz + \oint_{\tilde{C}_0} \frac{f(z)}{z - z_0} \, dz ,$$

so that

$$\oint_C \frac{f(z)}{z - z_0} \, dz = -\oint_{\tilde{C}_0} \frac{f(z)}{z - z_0} \, dz .$$

At this point we note that considered as a contour in its own right, i.e., not just as a part of C', $\tilde{C}_0$ is traversed in a clockwise direction. Let us therefore define $C_0 = -\tilde{C}_0$ so that C_0 is a counterclockwise contour (as is C). Then we may write

$$\oint_C \frac{f(z)}{z - z_0} \, dz = \oint_{C_0} \frac{f(z)}{z - z_0} \, dz .$$

(Note that for the purposes of what we have just done, C_0 need not be a circle; it could equally well be *any* closed contour lying completely inside C and oriented in the same sense as C.) We may rewrite the last equation as

$$\oint_C \frac{f(z)}{z - z_0} \, dz = f(z_0) \oint_{C_0} \frac{dz}{z - z_0} + \oint_{C_0} \frac{f(z) - f(z_0)}{z - z_0} \, dz .$$

We now use the fact that C_0 is a circle to write $z - z_0 = re^{i\theta}$ on C_0. Thus the first integral on the right becomes

$$\oint_{C_0} \frac{dz}{z - z_0} = \int_0^{2\pi} \frac{ire^{i\theta} d\theta}{re^{i\theta}} = 2\pi i , \qquad \text{for all } r > 0 \text{ within } C .$$

Cauchy's formula will therefore be established if we can show that the second integral vanishes for some choice of the contour C_0. The continuity of $f(z)$ at z_0 tells us that for all $\epsilon > 0$ there exists a δ such that if $|z - z_0| \le \delta$, then $|f(z) - f(z_0)| < \epsilon$. So by taking $r = \delta$, we satisfy the equation $|z - z_0| = \delta$, which in turn implies that

$$\left| \oint_{C_0} \frac{f(z) - f(z_0)}{z - z_0} \, dz \right| \le \oint_{C_0} \frac{|f(z) - f(z_0)|}{|z - z_0|} \, |dz| < \frac{\epsilon}{\delta} (2\pi\delta) = 2\pi\epsilon .$$

Thus by taking r small enough, but still greater than zero, the absolute value of the integral can be made smaller than any preassigned number. Thus

$$\oint_C \frac{f(z)}{z - z_0} \, dz = 2\pi i \, f(z_0) .$$

for all z. Therefore, by Liouville's theorem, $1/P(z) = $ const, a contradiction, since $P(z)$ is of degree one or greater. Hence $P(z) = 0$, for at least one value of z. QED

6.5 HILBERT TRANSFORMS AND THE CAUCHY PRINCIPAL VALUE

It is often the case that in the study of some physical system one has to deal with complex-valued functions—indices of refraction, susceptibilities, scattering amplitudes, impedances, etc.—which have a physical meaning only when the argument of the function (which might, for example, be a frequency or an energy) takes on *real* values. In many cases it is possible to obtain, from the laws governing the system, information about the general properties of such functions when the argument is *complex*; for example, it may be that the function is analytic in some region of the complex plane. Since experimental data can only be obtained for real values of the argument, it is of interest to see whether we can use general properties such as analyticity to deduce relations between real quantities of direct physical significance. The key to such a program can be found in the study of Hilbert transform pairs, which we shall investigate in this section.

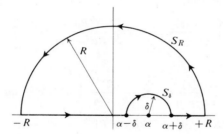

Fig. 6.12 The contour, C, used to obtain Eq. (6.18). The radius, R, of the semi-circle, S_r, may be made as large as necessary, and the radius, S, of the semi-circle, S_δ, may be made as small as we please.

Let us begin by considering a function $f(z)$, which is analytic in the upper half of the complex plane, and which is such that $|f(z)| \to 0$ as $|z| \to \infty$ in the upper half-plane. (Note that the only function which can satisfy these conditions in the *entire* plane is $f \equiv 0$). Now consider the contour integral

$$\oint_C \frac{f(z)}{z - \alpha}\, dz\,,$$

where C is the contour shown in Fig. 6.12 and α is real. By assumption, $f(z)$ is analytic within and on C; so is $1/(z - \alpha)$. Thus

$$\oint_C \frac{f(z)}{z - \alpha}\, dz = 0\,.$$

Let us break this up as follows:

$$\oint_C \frac{f(z)}{z - \alpha}\, dz \equiv \int_{-R}^{\alpha - \delta} \frac{f(x)}{x - \alpha}\, dx + \int_{S_\delta} \frac{f(z)}{z - \alpha}\, dz$$
$$+ \int_{\alpha + \delta}^{R} \frac{f(x)}{x - \alpha}\, dx + \int_{S_R} \frac{f(z)}{z - \alpha}\, dz = 0 \ .$$

Here δ is the radius of the small semicircle S_δ, centered at $x = \alpha$, and R is the radius of the large semicircle S_R, centered at the origin, as shown in Fig. 6.12. The radius δ can be chosen as small as we please, and R can be chosen as large as we please. In the limit of arbitrarily small δ, the quantity

$$\int_{-R}^{\alpha - \delta} \frac{f(x)}{x - \alpha}\, dx + \int_{\alpha + \delta}^{R} \frac{f(x)}{x - \alpha}\, dx$$

is called the *principal-value integral* of $f(x)/(x - \alpha)$ and is denoted by

$$P \int_{-R}^{R} \frac{f(x)}{x - \alpha}\, dx \ .$$

We will say more about this integral below. Now, along the large semicircle S_R, we set $z = Re^{i\theta}$, so that

$$\int_{S_R} \frac{f(z)}{z - \alpha}\, dz = i \int_0^\pi \frac{f(Re^{i\theta})}{Re^{i\theta} - \alpha}\, Re^{i\theta}\, d\theta \ ,$$

and hence

$$\left| \int_{S_R} \frac{f(z)}{z - \alpha}\, dz \right| \leq \frac{R}{|R - \alpha|} \int_0^\pi |f(Re^{i\theta})|\, d\theta \ ,$$

since $|Re^{i\theta} - \alpha| = [R^2 + \alpha^2 - 2R\alpha \cos \theta]^{1/2} \geq [R^2 + \alpha^2 - 2R\alpha]^{1/2} = |R - \alpha|$. But as $R \to \infty$, $|f(z)| \to 0$ and $R/|R - \alpha| \to 1$. Therefore the integral over the semicircle of radius R can be made arbitrarily small by choosing R sufficiently large. Thus we may write

$$\lim_{R \to \infty} P \int_{-R}^{R} \frac{f(x)}{x - \alpha}\, dx = - \int_{S_\delta} \frac{f(z)}{z - \alpha}\, dz = -f(\alpha) \int_{S_\delta} \frac{dz}{z - \alpha} - \int_{S_\delta} \frac{f(z) - f(\alpha)}{z - \alpha}\, dz \ ,$$

where we have added and subtracted the term $\int_{S_\delta} [f(\alpha)/(z - \alpha)]\, dz$. Setting $z - \alpha = \delta e^{i\theta}$ in the first integral on the right-hand side of this equation, we find that

$$-f(\alpha) \int_{S_\delta} \frac{dz}{z - \alpha} = -if(\alpha) \int_\pi^0 d\theta = i\pi f(\alpha) \ .$$

Thus

$$\lim_{R \to \infty} P \int_{-R}^{R} \frac{f(x)}{x - \alpha}\, dx = i\pi f(\alpha) - \int_{S_\delta} \frac{f(z) - f(\alpha)}{z - \alpha}\, dz \ .$$

Since $f(z)$ is continuous at $z = \alpha$, the argument used in deriving Cauchy's integral formula tells us that this last integral over S_δ vanishes. Hence

$$\lim_{R \to \infty} P \int_{-R}^{R} \frac{f(x)}{x - \alpha} \, dx = i\pi f(\alpha) .$$

For the sake of brevity, we write this simply as

$$P \int_{-\infty}^{\infty} \frac{f(x)}{x - \alpha} \, dx = i\pi f(\alpha) , \tag{6.18}$$

where $f(x)$ is a complex-valued function of a real variable. We may write it as

$$f(x) \equiv f_R(x) + i f_I(x) .$$

Equating real and imaginary parts in Eq. (6.18), we get

$$f_R(\alpha) = \frac{1}{\pi} P \int_{-\infty}^{\infty} \frac{f_I(x)}{x - \alpha} \, dx , \tag{6.19a}$$

$$f_I(\alpha) = -\frac{1}{\pi} P \int_{-\infty}^{\infty} \frac{f_R(x)}{x - \alpha} \, dx . \tag{6.19b}$$

Any pair of functions which satisfy Eqs. (6.19a) and (6.19b) is called a *Hilbert transform pair*. Note that these equations tell us that if $f_I(x) \equiv 0$, then $f_R(x) \equiv 0$.

The principal-value integral is seen to be a way of avoiding singularities on a path of integration: one integrates to within δ of the singularity in question, skips over the singularity, and begins integrating again a distance δ beyond the singularity. This prescription enables one to make sense out of integrals like

$$\int_{-R}^{R} \frac{dx}{x} .$$

One would like this integral to be zero, since we are integrating an odd function over a symmetric domain. However, unless we insert a P in front of this integral, the singularity at the origin makes the integral meaningless. Following the prescription for principal-value integrals, we can easily evaluate the above integral. We have

$$P \int_{-R}^{R} \frac{dx}{x} = \lim_{\delta \to 0} \left[\int_{-R}^{-\delta} \frac{dx}{x} + \int_{\delta}^{R} \frac{dx}{x} \right] .$$

In the first integral on the right-hand side, set $x = -y$. Then

$$P \int_{-R}^{R} \frac{dx}{x} = \lim_{\delta \to 0} \left[\int_{R}^{\delta} \frac{dy}{y} + \int_{\delta}^{R} \frac{dx}{x} \right] .$$

The sum of the two integrals inside the brackets is zero, since

$$\int_{R}^{\delta} = - \int_{\delta}^{R} .$$

Thus

$$P \int_{-R}^{R} \frac{dx}{x} = 0 .$$

In a similar manner, we may evaluate

$$P \int_{-R}^{R} \frac{dx}{x - a}$$

when $-R < a < R$. As above, we write

$$P \int_{-R}^{R} \frac{dx}{x - a} = \lim_{\delta \to 0} \left[\int_{-R}^{a - \delta} \frac{dx}{x - a} + \int_{a + \delta}^{R} \frac{dx}{x - a} \right].$$

Again setting $x = -y$ in the first integral on the right-hand side, we find that

$$P \int_{-R}^{R} \frac{dx}{x - a} = \lim_{\delta \to 0} \left[\int_{R}^{\delta - a} \frac{dy}{y + a} + \ln (R - a) - \ln \delta \right]$$

$$= \lim_{\delta \to 0} \left[\ln \delta - \ln (R + a) + \ln (R - a) - \ln \delta \right].$$

Thus

$$P \int_{-R}^{R} \frac{dx}{x - a} = \ln \left(\frac{R - a}{R + a} \right), \qquad -R < a < R. \tag{6.20}$$

For the case

$$P \int_{-R}^{R} \frac{f(x)}{x - a},$$

the result of Eq. (6.20) leads to

$$P \int_{-R}^{R} \frac{f(x)}{x - a} dx = P \int_{-R}^{R} \frac{f(a)}{x - a} dx + P \int_{-R}^{R} \frac{f(x) - f(a)}{x - a} dx,$$

or

$$P \int_{-R}^{R} \frac{f(x)}{x - a} dx = f(a) \ln \left(\frac{R - a}{R + a} \right) + P \int_{-R}^{R} \frac{f(x) - f(a)}{x - a} dx. \tag{6.21}$$

It will often happen that the second integral on the right-hand side of Eq. (6.21) will not be singular at $x = a$ [for example, this will be the case if $f(x)$ is differentiable at $x = a$] so the P symbol there can be dropped. We leave it to the reader to obtain the closely related result:

$$P \int_{0}^{R} \frac{f(x)}{x^2 - a^2} dx = f(a) \frac{1}{2a} \ln \left(\frac{R - a}{R + a} \right) + P \int_{0}^{R} \frac{f(x) - f(a)}{x^2 - a^2} dx. \tag{6.22}$$

To illustrate the use of the principal-value method and also the use of Eqs. (6.19a) and (6.19b), we consider the function $f(z) = 1/(z + i)$. This function satisfies all the hypotheses made in deriving Eqs. (6.19a) and (6.19b). We see that

$$f_R(x) = \frac{x}{x^2 + 1}, \qquad f_I(x) = -\frac{1}{x^2 + 1}.$$

Let us examine Eq. (6.19b). We write it as

$$\lim_{R \to \infty} P \int_{-R}^{R} \frac{f_R(x)}{x - \alpha} dx = -\pi f_I(\alpha).$$

We want to see if $f(z) = 1/(z + i)$ satisfies this relation. Using Eq. (6.21), we have

$$\lim_{R \to \infty} P \int_{-R}^{R} \frac{f_R(x)}{x - \alpha} dx = \lim_{R \to \infty} \left[f_R(\alpha) \ln \left(\frac{R - \alpha}{R + \alpha} \right) + P \int_{-R}^{R} \frac{f_R(x) - f_R(\alpha)}{x - \alpha} dx \right].$$

(6.23)

Now, since $f_R(x) = x/(x^2 + 1)$, we find that

$$\frac{f_R(x) - f_R(\alpha)}{x - \alpha} = \frac{1 - \alpha x}{(\alpha^2 + 1)(x^2 + 1)},$$

so we may drop the principal-value sign on the right-hand side of Eq. (6.23). Also,

$$\lim_{R \to \infty} \ln \left(\frac{R - \alpha}{R + \alpha} \right) = 0,$$

so Eq. (6.23) becomes

$$\lim_{R \to \infty} P \int_{-R}^{R} \frac{f_R(x)}{x - \alpha} dx = \frac{1}{\alpha^2 + 1} \lim_{R \to \infty} \int_{-R}^{R} \frac{1 - \alpha x}{x^2 + 1} dx = \frac{1}{\alpha^2 + 1} \lim_{R \to \infty} \int_{-R}^{R} \frac{dx}{x^2 + 1},$$

since $x/(x^2 + 1)$ is an odd function. Thus

$$\lim_{R \to \infty} P \int_{-R}^{R} \frac{f_R(x)}{x - \alpha} dx = \frac{2}{\alpha^2 + 1} \lim_{R \to \infty} \tan^{-1} R = \frac{\pi}{\alpha^2 + 1} = -\pi f_I(\alpha),$$

so Eq. (6.19b) is indeed satisfied. We leave it to the reader to show that Eq. (6.19a) is also satisfied. Clearly Eq. (6.21) is very useful in conjunction with Eqs. (6.19a) and (6.19b) because under the assumptions made in deriving these equations, $f(z)$ is differentiable at $z = \alpha$. Thus

$$f_R(\alpha) = \frac{1}{\pi} \int_{-\infty}^{\infty} \frac{f_I(x) - f_I(\alpha)}{x - \alpha} dx,$$

(6.24a)

$$f_I(\alpha) = -\frac{1}{\pi} \int_{-\infty}^{\infty} \frac{f_R(x) - f_R(\alpha)}{x - \alpha} dx,$$

(6.24b)

where, in case of any ambiguity,

$$\int_{-\infty}^{\infty} \equiv \lim_{R \to \infty} \int_{-R}^{R}.$$

These methods can sometimes be used to evaluate real definite integrals. For example, consider the function $f(z) = e^{iz}$. This function is analytic everywhere, and if we write $z = Re^{i\theta}$, then $|f(z)| \to 0$ as $R \to \infty$ for all θ such that $0 < \theta < \pi$. This is not quite what we used above to show that the integral around a large semicircle of $f(z)/(z - \alpha)$ vanishes (although it would be the same if we had $0 \le \theta \le \pi$). However, the reader can show for $f(z) = e^{iz}$ that the contribution from the large semicircle vanishes and Eqs. (6.19a) and (6.19b) are satisfied. In this case, $f_R(x) = \cos x$ and $f_I(x) = \sin x$, so using Eq.

(6.24a), we obtain

$$\cos \alpha = \frac{1}{\pi} \int_{-\infty}^{\infty} \frac{\sin x - \sin \alpha}{x - \alpha} \, dx \; .$$

Since $\sin x - \sin \alpha = 2 \sin \frac{1}{2} (x - \alpha) \cos \frac{1}{2} (x + \alpha)$, we see that indeed there is no singularity of the integrand at $x = \alpha$. For the special case $\alpha = 0$, we find that

$$1 = \frac{1}{\pi} \int_{-\infty}^{\infty} \frac{\sin x}{x} \, dx \; ,$$

that is,

$$\int_{-\infty}^{\infty} \frac{\sin x}{x} \, dx = \pi \; .$$

From this result, we also obtain by symmetry

$$\int_{0}^{\infty} \frac{\sin x}{x} \, dx = \frac{\pi}{2} \; .$$

Here we see that the oscillations of $\sin x$, when x is large, make the integral converge, even though

$$\int_{1}^{\infty} \frac{1}{x} \, dx$$

diverges. This is analogous to the fact that the *alternating* series

$$\sum_{n=1}^{\infty} (-1)^{n+1} \frac{1}{n} \; (= \ln 2)$$

converges, whereas $\sum_{n=1}^{\infty} (1/n)$ diverges.

6.6 AN INTRODUCTION TO DISPERSION RELATIONS

As mathematical results, the equations derived in the previous section are interesting in their own right. However, a scientist naturally wants to know if there are any physical systems to which these results can be applied. What we shall now show is that under fairly broad physically motivated assumptions, one can find physical quantities which possess the analytic properties necessary for them to satisfy a Hilbert transform relation. In our detailed applications, we will focus our attention on electromagnetic theory, but many of our results will be more general than this.

We begin by considering a physical system for which an input, $I(t)$, is related to a response, $R(t)$, in the following *linear* manner:

$$R(t) = \frac{1}{\sqrt{2\pi}} \int_{-\infty}^{\infty} G(t - t') I(t') \, dt' \; . \tag{6.25}$$

For example, $I(t')$ might be the electric field at a time t', and $R(t)$ might be the resulting polarization field at time t. We have assumed that G depends only on

$t - t'$ because we want the system to respond to a sharp input at t_0, $I(t')$ $= I_0\delta(t' - t_0)$, in the same way it would respond to a sharp input at $t_0 + \tau$, that is, at a time τ later. For the first case, we have

$$R_1(t) = \frac{1}{\sqrt{2\pi}} \int_{-\infty}^{\infty} G(t - t') I_0 \delta(t' - t_0) \, dt' = \frac{1}{\sqrt{2\pi}} I_0 G(t - t_0) \ .$$

For the second case, we have

$$R_2(t) = \frac{1}{\sqrt{2\pi}} \int_{-\infty}^{\infty} G(t - t') I_0 \delta(t' - t_0 - \tau) \, dt' = \frac{1}{\sqrt{2\pi}} I_0 G(t - t_0 - \tau) \ ,$$

or, in other words,

$$R_2(t + \tau) = \frac{1}{\sqrt{2\pi}} I_0 G(t - t_0) = R_1(t) \ .$$

Thus if we shift the input by τ, then we shift the response by τ.

Now, what can we say about $G(\tau)$ on general physical grounds? First we see that an input at t should not give rise to a response at times prior to t, that is, $G(\tau) = 0$ for $\tau < 0$, so

$$R(t) = \int_{-\infty}^{t} G(t - t') I(t') \, dt' \ ,$$

which shows that the response at t is the weighted linear superposition of all inputs *prior* to t. This is the *causality requirement*. The possibility that $G(\tau)$ is singular for any finite τ is excluded since the response from a sharp input, $I(t') = I_0 \delta(t' - t_0)$, is

$$R(t) = \frac{1}{\sqrt{2\pi}} I_0 G(t - t_0) \ , \qquad t > t_0 \ ,$$

and since on physical grounds we require that this response always be finite, $G(\tau)$ is finite for all τ. Furthermore, we make the physically reasonable assumption that the effect of an input in the *remote* past does not appreciably influence the present. This may be stated as the requirement that $G(\tau) \to 0$ as $\tau \to \infty$ since, from the previous equation, it amounts to the assumption that the response to any impulse dies down after a sufficiently long time (i.e., any system has some dissipative mechanism).

Now consider the Fourier transform of Eq. (6.25). Using the convolution theorem (see Section 5.7), we find that

$$r(\omega) = g(\omega) i(\omega) \ ,$$

where

$$r(\omega) = \frac{1}{\sqrt{2\pi}} \int_{-\infty}^{\infty} R(t) e^{i\omega t} \, dt \ , \qquad g(\omega) = \frac{1}{\sqrt{2\pi}} \int_{-\infty}^{\infty} G(t) e^{i\omega t} \, dt \ ,$$

$$i(\omega) = \frac{1}{\sqrt{2\pi}} \int_{-\infty}^{\infty} I(t) e^{i\omega t} \, dt \ .$$

In electromagnetic theory, where I is the applied electric field $\mathbf{E}$, and R is the polarization field $\mathbf{P}$, it is customary to denote $g(\omega)$ by $\chi(\omega)$, which is referred to as the electric susceptibility. Thus

$$P(\omega) = \chi(\omega) E(\omega) .$$

By assuming that $G(\tau)$ satisfies

$$\int_0^\infty |G(\tau)| \, d\tau < \infty ,$$

we can guarantee the existence of a bounded $g(\omega)$ for all ω. We may now summarize our physically motivated assumptions on $G(\tau)$:

a) $G(\tau)$ is bounded for all τ;
b) $|G(\tau)|$ is integrable, so $G(\tau) \to 0$ faster than $1/\tau$ as $\tau \to \infty$;
c) $G(\tau) = 0$ for $\tau < 0$.

We may remark that (a) and (b) taken together imply that $G(\tau)$ is square integrable and hence (see Section 9.6) $g(\omega)$ is square integrable.

We now want to show that we can extend $g(\omega)$ into the complex z-plane in such a way that $g(z)$ satisfies the conditions under which we derived the Hilbert transform pair [Eqs. (6.19a) and (6.19b)] of the previous section. First, since $G(\tau) = 0$ for $\tau < 0$, we write

$$g(\omega) = \frac{1}{\sqrt{2\pi}} \int_0^\infty G(t) e^{i\omega t} \, dt .$$

We extend this relation into the complex plane by using the definition

$$g(z) \equiv \frac{1}{\sqrt{2\pi}} \int_0^\infty G(t) e^{izt} \, dt$$

$$= \frac{1}{\sqrt{2\pi}} \int_0^\infty G(t) e^{i\omega t} e^{-\omega' t} \, dt ,$$

where we have written $z = \omega + i\omega'$. We now restrict our attention to the upper half-plane ($\omega' > 0$) where, because of the causality requirement given in assumption (c) above, ($t > 0$ in the above integral), the term $e^{-\omega' t}$ is a *decaying* exponential. For $0 < \theta < \pi$, we have

$$|g(z)| \le \frac{1}{\sqrt{2\pi}} M_G \int_0^\infty e^{-[|z| \sin \theta] t} \, dt ,$$

where we have replaced $G(t)$ by its maximum value, M_G [assumption (a) above]. Thus

$$|g(z)| \le \frac{M_G}{\sqrt{2\pi} \, |z| \sin \theta} ,$$

which tends to zero when $|z| \to \infty$. For $\theta = 0$ or π, we have

$$g(\omega, \omega' = 0) = \frac{1}{\sqrt{2\pi}} \int_0^\infty G(t) e^{i\omega t} \, dt .$$

Since $G(t)$ is square integrable, so is $g(\omega, \omega' = 0)$ as a function of ω (see Section 9.6), and hence $|g(\omega, \omega' = 0)|$ tends to zero as $\omega \to \infty$. Thus in any direction in the upper half-plane, $|g(z)| \to 0$ as $|z| \to \infty$.

Now we want to show that $g(z)$ is analytic in the upper half-plane. Using

$$g(z) = \frac{1}{\sqrt{2\pi}} \int_0^\infty G(t) e^{izt}\, dt = \frac{1}{\sqrt{2\pi}} \int_0^\infty G(t) e^{i\omega t} e^{-\omega' t}\, dt , \qquad (6.26)$$

we see that for $\omega' > 0$,

$$\frac{d^n g}{dz^n} = \frac{1}{\sqrt{2\pi}} \int_0^\infty G(t) \frac{d^n}{dz^n} e^{izt}\, dt = \frac{i^n}{\sqrt{2\pi}} \int_0^\infty t^n G(t) e^{i\omega t} e^{-\omega' t}\, dt , \qquad (6.27)$$

since in this case the integrals in both (6.26) and (6.27) are uniformly convergent because of the term $e^{-\omega' t} (\omega' > 0, t > 0)$. Thus $g(z)$ is analytic in the upper half-plane ($\omega' > 0$). However, it is clear that our assumptions on $G(t)$ do not enable us to extend the domain of analyticity to $\omega' \geq 0$. Nevertheless, we can say that $g(z)$ is bounded on the real axis, so the only singularities when $\omega' = 0$ will be of the branch point variety, and even then such branch singularities as $1/\sqrt{z}$ or $\log z$ are excluded by the boundedness requirement. The reader can see by looking back at the derivation of the original pair of Hilbert transform equations [Eqs. (6.19a) and (6.19b)] that it can be modified to include bounded branch point singularities on the real axis by taking a small semicircular detour around any such point. Thus Eqs. (6.19a) and (6.19b) remain unaltered by the presence of such singularities (the branches can always be chosen to avoid the upper half-plane). To eliminate the possibility of these branch singularities, one would have to assume an exponential type falloff of $G(\tau)$ as $\tau \to \infty$. Hence for any $g(z)$ arising from a $G(t)$ which satisfies assumptions (a), (b), and (c), we may write

$$g_R(\omega) = \frac{1}{\pi} P \int_{-\infty}^\infty \frac{g_I(\bar\omega)}{\bar\omega - \omega}\, d\bar\omega , \qquad (6.28a)$$

$$g_I(\omega) = -\frac{1}{\pi} P \int_{-\infty}^\infty \frac{g_R(\bar\omega)}{\bar\omega - \omega}\, d\bar\omega . \qquad (6.28b)$$

Thus by making a few very reasonable assumptions about the system in question, we can show that the real and imaginary parts of the physical quantity $g(\omega)$ are intimately related to each other for *real* values of the argument by what is essentially a dispersion relation. The key assumption is the *causality requirement*; we may say that causality implies the existence of dispersion relations in the case we have considered. In actual practice, one often restricts the term "dispersion relation" to mean an integral relation between two observable quantities which involves only an integration over values of the argument which are physically meaningful. Thus in Eqs. (6.28a) and (6.28b) only positive frequencies are accessible to experiment, so they are not directly useful as they stand. However, $G(t)$ is real, so we may proceed as follows:

$$g(z) = \frac{1}{\sqrt{2\pi}} \int_0^\infty G(t) e^{izt}\, dt ,$$

$$g^*(z) = \frac{1}{\sqrt{2\pi}} \int_0^\infty G^*(t) e^{-iz^* t}\, dt = \frac{1}{\sqrt{2\pi}} \int_0^\infty G(t) e^{-iz^* t}\, dt = g(-z^*) .$$

Thus we have $g^*(z) = g(-z^*)$, which is often referred to as the *reality condition*. If z is real $(z = \omega)$, we find that

$$g_R(\omega) - ig_I(\omega) = g_R(-\omega) + ig_I(-\omega) \ ,$$

or

$$g_R(\omega) = g_R(-\omega) \ , \tag{6.29a}$$

$$g_I(\omega) = -g_I(-\omega) \ , \tag{6.29b}$$

that is, g_R is an *even* function of ω and g_I is an *odd* function of ω. Note that if Eqs. (6.29a) and (6.29b) are satisfied, then the function

$$G(t) = \frac{1}{\sqrt{2\pi}} \int_{-\infty}^{\infty} g(\omega)e^{-i\omega t} \, d\omega$$

is a real function.

Now in Eq. (6.28a), let us write

$$g_R(\omega) = \frac{1}{\pi} P \int_{-\infty}^{0} \frac{g_I(\bar{\omega})}{\bar{\omega} - \omega} \, d\bar{\omega} + \frac{1}{\pi} P \int_{0}^{\infty} \frac{g_I(\bar{\omega})}{\bar{\omega} - \omega} \, d\bar{\omega} \ .$$

In the first integral, we let $\bar{\omega} \to -\bar{\omega}$. Thus

$$g_R(\omega) = \frac{1}{\pi} P \int_{\infty}^{0} \frac{g_I(-\bar{\omega})}{\bar{\omega} + \omega} \, d\bar{\omega} + \frac{1}{\pi} P \int_{0}^{\infty} \frac{g_I(\bar{\omega})}{\bar{\omega} - \omega} \, d\bar{\omega} \ .$$

Using Eq. (6.29b), we finally obtain

$$g_R(\omega) = \frac{2}{\pi} P \int_{0}^{\infty} \frac{\bar{\omega} g_I(\bar{\omega})}{\bar{\omega}^2 - \omega^2} \, d\bar{\omega} \ , \tag{6.30a}$$

and in an identical manner,

$$g_I(\omega) = -\frac{2\omega}{\pi} P \int_{0}^{\infty} \frac{g_R(\bar{\omega})}{\bar{\omega}^2 - \omega^2} \, d\bar{\omega} \ . \tag{6.30b}$$

These expressions involve only positive, experimentally accessible frequencies. For the electric susceptibility, for example, we have

$$\chi_R(\omega) = \frac{2}{\pi} P \int_{0}^{\infty} \frac{\bar{\omega} \chi_I(\bar{\omega})}{\bar{\omega}^2 - \omega^2} \, d\bar{\omega} \ , \tag{6.31a}$$

$$\chi_I(\omega) = -\frac{2\omega}{\pi} P \int_{0}^{\infty} \frac{\chi_R(\bar{\omega})}{\bar{\omega}^2 - \omega^2} \, d\bar{\omega} \ . \tag{6.31b}$$

Equations (6.31a) and (6.31b) were first derived by H. A. Kramers and R. de L. Kronig and are referred to as the Kramers-Kronig dispersion relations.

Now, according to electromagnetic theory, we may write

$$n^2(\omega) = 1 + 4\pi\chi(\omega) \ ,$$

where $n(\omega)$ is the (complex) index of refraction. Since $\chi(z)$ is analytic in the upper half-z-plane, so is $n^2(z)$, and the function

$$n(z) = \sqrt{1 + 4\pi\chi(z)} \tag{6.32}$$

is also analytic in this region *if* $1 + 4\pi\chi(z)$ has no zeroes in the upper half-plane. If $1 + 4\pi\chi(z)$ vanishes for some $z = z_0$ in the upper half-plane, then according to the reality condition

$$\chi^*(z_0) = \chi(-z_0^*) ,$$

we find that $1 + 4\pi\chi(z)$ also vanishes at $z = -z_0^*$. Since $-z_0^*$ lies in the upper half-plane with the imaginary part equal to Im z_0, there will be a cut in the upper half-plane running from $-z_0^*$ to z_0. In this case, the dispersion relations of Eqs. (6.31a) and (6.31b) would have to be modified. We will assume that $n(z)$ has no zeroes in the upper half-plane and is therefore analytic in this region. However, because of Eq. (6.32), $|n(z)|$ does not tend to zero as $|z| \to \infty$. In fact,

$$n(z) \to 1 \quad \text{as} \quad |z| \to \infty$$

in the upper half-plane. This necessitates a modification in the treatment of the term coming from the large semicircle of Fig. 6.12 in obtaining Eq. (6.18). We have, in the case of $n(z)$,

$$\int_{S_R} \frac{n(z)}{z - \alpha} \, dz \xrightarrow{|z| \to \infty} \int_0^\pi \frac{dz}{z} = i\pi$$

in the notation of the previous section (see Fig. 6.12). Thus, for the case of $n(z)$, Eq. (6.18) must be replaced by

$$i\pi n(\omega) = i\pi + P \int_{-\infty}^\infty \frac{n(\bar\omega)}{\bar\omega - \omega} \, d\bar\omega .$$

Separating real and imaginary parts, we obtain

$$n_R(\omega) = 1 + \frac{1}{\pi} P \int_{-\infty}^\infty \frac{n_I(\bar\omega)}{\bar\omega - \omega} \, d\bar\omega , \tag{6.33a}$$

$$n_I(\omega) = -\frac{1}{\pi} P \int_{-\infty}^\infty \frac{n_R(\bar\omega)}{\bar\omega - \omega} \, d\bar\omega . \tag{6.33b}$$

Making use of the reality condition, we can write these equations as

$$n_R(\omega) = 1 + \frac{2}{\pi} P \int_0^\infty \frac{\bar\omega n_I(\bar\omega)}{\bar\omega^2 - \omega^2} \, d\bar\omega , \tag{6.34a}$$

$$n_I(\omega) = -\frac{2\omega}{\pi} P \int_0^\infty \frac{n_R(\bar\omega)}{\bar\omega^2 - \omega^2} \, d\bar\omega . \tag{6.34b}$$

The quantity $\mu(\omega) \equiv (2\omega/c)n_I(\omega)$, when c is the speed of light in vacuum, is called the *absorption coefficient* and is the inverse of the distance a wave

$$\phi(x, t) = A \exp\left\{i\omega\left[\frac{n(\omega)}{c} x - t\right]\right\}$$

travels before its intensity drops to $1/e$ of its value at $x = 0$. In terms of μ, we have

$$n_R(\omega) = 1 + \frac{c}{\pi} P \int_0^\infty \frac{\mu(\bar\omega)}{\bar\omega^2 - \omega^2} \, d\bar\omega . \tag{6.35}$$

Thus the real part of the index of refraction is completely specified by knowing the absorption coefficient at all frequencies ! It is from Eq. (6.35) that dispersion relations derive their name. Equation (6.35) relates a substance's absorption to its dispersive effects, i.e., to the way the real index of refraction varies with frequency. It is this variation with frequency which produces the well-known separation (dispersion) of different wavelengths of light by a prism.

In more recent times, the term dispersion relation has continued to be used to denote any relationship between real and imaginary parts of a physical quantity (a scattering amplitude in quantum mechanics, for example) which has the general appearance of a Hilbert transform. Note that since $\mu(\omega)$ must be positive for all frequencies on physical grounds (i.e., we do not expect to find waves which grow in time as they pass through a substance), Eq. (6.35) specifies that

$$n_R(0) = 1 + \frac{c}{\pi} P \int_0^\infty \frac{\mu(\bar{\omega})}{\bar{\omega}^2} \, d\bar{\omega} , \qquad (6.36)$$

so we see that $n_R(0) > 1$. Thus the familiar static dielectric constant ϵ, given by $\epsilon = n^2(0)$ is always greater than unity. Since $\chi_I(0) = 0$, we see that the integral in Eq. (6.36) converges without our using the principal-value technique. Thus using $n(0) = \sqrt{\epsilon}$, we may write Eq. (6.36) as

$$\sqrt{\epsilon} - 1 = \frac{c}{\pi} \int_0^\infty \frac{\mu(\bar{\omega})}{\bar{\omega}^2} \, d\bar{\omega} .$$

This relation is known as a "sum rule" for the absorption coefficient; it relates the weighted integral over all values of the absorption coefficient to a simple, experimentally accessible constant.

The derivation of the dispersion relation for the index of refraction exhibits certain features which are often encountered in deriving dispersion relations. Namely, it often happens that the quantity in question does not tend toward zero as $|z|$ tends toward infinity, and, furthermore, one is not usually fortunate enough to know the precise behavior of the quantity as $|z|$ tends to infinity, except, for example, to say that it is *bounded* for large values of $|z|$. In this case, we can proceed as follows. Let α_0 be some point on the real axis at which $f(z)$ is analytic. Then the function

$$\frac{f(z) - f(\alpha_0)}{z - \alpha_0} \equiv \phi(z)$$

is not singular at $z = \alpha_0$, and $|\phi(z)| \to 0$ as $|z| \to \infty$. Also, if $f(z)$ is analytic in the upper half-plane, so is $\phi(z)$, and we can write a dispersion relation for $\phi(z)$:

$$i\pi \left[\frac{f(\alpha) - f(\alpha_0)}{\alpha - \alpha_0} \right] = P \int_{-\infty}^\infty \frac{f(x) - f(\alpha_0)}{(x - \alpha)(x - \alpha_0)} \, dx .$$

But

$$\frac{1}{(x - \alpha)(x - \alpha_0)} = \frac{1}{\alpha - \alpha_0} \left[\frac{1}{x - \alpha} - \frac{1}{x - \alpha_0} \right].$$

Therefore, our dispersion relation takes the form

$$i\pi f(\alpha) = i\pi f(\alpha_0) + (\alpha - \alpha_0) P \int_{-\infty}^{\infty} \frac{f(x)\,dx}{(x-\alpha)(x-\alpha_0)} - f(\alpha_0) P \int_{-\infty}^{\infty} \frac{dx}{x-\alpha}$$

$$+ f(\alpha_0) P \int_{-\infty}^{\infty} \frac{dx}{x-\alpha_0} \, .$$

According to the work of the previous section, these last two principal-value integrals vanish, so we have just

$$i\pi f(\alpha) = i\pi f(\alpha_0) + (\alpha - \alpha_0) P \int_{-\infty}^{\infty} \frac{f(x)\,dx}{(x-\alpha)(x-\alpha_0)} \, .$$

Separating the real and imaginary parts, we finally obtain

$$f_R(\alpha) = f_R(\alpha_0) + \frac{1}{\pi}(\alpha - \alpha_0) P \int_{-\infty}^{\infty} \frac{f_I(x)}{(x-\alpha)(x-\alpha_0)}\,dx \, , \qquad (6.37a)$$

$$f_I(\alpha) = f_I(\alpha_0) - \frac{1}{\pi}(\alpha - \alpha_0) P \int_{-\infty}^{\infty} \frac{f_R(x)}{(x-\alpha)(x-\alpha_0)}\,dx \, . \qquad (6.37b)$$

Relations of the type of Eqs. (6.37a) and (6.37b) are referred to as *once-sub-tracted dispersion relations*. For them to be of use in a particular physical problem, one must have a means of determining, say, $f_R(\alpha_0)$ for *some* α_0 in addition to possessing the usual information required by an ordinary dispersion relation of the type of Eq. (6.19a). If the properties of $f(z)$ for large $|z|$ are even "worse" than assumed above [for example, suppose that $|f(z)/z|$ tended toward a nonzero constant as $|z|$ tended toward infinity], then one could introduce more subtraction points, α_1, α_2, etc, in a similar manner.

We have already seen that causality implies certain analyticity properties; we conclude this section by showing that the converse is also true, namely, analyticity implies causality ! We will do this by using the analytic properties of $n(z)$ to show that electromagnetic signals will not propagate in any medium faster than the speed of light. Consider a wave front traveling in the x-direction in a dielectric medium with a complex index of refraction, $n(z)$. Assume that at $x = 0$ there is no disturbance before $t = 0$, that is, $\phi(0, t) = 0$ for $t < 0$. We can write a general wave, as $\phi(x, t)$, a superposition of plane waves of all frequencies:

$$\phi(x, t) = \int_{-\infty}^{\infty} \phi(\omega) \exp\left\{ i\omega \left[\frac{n(\omega)}{c} x - t \right] \right\}\,d\omega \, .$$

Note that

$$\phi(0, t) = \int_{-\infty}^{\infty} \phi(\omega) e^{-i\omega t}\,d\omega \, ,$$

so

$$\phi(\omega) = \frac{1}{2\pi} \int_{-\infty}^{\infty} \phi(0, t) e^{i\omega t}\,dt \, . \qquad (6.38)$$

We may now use Eq. (6.38) to define $\phi(z)$ for z complex:

$$\phi(z) \equiv \frac{1}{2\pi} \int_0^{\infty} \phi(0, t) e^{i\omega' t} e^{-\omega'' t}\,dt \, ,$$

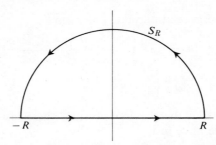

Fig. 6.13 The contour, C, used in evaluating Eq. (6.39). R may become as large as we please.

where we have made use of the fact that $\phi(0, t) = 0$ for $t < 0$ and have written, as usual, $z = \omega + i\omega'$. By our previous arguments, $\phi(z)$ is analytic in the upper half-plane and tends in norm toward zero as $|z|$ tends toward infinity in this region. Now let us consider

$$\oint_C \phi(z) \exp\left[iz\left(\frac{n(z)}{c}x - t\right)\right] dz$$

around the contour shown in Fig. 6.13. Since $\phi(z)$ and $n(z)$ are analytic in the upper half-plane,

$$\oint_C \phi(z) \exp\left[iz\left(\frac{n(z)}{c}x - t\right)\right] dz = 0 .$$

Thus

$$\int_{-R}^{R} \phi(\omega) \exp\left[i\omega\left(\frac{n(\omega)}{c}x - t\right)\right] d\omega + \int_{S_R} \phi(z) \exp\left[iz\left(\frac{n(z)}{c}x - t\right)\right] dz = 0 .$$

$$(6.39)$$

Calling the second integral in Eq. (6.39) I_R, we have

$$|I_R| \le \int_0^{\pi} |\phi(z)| \exp\left[-R \sin\theta \left(\frac{n_R}{c}x - t\right) - R \cos\theta \frac{n_I}{c}x\right] R \, d\theta ,$$

where R is some arbitrarily large number. Now as $R \to \infty$, $n_I \to 0$ and $n_R \to 1$, as we have seen above. Thus, under these circumstances,

$$|I_R| \le 2R \int_0^{\pi/2} |\phi(z)| \exp\left[-R\left(\frac{x}{c} - t\right)\sin\theta\right] d\theta .$$

But $\sin\theta \ge 2\theta/\pi$ for $0 \le \theta \le \pi/2$. (To see this, note that $g(\theta) = \sin\theta - 2\theta/\pi$ vanishes at $\theta = 0$ and $\theta = \pi/2$. It is positive at $\theta = \pi/4$, so if it is to become zero or negative inside $[0, \pi/2]$, it must take on a minimum in this region. However, $g''(\theta)$ is always *negative* in $[0, \pi/2]$ so the function cannot possibly take on a minimum value. This can also be seen by drawing a graph of $\sin\theta$ and $2\theta/\pi$.) Therefore, if $(x/c - t)$ is positive,

$$|I_R| \le 2R \int_0^{\pi/2} |\phi(z)| \exp\left[-\frac{2R}{\pi}\left(\frac{x}{c} - t\right)\theta\right] d\theta .$$

Now $|\phi(z)| \to 0$ as $R \to \infty$, so let us write for large R, $|\phi(z)| \leq aR^{-\lambda}(\lambda > 0)$. Then

$$|I_R| \leq 2aR^{1-\lambda} \int_0^{\pi/2} \exp\left[-\frac{2}{\pi} R\left(\frac{x}{c} - t\right)\theta\right]d\theta\,,$$

or

$$|I_R| \leq \frac{\pi a}{R^2[(x/c) - t]}\left[1 - \exp\left\{-R\left(\frac{x}{c} - t\right)\right\}\right].$$

If we assume that $x/c > t$, then as $R \to \infty$, we see that $|I_R| \to 0$. Note that if $x/c < t$, we cannot draw this conclusion because of the *growing* exponential in the above inequality. Thus as $R \to \infty$, Eq. (6.39) becomes

$$\phi(x, t) = \int_{-\infty}^{\infty} \phi(\omega) \exp\left\{i\omega\left[\frac{n(\omega)}{c} x - t\right]\right\}d\omega = 0$$

for $x/c > t$. Thus we reach the satisfying conclusion that if no signal is present at $x = 0$ when $t = 0$, then there will be no signal at $x = x_0 > 0$ before $t = x_0/c$, that is, a signal can propagate with at most the speed of light, c, even though $c/n(\omega)$ may be greater than c, since $n(\omega)$ is known experimentally to become less than 1 at high frequencies [it clearly *cannot* do so at very low frequencies, since we have already shown that $n(0) \geq 1$].

6.7 THE EXPANSION OF AN ANALYTIC FUNCTION IN A POWER SERIES

We now come to one of the most important applications of the Cauchy-Goursat theorem, namely, the possibility of expanding an analytic function in a power series. The main result may be stated as follows:

Laurent's theorem. Let $f(z)$ be analytic throughout the closed annular region between the two circles C_1 and C_2 with common center z_0. Then at each point in this annulus

$$f(z) = \sum_{n=-\infty}^{\infty} A_n(z - z_0)^n\,, \tag{6.40}$$

with the series converging uniformly in any closed region, R, lying wholly within the annulus. Here

$$A_n = \frac{1}{2\pi i} \oint_C \frac{f(z')}{(z' - z_0)^{n+1}} dz'\,, \tag{6.41}$$

for $n = 0, \pm 1, \pm 2, \cdots$, and C is any closed contour in the annulus which encircles z_0.

Proof. Consider the contour K enclosing the region R as shown in Fig. (6.14); it may be written symbolically as $K = C_1 + L_1 - C_2 + L_2$. Here we adhere to the convention that simple circular contours are always traversed in a counter-clockwise direction. Since the inner circle is traversed in a clockwise direction

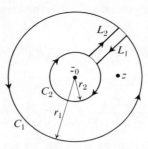

Fig. 6.14

when considered as a part of K, we write it is $-C_2$, where C_2 is a conventionally oriented curve. Since $f(z)$ is analytic within and on K,

$$2\pi i f(z) = \oint_K \frac{f(z')}{z' - z} dz' = \int_{C_1} \frac{f(z')}{z' - z} dz'$$

$$+ \int_{L_1} \frac{f(z')}{z' - z} dz + \int_{-C_2} \frac{f(z')}{z' - z} dz' + \int_{L_2} \frac{f(z')}{z' - z} dz' ,$$

where $z \in R$. By the same argument used in deriving Cauchy's integral formula we see that if L_1 and L_2 are taken to be arbitrarily close together the integrals along L_1 and L_2 cancel, and

$$f(z) = \frac{1}{2\pi i} \oint_{C_1} \frac{f(z')}{z' - z} dz' - \frac{1}{2\pi i} \oint_{C_2} \frac{f(z')}{z' - z} dz' , \qquad (6.42)$$

where we have used Eq. (6.11). Equation (6.42) is the starting point for the proof of Laurent's theorem. To proceed further we make use of the identity (for $\alpha \neq 0$)

$$\frac{1}{\alpha - \beta} = \frac{1}{\alpha} + \frac{\beta}{\alpha(\alpha - \beta)} .$$

The second term is just $(\beta/\alpha)[1/(\alpha - \beta)]$, that is, β/α times the originally expanded quantity, so upon iterating N times we get

$$\frac{1}{\alpha - \beta} = \sum_{n=0}^{N} \frac{\beta^n}{\alpha^{n+1}} + \left(\frac{\beta}{\alpha}\right)^{N+1} \frac{1}{\alpha - \beta} . \qquad (6.43)$$

Keeping this last equation in mind, let us write Eq. (6.42) in the form

$$f(z) = \frac{1}{2\pi i} \oint_{C_1} \frac{f(z')}{[(z' - z_0) - (z - z_0)]} dz' + \frac{1}{2\pi i} \oint_{C_2} \frac{f(z')}{[(z - z_0) - (z' - z_0)]} dz' .$$

Using Eq. (6.43) we can rewrite this as

$$
f(z) = \frac{1}{2\pi i} \sum_{n=0}^{N} \oint_{C_1} \frac{(z - z_0)^n}{(z' - z_0)^{n+1}} f(z')\, dz' + \frac{1}{2\pi i} \oint_{C_1} \left[\frac{z - z_0}{z' - z_0} \right]^{N+1} \frac{f(z')}{z' - z}\, dz'
$$

$$
+ \frac{1}{2\pi i} \sum_{m=0}^{N} \oint_{C_2} \frac{(z' - z_0)^m}{(z - z_0)^{m+1}} f(z')\, dz' + \frac{1}{2\pi i} \oint_{C_2} \left[\frac{z' - z_0}{z - z_0} \right]^{N+1} \frac{f(z')}{z - z'}\, dz' .
$$

(6.44)

According to by now familiar arguments the contours C_1 and C_2 in the first and third terms of the above equation may be replaced by any contour C about z_0 which is contained in the annulus bounded by C_1 and C_2. Making the change of index $m = n + 1$ in the third term, we obtain

$$
f(z) = \sum_{n=-N-1}^{N} A_n (z - z_0)^n + R_N(z) ,
$$

where A_n is given by Eq. (6.41) and

$$
R_N(z) = \frac{1}{2\pi i} \oint_{C_1} \left[\frac{z - z_0}{z' - z_0} \right]^{N+1} \frac{f(z')}{z' - z}\, dz' + \frac{1}{2\pi i} \oint_{C_2} \left[\frac{z' - z_0}{z - z_0} \right]^{N+1} \frac{f(z')}{z - z'}\, dz' .
$$

If we can show that the magnitude of $R_N(z)$ can be made less than any pre-assigned ϵ for N sufficiently large, where N is independent of z, then the proof will be complete. Letting r_1 be the radius of C_1 and r_2 be the radius of C_2, we have

$$
|R_N(z)| \leq \frac{1}{2\pi} \left[\int_0^{2\pi} \frac{|z - z_0|^{N+1}}{r_1^{N+1}} \frac{|f(z')|}{|z' - z|} r_1\, d\theta + \int_0^{2\pi} \frac{r_2^{N+1}}{|z - z_0|^{N+1}} \frac{|f(z')|}{|z - z'|} r_2\, d\theta \right] .
$$

Now we define

$$
M_1 \equiv \operatorname*{Max}_{z \in C_1} |f(z)| , \qquad M_2 \equiv \operatorname*{Max}_{z \in C_2} |f(z)| ,
$$

$$
l_1 \equiv \operatorname*{Max}_{z \in R} |z - z_0| , \qquad l_2 \equiv \operatorname*{Min}_{z \in R} |z - z_0| ,
$$

$$
d_1 \equiv \operatorname*{Min}_{\substack{z \in R \\ z' \in C_1}} |z' - z| , \qquad d_2 \equiv \operatorname*{Min}_{\substack{z \in R \\ z' \in C_2}} |z' - z| .
$$

Since R is a domain within the annulus bounded by C_1 and C_2,

$$
l_1 < r_1 , \qquad l_2 > r_2 ,
$$

(6.45)

Thus,

$$
|R_N(z)| \leq \frac{M_1 r_1}{d_1} \left(\frac{l_1}{r_1} \right)^{N+1} + \frac{M_2 r_2}{d_2} \left(\frac{r_2}{l_2} \right)^{N+1} .
$$

(6.46)

But according to Eq. (6.45), $(l_1/r_1) < 1$ and $(r_2/l_2) < 1$, independent of z, so the magnitude of $R_N(z)$ can be made as small as we please for N sufficiently large. Since the bound of Eq. (6.46) is independent of z we have completed the proof of the uniform convergence of the series in Eq. (6.40). This series is known as the *Laurent expansion* of $f(z)$ about the point z_0.

Example 1. Consider the function

$$f(z) = \frac{z^3 + 2z^2 + 4}{(z - 1)^3} .$$

We shall obtain the Laurent expansion of $f(z)$ about the singular point $z = 1$. Writing $z \equiv (z - 1) + 1$, we have

$$f(z) = \frac{[(z - 1) + 1]^3 + 2[(z - 1) + 1]^2 + 4}{(z - 1)^3}$$

$$= 1 + \frac{5}{z - 1} + \frac{7}{(z - 1)^2} + \frac{7}{(z - 1)^3} .$$

Clearly this is the Laurent expansion of $f(z)$ about $z = 1$, and the reader is urged to verify this by evaluating the coefficients A_n of Eq. (6.41) which are non-vanishing for this particular $f(z)$.

Example 2. We now consider the Laurent series for a less trivial case, namely the function $\cosh(z + 1/z)$. The hyperbolic cosine is an entire function. Its argument, $z + 1/z$, is analytic everywhere except at the origin, and therefore $\cosh(z + 1/z)$ is analytic everywhere except at the origin. Thus we can pick C_2 to be an arbitrarily small circle about the origin and C_1 to be an arbitrarily large circle about the origin. Then

$$\cosh\left(z + \frac{1}{z}\right) = \sum_{-\infty}^{\infty} A_n z^n , \quad \text{where} \quad A_n = \frac{1}{2\pi i} \oint_C \frac{\cosh(z' + 1/z')}{(z')^{n+1}} dz' ,$$

and C is any closed contour about the origin. Let C be the unit circle. Then $z' = e^{i\theta}$ on C, so the integral becomes

$$A_n = \frac{1}{2\pi} \int_{-\pi}^{\pi} \cosh(2\cos\theta) e^{-in\theta} d\theta$$

$$= \frac{1}{\pi} \int_0^{\pi} \cosh(2\cos\theta) \cos n\theta \, d\theta .$$

This integral may be evaluated by using the integral representation of the Bessel function, which will be discussed in Section 6.9. We will obtain A_n by still another method later in this section but will give the result here for the sake of completeness:

$$A_{2n} = \sum_{m=0}^{\infty} \frac{1}{m!(m + 2|n|)!} ,$$

$$A_{2n+1} = 0 \quad \text{for} \quad n = 0, \pm 1, \pm 2, \cdots$$

(6.47)

Example 3. To illustrate another kind of problem involving Laurent expansions, consider the function $f(z) = (z^2 - 1)^{-1/2}$. According to the discussion in

Section 6.2, this function has branch points at $z = -1$ and $z = +1$. We can choose the cut to run between these two points along the real axis, defining a single-valued branch by

$$f(z) = (\rho_1\rho_2)^{-1/2} e^{-i\phi_1/2} e^{-i\phi_2/2} ,$$

where $0 \leq \phi_1 < 2\pi$, $0 \leq \phi_2 < 2\pi$, $\rho_1 = |z - 1|$, $\rho_2 = |z + 1|$ and $(\rho_1\rho_2)^{-1/2}$ denotes the positive square root of $1/\rho_1\rho_2$ (see Fig. (6.15)). With these definitions $f(z)$ is analytic everywhere except on the real axis between $z = -1$ and $z = +1$. Thus, if we take C_2 to be a circle centered at $z = 0$ with radius infinitesimally larger than 1 and C_1 to be a circle of arbitrarily large radius, we can obtain a Laurent expansion of $f(z)$ in the annulus defined by C_1 and C_2. As usual

$$(z^2 - 1)^{-1/2} = \sum_{n=-\infty}^{\infty} A_n z^n ,$$

where

$$A_n = \frac{1}{2\pi i} \oint_C \frac{(z'^2 - 1)^{-1/2}}{(z')^{n+1}} dz' .$$

For $n \geq 0$ we choose C to be a circle of arbitrarily large radius; it is clear that for this contour the relevant integral vanishes, so $A_n = 0$ for $n \geq 0$. To deal with the case of negative n, we choose as contour any circle with radius greater than 1 (see Fig. 6.15). According to our results on path independence, this contour can be deformed into a "dogbone" contour as shown in Fig. 6.15. The

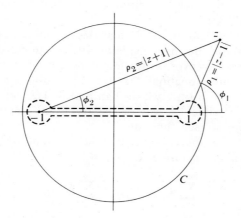

Fig. 6.15 The circular contour C is the starting point for the evaluation of the Laurent series coefficients, A_n of $(z^2 - 1)^{-1/2}$ when n is negative. ρ_1, ρ_2, ϕ_1, and ϕ_2 define the single-valued branch of this function, and the dashed "dogbone" contour is the deformation of C which enables us to evaluate the coefficients.

contribution to A_n from the infinitesimally small circles at the ends of the bone is vanishingly small, so we have simply

$$A_n = \frac{1}{2\pi i}\left[\int_1^{-1} \frac{1}{\sqrt{1-x^2}} e^{-i\pi/2} x^m \, dx + \int_{-1}^1 \frac{1}{\sqrt{1-x^2}} e^{-i(\pi+2\pi)/2} x^m \, dx\right]$$

$$= \frac{1}{\pi}\int_{-1}^1 \frac{x^m}{\sqrt{1-x^2}} \, dx \,,$$

where $m = -n - 1$ (note that for the range of n in question m is never negative). Clearly, for m odd (n even) A_n vanishes. For m even (n odd) the integral is elementary; we have

$$A_n = \frac{2}{\pi}\int_0^1 \frac{x^m}{\sqrt{1-x^2}} \, dx = \frac{2}{\pi}\int_0^{\pi/2} \sin^m \theta \, d\theta = \frac{m!}{2^m[(m/2)!]^2} \cdot$$

Thus,

$$(z^2 - 1)^{-1/2} = \sum_{m=0}^{\infty}{}' \frac{m!}{2^m[(m/2)!]^2} \frac{1}{z^{m+1}} \,,$$

where the prime indicates that only even values of m are included in the summation. Setting $m = 2\nu$, we have finally

$$(z^2 - 1)^{-1/2} = \sum_{\nu=0}^{\infty} \frac{(2\nu)!}{4^\nu (\nu!)^2} \frac{1}{z^{2\nu+1}} = \frac{1}{z} + \frac{1}{2}\frac{1}{z^3} + \frac{3}{8}\frac{1}{z^5} + \frac{5}{16}\frac{1}{z^7} + \cdots .$$

This result is not surprising: it is just what we would have obtained by expanding $(z^2 - 1)^{-1/2}$ using real variable techniques. Note that in keeping with our definition of the single-valued branch of $(z^2 - 1)^{-1/2}$ the Laurent series gives a value of the square root which is positive on the positive real axis and negative on the negative real axis.

Until now we have spoken of singularities as points where the function in question is not analytic, but have made no attempt to classify singular points. There are differences, however, as we might expect if we look at the singular point $z = 0$ of the three functions $1/z$, $1/z^2$, and $\cosh (z + 1/z)$. We feel that the singularity of $1/z^2$ is a little worse than that of $1/z$ and that the singularity of $\cosh (z + 1/z)$ is terrible. A way of classifying the singularities is provided by the Laurent series of each function.

Suppose that $f(z)$ is analytic in a domain R except at $z = z_0$. Expand $f(z)$ in a Laurent series about z_0 inside R:

$$f(z) = \sum_{n=0}^{\infty} a_n(z - z_0)^n + \sum_{n=1}^{\infty} b_n \frac{1}{(z - z_0)^n} \cdot$$

If $b_n = 0$ for $n = N + 1, N + 2, \cdots, \infty$, that is, if the series of negative powers of $(z - z_0)$ terminates with the Nth power, then $f(z)$ is said to have a *pole of order N* at z_0. The functions $1/z$ and $1/z^2$ have poles of order 1 and 2 respectively. But the Laurent expansion of $\cosh (z + 1/z)$ has an *infinite* number of negative powers of z; so does the Laurent expansion of $e^{1/z}$ as we shall soon see. The singularities of these functions at the origin are called *essential* singularities. They cannot be removed by multiplying the function by some finite power of z, as is the case with the poles of $1/z$ and $1/z^2$. Notice, however, that the presence of an infinite number of negative powers of z in a Laurent series does not guarantee the presence of an essential singularity. Example 3 above shows that a branch cut singularity can also give rise to an infinite number of negative powers of z in a Laurent series. Only if we know that the singularity in question is confined within an arbitrarily small region can we conclude that an infinite number of negative powers of z implies the existence of an essential singularity. A function with no essential singularities in a region—although it may have poles there—is said to be a *meromorphic* function.

A particularily important consequence of Laurent's theorem arises when there are *no singularities* contained within the inner circle C_2, that is, if $f(z)$ is analytic everywhere inside C_1. Using Laurent's theorem, we can write

$$f(z) = \sum_{n=-\infty}^{\infty} A_n (z - z_0)^n,$$

where

$$A_n = \frac{1}{2\pi i} \oint_C \frac{f(z')}{(z' - z_0)^{n+1}} \, dz' . \qquad (6.48)$$

But if $f(z')$ is analytic inside C_1, then for $n = -1, -2, \cdots$, the integrand in Eq. (6.48) is analytic within and on C (since C lies within C_1). Therefore, according to the Cauchy-Goursat theorem, $A_n = 0$ for $n \leqslant -1$. Furthermore, for $n \geqslant 0$, we have, using Eq. (6.17),

$$\frac{1}{2\pi i} \oint_C \frac{f(z')}{(z' - z_0)^{n+1}} \, dz' = \frac{1}{n!} f^{(n)} (z_0) ,$$

where $f^{(n)} (z_0)$ denotes the nth derivative of $f(z)$ at $z = z_0$ and $f^{(0)} (z) \equiv f(z_0)$. Thus,

$$f(z) = \sum_{n=0}^{\infty} \frac{1}{n!} f^{(n)} (z_0) (z - z_0)^n . \qquad (6.49)$$

This result is known as Taylor's theorem, and the series in Eq. (6.49) is called Taylor's series for $f(z)$ about z_0. This very important result may be stated formally as follows:

Taylor's Theorem. If $f(z)$ is analytic at all points interior to a circle C centered about z_0 then in any closed region contained wholly inside C

$$f(z) = \sum_{n=0}^{\infty} \frac{1}{n!} f^{(n)} (z_0) (z - z_0)^n , \qquad (6.50)$$

and the series converges uniformly.

We can now express the analytic function $f(z)$ as a uniformly convergent series of analytic functions (it is a simple matter to show that *any* uniformly convergent series of analytic functions is analytic). Because of the uniformity of the convergence, it can readily be shown that the integral of $f(z)$ along any path in the region of convergence of the power series in Eq. (6.49) can be evaluated by integrating the series term-by-term (see Problem 6.28). Using Eq. (6.17), we see that this also means that the derivatives of $f(z)$ can be evaluated similarly by term-by-term differentiation. Thus Eq. (6.49) provides $f(z)$ and all its derivatives throughout the region of convergence.

Examples

1. $e^z = \sum_{n=0}^{\infty} \frac{z^n}{n!}$,   for $|z| < \infty$.

2. $\sin z = \sum_{n=0}^{\infty} (-1)^n \frac{z^{2n+1}}{(2n+1)!}$,   for $|z| < \infty$.

3. $(1-z)^{-1} = \sum_{n=0}^{\infty} z^n$,   for $|z| < 1$.

These series all reduce to familiar results for real values of z.

It is often possible to obtain the *Laurent* expansion of some function by using a related Taylor series. Thus, Example 1, above, gives us

$$e^{1/z} = \sum_{n=0}^{\infty} \frac{1}{n!\, z^n} \qquad (|z| > 0) .$$

This show clearly that $e^{1/z}$ has an essential singularity at $z = 0$. A slightly more substantial example is provided by the Taylor expansion of $\cosh z$. It is a simple matter to show that

$$\cosh z = \sum_{n=0}^{\infty} \frac{z^{2n}}{(2n)!}$$

For $|z| < \infty$. Thus for $|z| > 0$ we have

$$\cosh (z + 1/z) = \sum_{n=0}^{\infty} \frac{1}{(2n)!} (z + 1/z)^{2n} .$$

Using the binomial theorem, we find

$$\cosh (z + 1/z) = \sum_{n=0}^{\infty} \sum_{m=0}^{2n} \frac{z^{2(n-m)}}{(2n-m)!\, m!} = \sum_{n=0}^{\infty} \sum_{\mu=-n}^{n} \frac{z^{2\mu}}{(n+\mu)!\, (n-\mu)!} .$$

If in Eq. (6.50) we interchange the order of summation and then make the change of variable $\nu = n - \mu$, we obtain

$$\cosh (z + 1/z) = \sum_{\mu=-\infty}^{\infty} z^{2\mu} \left[\sum_{\nu=0}^{\infty} \frac{1}{(\nu + 2|\mu|)!\, \nu!} \right] ,$$

in agreement with the result of Eqs. (6.47).

The region in which a Taylor series expansion of a function about a point z_0 is valid is limited by the presence of a singularity of $f(z)$. We have seen that if this singularity is at the point α_0, the Taylor's expansion holds within a circular region of radius $|\alpha_0 - z_0|$ about z_0. Now the Taylor expansion gives the values of the analytic function and all its derivatives at every point in the region of analyticity. In particular, these quantities are known at a point z_1 (see Fig. 6.16) near the region's border. We may now use the point z_1 as a point about which to expand the function in another Taylor series. We can do this because $f^{(n)}(z_1)$ is known for all n from the first Taylor expansion about z_0. The radius of convergence of this second series expansion about z_1 is determined by the distance from z_1 to the nearest singularity. Continuing in this way (Fig. 6.16), we can determine the function throughout the entire plane except the points at which it is singular. To get started, we need only know the values of the analytic function in some *region*, however small. This process is called *analytic continuation*. It is as though a paleontologist could reconstruct a whole dinosaur from the fossil remains of a single toenail.

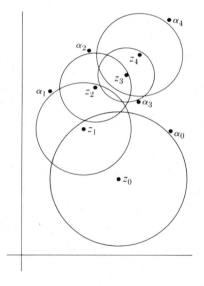

Fig. 6.16 A sequence of Taylor expansions which analytically continue a function originally known in some region around z_0. The first expansion about z_0 is limited in its radius of expansion by the singularity at α_0. The next Taylor expansion about z_1 (inside the first expansion's radius of convergence) is limited by a second singularity at α_1, and so on.

The process of analytic continuation is the best demonstration of the rigid inner structure of *analytic* functions. Again we see how interdependent are the values of an analytic function: its values in *any* region on the plane determine its values *everywhere* that it is analytic. This blueprint for the construction of all the values of an analytic function also demonstrates the necessity of the property that all derivatives of analytic functions are analytic. For if this were not the case, we could not continue a function analytically by a chain of Taylor expansions. To do this requires that we be able to approximate the function arbitrarily well, and this in turn means that all its derivatives must exist so the Taylor series can be extended to achieve arbitrary accuracy.

An immediate consequence of the fact that an analytic function may be continued is that a function which is zero along any curve in a region R, throughout which it is analytic, must be zero everywhere in R. This means that if two functions $f(z)$ and $g(z)$ are equal on any curve inside a simply-connected region R in which both are single-valued and analytic, then they are equal everywhere in R, since $f(z) - g(z)$ is zero on the curve and therefore throughout R. It will be recalled that the analytic functions e^z, sin z, sinh z, etc., were defined for complex arguments in a way that reduced to the usual definitions on the real axis. The principle discussed above shows that these functions could not have been defined otherwise away from the real axis and still be analytic. Furthermore, this explains why all the familiar identities satisfied by the functions for real values continue to hold throughout the complex plane.

It should also be noted that the process of analytic continuation is closely related to the problem of multivalued functions and Riemann surfaces discussed in Section 6.2. Suppose that we are given an analytic power series for a function in some region, for example,

$$w(z) = \sqrt{z} = \sqrt{1 - (1 - z)} = 1 - \tfrac{1}{2}(1 - z) - \tfrac{1}{8}(1 - z)^2 + \cdots$$

in the region consisting of the interior of a circle of unit radius about the point $z = 1$. If we try to continue such a function along certain paths in the z-plane (in the case above, any path enclosing the origin), it may happen that upon returning to the original region of definition, we do *not* return to the original values of the function. This leads in a natural way to the construction of Riemann surfaces of the type discussed in Section 6.2.

6.8 RESIDUE THEORY—EVALUATION OF REAL DEFINITE INTEGRALS AND SUMMATION OF SERIES

There is really nothing fundamentally new in this section. All the theorems have been proved; here we just apply them in certain ways to determine the values of some real definite integrals.

The Residue Theorem. The integral of $f(z)$ around a closed contour C containing a finite number n of singular points of $f(z)$ equals the sum of n integrals of $f(z)$ about n circles, each enclosing one (and only one) of the n singular points.

Proof. If we apply Cauchy's theorem to the region shown in Fig. 6.17, we obtain

$$\int_C f(z)\ dz + \int_{C_1} f(z)\ dz + \int_{C_2} f(z)\ dz + \cdots + \int_{C_n} f(z)\ dz = 0.$$

Note that the contours C_j are traversed clockwise in Fig. (6.17). It follows that

$$\oint_C f(z)\ dz = 2\pi i \sum_{j=1}^{n} R_j\ ,$$

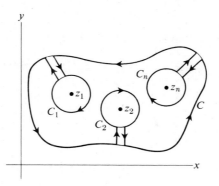

Fig. 6.17

where $R_j = (1/2\pi i) \oint_{C_j} f(z)\, dz$ is called the *residue* at the point z_j. In this equation for R_j the integral sign has its conventional meaning, that is, the contours C_j are traversed counterclockwise.

There is nothing new in this theorem except the name "residue." To compute the residues we shall often use Cauchy's integral formula or the formula for the derivative of an analytic function derived from Cauchy's formula by differentiation.

There is another way to compute residues, however, which is sometimes useful. We expand $f(z)$ in a Laurent series about the singular point z_0:

$$f(z) = \sum_{n=0}^{\infty} a_n(z - z_0)^n + \sum_{n=1}^{\infty} b_n(z - z_0)^{-n}.$$

Now $b_1 = (1/2\pi i) \oint_{C_0} f(z)\, dz = R_0$. It is instructive to check this by integrating both sides of the Laurent series expansion about a circle which includes z_0 but no other singularities. Interchanging summation and integration, which is permissible because these series converge uniformly, we get

$$\oint_{C_0} f(z)\, dz = \sum_{n=0}^{\infty} a_n \oint_{C_0} (z - z_0)^n\, dz + \sum_{n=1}^{\infty} b_n \oint_{C_0} \frac{dz}{(z - z_0)^n}.$$

The first integral vanishes for all n because $(z - z_0)^n$ is analytic. For $n = 1$, the second integral gives $2\pi i b_1$ by Cauchy's integral formula. For $n > 1$, we write $b_n \equiv g(z)$; then by Eq. (6.17)

$$\oint_{C_0} \frac{b_n\, dz}{(z - z_0)^n} = \oint_{C_0} \frac{g(z)\, dz}{(z - z_0)^n} = \frac{2\pi i}{(n - 1)!} g^{(n-1)}(z_0) = 0,$$

since $g(z) = b_n = $ const. Thus $(1/2\pi i) \oint_{C_0} f(z)\, dz = b_1 = $ the residue at z_0, so the residue at a point can be found by expanding the function about the point in a Laurent series and picking out the coefficient of the term in $(z - z_0)^{-1}$. There is nothing mysterious about this; it is a simple consequence of Cauchy's integral formula.

Examples.

1. $I = \oint_C e^{1/z} \, dz$, C = unit circle about the origin.

$$e^{1/z} = \sum_{n=0}^{\infty} \frac{1}{n! \, z^n}, \qquad \text{so } b_1 = 1 .$$

Therefore $I = 2\pi i$.

2. $I = \oint_C \dfrac{3z^2 + 2}{z(z + 1)} \, dz$,

where C is the circle: $|z| = 3$. The quickest way to do this integral is to write it as

$$\oint_C = \oint_{C_0} + \oint_{C_1} = \oint_{C_0} \frac{(3z^2 + 2)/(z + 1)}{z} \, dz + \oint_{C_1} \frac{(3z^2 + 2)/z}{(z + 1)} \, dz ,$$

where C_0 is a little circle inside C enclosing $z = 0$, but not $z = -1$, and C_1 is a little circle inside C enclosing $z = -1$, but not $z = 0$. Then using Cauchy's integral formula to evaluate both integrals, we obtain $I = 2\pi i(2 - 5) = -6\pi i$.

3. $I = \oint_C \dfrac{3z + 2}{z(z + 1)^3} \, dz$,

where C is the circle $|z| = 3$. We break up the integral as before:

$$I = \oint_{C_0} \frac{(3z + 2)/(z + 1)^3}{z} \, dz + \oint_{C_1} \frac{(3z + 2)/z}{(z + 1)^3} \, dz$$

$$= 2\pi i[2] + 2\pi i \left[\frac{f''(z)}{2!} \right]_{z=-1}$$

where $f(z) = (3z + 2)/z$. Therefore $f''(-1) = -4$, so the residue at $z = -1$ is -2, thus $I = 2\pi i(2 - 2) = 0$.

In this last example we evaluated the residue of a function of the form $f(z)/(z - z_0)^n$ at the singular point z_0 by using Cauchy's formula for the derivative of an analytic function. In general, if $f(z)$ is analytic within and on some contour C surrounding z_0, then the residue of the function $f(z)/(z - z_0)^n$ at z_0 is

$$\frac{1}{2\pi i} \oint_C \frac{f(z)}{(z - z_0)^n} \, dz = \frac{f^{n-1}(z_0)}{(n - 1)!} .$$

An instructive way to view this formula is to expand $f(z)$ in a Taylor series about z_0. This is possible because $f(z)$ is analytic in some region about z_0, since the singularities are isolated. Then

$$f(z) = f(z_0) + f'(z_0)(z - z_0) + \cdots + \frac{f^{n-1}(z_0)(z - z_0)^{n-1}}{(n - 1)!} + \cdots .$$

If we now form the quantity $f(z)/(z - z_0)^n$ by dividing both sides by $(z - z_0)^n$, the coefficient of the term in $1/(z - z_0)$, which is just the residue of $f(z)/(z - z_0)^n$, is $f^{(n-1)}(z_0)/(n - 1)!$, in agreement with the above.

$f'(z) = -\dfrac{2}{z^2}$

$f''(z) = +\dfrac{4}{z^3}$

same as
6.17

We now use these techniques to evaluate various definite integrals.

a) $\int_0^{2\pi} R(\cos\theta, \sin\theta)\, d\theta$, where R is a rational function, that is,

$$R = \frac{a_1\cos\theta + a_2\sin\theta + a_3\cos^2\theta + \cdots}{b_1\cos\theta + b_2\sin\theta + b_3\cos^2\theta + b_4\sin^2\theta + \cdots}.$$

To evaluate this integral, let $z = e^{i\theta}$, so that

$$\cos\theta = \frac{1}{2}\left(z + \frac{1}{z}\right), \qquad \sin\theta = \frac{1}{2i}\left(z - \frac{1}{z}\right),$$

and $d\theta = -i(dz/z)$. The integral becomes

$$-i\oint_C R\left[\frac{1}{2}\left(z + \frac{1}{z}\right), \frac{1}{2i}\left(z - \frac{1}{z}\right)\right]\frac{dz}{z},$$

where C is the unit circle.

Example.

$$I = \int_0^{2\pi} \frac{d\theta}{a + \cos\theta}, \qquad a > 1.$$

$$I = -i\oint_{|z|=1} \frac{1}{\left(a + \dfrac{z}{2} + \dfrac{1}{2z}\right)}\frac{dz}{z} = -2i\oint_{|z|=1} \frac{dz}{z^2 + 2az + 1}.$$

The denominator can be factored into $(z - \alpha)\,(z - \beta)$, where

$$\alpha = -a + (a^2 - 1)^{1/2}, \qquad \beta = -a - (a^2 - 1)^{1/2}.$$

Since $a > 1$, it follows readily that $|\alpha| < 1$ and $|\beta| > 1$. Thus the integrand has one singularity, at $z = \alpha$, within the unit circle, and

$$I = -2i(2\pi i)\frac{1}{\alpha - \beta} = \frac{2\pi}{(a^2 - 1)^{1/2}}.$$

Next we consider integrals of the form:

b) $\int_{-\infty}^{\infty} R(x)\, dx$, where $R(x)$ is a rational function (i.e., a ratio of two poly-nomials), without poles on the real axis.

If there are no poles on the real axis, then this integral exists if the degree of the denominator of $R(x)$ is at least two units higher than the degree of the numerator. This means that $|R(z)| \to 1/|z^2|$ as $|z| \to \infty$. Now

$$\oint_C R(z)\, dz = \int_{-\rho}^{\rho} R(x)\, dx + \int_{\text{semicircle}} R(z)\, dz$$

(see Fig. 6.18). As $\rho \to \infty$, the closed contour C encloses all the singularities of $R(z)$ in the upper half-plane, so

$$\oint_C R(z)\, dz = 2\pi i \sum_{y>0} \text{Res}\, R(z),$$

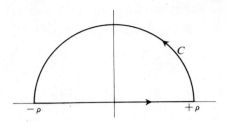

Fig. 6.18

where this notation means to form the sum of all the residues of $R(z)$ in the upper half-plane. Now in the limit of large $|z|$,

$$\left| \int_{semicircle} R(z)\ dz \right| \leq \int \frac{|const|\ \rho\ d\theta}{\rho^2} = \frac{|const|}{\rho} ,$$

which goes to zero as $\rho \to \infty$. Thus

$$\oint_C R(z)\ dz = \int_{-\infty}^{\infty} R(x)\ dx = 2\pi i \sum_{y>0} \text{Res } R(z) .$$

When we say that an integral over a "contour at infinity" vanishes, we really mean, of course, that given any $\epsilon > 0$ there exists a *finite* contour C such that $\left| \oint_C f(z)\ dz \right| < \epsilon$. If this is so, we say that the integral over the contour at ∞ is zero; all contours are really finite.

Example.

$$I = \int_{-\infty}^{\infty} \frac{dx}{(x^2 + 1)^2} .$$

To find the zeros of the denominator in the upper half-plane, we must solve $z^2 = -1$. We get $z = \pm i$. Only the root $+i$ is in the upper half-plane. Therefore

$$I = \oint \frac{dz}{(z + i)^2(z - i)^2} = \frac{2\pi i}{1!} \frac{d}{dz} \left(\frac{1}{(z + i)^2} \right) \bigg]_{z=i}$$

$$= (2\pi i) \cdot (-2) \cdot \frac{1}{(z + i)^3} \bigg]_{z=i} = \frac{\pi}{2} .$$

c) Another very important class of integrals is $\int_{-\infty}^{\infty} R(x)e^{ix}\ dx$. This is the Fourier integral of the rational function $R(x)$. Its real and imaginary parts determine the integrals:

$$\int_{-\infty}^{\infty} R(x) \cos x\ dx \qquad \text{and} \qquad \int_{-\infty}^{\infty} R(x) \sin x\ dx .$$

We retain the assumption that there are no poles on the real axis. Here, too, we consider the integral $\oint_C R(z)e^{iz}\ dz$ over a semicircle. Since $|e^{iz}| = e^{-y} \leq 1$

Fig. 6.19

for any point in the upper half-plane, this integral will exist if the rational function $R(z)$ has a zero of at least order two at infinity. Then, just as before, the integral over the infinite semicircle vanishes, leaving

$$\oint_C R(z)e^{iz}\,dz = \int_{-\infty}^{\infty} R(x)e^{ix}\,dx = 2\pi i \sum_{y>0} \text{Res}\,[R(z)e^{iz}] .$$

Example.

$$I = \int_{-\infty}^{\infty} \frac{e^{ikr}}{k^2 + \mu^2}\,dk .$$

If $r > 0$, then letting $x = rk$, we find that the integral becomes

$$I = r\int_{-\infty}^{\infty} \frac{e^{ix}}{x^2 + (\mu r)^2}\,dx = r\oint \frac{e^{iz}}{z^2 + (\mu r)^2}\,dz = 2\pi i r \sum_{y>0} \text{Res}\left(\frac{e^{iz}}{z^2 + (\mu r)^2}\right)$$

$$= 2\pi i r\,\frac{e^{iz}}{z + i\mu r}\bigg]_{z=i\mu r} = \pi\,\frac{e^{-\mu r}}{\mu} .$$

Note that

$$I = \int_{-\infty}^{\infty} \frac{\cos kr}{k^2 + \mu^2}\,dk$$

and hence the result above is actually independent of the sign of r. Therefore

$$\int_{-\infty}^{\infty} \frac{e^{ikr}}{k^2 + \mu^2}\,dk = \pi\,\frac{e^{-\mu|r|}}{\mu} .$$

Another way to see this is to compute the integral assuming $r < 0$. Then we must take the contour in the *lower* half-plane, since $|e^{ikr}| = e^{-(\text{Im } k)r}$, which is bounded only for $\text{Im}\,(k) < 0$, if $r < 0$. As before, for a large enough semicircle (Fig. 6.19),

$$\oint_C = \int_{-\infty}^{\infty} = -2\pi i \sum_{y<0} \text{Res} .$$

The minus sign arises because the contour C is traversed clockwise. Thus

$$I = -2\pi i r\,\frac{e^{iz}}{z - i\mu r}\bigg]_{z=-i\mu r} = \frac{\pi e^{\mu r}}{\mu} ,$$

which for $r < 0 = \pi e^{-\mu|r|}/\mu$. Here the residue was computed at the only pole in the lower half-plane, $z = -i\mu r$.

d)   There arise integrals of the form $\int_{-\infty}^{\infty} R(x)e^{i\alpha x}\,dx$, where the rational function $R(x)$ has a zero of order one at infinity. The integrals

$$\int_{-\infty}^{\infty} R(x)\cos \alpha x\,dx \qquad \text{and} \qquad \int_{-\infty}^{\infty} R(x)\sin \alpha x\,dx$$

are the real and imaginary parts, respectively, of this integral.

From the preceding discussion, it is not clear that these integrals exist. Jordan's lemma, which we now prove, tells us that they do. Again we assume that there are no poles on the real axis.

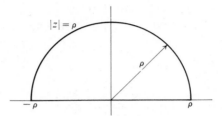

Fig. 6.20

Jordan's Lemma.   If as $\rho \to \infty$ (in Fig. 6.20), $|R(z)| \to 0$ uniformly in θ for $0 < \theta < \pi$, then $\lim_{\rho \to \infty} \int_{|z|=\rho} R(z)e^{i\alpha z}\,dz = 0$, for $\alpha > 0$.

Proof.   We have almost proved this result in the section on dispersion relations. There, however, the analyticity of $R(z)$ in the upper half-plane was used.   Here we use the hypothesis on the uniformity of the approach of $|R(z)|$ to zero.   Let $M(\rho)$ be the maximum of $|R(z)|$ on the semicircle $|z| = \rho$.   Then the statement that $|R(z)| \to 0$ uniformly means that $|R(z)| \le M(\rho)$, where $\lim_{\rho \to \infty} M(\rho) = 0$, *independent of θ.*

Let

$$I = \int_{|z|=\rho} R(z)e^{i\alpha z}\,dz\ .$$

Then

$$|I| \le M(\rho) \int_0^\pi |e^{i\alpha(\rho \cos \theta + i\rho \sin \theta)}|\,|\rho i e^{i\theta}|\,d\theta$$

$$= \rho M(\rho) \int_0^\pi e^{-\alpha \rho \sin \theta}\,d\theta\ .$$

Treating this integral exactly as in Section 6.6, we obtain

$$|I| < \pi M(\rho)\,\frac{(1 - e^{-\alpha \rho})}{\alpha} \to 0 \qquad \text{as } \rho \to \infty\ ,$$

since $\alpha > 0$, and $M(\rho) \to 0$ as $\rho \to \infty$.   Thus we arrive at the formula

$$\int_{-\infty}^{\infty} R(x)e^{i\alpha x}\,dx = 2\pi i \sum_{y>0} \text{Res}\,[R(z)e^{i\alpha z}]$$

for $\alpha > 0$. For $\alpha < 0$, the derivation works only in the lower half-plane $(y < 0)$, and changes in the above formula must be made accordingly.

Example.

$$I = \int \frac{e^{i\mathbf{k}\cdot\mathbf{r}}}{k^2 + \mu^2} \, d\mathbf{k}$$

$$= \int_0^{2\pi} k \, d\phi \int_0^\pi k \sin\theta \, d\theta \int_0^\infty dk \, \frac{e^{ik|r|\cos\theta}}{k^2 + \mu^2}$$

$$= 2\pi \int_{-1}^1 dt \int_0^\infty dk \, \frac{k^2 e^{ik|r|t}}{k^2 + \mu^2}$$

$$= \frac{2\pi}{i|r|} \int_0^\infty dk \, \frac{k(e^{ik|r|} - e^{-ik|r|})}{k^2 + \mu^2}$$

$$= \frac{2\pi}{i|r|} \int_{-\infty}^\infty dk \, \frac{k e^{ik|r|}}{k^2 + \mu^2} \, .$$

Jordan's lemma tells us that this integral for complex k vanishes over the infinite semicircle. Therefore

$$I = \frac{2\pi}{i|r|} \, 2\pi i \sum_{y>0} \text{Res} \, \frac{k e^{ik|r|}}{k^2 + \mu^2} = \frac{4\pi^2}{|r|} \frac{i\mu e^{i\cdot i\mu|r|}}{2i\mu} = \frac{2\pi^2}{|r|} e^{-\mu|r|} , \qquad (6.51)$$

since there is only one pole in the upper half-plane $(k = +i\mu)$.

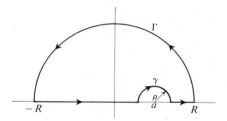

Fig. 6.21

e) We have not as yet allowed the integrand to have poles on the real axis. If $Q(z)$ is a meromorphic function in the upper half-plane, if it only has poles of order one (i.e., simple poles) on the real axis, and if $Q(z)$ behaves at infinity like any of the integrands of class b, c, or d, then the techniques of these cases can be extended to evaluate integrals of the form

$$P \int_{-\infty}^\infty Q(x) \, dx,$$

where the P stands for Cauchy's principal value, which arises because of the presence of the poles on the real axis.

Let $Q(z)$ have a single simple pole on the real axis at $z = a$. Consider the indented contour C (Fig. 6.21) consisting of the small semicircle γ about point a, the large semicircle Γ about the origin, and the two straight line segments on the real axis from $-R$ to $a - \rho$ and from $a + \rho$ to R. We take γ small enough so it encloses only the pole at a; Γ is taken large enough to enclose all the poles in the upper half-plane and large enough so the integral over Γ approaches 0 as $R \to \infty$. We have

$$\left(\int_\Gamma + \int_{-R}^{a-\rho} + \int_\gamma + \int_{a+\rho}^R \right) Q(z)\, dz = 2\pi i \sum_{y>0} \operatorname{Res} Q(z) \ .$$

Taking the limit as $R \to \infty$, we get

$$\left[\lim_{R \to \infty} \left(\int_{-R}^{a-\rho} + \int_{a+\rho}^R \right) + \int_\gamma \right] Q(z)\, dz = P \int_{-\infty}^\infty Q(x)\, dx + \int_\gamma Q(z)\, dz$$

$$= 2\pi i \sum_{y>0} \operatorname{Res} Q(z) \ .$$

We now consider $\int_\gamma Q(z)\, dz$. On γ, $z = a + \rho e^{i\theta}$, so that

$$\int_\gamma Q(z)\, dz = \int_\pi^0 Q(a + \rho e^{i\theta}) \rho e^{i\theta} i\, d\theta \ .$$

Since $Q(z)$ has a simple pole at $z = a$, it contains the factor $(z-a)^{-1}$. We may therefore write $Q(z) = \phi(z)/(z-a) + \psi(z)$, where $\phi(z)$ and $\psi(z)$ are analytic at and near $z = a$. Clearly $\psi(z)$ does not contribute to the integral over γ as $\rho \to 0$, so since $z - a = \rho e^{i\theta}$, we have

$$\int_\gamma Q(z)\, dz = \int_\pi^0 \phi(a + \rho e^{i\theta}) i\, d\theta \ .$$

We now expand ϕ in a Taylor series about a (it is analytic there):

$$\phi(a + \rho e^{i\theta}) = \phi(a) + \text{terms in } \rho \ .$$

Therefore, letting $\rho \to 0$, we get

$$\int_\gamma Q(z)\, dz = \int_\pi^0 \phi(a) i\, d\theta = -i\pi \phi(a) \ .$$

Now $\phi(a)$ is the residue of $Q(z) = \phi(z)/(z-a)$ at $z = a$, so the final answer may be written as

$$P \int_{-\infty}^\infty Q(x)\, dx = 2\pi i \sum_{y>0} \operatorname{Res} Q(z) + \pi i \sum_{y=0} \operatorname{Res} Q(z) \ ,$$

where $\sum_{y=0} \operatorname{Res} Q(z)$ denotes the sum of the residues of $Q(z)$ at each of its simple poles on the real axis (generalizing from one to several simple poles).

Example.

$$I = \int_{-\infty}^\infty \frac{\sin x}{x}\, dx \ .$$

The value of this integral may be determined from the following simple result:

$$P \int_{-\infty}^\infty \frac{e^{ix}}{x}\, dx = \pi i \sum_{y=0} \operatorname{Res}\left(\frac{e^{iz}}{z}\right) = \pi i \ .$$

Here the only pole is on the real axis at $z = x = 0$.

Equating real and imaginary parts, we have

$$P\int_{-\infty}^{\infty} \frac{\cos x}{x}\, dx = 0 \, ,$$

which is trivial because the integrand is an odd function, and

$$P\int_{-\infty}^{\infty} \frac{\sin x}{x}\, dx = \pi \, ,$$

a result derived previously from Hilbert transform theory. In this formula the P is superfluous because the integrand has no pole. Many integrals involving $\sin x$ or $\cos x$ may be evaluated, as we have done here, by replacing the trigonometric function with e^{iz}, and later taking real and imaginary parts.

f) Next we consider integrals of the form $\int_0^{\infty} x^{\lambda-1} R(x)\, dx$, where $R(z)$ is rational, analytic at $z = 0$, and has no poles on the positive real axis, and where $|z^2 R(z)|$ $\to 0$ uniformly as $|z| \to 0$ and as $|z| \to \infty$. Since the case of integral λ can be handled by the methods described earlier, we will assume that λ is not equal to an integer.

This problem involves branch points and branch cuts because $z^{\lambda-1}$ is not in general, a single-valued function. The power function $z^{\lambda-1}$ has a branch point at the origin. Let $z^{\lambda-1}$ denote the following branch of the power function:

$$z^{\lambda-1} = \exp\left[(\lambda - 1) \log z \right] = \exp\left[(\lambda - 1)(\log r + i\theta) \right] ,$$

where $0 < \theta < 2\pi$, $r > 0$. Then

$$z^{\lambda-1} = r^{\lambda-1} e^{i(\lambda-1)\theta} , \qquad 0 < \theta < 2\pi, r > 0 \, .$$

The branch cut has been chosen to be the positive real axis. For $\theta = 0$, the power function has the value

$$z^{\lambda-1} = r^{\lambda-1} = x^{\lambda-1} \, .$$

Now consider the contour integral $\oint_{C'} z^{\lambda-1} R(z)\, dz$, where the closed contour C' is shown in Fig. 6.22. Here C' consists of a small circle about $z = 0$, whose radius will later be shrunk to zero, a large circle whose radius will later be expanded to ∞, and two integrals along the positive real axis in opposite directions and on opposite sides of the branch cut. Since the integrand is discontinuous along the branch cut, these two integrals will not cancel. To do the integral, the phase of $z^{\lambda-1}$ must be prescribed everywhere. We have done this above by defining it to be 0 on the positive real axis so that $z^{\lambda-1} = x^{\lambda-1}$ there, which is the usual convention. Therefore, on the line just below the real axis, $z^{\lambda-1}$ $= x^{\lambda-1} e^{i2\pi(\lambda-1)}$. The integrals over the little and big circles vanish, because $|z^2 R(z)| \to 0$ as $|z| \to 0$, and as $|z| \to \infty$. Therefore

$$\oint_{C'} z^{\lambda-1} R(z)\, dz = -\int_0^{\infty} e^{2\pi i(\lambda-1)} x^{\lambda-1} R(x)\, dx + \int_0^{\infty} x^{\lambda-1} R(x)\, dx \, ,$$

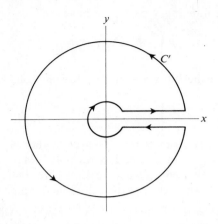

Fig. 6.22

where the first integral on the right is the contribution from the line below the positive x-axis and the second is the contribution from the line above the x-axis. Together these integrals give

$$[1 - e^{2\pi i(\lambda-1)}] \int_0^\infty x^{\lambda-1}R(x)\,dx = \left(\frac{-2i\sin\pi\lambda}{e^{-\pi i\lambda}}\right) \int_0^\infty x^{\lambda-1}R(x)\,dx\,.$$

Since

$$\oint_{C'} z^{\lambda-1}R(z)\,dz = 2\pi i \sum_{\text{inside } C'} \mathrm{Res}\,[z^{\lambda-1}R(z)]\,,$$

we obtain

$$\int_0^\infty x^{\lambda-1}R(x)\,dx = \frac{-\pi e^{-\pi i\lambda}}{\sin\pi\lambda} \sum_{\text{inside } C'} \mathrm{Res}\,[z^{\lambda-1}R(z)] \tag{6.52}$$

$$= \frac{\pi(-1)^{\lambda-1}}{\sin\pi\lambda} \sum_{\text{inside } C'} \mathrm{Res}\,[z^{\lambda-1}R(z)]\,,$$

since $e^{-i\pi\lambda} = (-1)^\lambda$. This is as far as we can go without choosing a specific function $R(z)$. A very simple example of this type is the following integral:

$$I = \int_0^\infty \frac{x^{\lambda-1}}{1+x}\,dx\,, \qquad 0 < \lambda < 1\,.$$

After evaluating it, we shall use it to prove some results involving the beta and gamma functions.

First since $0 < \lambda < 1$, $|z^\lambda/(1+z)| \to 0$ as $|z| \to \infty$ and as $z \to 0$. Therefore

$$\int_0^\infty \frac{x^{\lambda-1}}{1+x}\,dx = \frac{\pi(-1)^{\lambda-1}}{\sin\pi\lambda}\,\mathrm{Res}\left(\frac{z^{\lambda-1}}{1+z}\right)_{z=-1} = \frac{\pi}{\sin\pi\lambda}\,.$$

The beta function $\beta(x,y)$ is defined as

$$\beta(x,y) \equiv \int_0^1 t^{x-1}(1-t)^{y-1}\,dt = \frac{\Gamma(x)\Gamma(y)}{\Gamma(x+y)}\,, \qquad x,y > 0\,, \tag{6.53}$$

where $\Gamma(x)$ is the gamma function:

$$\Gamma(x) = \int_0^\infty t^{x-1} e^{-t} \, dt \,. \tag{6.54}$$

The proof of the identity in Eq. (6.53) may be found in many books on analysis. We note that

$$\beta(x, 1 - x) = \Gamma(x)\Gamma(1 - x) = \int_0^1 t^{x-1}(1 - t)^{-x} \, dt \,, \qquad \text{if } 0 < x < 1.$$

If in the last integral we make the change of variable

$$t = \frac{u}{1 + u} = 1 - \frac{1}{1 + u} \,,$$

it becomes

$$\int_0^\infty \frac{u^{x-1}}{1 + u} \, du \,,$$

which is precisely the integral we have just evaluated. Thus

$$\beta(x, 1 - x) = \Gamma(x)\Gamma(1 - x) = \frac{\pi}{\sin \pi x} \,, \qquad \text{for } 0 < x < 1 \,. \tag{6.55}$$

This formula may be extended by analytic continuation to all z in the complex plane. In particular, for $x = \frac{1}{2}$, we have $[\Gamma(\frac{1}{2})]^2 = \pi$. Therefore

$$\pi^{1/2} = \Gamma(\tfrac{1}{2}) \equiv \int_0^\infty t^{-1/2} e^{-t} \, dt = 2 \int_0^\infty e^{-u^2} \, du = \int_{-\infty}^\infty e^{-u^2} \, du \,, \tag{6.56}$$

where we have made the substitution $t = u^2$.

We close this section on residue theory with an illustration of how series can be summed by contour integration. The result we shall obtain depends on the fact that $\pi \cot \pi z$ has poles of order one at the zeros of $\sin \pi z$, (that is, at $z = n, n = 0, \pm 1, \pm 2, \cdots$), and the fact that the residue at each of these poles is 1.

Theorem. Let $f(z)$ be a meromorphic function and let C be a contour which encloses the zeros of $\sin \pi z$, located at $z = \rho, \rho + 1, \cdots, n$. If we assume that the poles of $f(z)$ and $\sin \pi z$ are distinct, then

$$\sum_{m=\rho}^n f(m) = \frac{1}{2\pi i} \oint_C \pi \cot \pi z \, f(z) \, dz - \sum_{\substack{\text{poles of } f(z) \\ \text{inside } C}} \text{Res} \, [\pi \cot (\pi z) \, f(z) \,] \,. \tag{6.57}$$

Proof.

$$\oint_C \pi \cot \pi z f(z) \, dz = 2\pi i \sum (\text{Residues at all the poles of the integrand})$$

$$= 2\pi i \left[\sum_{m=\rho}^n f(m) + \sum_{\substack{\text{poles of } f(z) \\ \text{inside } C}} \text{Res} \, [\pi \cot \pi z \, f(z) \,] \right] \,. \quad \text{QED}$$

Example. We shall use this theorem to establish the equivalence of Langevin's function $(\coth x - 1/x)$ and the sum

$$\sum_{n=1}^{\infty} \frac{2x}{x^2 + n^2\pi^2} .$$

We shall then use this result to derive an infinite *product* expression for $\sin \theta$, which is of considerable interest in its own right.

Letting $f(z) = 2x/(x^2 + z^2\pi^2)$, and using the formula above, we obtain

$$\sum_{m=-N}^{N} \frac{2x}{x^2 + m^2\pi^2} = \frac{1}{2\pi i} \oint_C \pi \cot \pi z \, f(z) \, dz - \sum_{\substack{\text{poles of } f(z) \\ \text{inside } C}} \text{Res} \left[\pi \cot \pi z \, f(z) \right] ,$$

where C is a closed contour, say, a rectangle, enclosing the points $z = -N$, $-N+1, \cdots, 0, 1, \cdots, N-1, N$. Now let the length and width of the rectangle C approach ∞. As this happens,

$$\left| \frac{1}{2\pi i} \oint_C \pi \cot \pi z \, f(z) \, dz \right| \leq \frac{1}{2} \oint_C |\cot \pi z| \left| \frac{2x}{x^2 + z^2\pi^2} \right| |dz| \to 0 .$$

To see that this integral vanishes as $z \to \infty$, we observe that

$$|\cot \pi z| = \frac{|\cos \pi z|}{|\sin \pi z|} = \left(\frac{\cos^2 \pi x + \sinh^2 \pi y}{\sin^2 \pi x + \sinh^2 \pi y} \right)^{1/2} .$$

Now, arbitrarily high accuracy can be achieved in summing the series by choosing the rectangle so that its vertical sides cross the x-axis at a large enough half-integer, for example $(10^{97} + \frac{1}{2})$, where $\cos \pi(10^{97} + \frac{1}{2}) = 0$ and $\sin \pi(10^{97} + \frac{1}{2}) = 1$. Then, over these sides of the rectangle

$$|\cot \pi z| = \left| \left(\frac{\sinh^2 \pi y}{1 + \sinh^2 \pi y} \right)^{1/2} \right| = |\tanh \pi y| \leq 1 .$$

Over the horizontal sides of the rectangle, $\lim_{z \to \infty} |\cot \pi z| = 1$. Thus the integrand goes as $|1/z^2|$ as $|z| \to \infty$, and the integral vanishes.

If we take an infinite rectangular contour, then

$$\sum_{m=-\infty}^{\infty} \frac{2x}{x^2 + m^2\pi^2} = - \text{Res} \left[\frac{(\pi \cot \pi z) \, 2x}{x^2 + z^2\pi^2} \right]_{z=\pm ix/\pi}$$

$$= -\frac{2x}{\pi} \left[\frac{\cot \pi(ix/\pi)}{2ix/\pi} + \frac{\cot \pi(-ix/\pi)}{-2ix/\pi} \right] = 2i \cot ix = 2 \coth x .$$

Therefore

$$2 \sum_{m=1}^{\infty} \frac{2x}{x^2 + m^2\pi^2} + \frac{2}{x} = 2 \coth x$$

or

$$\coth x - \frac{1}{x} = \sum_{m=1}^{\infty} \frac{2x}{x^2 + m^2\pi^2} , \qquad (6.58)$$

which establishes the result stated at the outset.

Aside from illustrating this summation technique, this particular result is not of much interest. However, if we integrate both sides from 0 to x, we get

$$\sum_{m=1}^{\infty} \ln\left(1 + \frac{x^2}{m^2\pi^2}\right) = \ln\left(\frac{\sinh x}{x}\right).$$

Hence

$$\ln\left(\frac{\sinh x}{x}\right) = \sum_{m=1}^{\infty} \ln\left(1 + \frac{x^2}{m^2\pi^2}\right) = \ln \prod_{m=1}^{\infty}\left(1 + \frac{x^2}{m^2\pi^2}\right),$$

so

$$\frac{\sinh x}{x} = \prod_{m=1}^{\infty}\left(1 + \frac{x^2}{m^2\pi^2}\right). \tag{6.59}$$

We may extend this result to all z in the complex plane by analytic continuation. Then setting $x = i\theta$ (θ real), we obtain

$$\sin\theta = \theta \prod_{n=1}^{\infty}\left(1 - \frac{\theta^2}{n^2\pi^2}\right). \tag{6.60}$$

This infinite product formula displays *explicitly* all the zeros of $\sin\theta$. It represents the complete factorization of the Taylor series. It can, in fact, be taken as the definition of the sine function.

By equating coefficients of the θ^3 term of both sides of the above equation, we obtain a useful sum:

$$\sum_{n=1}^{\infty} \frac{1}{n^2} = \frac{\pi^2}{6}. \tag{6.61}$$

This is a special value of the Riemann zeta function,

$$\zeta(z) = \sum_{n=1}^{\infty} \frac{1}{n^z}. \tag{6.62}$$

There are many other special tricks for evaluating integrals and summing series. We have surveyed only the principal techniques, but the reader will have no trouble understanding any particular evaluation procedure he may encounter if he understands this section. Problem 31 provides applications of all the basic techniques of residue calculus developed above.

6.9 APPLICATIONS TO SPECIAL FUNCTIONS AND INTEGRAL REPRESENTATIONS

In this section we use the formula for the derivative of an analytic function to find generating functions for certain special functions from their Rodrigues formulas. Also, we shall derive integral representations for Bessel functions and Legendre polynomials.

Bessel Functions

The function $e^{(1/2)z(w-1/w)}$ is analytic everywhere in the w-plane except at $w = 0$, so it can be expanded in a Laurent series in any annulus $R_2 < |w| < R_1$, no matter how small $R_2(> 0)$ or how large R_1. Denoting the expansion coefficients by $J_n(z)$, we have

$$e^{(1/2)z(w-1/w)} = \sum_{n=-\infty}^{\infty} J_n(z)w^n .$$

(6.63)

The expansion coefficients are functions of the complex variable z. The notation chosen for them anticipates the fact that they will turn out to be Bessel functions of integral order. In other words, $e^{(1/2)z(w-1/w)}$ is a generating function for Bessel functions.

We now prove that the functions $J_n(z)$ do satisfy Bessel's differential equation:

$$z^2 \frac{d^2 J_n}{dz^2} + z \frac{dJ_n}{dz} + (z^2 - n^2)J_n = 0 .$$

(6.64)

Along the way to this result we shall find an integral representation for Bessel functions and also an explicit formula for them.

By Laurent's theorem,

$$J_n(z) = \frac{1}{2\pi i} \oint_C \frac{f(w)}{(w - w_0)^{n+1}} \, dw ,$$

(6.65)

where C is any closed contour in the annulus. We take C to be the unit circle: $w = e^{i\theta}$. Then in Eq. (6.65), $w_0 = 0$ and $f(w) = e^{(1/2)z(w-1/w)}$. On the unit circle $w - 1/w = 2i \sin \theta$. Therefore

$$J_n(z) = \frac{1}{2\pi} \int_{-\pi}^{\pi} e^{iz \sin \theta} e^{-in\theta} \, d\theta = \frac{1}{2\pi} \int_{-\pi}^{\pi} e^{-i(n\theta - z \sin \theta)} \, d\theta$$

$$= \frac{1}{2\pi} \int_{-\pi}^{\pi} \cos (n\theta - z \sin \theta) \, d\theta - \frac{i}{2\pi} \int_{-\pi}^{\pi} \sin (n\theta - z \sin \theta) \, d\theta .$$

But the second integral is zero because the integrand is odd in θ. Since the first integrand is even in θ,

$$J_n(z) = \frac{1}{\pi} \int_0^{\pi} \cos (n\theta - z \sin \theta) \, d\theta .$$

(6.66)

This is an integral representation for the function $J_n(z)$, which we now prove is a solution of Bessel's equation by substituting it into Eq. (6.64). The verification is trickier than one might expect. We therefore resist the temptation to "leave it to the reader." He is, of course, welcome to have a try at it before reading further. We have

$$J_n'(z) = \frac{1}{\pi} \int_0^{\pi} \sin \theta \sin (n\theta - z \sin \theta) \, d\theta$$

(6.67a)

$$= -\frac{1}{\pi} \cos \theta \sin (n\theta - z \sin \theta) \Big]_0^{\pi}$$

$$+ \frac{1}{\pi} \int_0^{\pi} \cos \theta \cos (n\theta - z \sin \theta)(n - z \cos \theta) d\theta ,$$

(6.67b)

where we have integrated by parts. The first term is zero. Differentiating Eq. (6.67a) again, we have

$$J_n''(z) = -\frac{1}{\pi} \int_0^\pi \sin^2 \theta \cos (n\theta - z \sin \theta) d\theta .$$

We now form the quantity $z^2 (J_n'' + J_n) + zJ_n' - n^2 J_n$, using Eq. (6.67b) for $J_n'(x)$. It must be identically zero if the $J_n(z)$ are Bessel functions. We get

$$\frac{1}{\pi} \int_0^\pi \cos (n\theta - z \sin \theta)[z^2 - z^2 \sin^2 \theta + z \cos \theta (n - z \cos \theta) - n^2] d\theta$$

$$= \frac{-n}{\pi} \int_0^\pi [\cos (n\theta - z \sin \theta)(n - z \cos \theta)] d\theta .$$

The function $\sin (n\theta - z \sin \theta)$ is an antiderivative of the integrand. It vanishes at both 0 and π, so the proof is complete: the $J_n(z)$ are solutions of Bessel's equation. It is easy to show that

$$J_0(0) = 1 , \qquad J_n(0) = 0 \quad \text{for } n \neq 0 ,$$
$$J_1'(0) = \tfrac{1}{2} , \qquad J_n'(0) = 0 \quad \text{for } n \neq 1 , \tag{6.68}$$

so these functions are indeed that solution of Bessel's equation, known as Bessel functions of nth (integral) order of the *first* kind (which are analytic at the origin).

Usually, the solution of Bessel's equation is expressed as an infinite series, not as an integral. We now derive the infinite series solution from the generating function:

$$e^{(1/2)z(w-1/w)} = e^{(1/2)zw}e^{-z/2w}$$

$$= \sum_{r=0}^\infty \frac{(z/2)^r w^r}{r!} \sum_{m=0}^\infty \frac{(-z/2)^m w^{-m}}{m!} = \sum_{n=-\infty}^\infty w^n J_n(z) .$$

To obtain $J_n(z)$, the coefficient of the term in $w^n (n \geq 0)$, we multiply each term in w^{-m} in the second series by the term w^{n+m} in the first series, and then sum over all m:

$$J_n(z) w^n = \sum_{m=0}^\infty \frac{(z/2)^{n+m} w^{n+m} (-z/2)^m w^{-m}}{(n+m)! \, m!}$$

$$= \sum_{m=0}^\infty \left[\frac{(-1)^m (z/2)^{2m+n}}{(n+m)! \, m!} \right] w^n .$$

Thus

$$J_n(z) = \sum_{m=0}^\infty \frac{(-1)^m (z/2)^{2m+n}}{(n+m)! \, m!} . \tag{6.69}$$

This is the infinite series solution for integral $n \geq 0$. The reader may show that, for integral n,

$$J_{-n}(z) = (-1)^n J_n(z) . \tag{6.70}$$

Thus these solutions are linearly dependent, and there must exist another set of linearly independent solutions. They are called the Neumann functions, and are denoted by $N_n(z)$. A whole family of equations and solution functions may be constructed from Bessel's equations and Bessel functions by permitting the index n to be nonintegral and half-integral. Also, various linear combinations of Bessel and Neumann functions of real and imaginary argument give rise to the modified Bessel functions and the Hankel functions. The spherical Bessel functions (which we discuss in Chapter 7) are still another set of functions that are defined in terms of the Bessel functions. Each of these sets of functions is a Sturm-Liouville system. It is not our purpose to provide an exhaustive (and exhausting) account of them, but merely to derive and discuss the fundamental results so the reader can dig the particular facts he needs for his work out of a treatise on the subject.

Legendre polynomials

Previously we have shown that the Legendre polynomials, defined by the Rodrigues formula

$$P_n(x) = \frac{1}{2^n n!} \frac{d^n}{dx^n} (x^2 - 1)^n ,$$

are an orthogonal set on the interval $[-1, 1]$ and satisfy Legendre's equation:

$$(1 - x^2) P_n'' - 2x P_n' + n(n + 1) P_n = 0 .$$

It was mentioned in Section 1.8, but not proved, (except for P_0, P_1, and P_2), that a generating function for the Legendre polynomials is

$$\frac{1}{(1 - 2xt + t^2)^{1/2}} = \sum_{n=0}^{\infty} P_n(x) t^n , \qquad 0 < t < 1 , \qquad |x| \le 1 . \quad (6.71)$$

In the comparison of this equation with Eq. (1.101), the reader will note that we have set $t \equiv r'/r$ and $x \equiv \cos \theta$. We now prove this relation for all n. We begin by expressing the Rodrigues formula as a contour integral by making use of the formula for the nth derivative of an analytic function:

$$P_n(x) = \frac{(-1)^n}{2^n n!} \frac{d^n}{dx^n} (1 - x^2)^n = \frac{(-1)^n}{2^n} \frac{1}{2\pi i} \oint_C \frac{(1 - z^2)^n}{(z - x)^{n+1}} dz . \quad (6.72)$$

Here we have used the fact that the function $(1 - z^2)^n$ is entire (C is a closed contour that encloses the point x). This integral representation of the Legendre polynomials is known as Schläfli's integral formula. If we now form the series $S = \sum_{n=0}^{\infty} P_n(x) t^n$, using this integral representation for $P_n(x)$, and interchange the order of summation and integration, we get

$$S = \frac{1}{2\pi i} \oint_C \frac{dz}{z - x} \sum_{n=0}^{\infty} \frac{(-1)^n}{2^n} t^n \left(\frac{1 - z^2}{z - x} \right)^n .$$

This is a simple geometric series, which converges and is easily summed if

$$\left| \frac{t}{2} \frac{1 - z^2}{z - x} \right| < 1 .$$

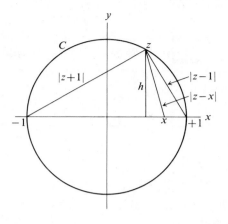

Fig. 6.23

We must show, however, that a contour C, enclosing the point x, can always be chosen so that this is true for all x and t in their prescribed ranges. Let C be the unit circle; z is a point anywhere on C, and x is on the real axis inside or on C as shown in Fig. 6.23. The area A of the right triangle with vertices at -1, z, and $+1$ is given by

$$A = \tfrac{1}{2} |z + 1| \, |z - 1| = \tfrac{1}{2} |1 - z^2| \, .$$

It is also given by $\tfrac{1}{2}(2h) = h$. But $|z - x| \geq h$ for all z and x, so

$$|z - x| \geq h = A = \tfrac{1}{2} |1 - z^2| \Longrightarrow \left| \tfrac{1}{2} \cdot \frac{1 - z^2}{z - x} \right| \leq 1 \, .$$

Consequently,

$$\left| \frac{t}{2} \frac{1 - z^2}{z - x} \right| < 1$$

since $t < 1$. A purely algebraic proof is also possible, but this geometric one is simpler. We now sum the geometric series to obtain

$$S = \frac{1}{2\pi i} \oint_C \frac{dz}{z - x} \frac{1}{1 - \left[\dfrac{-t}{2} \dfrac{(1 - z^2)}{(z - x)} \right]} = -\frac{1}{2\pi i} \oint_C \frac{2/t \, dz}{z^2 - \dfrac{2}{t} z - \left(1 - \dfrac{2}{t} x \right)} \, .$$

The denominator has two roots;

$$z_{\pm} = \frac{1}{t} \pm \left(\frac{1}{t^2} - \frac{2x}{t} + 1 \right)^{1/2} = \frac{1}{t} [1 \pm (1 - 2xt + t^2)^{1/2}] \, .$$

Remembering that $0 < t < 1$ and $-1 \leq x \leq 1$, it is easy for us to show that $z_+ > 0$ and $-1 < z_- < 1$, so z_- is the root enclosed by the contour C. Evaluating the residue at z_-, we have

$$S = \sum_{n=0}^{\infty} P_n(x) t^n = \frac{-1}{2\pi i} \frac{2}{t} 2\pi i \frac{1}{z_- - z_+} = \frac{1}{(1 - 2xt + t^2)^{1/2}} \, . \qquad \text{QED}$$

Table 6.1

PROPERTIES OF ORTHOGONAL FUNCTIONS
ARISING FROM STURM-LIOUVILLE SYSTEMS

Name and physical application	Rodrigues formula	Generating function
Legendre polynomials: 1) Multipole expansion 2) ∇^2 in spherical coordinates	$P_n(x) = \dfrac{1}{2^n n!} \dfrac{d^n}{dx^n}(x^2 - 1)^n$	$\displaystyle\sum_{n=0}^{\infty} P_n(x) t^n$ $= \dfrac{1}{\sqrt{1 - 2xt + t^2}}$ $(0 < t < 1)$
Hermite polynomials: Quantum oscillator	$H_n(x) = (-1)^n e^{x^2} \dfrac{d^n e^{-x^2}}{dx^n}$	$\displaystyle\sum_{n=0}^{\infty} \dfrac{H_n(x)}{n!} t^n = e^{-t^2 + 2tx}$ $(t > 0)$
Laguerre polynomials: Hydrogen atom (radial equation)	$L_n(x) = e^x \dfrac{d^n}{dx^n} x^n e^{-x}$	$\displaystyle\sum_{n=0}^{\infty} \dfrac{L_n(x)}{n!} t^n = \dfrac{e^{-xt/(1-t)}}{1 - t}$ $(0 < t < 1)$
	Series representation	
Bessel's function (of integral order) ∇^2 in cylindrical coordinates	$J_n(x) = \displaystyle\sum_{m=0}^{\infty} \dfrac{(-1)^m (x/2)^{2m+n}}{(n+m)! \, m!}$	$\displaystyle\sum_{n=-\infty}^{\infty} J_n(x) t^n = e^{(1/2) x(t - 1/t)}$ $(t > 0)$
Trigonometric functions: Classical oscillator	$f_n = \sin nx$ $= \displaystyle\sum_{m=0}^{\infty} (-1)^m \dfrac{(nx)^{2m+1}}{(2m+1)!}$ $g_n = \cos nx$ $= \displaystyle\sum_{m=0}^{\infty} (-1^m) \dfrac{(nx)^{2m}}{(2m)!}$	

Differential equation	Differential equation in Sturm-Liouville form	Orthonormality
$(1 - x^2) P_n'' - 2x P_n'$ $+ n(n + 1) P_n = 0$	$\dfrac{d}{dx}((1 - x^2) P_n')$ $+ n(n + 1) P_n = 0$	$\displaystyle\int_{-1}^{1} P_n P_m \, dx$ $= \delta_{nm} \dfrac{2}{2n + 1}$
$H_n'' - 2xH' + 2nH_n = 0$	$\dfrac{d}{dx}(e^{-x^2} H_n') + 2ne^{-x^2} H_n = 0$	$\displaystyle\int_{-\infty}^{\infty} H_n H_m e^{-x^2} \, dx$ $= \delta_{nm} \sqrt{\pi} \, 2^n n!$
$x L_n'' + (1 - x) L_n'$ $+ n L_n = 0$	$\dfrac{d}{dx}(xe^{-x} L_n') + ne^{-x} L_n = 0$	$\displaystyle\int_{0}^{\infty} L_n L_m e^{-x} \, dx$ $= \delta_{nm} (n!)^2$
$x^2 J_n'' + x J_n'$ $+ (x^2 - n^2) J_n = 0$	$\dfrac{d}{dx}(x J_n') + \left(x - \dfrac{n^2}{x}\right) J_n = 0$	See Problem 5.23
$f_n'' + n^2 f_n = 0$ $g_n'' + n^2 g_n = 0$	$\dfrac{d}{dx}(f_n') + n^2 f_n = 0$ $\dfrac{d}{dx}(g_n') + n^2 g_n = 0$	$\displaystyle\int_{-\pi}^{\pi} f_n f_m \, dx = \delta_{nm} \pi$ $\displaystyle\int_{-\pi}^{\pi} g_n g_m \, dx = \delta_{nm} \pi$ $\displaystyle\int_{-\pi}^{\pi} f_n g_m \, dx = 0$

In exactly the same way, the generating functions for the Hermite polynomials and the Laguerre polynomials can be derived from their Rodrigues formulas (see Problems 36 and 37).

Let us return to Schläfli's integral representation of the Legendre polynomials:

$$P_n(x) = \frac{1}{2\pi i} \oint_C \frac{(z^2 - 1)^n}{2^n (z - x)^{n+1}} \, dz \, . \tag{6.73}$$

It can be proved directly from this integral representation that the $P_n(x)$ satisfy Legendre's differential equation. But we have already proved that the $P_n(x)$ as given by Rodrigues' formula satisfy Legendre's equation, so we omit this proof. Here we derive another integral representation: a real integral.

For the contour C, we take a circle about x of radius $|(x^2 - 1)^{1/2}|$. Then for any point z on C, we may put $z = x + (x^2 - 1)^{1/2} e^{i\theta}$, where θ increases from $-\pi$ to π. Making this substitution in Schläfli's formula, we obtain

$$P_n(x) = \frac{1}{2\pi i} \int_{-\pi}^{\pi} \left[\frac{(x - 1 + (x^2 - 1)^{1/2} e^{i\theta})(x + 1 + (x^2 - 1)^{1/2} e^{i\theta})}{2(x^2 - 1)^{1/2} e^{i\theta}} \right]^n i \, d\theta \, ,$$

where we have written $(z^2 - 1)^n$ in the form $[(z - 1)(z + 1)]^n$ before substituting $z = x + (x^2 - 1)^{1/2} e^{i\theta}$. Now everything in square brackets above simplifies after a little algebra to $x + (x^2 - 1)^{1/2} \cos \theta$, an even function of θ. Thus we have a real integral representation of the Legendre polynomials due to Laplace:

$$P_n(x) = \frac{1}{\pi} \int_0^{\pi} [x + (x^2 - 1)^{1/2} \cos \theta]^n \, d\theta \, , \qquad \text{for } |x| \le 1 \, . \tag{6.74}$$

Note how obvious it is from this representation that $P_n(1) = 1$, and $P_n(-1) = (-1)^n$. It is instructive to compute P_0, P_1, and P_2 from this formula. Although $(x^2 - 1)^{1/2}$ is pure imaginary for $|x| < 1$, all the terms in $(x^2 - 1)^{1/2}$ vanish when the integral is performed because $\int_0^{\pi} \cos^m \theta \, d\theta = 0$ for odd m.

We conclude this section with Table 6.1. It summarizes some of the more useful information concerning the special functions of mathematical physics.

PROBLEMS

1. Let

$$f(z) = \frac{xy^2(x + iy)}{x^2 + y^2} \qquad \text{for } z \ne 0, \quad f(0) = 0 \, .$$

Determine where, if anywhere, this function is a) differentiable, b) analytic.

2. Show that the complex numbers z_1, z_2, z_3 lie on a straight line if and only if $(z_1 - z_3)/(z_2 - z_3)$ is a real number.
   [*Hint*: This problem can be done very simply if one thinks of the complex numbers geometrically (as vectors). It can be done algebraically also, but the geometric proof is certainly easier.]

3. Prove that $u = \sin x \cosh y + 2 \cos x \sinh y + x^2 - y^2 + 4xy$ is a harmonic function and find a conjugate harmonic function v. Find a complex function of the complex variable z such that $f(z) = u + iv$.

4. a) Determine all the values of the constants a, b, c, d for which the polynomial $u(x, y) = ax^3 + bx^2y + cxy^2 + dy^3$ is harmonic, i.e., satisfies the two-dimensional Laplace equation in the entire plane.

   b) Find a harmonic conjugate, $v(x, y)$, of $u(x, y)$.

   c) Find an analytic function $f(z) = u(x, y) + iv(x, y)$, where $z = x + iy$.

5. A complex function $E^*(z)$ is defined by $E^*(z) = E_x(x, y) - iE_y(x, y)$, where E_x and E_y are the components of the electric field in two dimensions. Show that the static Maxwell equations in free space imply that $E^*(z)$ is an analytic function of z.

6. Show that if we write $z = re^{i\theta}$, the Cauchy-Riemann equations become, in terms of r and θ,

$$\frac{\partial u}{\partial r} = \frac{1}{r}\frac{\partial v}{\partial \theta}, \qquad \frac{\partial v}{\partial r} = -\frac{1}{r}\frac{\partial u}{\partial \theta}.$$

7. Analyze the function $z^{1/3}$ in terms of the Riemann sheet concepts discussed in Section 6.2.

8. Using the results of Problem 6.6, show that $\log z$, $z^{1/2}$, and $z^{1/3}$ are analytic everywhere on their appropriate Riemann sheets except at $z = 0$.

9. Show that the two-sheeted Riemann surface for $w(z) = \sqrt{(z - a)(z - b)}$ can be cut and joined along the line segment $[a, b]$ of the real axis (assume for convenience that a and b are real). Make an appropriate definition of $w(z)$ in terms of the polar representation of complex numbers, including a definition of the range of the phases.

10. Find the Riemann surface on which $\sqrt{z - a} + \sqrt{z - b}$ (a, b real and positive) is a single-valued function, analytic except at $z = a$ and $z = b$.

11. Find the Riemann surface on which $\sqrt{(z - 1)(z - 2)(z - 3)}$ is a single-valued function, analytic except at $z = 1, 2, 3$.

12. Show that $w(z) = z^\alpha$ ($0 < \alpha < 1$), where α is irrational, can be made single-valued only on an infinite-sheeted Riemann surface. Discuss how the sheets should be connected.

13. Show that, according to the definitions of Section 6.2,

$$\tan(\tan^{-1} z) = z, \qquad \log(e^z) = z + 2\pi ni.$$

14. *The mean-value theorem.* Prove that for charge-free two-dimensional space the value of the electrostatic potential at any point is equal to the average of the potential over the surface of *any* circle centered on that point. Do this by considering the electrostatic potential as the real part of an analytic function.

15. Find all the singularities of $\tanh z$.

16. Explain why one of the following definite integrals is meaningful and the other meaningless. Evaluate the one that makes sense, writing the answer in the form $a + bi$.

   a) $\displaystyle\int_{-1}^{1} z^* \, dz$,   b) $\displaystyle\int_{0}^{i} \sin 2z \, dz$.

17. Compute, using Cauchy's integral formula,

a) $\oint_c \dfrac{e^z\,dz}{z - \pi i/2}$, C = boundary of a square with sides $x = \pm 2$, $y = \pm 2$.

b) $\oint_c \dfrac{dz}{z^2 + 2}$, C = circle of radius 1, center i.

(Both contours are oriented counterclockwise.)

18. Show that

a) $\oint_c \dfrac{z^4 + 2z + 1}{(z - z_0)^4}\,dz = 8\pi i z_0$, where C is any closed contour containing z_0.

b) $\oint_c \dfrac{\cosh z}{z^{n+1}}\,dz = \dfrac{2\pi i}{n!}\dfrac{[1 + (-1)^n]}{2}$, where C is any closed contour containing the origin.

19. *Cauchy's integral formula for a polynomial.* Let $P(z)$ be a polynomial. Using Cauchy's Theorem, prove that

$$\frac{1}{2\pi i}\oint_c \frac{P(z)}{z - a}\,dz = P(a)\,,$$

where C encloses the point a. [*Hint:* Consider

$$Q(z) = \frac{P(z) - P(a)}{z - a}\,,$$

which is also a polynomial (why?), and evaluate the integral you want from this expression.]

20. Prove that if $f(z)$ is analytic within and on a closed contour C, and α and β are two distinct points within C, then

$$\frac{1}{2\pi i}\oint_c \frac{f(z)}{(z - \alpha)(z - \beta)}\,dz = \frac{f(\alpha)}{\alpha - \beta} + \frac{f(\beta)}{\beta - \alpha}.$$

From this result, deduce Liouville's theorem, which states that a function must be a constant. [*Hint:* If for arbitrary α and β, $f(\alpha) = f(\beta)$, then $f(z) = $ const.]

21. *Morera's theorem.* Morera's theorem is a kind of converse to the Cauchy-Goursat theorem. It states that if $f(z)$ is continuous in a region R and if $\oint f(z)\,dz = 0$ for any C inside R, then $f(z)$ is analytic inside R. Prove this theorem. Morera's theorem gives us another way of establishing the analyticity of a function. We can use it instead of checking the Cauchy-Riemann conditions *and* the sometimes troublesome additional requirement for analyticity, the continuity of the derivative of $f(z) = u + iv$, that is, continuity of the four first partial derivatives of u and v.

22. *Conformal mappings.* Consider the analytic function $w = f(z)$ as transforming the complex z-plane into a complex w-plane. Suppose that two curves in the z-plane, F_z^1 and F_z^2, meet at an angle α at the point z_0 in the z-plane. Prove that the transformed curves in the w-plane, F_w^1 and F_w^2, meet at the same angle in the w-plane if $f'(z_0) \neq 0$. The requirement that $f'(z_0) \neq 0$ is essential for conformality at z_0. Consider the analytic function $w = z^2$, for which $w'(0) = 0$. The coordinate axes themselves, which pass through the origin and are separated by an angle of $90°$, are mapped into lines that are separated by $180°$. The angle between any two straight lines through the origin in the z-plane will be doubled in the w-plane. Thus the mapping is not conformal at the origin. However, it is conformal everywhere else.

23. *Poisson's formula*

   a) Let $f(z)$ be an analytic function within and on the circle C of radius a. Prove that

$$f(z') = \frac{1}{2\pi i} \oint_C \left[\frac{f(z)}{z - z'} - \frac{f(z)}{z - (a^2/z'^*)} \right] dz ,$$

   if $z' = re^{i\phi}$, $r < a$, in polar coordinates located at the center of C.

   b) From the above formula, derive Poisson's formula:

$$f(re^{i\phi}) = \frac{1}{2\pi} \int_0^{2\pi} \frac{a^2 - r^2}{a^2 + r^2 - 2ar \cos(\theta - \phi)} f(ae^{i\theta}) \, d\theta .$$

   c) From Poisson's formula, prove that if a function is analytic throughout and on a circle, then the value of the function at the center of the circle, $f(0)$, is the average of its boundary values on the circle (mean value theorem).

   d) Now, starting with the equation

$$f(z') = \frac{1}{2\pi i} \oint_C \left[\frac{f(z)}{z - z'} + \frac{f(z)}{z - (a^2/z'^*)} \right] dz ,$$

   [which differs from the equation of part (a) by the $+$ sign, but holds for the same reason], derive [using part (c) eventually]

$$f(z') = f(0) - \frac{iar}{\pi} \int_0^{2\pi} \frac{\sin(\theta - \phi) f(ae^{i\theta})}{a^2 + r^2 - 2ar \cos(\theta - \phi)} \, d\theta .$$

   e) Letting $f(z') = f(re^{i\phi}) = u(r, \phi) + iv(r, \phi)$, etc., deduce from (d) the formulas

$$u(a, \phi) = u(0) + \frac{1}{2\pi} P \int_0^{2\pi} v(a, \theta) \cot\left(\frac{\theta - \phi}{2} \right) d\theta ,$$

$$v(a, \phi) = v(0) - \frac{1}{2\pi} P \int_0^{2\pi} u(a, \theta) \cot\left(\frac{\theta - \phi}{2} \right) d\theta .$$

   These formulas express the real part of an analytic function on a circle in terms of its imaginary part on the circle, and vice versa. Many further applications of these formulas are possible.

24. *An alternative approach to Hilbert transforms*

   a) Show that if $f(z)$ is analytic in the upper half z-plane, then if $a = \alpha + i\beta$ $(\beta > 0)$,

$$\frac{1}{2\pi i} \oint_C \left[\frac{f(z)}{z - a} + \frac{f(z)}{z - a^*} \right] dz = f(a) ,$$

   where C is a semicircle of arbitrarily large radius with the real axis for its base.

   b) If $|f(z)| \to 0$ as $|z| \to \infty$ in the upper half-plane, then show that

$$\frac{1}{2\pi i} \int_{-\infty}^{\infty} \left[\frac{f(x)}{x - a} + \frac{f(x)}{x - a^*} \right] dx = f(a) .$$

   Combine fractions to obtain

$$\frac{1}{i\pi} \int_{-\infty}^{\infty} \frac{(x - \alpha) f(x)}{(x - \alpha)^2 + \beta^2} \, dx = f(a) .$$

   c) If $f(z) = u(x, y) + iv(x, y)$, show that (b) reduces to

$$u(\alpha, \beta) = \frac{1}{\pi} \int_{-\infty}^{\infty} \frac{(x - \alpha) v(x, 0)}{(x - \alpha)^2 + \beta^2} \, dx , \quad v(\alpha, \beta) = -\frac{1}{\pi} \int_{-\infty}^{\infty} \frac{(x - \alpha) u(x, 0)}{(x - \alpha)^2 + \beta^2} \, dx .$$

d) Hence show that if we let $\beta = 0$,

$$u(\alpha, 0) = \frac{1}{\pi} P \int_{-\infty}^{\infty} \frac{v(x, 0)}{x - \alpha} \, dx, \qquad v(\alpha, 0) = -\frac{1}{\pi} P \int_{-\infty}^{\infty} \frac{u(x, 0)}{x - \alpha} \, dx,$$

which is, apart from notation, the Hilbert transform pair derived in Section 6.5 [Eqs. (6.19a) and (6.19b)].

25. Consider the integral

$$I_{\pm} = \lim_{\epsilon \to 0} \int_{-A}^{+B} \frac{f(x)}{x \pm i\epsilon} \, dx,$$

where A and B are positive real numbers and $\epsilon > 0$.

a) Show that $I_{\pm}$ can be written as

$$I_{\pm} = \lim_{\epsilon \to 0} \int_{-A}^{-\delta} \frac{xf(x)}{x^2 + \epsilon^2} \, dx + \lim_{\epsilon \to 0} \int_{+\delta}^{+B} \frac{xf(x)}{x^2 + \epsilon^2} \, dx + \lim_{\epsilon \to 0} \int_{-\delta}^{+\delta} \frac{xf(x)}{x^2 + \epsilon^2} \, dx$$
$$\mp i \lim_{\epsilon \to 0} \epsilon \int_{-A}^{B} \frac{f(x)}{x^2 + \epsilon^2} \, dx,$$

where δ is a small positive number.

b) Use plausible arguments (of the type found, for example, in Section 5.3) to show that $I_{\pm}$ can be written as

$$I_{\pm} = \int_{-A}^{-\delta} \frac{f(x)}{x} \, dx + \int_{\delta}^{+B} \frac{f(x)}{x} \, dx + f(0) \lim_{\epsilon \to 0} \int_{-\delta}^{\delta} \frac{x \, dx}{x^2 + \epsilon^2} \mp i f(0) \lim_{\epsilon \to 0} \epsilon \int_{-A}^{B} \frac{dx}{x^2 + \epsilon^2}.$$

c) Show that the third term of the equation in (b) vanishes by symmetry. Doing the fourth integral explicitly, show that

$$I_{\pm} = P \int_{-A}^{B} \frac{f(x)}{x} \, dx \mp i f(0) \lim_{\epsilon \to 0} \left[\tan^{-1}\left(\frac{B}{\epsilon}\right) + \tan^{-1}\left(\frac{A}{\epsilon}\right) \right].$$

d) Let $\epsilon \to 0$ and use the definition of the δ-function to write, finally,

$$\lim_{\epsilon \to 0} \int_{-A}^{+B} \frac{f(x)}{x \pm i\epsilon} \, dx = P \int_{-A}^{+B} \frac{f(x)}{x} \, dx \mp i\pi f(0) = P \int_{-A}^{B} \frac{f(x)}{x} \, dx \mp i\pi \int_{-A}^{B} \delta(x) f(x) \, dx.$$

This is often written, rather cryptically, as the symbolic formula

$$\lim_{\epsilon \to 0} \frac{1}{x \pm i\epsilon} = P \frac{1}{x} \mp i\pi \delta(x).$$

26. Solve the integral equation

$$\frac{1}{\pi} P \int_{-\infty}^{\infty} \frac{u(x)}{x - t} \, dx = \frac{1}{1 + t^2} \equiv -v(t)$$

by finding the Hilbert transform of $v(t)$. Find a complex function $f(z) = u(x, y) + iv(x, y)$ such that $u(x, 0) \equiv u(x) = Re(f(z))$ and $v(x, 0) \equiv v(x) = Im(f(z))$ and verify that this complex function has the two properties (what are they?) that ensure that $u(x)$ and $v(x)$ are a Hilbert transform pair.

27. Derive a dispersion relation for $f(z)$ when $|f(z)/z|$ tends to a constant as $|z| \to \infty$.

28. Prove that a uniformly convergent series of analytic functions can be integrated term by term. Hence show that a uniformly convergent series of analytic functions is an analytic function.
[*Hint*: Use Morera's theorem of Problem 22.]

29. Find the order of the pole at the origin, the residue there, and the integral around a (small) path C enclosing the origin, but no other singularities, for each of the following functions:

a) $\cot z$,   b) $\csc^2 z \log (1 - z)$,   c) $\dfrac{z}{\sin z - \tan z}$.

30. What are the positions and natures of the singularities and the residues at these singularities of the following functions in the z-plane, excluding the point at infinity?

a) $f_1(z) = \dfrac{\cot \pi z}{(z - 1)^2}$,   b) $f_2(z) = \dfrac{1}{z(e^z - 1)}$.

[*Note*: Both these functions have nonisolated and hence essential singularities at infinity because the origin for $f_1(1/z)$ and $f_2(1/z)$ is a limit point of poles.]

31. Problems on the evaluation of real definite integrals by contour integration:

a) $\displaystyle\int_0^{2\pi} \dfrac{d\theta}{a + b \sin \theta} = \dfrac{2\pi}{(a^2 - b^2)^{1/2}}$, $a > b > 0$.

b) $\displaystyle\int_0^{2\pi} \dfrac{\sin^2\theta \, d\theta}{a + b \cos \theta} = \dfrac{2\pi}{b^2}[a - (a^2 - b^2)^{1/2}]$, $a > b > 0$.

c) $\displaystyle\int_0^{2\pi} \dfrac{d\theta}{(a + b \cos \theta)^2} = \dfrac{2\pi a}{(a^2 - b^2)^{3/2}}$, $a > b > 0$.

d) $\displaystyle\int_0^\infty \dfrac{dx}{1 + x^4} = \dfrac{\pi}{2\sqrt{2}}$.   e) $\displaystyle\int_0^\infty \dfrac{x^2 \, dx}{(a^2 + x^2)^3} = \dfrac{\pi}{16a^3}$.

f) $\displaystyle\int_0^\infty \dfrac{\sin x \, dx}{x(a^2 + x^2)} = \dfrac{\pi}{2a^2}(1 - e^{-a})$.   g) $\displaystyle\int_{-\infty}^\infty \dfrac{\sin^2 x}{x^2} \, dx = \pi$.

h) $\displaystyle\int_0^\infty \dfrac{x^{2a-1}}{b^2 + x^2} \, dx = \dfrac{\pi b^{2(a-1)}}{2} \csc \pi a$, $0 < a < 1$.

i) $\displaystyle\int_0^\infty \dfrac{\log x}{b^2 + x^2} \, dx = \dfrac{\pi \log b}{2b}$.

j) $\displaystyle P\int_{-\infty}^\infty \dfrac{1}{(\omega' - \omega_0)^2 + a^2} \dfrac{1}{\omega' - \omega} \, d\omega' = \dfrac{\pi}{a} \dfrac{\omega_0 - \omega}{(\omega_0 - \omega)^2 + a^2}$.

k) $\displaystyle\int_0^\infty \dfrac{dx}{x^3 + a^3} = \dfrac{2\pi}{3a^2\sqrt{3}}$.

l) Consider the real integral

$$G(x, x', \tau) = \frac{1}{2\pi} \int_{-\infty}^\infty e^{ik(x-x')} e^{-k^2\tau} \, dk,$$

where τ is real. In this case it is easy to show that

$$G(x, x', \tau) = \frac{1}{(4\pi\tau)^{1/2}} e^{-(x-x')^2/4\tau}.$$

Prove that this result still holds when τ is pure imaginary. [*Hint*: The value of the integral

$$\int_0^\infty e^{-iu^2} \, du$$

may be found by considering the integral of e^{-z^2} around the boundary of the circular sector $0 \le \theta \le \pi/4$, $0 \le r \le R$. In the limit $R \to \infty$, *prove* that the contribution to the integral over the circular arc goes to zero. The contributions over the remaining straight segments of the contour provide the value of the integral needed in the problem.]

Note: This contour integral provides the values of the two real definite integrals:

$$\int_{-\infty}^{\infty} \sin{(x^2)}\, dx = \int_{-\infty}^{\infty} \cos{(x^2)}\, dx = (\pi/2)^{1/2},$$

by taking real and imaginary parts. By making the change of variable $x^2 = t$, this result can be transformed into

$$\int_{0}^{\infty} \frac{\sin t}{\sqrt{t}}\, dt = \int_{0}^{\infty} \frac{\cos t}{\sqrt{t}}\, dt = (\pi/2)^{1/2}.$$

32. We have seen how the function $\pi \cot \pi z$ may be used to sum certain series. But it is useless if the series is an alternating one. Show how alternating series may be summed by using the function $\pi \csc{(\pi z)}$ in place of $\pi \cot{(\pi z)}$. Use the general result to prove that

$$\sum_{n=1}^{\infty} (-1)^{n+1} \frac{1}{n^2} = \pi^2/12 .$$

33. Consider the problem of evaluating the integral of $z^{1/2}$ from A to D along the circular path C, shown in Fig. 6.24. We take the cut to lie along the ray $\theta = \alpha$ and define $z^{1/2} \equiv r^{1/2} e^{i\theta/2}$ for $\alpha \leq \theta < \alpha + 2\pi$. Compare this with the value obtained by integrating $z^{1/2}$ from A to D along the "keyhole" path $ABCD$. Do the results agree? Should they agree? Why?

Fig. 6.24 The contours for Problem 6-34. The angles, ϵ, for the "keyhole" path are arbitrarily small. The radius of the circle, C_0, is l, and the cut is along the ray $\theta = \alpha$.

34. Consider the following response function, $G(t)$, which vanishes for negative values of the argument and which, for positive values, is given by

$$G(t) = G_0 \frac{\sin^2 \mu t}{t^{3/2}}.$$

Note that this function satisfies conditions (a), (b), (c) at the beginning of Section

6.6. Show that the Fourier transform, $g(\omega)$, is given by

$$g(\omega) = \frac{i-1}{2}G_0[\sqrt{\omega} - \tfrac{1}{2}\sqrt{\omega + 2\mu} - \tfrac{1}{2}\sqrt{\omega - 2\mu}], \qquad \omega \geq 2\mu ;$$

$$= \frac{i-1}{2}G_0[\sqrt{\omega} - \tfrac{1}{2}\sqrt{\omega + 2\mu}] + \frac{i+1}{2}G_0[\tfrac{1}{2}\sqrt{2\mu - \omega}], \qquad 0 \leq \omega \leq 2\mu ,$$

$g(-\omega) = g^*(\omega)$.

Show that the complex-valued function of z which reduces to the above result on the real axis is

$$g(z) = \frac{i-1}{2}G_0[\sqrt{z} - \tfrac{1}{2}\sqrt{z + 2\mu} - \tfrac{1}{2}\sqrt{z - 2\mu}] .$$

Thus we see that $g(z)$ has branch points on the real axis, a possibility which is *not* excluded by conditions (a), (b), and (c). Note that we can choose the cuts to lie in the lower half-plane, so $g(z)$ is analytic in the upper half-plane.
[*Hint*: the integrals mentioned in the note following Problem 6.32 will be of use.]

35. The θ-function (or step function) is defined as

$$\theta(x) = \begin{cases} 0 & \text{for } x < 0 , \\ \tfrac{1}{2} & \text{for } x = 0 , \\ 1 & \text{for } x > 0 . \end{cases}$$

Prove

a) $\theta(x) = \dfrac{1}{2} + \dfrac{1}{2\pi i} P\displaystyle\int_{-\infty}^{\infty} \dfrac{e^{i\omega x}}{\omega} d\omega ,$ \qquad b) $\dfrac{d\theta(x)}{dx} = \delta(x)$.

[*Hint*: See Eq. (5.63)]

36. The Laguerre polynomials are generated by the generating function

$$\phi(x, t) = \frac{e^{-xt/(1-t)}}{1 - t} = \sum_{n=0}^{\infty} \frac{L_n(x)}{n!}t^n , \qquad 0 < t < 1 .$$

They are given directly by the formula

$$L_n(x) = e^x \frac{d^n}{dx^n}(x^n e^{-x}) , \qquad 0 \leq x \leq \infty ,$$

analogous to Rodrigues' formula for Legendre polynomials.

a) By differentiating the generating function with respect to x [getting $(1 - t)\phi' = - t\phi$], derive the recursion relation

$$L_n' - nL_{n-1}' = -nL_{n-1} .$$

By differentiating $\phi(x, t)$ with respect to t, another recursion relation can be derived. Show that

$$L_{n+1} - (2n + 1 - x)L_n + n^2 L_{n-1} = 0 .$$

b) From these two recursion relations, derive Laguerre's differential equation

$$xL_n'' + (1 - x)L_n' + nL_n = 0 .$$

c) Show that $L_n(0) = n!$
d) Derive the generating function from Rodrigues' formula by contour integration.

37. In Section 5.10, we defined the Hermite polynomials in terms of the generating function

$$e^{-t^2+2tx} = \sum_{n=0}^{\infty} \frac{H_n(x)}{n!} t^n , \qquad t > 0 ,$$

and deduced from this the Rodrigues formula:

$$H_n(x) = (-1)^n e^{x^2} \frac{d^n}{dx^n} e^{-x^2} .$$

Now prove the converse: that Rodrigues' formula implies the generating function. Enroute, establish the integral representation

$$H_n(x) = \frac{(-1)^n n!}{2\pi i} e^{x^2} \oint_C \frac{e^{-z^2}}{(z-x)^{n+1}} dz ,$$

where C encloses the point x.

38. Prove the integral representation for the Hermite polynomials:

$$H_n(x) = \frac{2^n}{\pi^{1/2}} \int_{-\infty}^{\infty} (x+it)^n e^{-t^2} dt .$$

Use this result to derive an explicit series for the Hermite polynomials:

$$H_n(x) = \sum_{\substack{r=0 \\ (2r \le n)}}^{n} \frac{(-1)^r n!}{r!(n-2r)!} (2x)^{n-2r} .$$

39. Show that
   a) $\Gamma(x+1) = x\Gamma(x)$ for $x > 0$
   b) $\Gamma(n+1) = n!$, where n is a positive integer.

FURTHER READINGS

CHURCHILL, R. V., *Complex Variables and Applications*. Second edition. New York: McGraw-Hill, 1960. An excellent text of great clarity, it is ideal for self-study. Churchill's books have influenced a generation of physicists (including the authors).

FRANKLIN, P., *Functions of Complex Variables*. Englewood Cliffs, N. J.: Prentice Hall, 1958.

GOURSAT, E., *Functions of a Complex Variable*. New York: Dover Publications, 1966. Very readable.

HILLE, E., *Analytic Function Theory*, Volumes I and II. Boston: Ginn, 1959. An exhaustive account.

KNOPP, K., *Theory of Functions*, Parts I and II. New York: Dover, 1945. There are two accompanying problem books.

LANDAU, E., *Foundations of Analysis*. New York: Chelsea, 1960. An axiomatic treatment of the various number systems, including complex numbers.

SESHU, S., and N. BALABARIAN, *Linear Network Analysis*. New York: Wiley, 1959. This book treats engineering applications of dispersion relations.

SCHWEBER, S., *An Introduction to Relativistic Quantum Field Theory*. Evanston, Ill.: Row Peterson, 1961. See p. 411 for a discussion of causality and dispersion relations.

TITCHMARSH, E. C., *Introduction to the Theory of Fourier Integrals*. New York: Oxford University Press, 1937. Chapter 5 provides a rigorous treatment of the Hilbert transform pair.

WEYL, H., *Philosophy of Mathematics and Natural Science*. Princeton, N. J.: Princeton University Press, 1949. Chapter II is devoted to the various number systems.

CHAPTER 7

GREEN'S FUNCTIONS

INTRODUCTION

In this chapter, we turn our attention to integral operators. It turns out that there is a particularly close connection between differential and integral operators; and the boundary conditions with which one is familiar from the theory of differential equations play a crucial role in linking the two. The connection between them is essentially the theory of Green's functions, an area in theoretical physics which has become particularly important in connection with modern developments in quantum mechanics. We cannot hope to give a comprehensive treatment of this enormous subject in just one chapter, but we shall try to illustrate the main ideas. Green's functions can be useful in classical physics, but our emphasis here will be primarily on their role in quantum mechanics, for it has been largely through the formulation in terms of Green's functions that the mathematical structure of quantum mechanics, both in the relativistic and nonrelativistic regimes, has been clarified.

7.1 A NEW WAY TO SOLVE DIFFERENTIAL EQUATIONS

The simplest of all differential equations is undoubtedly

$$-i\frac{dy}{dx} = f(x) \ . \tag{7.1}$$

(We have put the i in front of the derivative for future convenience; note the analogy with the quantum-mechanical operator $p_x = -i\hbar d/dx$.) If we choose the initial condition to be $y(a) = y_0$, the solution to Eq. (7.1) may be written immediately:

$$y(x) = y_0 + i\int_a^x f(x') \ dx' \ . \tag{7.2}$$

Thus we have already solved a simple differential equation by integration.

But this is really a trivial example, because in these terms every integral one writes may be dignified by the title "A Solution to a Differential Equation." However, let us push the problem a bit further. Imagine that x lies within some closed interval $[a, b]$. Then we may rewrite Eq. (7.2) as

$$y(x) = y_0 + i\int_a^b \theta(x - x')f(x') \ dx' \ , \tag{7.3}$$

Fig. 7.1 The Heaviside function.

where $\theta(t)$ is the discontinuous step function defined by

$$\theta(t) = \begin{cases} 1, & t > 0, \\ 0, & t \le 0, \end{cases} \tag{7.4}$$

$\theta(t)$ is sometimes called the Heaviside function (Fig. 7.1). Its presence in the integrand in Eq. (7.3) serves to cut off the integration over x' at $x = x'$; thus Eq. (7.3) is equivalent to Eq. (7.2). We note that $y(x)$ has the form

$$y(x) = y_0 + Kf(x), \tag{7.5}$$

where K is an integral operator defined by

$$Kf(x) \equiv i \int_a^b \theta(x - x')f(x')\,dx'. \tag{7.6}$$

Here $i\theta(x - x')$ is the *kernel* of the integral operator K, and when the kernel comes from the solution of an equation involving a differential operator, it is often referred to as the *Green's function* of that differential operator *for the relevant boundary conditions.* Thus

$$G_1(x, x') = i\theta(x - x') \tag{7.3'}$$

is the Green's function belonging to id/dx for a system subject to the boundary condition $y(a) = y_0$.

A more interesting example is the equation

$$\frac{d^2y}{dx^2} = f(x), \tag{7.7}$$

where $y(x)$ is subject to the one-point boundary conditions, $y(a) = y_0$, $y'(a) = \tilde{y}_0$. Integrating Eq. (7.7) once, we obtain

$$\frac{dy}{dx} = \tilde{y}_0 + \int_a^x f(x')\,dx';$$

a second integration gives

$$y(x) = y_0 + \tilde{y}_0(x - a) + \int_a^x dx'' \int_a^{x''} dx'\,f(x').$$

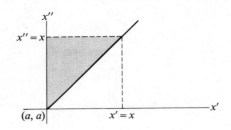

Fig. 7.2

In this expression we are integrating over a triangular region in the $x'x''$ plane (the shaded region in Fig. 7.2) by first integrating x' from $x' = a$ to $x' = x''$, and then integrating x'' from a to x. However, we can equally well integrate x'' from $x'' = x'$ to $x'' = x$ and then integrate x' from a to x. Since the function being integrated depends only on x', it is advantageous to change the order and limits of integration in this manner. We get

$$y(x) = y_0 + \bar{y}_0(x - a) + \int_a^x dx' \, f(x') \int_{x'}^x dx''$$

so that

$$y(x) = y_0 + \bar{y}_0(x - a) + \int_a^x (x - x')f(x') \, dx' . \tag{7.8}$$

The reader may check this by differentiating $y(x)$ twice and comparing the result with Eq. (7.3). Again, if we restrict x to the interval $[a, b]$, we can write

$$y(x) = y_0 + \bar{y}_0(x - a) + \int_a^b (x - x')\theta(x - x')f(x') \, dx' . \tag{7.9}$$

This solution for $y(x)$ has exactly the same form as the solution to Eq. (7.1). Using the terminology introduced earlier, we may say that the function

$$G_2(x, x') = (x - x')\theta(x - x') \tag{7.9'}$$

is the Green's function corresponding to the operator d^2/dx^2 for the boundary conditions $y(a) = y_0$, $y'(a) = \bar{y}_0$. Note that this Green's function is continuous while the Green's function of the operator d/dx is discontinuous (at $x = x'$).

In both Eqs. (7.3) and (7.9), the term on the right-hand side which is not under the integral is a solution of the homogeneous equation for the given boundary condition. We have

$$\frac{dy}{dx} = 0$$

in the case of Eq. (7.3), and

$$\frac{d^2y}{dx^2} = 0$$

in the case of Eq. (7.9). Therefore, the general solution to Eq. (7.7) is

$$y(x) = \alpha + \beta x + \int_a^b (x - x')\theta(x - x')f(x')\,dx' , \qquad (7.10)$$

where α and β are to be determined by the boundary conditions.

For example, if we have a two-point boundary condition

$$y(0) = y_0, \; y(1) = y_1 ,$$

the solution interior to the interval $[0, 1]$ will be

$$y(x) = \alpha + \beta x + \int_0^1 (x - x')\theta(x - x')f(x')\,dx' ,$$

where α and β are determined via the equations

$$y_0 = \alpha - \int_0^1 x'\theta(- x')f(x')\,dx' = \alpha ,$$

$$y_1 = \alpha + \beta + \int_0^1 (1 - x')\theta(1 - x')f(x')\,dx' .$$

Thus

$$\alpha = y_0 , \qquad \beta = y_1 - y_0 - \int_0^1 (1 - x')f(x')dx' .$$

Hence the solution looks like

$$y(x) = y_0 + (y_1 - y_0)x - \int_0^1 x(1 - x')f(x')\,dx'$$
$$+ \int_0^1 (x - x')\theta(x - x')f(x')\,dx' .$$

Calling

$$G_3(x, x') = -x(1 - x') + (x - x')\theta(x - x') ,$$

we have

$$y(x) = y_0 + (y_1 - y_0)x + \int_0^1 G_3(x, x')f(x')\,dx' . \qquad (7.11)$$

Let us look at $G_3(x, x')$ more closely. When $0 \le x' \le x$,

$$G_3(x, x') = -x(1 - x') + (x - x') = -x'(1 - x) ;$$

when $x \le x' \le 1$,

$$G_3(x, x') = -x(1 - x') .$$

To summarize, the solution to Eq. (7.7) is given by Eq. (7.11), where $G_3(x, x')$ is

$$G_3(x, x') = \begin{cases} -x'(1 - x) , & 0 \le x' \le x , \\ -x(1 - x') , & x \le x' \le 1 . \end{cases} \qquad (7.11')$$

Using the function $\theta(x)$, $G_3(x, x')$ can also be written conveniently as

$$G_3(x, x') = xx' - x'\theta(x - x') - x\theta(x' - x) . \qquad (7.11'')$$

Note that $G_3(x, x')$ vanishes at $x = 0$ and $x = 1$, and also at $x' = 0$ and $x' = 1$.

It is interesting to observe the dramatic effect which the boundary conditions have on the form of the Green's function. For one thing, the functional form changes. Moreover, the Green's function of Eq. (7.11'') is a symmetric function of x and x', since

$$G_3(x, x') = G_3(x', x);$$

but the Green's function of Eq. (7.9') is not symmetric. However, both $G_2(x, x')$ and $G_3(x, x')$ are Green's functions of the operator d^2/dx^2; the only difference lies in the boundary conditions.

Let us now examine the effect of changing boundary conditions in a first-order equation. We return to Eq. (7.1) and this time try the boundary condition $y(1) = Cy(0)$. The solution will have the general form

$$y(x) = A + i \int_0^1 \theta(x - x')f(x') \, dx' .$$

Now we require that

$$y(1) = A + i \int_0^1 f(x') \, dx' = Cy(0) = CA;$$

here we have substituted both $x=1$ and $x=0$ into the above equation. From this we find immediately that

$$A = -\frac{i}{1 - C} \int_0^1 f(x') \, dx' .$$

Thus

$$y(x) = -\frac{i}{1 - C} \int_0^1 f(x') \, dx' + i \int_0^1 \theta(x - x')f(x') \, dx' ,$$

or

$$y(x) = \int_0^1 G_4(x, x')f(x') \, dx' , \qquad (7.12)$$

where

$$G_4(x, x') = -i\left[\frac{1}{1 - C} - \theta(x-x') \right].$$

Thus

$$G_4(x, x') = \begin{cases} -\dfrac{iC}{1 - C}, & x > x' , \\[2mm] -\dfrac{i}{1 - C}, & x \leq x' . \end{cases}$$

If we demand that $|C| = 1$, then

$$G_4(x, x') = \begin{cases} -\dfrac{i}{C^* - 1}, & x > x', \\[2mm] +\dfrac{i}{C - 1}, & x \leq x', \end{cases} \qquad (7.12')$$

from which we see that $G_4(x, x')$ is symmetric in the sense that

$$G(x, x') = G(x', x)^* .$$

This definition of symmetry is motivated by the definition of a Hermitian matrix as being one whose elements satisfy

$$a_{ij} = a_{ji}^* .$$

As we shall see, the relationship between symmetric functions like $G_4(x, x')$ and Hermitian matrices is a very close and fruitful one. For the present, we may conclude that even in the simple case of a single derivative, the choice of boundary condition can mean the difference between a symmetric and a non-symmetric Green's function [since $G_1(x, x')$ of Eq. (7.3$'$) is not symmetric].

The fact that certain boundary conditions lead to a Green's function which is symmetric while others do not is readily made plausible. The reader can easily show that on the space of square-integrable functions which satisfy $f(1) = Cf(0)$ with $C = e^{i\phi}$ the differential operator $p = -id/dx$ is symmetric in the sense that $(f, pg) = (pf, g)$. Here $(\ ,\ )$ denotes the inner product of Eq. (5.3) with $a = 0$ and $b = 1$. However, p will not be symmetric if we require only that the functions in the space take on a fixed value at $x = 0$. Similar comments apply to the operator d^2/dx^2, if one remembers that in finding a Green's function for d^2/dx^2 acting on the space of square-integrable functions which take on fixed values at $x = 0$ and $x = 1$ one can always choose the endpoint values to be zero. This follows simply from the fact that if we solve

$$\frac{d^2\eta}{dx^2} = f(x)$$

subject to $\eta(0) = 0$ and $\eta(1) = 0$, then the solution to

$$\frac{d^2y}{dx^2} = f(x)$$

with $y(0) = y_0$ and $y(1) = y_1$ is just $y(x) = y_0 + (y_1 - y_0)x + \eta(x)$. Because the Green's functions $G_3(x, x')$ and $G_4(x, x')$ are symmetric functions of x and x', it is a simple matter to see that the integral operators K_3 and K_4 which have $G_3(x, x')$ and $G_4(x, x')$, respectively, as kernels are symmetric operators in the same sense that p was symmetric, that is, $(f, K_3g) = (K_3f, g)$ and $(f, K_4g) = (K_4f, g)$. Thus, it is not surprising that there appears to be a close relationship between symmetric differential operators and symmetric Green's functions.

The reader may well wonder why we have bothered developing such an elaborate way of integrating simple differential equations. One very important reason is the following. Suppose that, instead of Eq. (7.1), we had to solve

$$-i\frac{dy}{dx} = f(x, y) \ . \tag{7.13}$$

This is a true differential equation in the sense that it is not immediately integrable. By our previous work we have

$$y(x) = \alpha + \int_0^1 G(x, x')f[x', y(x')]\, dx' \ . \tag{7.14}$$

If the boundary condition is $y(0) = y_0$, then $\alpha = y_0$, and $G(x, x') = -i\theta(x - x')$; if the boundary condition is $y(1) = Cy(0)$, where $|C| = 1$, then $\alpha = 0$, and $G(x, x')$ is given by the symmetric function $G_4(x, x')$ of Eq. (7.12). Since the unknown function $y(x)$ now appears under the integral sign, we have transformed the *differential* equation into an *integral* equation. Similarly, if we have

$$\frac{d^2y}{dx^2} = f(x, y)$$

with $y(0) = y_0$, $y(1) = y_1$, we get as the corresponding integral equation

$$y(x) = y_0 + (y_1 - y_0)x + \int_0^1 G_3(x, x')f[x', y(x')]\, dx' \ ,$$

where $G_3(x, x')$ is the symmetric function given by Eq. (7.11'). For example, the well-known second-order linear differential equation

$$\frac{d^2y}{dx^2} + \lambda y = 0 \ , \qquad y(0) = 0 = y(1)$$

is transformed into the integral equation

$$y(x) = -\lambda \int_0^1 G_3(x, x')y(x')\, dx' \ .$$

There is one very interesting and tricky aspect of these equations which should be mentioned here. Crudely speaking, the differential operator id/dx is *unbounded* in the sense that it can act on functions of unit norm in Hilbert space and transform them into functions with arbitrarily large norm. For example, the norm of e^{inx} in the Hilbert space of square-integrable functions on $[0, 1]$ is 1, but the norm of

$$i\frac{d}{dx}[e^{inx}] = -ne^{inx}$$

is n, which can be as large as we like. As we shall see later, the theory of such unbounded operators is rather subtle.

However, the integral operator whose kernel is $G_4(x, x')$ is *bounded*, in the sense that it transforms any square-integrable function of unit norm into a function whose norm is less than some given number. As a general rule, let

$$f(x) = \int_0^1 K(x, y)\, g(y)\, dy \ .$$

If we assume that $g(y)$ is square-integrable and that $K(x, y)$ is square-integrable in y, for all x, then by Schwartz's inequality (Eq. 4.10),

$$|f(x)| \leq \left[\int_0^1 |K(x, y)|^2\, dy\right]^{1/2} \left[\int_0^1 |g(y)|^2\, dy\right]^{1/2}.$$

Thus, if g has unit norm, we get

$$|f(x)| \leq \left[\int_0^1 |K(x, y)|^2\, dy\right]^{1/2}.$$

But this means that

$$\int_0^1 |f(x)|^2\, dx \leq \int_0^1 \int_0^1 |K(x, y)|^2\, dx\, dy .$$

If $K(x, y)$ is square integrable in the xy-plane, which is the case for all the Green's functions discussed above, then calling

$$\int_0^1 \int_0^1 |K(x, y)|^2\, dx\, dy = C ,$$

we have

$$\int_0^1 |f(x)|^2\, dx \equiv ||f||^2 \leq C$$

for *any* function $g(x)$ of unit norm. Kernels of the square-integrable type actually have many other nice properties. For instance, the kernel $G_4(x, x')$ transforms the sequence of functions of unit norm $\{e^{inx}\}$ into a sequence of functions whose norms tend toward zero. In fact, for kernels of this type, *any* infinite bounded sequence of functions (i.e., functions $f_n(x)$ satisfying $||f_n|| \leq C$ for all n) will be transformed into a sequence containing a subsequence which is convergent in the mean. Operators of this type are said to be *completely continuous*, and we shall have a great deal more to say about them in Chapter 9. The analysis of these operators is much more straightforward than that of unbounded operators, and, in fact, bears a very close resemblance to ordinary matrix theory. Thus by turning a differential equation into an integral equation, or, in other words, by turning a differential operator into an integral operator, it is often possible to effect significant mathematical simplifications in a given problem.

7.2 GREEN'S FUNCTIONS AND DELTA FUNCTIONS

With the general idea of a Green's function in mind, let us now approach the problem of solving a differential equation in a slightly different manner. Suppose that we have the equation

$$Ly = f , \tag{7.15}$$

where L is some linear ordinary differential operator and f is a given function. Throwing aside questions of rigor, suppose now that L possesses a complete, orthonormal set of eigenfunctions $\{\phi_n(x)\}$ so that

$$L\phi_n(x) = \lambda_n\phi_n(x) .$$

Under these circumstances we could write (omitting the dots over the equal signs which denote mean convergence)

$$y(x) = \sum_{n=1}^{\infty} \alpha_n\phi_n(x) , \qquad (7.16a)$$

$$f(x) = \sum_{n=1}^{\infty} \beta_n\phi_n(x) . \qquad (7.16b)$$

The sum runs to infinity, which reflects the fact that in an infinite-dimensional Hilbert space, a complete orthonormal set contains an infinite number of elements.

If we now substitute Eqs. (7.16a) and (7.16b) into Eq. (7.15), we get

$$Ly = L \sum_{n=1}^{\infty} \alpha_n\phi_n = \sum_{n=1}^{\infty} L\alpha_n\phi_n = \sum_{n=1}^{\infty} \alpha_n\lambda_n\phi_n = f = \sum_{n=1}^{\infty} \beta_n\phi_n .$$

Thus

$$\sum_{n=1}^{\infty} (\alpha_n\lambda_n - \beta_n)\phi_n = 0 .$$

Since the ϕ_n are linearly independent, we conclude that

$$\alpha_n = \beta_n/\lambda_n;$$

thus

$$y(x) = \sum_{n=1}^{\infty} \frac{1}{\lambda_n} \beta_n\phi_n(x) , \qquad (7.17)$$

where $\beta_n = (\phi_n, f)$. If some $\lambda_n = 0$, then a solution exists only if the corresponding $\beta_n = 0$. In this case, the solution will not be unique; an arbitrary multiple of the ϕ_n corresponding to $\lambda_n = 0$ can be added to any solution (see Theorem 3.17). For the moment, then, we assume that $\lambda_n \neq 0$ for all n.

Let us write Eq. (7.17) in more detail:

$$y(x) = \sum_{n=1}^{\infty} \frac{1}{\lambda_n} \phi_n(x)(\phi_n, f)$$

$$= \sum_{n=1}^{\infty} \frac{1}{\lambda_n} \phi_n(x) \int \phi_n^*(x')f(x') \, dx'$$

$$= \int \sum_{n=1}^{\infty} \frac{\phi_n(x)\phi_n^*(x')}{\lambda_n} f(x') \, dx' .$$

Thus

$$y(x) = \int G(x, x')f(x') \, dx' , \qquad (7.18)$$

where

$$G(x, x') = \sum_{n=1}^{\infty} \frac{\phi_n(x)\phi_n^*(x')}{\lambda_n} . \tag{7.18'}$$

(Here we have interchanged sums and integrals in a rather cavalier manner, i.e., without establishing the uniform convergence of the sum.) Thus we obtain a representation of the Green's function in terms of an infinite eigenfunction expansion. If the λ_n are real, then $G(x, x')$ is symmetric:

$$G(x, x') = G(x', x)^* .$$

As an example, consider the operator

$$L = \frac{d^2}{dx^2}$$

for x in $[0, 1]$. The normalized eigenfunctions of L on $[0, 1]$, which vanish at the endpoints, are $\phi_n(x) = \sqrt{2} \sin (n\pi x)$, $n = 1, 2, \cdots$, with eigenvalues $\lambda_n = -n^2\pi^2$. Thus the Green's function for this case is

$$G(x, x') = -\frac{2}{\pi^2} \sum_{n=1}^{\infty} \frac{\sin (n\pi x) \sin (n\pi x')}{n^2} . \tag{7.19}$$

Since the series is dominated term by term by $1/n^2$, we have uniform convergence to a continuous function. In fact, the function to which the series of Eq. (7.19) converges must be precisely the function $G_3(x, x')$ given by Eq. (7.11'), since we have already determined by another (more rigorous) method that this is the Green's function of d^2/dx^2 with the two-endpoint boundary condition. It is interesting to calculate $G_3(x, x')$ at a few points to see whether Eqs. (7.11') and (7.19) agree. For example, at $x = x' = \frac{1}{2}$, $G_3(\frac{1}{2}, \frac{1}{2}) = -\frac{1}{4}$, while Eq. (7.19) gives

$$G\left(\frac{1}{2}, \frac{1}{2}\right) = -\frac{2}{\pi^2} \sum_{n=1}^{\infty}{}' \frac{1}{n^2} ,$$

where the prime on the summation sign means that the sum runs only over odd values of n. Using the results of Eq. (6.61) and Problem (6.32) one readily obtains the result

$$\sum_{n=1}^{\infty}{}' \frac{1}{n^2} = \frac{\pi^2}{8} ,$$

so that $G(\frac{1}{2}, \frac{1}{2}) = -\frac{1}{4}$, in agreement with the previously obtained result for $G_3(\frac{1}{2}, \frac{1}{2})$.

It is also instructive to look at the operator $p = -id/dx$ acting on the space of square-integrable functions on $[0, 1]$ which satisfy $f(1) = Cf(0)$, where $C = e^{i\phi}$ $(0 \le \phi < 2\pi)$. We have considered this operator from a different point of view in the previous section. The normalized eigenfunctions of p are readily seen to be $\phi_n = e^{i(2\pi n + \phi)x}$ $(n = 0, \pm 1, \pm 2, \cdots)$; the corresponding eigenvalues are $\lambda_n = 2\pi n + \phi$. Thus, the Green's function for this operator is

$$G(x, x') = \sum_{n=-\infty}^{\infty} \frac{e^{i(2\pi n + \phi)(x-x')}}{2\pi n + \phi} .$$

Note that if $\phi = 0$, that is, if $C = 1$, this expression for $G(x, x')$ is ill-defined because of a zero denominator when $n = 0$. This illustrates the type of difficulty that arises when an operator has an eigenvector with a zero eigenvalue. In the above case, $\lambda_0 = 0$, so the solution of Eq. (7.17) breaks down, and the problem posed in Eq. (7.15) does not have a solution unless $(\phi_0, f) = 0$. Even if $(\phi_0, f) = 0$, the solution to Eq. (7.15) is not unique. However, if $\phi \neq 0$, the problem is well-posed, and it is, in fact, a simple matter to determine $G(x, x')$. We shall see in the next section that the Green's function for p must be constant except when $x = x'$. To evaluate $G(x, x')$ when $x > x'$ we may take $x - x' = 1/2$ without loss of generality. Thus,

$$G(x, x') = \frac{1}{2\pi} e^{i\phi/2} \sum_{n=-\infty}^{\infty} \frac{(-1)^n}{n + \phi/2\pi} \qquad (x > x') ,$$

and similarly, taking $x - x' + -\frac{1}{2}$,

$$G(x, x') = \frac{1}{2\pi} e^{-i\phi/2} \sum_{n=-\infty}^{\infty} \frac{(-1)^n}{n + \phi/2\pi} \qquad (x < x') .$$

From the result of Problem 6.32 (see also Eq. (6.57)) the sum in question can be readily evaluated; the reader will find that the Green's function obtained in this way agrees precisely with the Green's function $G_4(x, x')$ of Eq. (7.12') which was obtained in a more elementary fashion for the operator p.

An interesting way of viewing the Green's function is to operate on $G(x, x')$ with L:

$$LG(x, x') = L \sum_{n=1}^{\infty} \frac{\phi_n(x)\phi_n^*(x')}{\lambda_n} .$$

If we interchange summation and the operation denoted by L, we have, using $L\phi_n(x) = \lambda_n\phi_n(x)$,

$$LG(x, x') = \sum_{n=1}^{\infty} \frac{L\phi_n(x)\phi_n^*(x')}{\lambda_n} = \sum_{n=1}^{\infty} \phi_n(x)\phi_n^*(x') \equiv I(x, x') .$$

For any function $f(x)$,

$$\int I(x, x')f(x') \, dx' = \sum_{n=1}^{\infty} \phi_n(x) \int \phi_n^*(x')f(x') \, dx'$$

$$= \sum_{n=1}^{\infty} \phi_n(x)(\phi_n, f) .$$

But since the ϕ_n are assumed to be a complete orthonormal set, this equation may be written

$$\int I(x, x')f(x')\, dx = f(x) \ .$$

We have already seen in Chapter 5 that the "function" $I(x, x')$ which has this property is just the Dirac δ-function, $\delta(x - x')$. Thus we may write

$$LG(x, x') = \delta(x - x') \ , \tag{7.20}$$

an equation which is perhaps better written in the form

$$LK = I \ , \tag{7.21}$$

where K is the integral operator defined by

$$Kf = \int G(x, x')f(x')\, dx' \ .$$

Thus, in terms of Eq. (7.21), finding the Green's function of an operator L is tantamount to *inverting* L, so that equations like $Ly = f$ can be solved according to

$$y = L^{-1}f = Kf = \int G(x, x')f(x')\, dx' \ .$$

This analysis tells us that if we go back to our simplest of Green's functions, $G_1(x, x')$ of Eq. (7.3'), we should find that

$$-i\frac{d}{dx}G_1(x, x') = \delta(x - x') \ .$$

Using Eq. (7.3'), we find that this becomes

$$\frac{d}{dx}\theta(x - x') = \delta(x - x')$$

or

$$\frac{d}{dt}\theta(t) = \delta(t) \ . \tag{7.22}$$

Let us see whether $d\theta/dt$ has the properties of a δ-function discussed in Section 5.3. Using the definition of $\theta(t)$, we see that

$$\int_{-\epsilon}^{\epsilon} \frac{d\theta(t)}{dt}\, dt = \theta(\epsilon) - \theta(-\epsilon) = 1 \ ,$$

so one basic property of the δ-function is trivially satisfied. Also, since $\theta(t)$ is a constant everywhere except at $t = 0$, $d\theta/dt$ vanishes everywhere except at $t = 0$. Now we investigate the effect of $d\theta(t)/dt$ as a factor in an integrand:

$$\int_{-\epsilon}^{\epsilon} \frac{d\theta(t)}{dt} f(t)\, dt = [\theta(t)f(t)]_{-\epsilon}^{\epsilon} - \int_{-\epsilon}^{\epsilon} \theta(t)f'(t)\, dt \ ,$$

where we have integrated once by parts. Using the definition of $\theta(t)$, we get

$$\int_{-\epsilon}^{\epsilon} \frac{d\theta}{dt} f(t) \, dt = f(\epsilon) - \int_{0}^{\epsilon} f'(t) \, dt$$

$$= f(\epsilon) - [f(\epsilon) - f(0)] = f(0) \ .$$

Hence $d\theta/dt$ has the most important of the δ-function properties, namely,

$$\int_{-\epsilon}^{\epsilon} \delta(t) f(t) \, dt = f(0) \ .$$

An intuitive way of seeing that $d\theta/dt = \delta(t)$ is to write an approximate $\theta(t)$ as

$$\theta_\epsilon(t) = \begin{cases} 0 \ , & t < -\epsilon \ , \\ \dfrac{1}{2} + \dfrac{1}{2\epsilon} t \ , & -\epsilon \leq t \leq \epsilon \ , \\ 1 \ , & t > \epsilon \ . \end{cases}$$

Clearly, $\theta_\epsilon(t) \to \theta(t)$ as $\epsilon \to 0$. Now we compute $d\theta_\epsilon(t)/dt$ and find that

$$\theta_\epsilon'(t) = \begin{cases} 0 \ , & t < -\epsilon \ , \\ 1/2\epsilon \ , & -\epsilon \leq t \leq \epsilon \ , \\ 0 \ , & t > \epsilon \ . \end{cases}$$

The sequence of functions $\{\theta_\epsilon'(t)\}$ is one of those we showed in Section 5.3, which approximated the δ-function. Figure 7.3 shows the function $\theta_\epsilon(t)$ and $\theta_\epsilon'(t)$. With these properties of the δ-function in mind, the reader should verify that all the Green's functions derived in the last section satisfy Eq. (7.20).

Fig. 7.3 The solid line represents the function $\theta_\epsilon(t)$; the dashed line represents the function $\theta'_\epsilon(t)$.

The differential representation of the δ-function in Eq. (7.22) is very useful, and for future reference we note a few of its simple consequences. First, since

$$\theta(at) = \theta(t) \qquad \text{if} \qquad a > 0 \ ,$$

$$\theta(at) = 1 - \theta(t) \qquad \text{if} \qquad a < 0 \ ,$$

we obtain by differentiation

$$a \frac{d\theta(at)}{d(at)} = \frac{d\theta}{dt} , \qquad a > 0 ,$$

$$a \frac{d\theta(at)}{d(at)} = - \frac{d\theta}{dt} , \qquad a < 0 .$$

Thus

$$a\delta(at) = \delta(t), \qquad a > 0 ,$$

$$a\delta(at) = -\delta(t) , \qquad a < 0 ,$$

or

$$\delta(at) = \frac{1}{|a|} \delta(t) . \tag{7.23}$$

A second useful result concerns the function signum(x), which is usually written sgn (x). This is a function which equals $+1$ when x is positive and -1 when x is negative. Clearly,

$$\text{sgn} \ (x) = \theta(x) - \theta(-x) ,$$

so

$$\frac{d}{dx} [\text{sgn} \ (x)] = \frac{d\theta(x)}{dx} + \frac{d\theta(-x)}{d(-x)} = \delta(x) + \delta(-x) = 2\delta(x) ,$$

that is,

$$\frac{d}{dx} \text{sgn} \ (x) = 2\delta(x) . \tag{7.24}$$

As an immediate consequence, we see that

$$\frac{d^2}{dx^2} |x| = \frac{d^2}{dx^2} [x \ \text{sgn} \ (x) \ ] = \frac{d}{dx} [\text{sgn} \ (x) + 2x\delta(x)] = \frac{d}{dx} [\text{sgn} \ (x)] = 2\delta(x) .$$

Here we have used the fact that $x\delta(x) = 0$ and Eq. (7.24).

With these rather informal interpretations of Green's functions and the δ-function in mind, we turn to some applications.

7.3 GREEN'S FUNCTIONS IN ONE DIMENSION

Having studied a few simple operators by way of introduction, we shall now try our hand at operators of a more general type and at the same time introduce another technique for the study of Green's functions. We shall begin with an example from classical mechanics, but before we are finished, it will be apparent that the applications arising from this special case are considerable indeed. We consider the equation of the forced, damped harmonic oscillator,

$$\ddot{x}(t) + 2\gamma \dot{x}(t) + \omega_0^2 x(t) = F(t) , \tag{7.25}$$

where we indicate differentiation with respect to time by a dot. We have chosen units of mass such that $m = 1$; γ is essentially the coefficient of frictional drag, ω_0 is the square root of the (positive) spring constant, and $F(t)$ is the external driving force. We assume that $F(t)$ has a Fourier transform,

$$\hat{F}(k) = \frac{1}{\sqrt{2\pi}} \int_{-\infty}^{\infty} e^{ikt} F(t)dt .$$

Since we have assumed that $F(t)$ has a Fourier transform, $F(t)$ must go to zero for large $|t|$. This, coupled with the presence of damping, makes it reasonable to assume that $x(t)$ and its first derivative go to zero for large $|t|$, and therefore their Fourier transforms exist. Taking the Fourier transform of both sides of Eq. (7.25), we get

$$\frac{1}{\sqrt{2\pi}} \int_{-\infty}^{\infty} (\ddot{x} + 2\gamma\dot{x} + \omega_0^2 x)e^{ikt} \, dt = \hat{F}(k) .$$

Let

$$\hat{x}(k) = \frac{1}{\sqrt{2\pi}} \int_{-\infty}^{\infty} e^{ikt} x(t) \, dt;$$

then

$$\frac{1}{\sqrt{2\pi}} \int_{-\infty}^{\infty} \frac{d^2 x}{dt^2} e^{ikt} \, dt + 2\gamma \frac{1}{\sqrt{2\pi}} \int_{-\infty}^{\infty} \frac{dx}{dt} e^{ikt} \, dt + \omega_0^2 \hat{x}(k) = \hat{F}(k) . \quad (7.26)$$

In the first term we integrate by parts once to get

$$\int_{-\infty}^{\infty} \frac{d^2 x}{dt^2} e^{ikt} dt = \left[\frac{dx}{dt} e^{ikt} \right]_{-\infty}^{\infty} - \int_{-\infty}^{\infty} \left(\frac{dx}{dt} \right) \frac{d}{dt} (e^{ikt}) \, dt$$

$$= -ik \int_{-\infty}^{\infty} \left(\frac{dx}{dt} \right) e^{ikt} \, dt .$$

Here the contribution from the endpoints vanishes since we assume that $x(t)$ and $\dot{x}(t)$ may be Fourier transformed and therefore vanish at large distances. Thus, Eq. (7.26) implies that

$$\frac{(2\gamma - ik)}{\sqrt{2\pi}} \int_{-\infty}^{\infty} \left(\frac{dx}{dt} \right) e^{ikt} \, dt + \omega_0^2 \hat{x}(k) = \hat{F}(k) . \quad (7.27)$$

Finally, we integrate by parts once more and use the boundary conditions at infinity to find

$$\frac{1}{\sqrt{2\pi}} \int_{-\infty}^{\infty} \left(\frac{dx}{dt} \right) e^{ikt} = -ik \frac{1}{\sqrt{2\pi}} \int_{-\infty}^{\infty} x(t) e^{ikt} \, dt = -ik\hat{x}(k) .$$

Hence Eq. (7.27) becomes

$$(-k^2 - 2i\gamma k + \omega_0^2)\hat{x}(k) = \hat{F}(k) . \quad (7.28)$$

Since $(\omega_0^2 - 2i\gamma k - k^2)$ has no zeroes on the real line,

$$\hat{x}(k) = \frac{\hat{F}(k)}{-k^2 - 2i\gamma k + \omega_0^2},$$

and by the basic result on Fourier transforms,

$$x(t) = \frac{1}{\sqrt{2\pi}} \int_{-\infty}^{\infty} \frac{\hat{F}(k)}{-k^2 - 2i\gamma k + \omega_0^2} e^{-ikt} \, dk \; .$$

Using the definition of $\hat{F}(k)$, we get

$$x(t) = \frac{1}{2\pi} \int_{-\infty}^{\infty} dt' \int_{-\infty}^{\infty} dk \, \frac{F(t')e^{ikt'}}{-k^2 - 2i\gamma k + \omega_0^2} e^{-ikt} \; .$$

Finally, we can add an arbitrary linear combination of solutions to the homogeneous equation to get the general solution

$$x(t) = Ax_1(t) + Bx_2(t) + \int_{-\infty}^{\infty} G(t, t')F(t') \, dt' \; , \tag{7.29a}$$

where

$$G(t, t') = \frac{1}{2\pi} \int_{-\infty}^{\infty} \frac{e^{-ik(t-t')}}{-k^2 - 2i\gamma k + \omega_0^2} \, dk \; , \tag{7.29b}$$

and A and B must be chosen to satisfy the boundary conditions. For the two linearly independent solutions of the homogeneous equation, we may take

$$x_1(t) = e^{-\gamma t} \sin \left[\sqrt{\omega_0^2 - \gamma^2}\, t \right] ,$$

$$x_2(t) = e^{-\gamma t} \cos \left[\sqrt{\omega_0^2 - \gamma^2}\, t \right] . \tag{7.30}$$

Let us now see if we can evaluate $G(t, t')$. First we write

$$G(t, t') = -\frac{1}{2\pi} \int_{-\infty}^{\infty} \frac{e^{-ik(t-t')} \, dk}{(k - k_1)(k - k_2)} \; , \tag{7.31}$$

where $k_1 = (\omega_0^2 - \gamma^2)^{1/2} - i\gamma$ and $k_2 = -(\omega_0^2 - \gamma^2)^{1/2} - i\gamma$. We will assume for definiteness that $\omega_0 > \gamma$, but this is in no way essential in what follows. The important fact about k_1 and k_2 is that their imaginary parts are always *negative*. Our work on complex variable theory puts us in a position to do this integral easily: we consider the integral in Eq. (7.31) as part of a contour integral in the complex k-plane. The relevant contour—which will be labeled C—runs along the real axis from $-K$ to $+K$ and then closes in the lower half-plane by

Fig. 7.4 The complex k-plane showing the contour used in evaluating the Green's function for the damped harmonic oscillator.

means of a semicircle of radius K about the origin (Fig. 7.4). We shall see that when $t - t' > 0$, this is the appropriate contour, whereas when $t - t' < 0$, the appropriate contour is one that closes in the upper half-plane:

$$I \equiv -\frac{1}{2\pi} \oint_c \frac{e^{-ik(t-t')} \, dk}{(k - k_1)(k - k_2)} = -\frac{1}{2\pi} \int_{-K}^{K} \frac{e^{-ik(t-t')}}{(k - k_1)(k - k_2)} \, dk$$
$$-\frac{1}{2\pi} \int_0^{-\pi} \frac{e^{-iK(t-t')e^{i\phi}}}{(Ke^{i\phi} - k_1)(Ke^{i\phi} - k_2)} \, iKe^{i\phi} \, d\phi \, . \tag{7.32}$$

In the first term on the right of Eq. (7.32), the integral is taken along the real axis; in the second term we integrate along the semicircle of radius K, on which

$$k = Ke^{i\phi} \, , \qquad dk = iKe^{i\phi} \, d\phi \, ,$$

and ϕ ranges from $\phi = 0$ to $\phi = -\pi$. Now we let K, the radius of the contour, become very large. Then since the imaginary parts of k_1 and k_2 are both in the lower half-plane, the contour C eventually encloses both of them, and we can evaluate the integral by the residue theorem. We get

$$-2\pi I = \lim_{K \to \infty} \oint_c \frac{e^{-ik(t-t')}}{(k - k_1)(k - k_2)} \, dk = (-1)(2\pi i)\left[\frac{e^{-ik_1(t-t')}}{k_1 - k_2} + \frac{e^{-ik_2(t-t')}}{k_2 - k_1}\right].$$

The factor (-1) enters because the contour is closed in the *lower* half-plane, and so is traversed *clockwise*. Inserting the values of k_1 and k_2, we obtain

$$I = \frac{e^{-\gamma(t-t')} \sin\left[\sqrt{\omega_0^2 - \gamma^2}(t - t')\right]}{\sqrt{\omega_0^2 - \gamma^2}} \, .$$

As $K \to \infty$, the first term on the right-hand side of Eq. (7.32) becomes just $G(t, t')$, Eq. (7.31), so

$$\frac{e^{-\gamma(t-t')} \sin\left[\sqrt{\omega_0^2 - \gamma^2}(t - t')\right]}{\sqrt{\omega_0^2 - \gamma^2}} = G(t, t') + \lim_{K \to \infty} R \, , \tag{7.33}$$

where

$$R = -\frac{1}{2\pi} \int_0^{-\pi} \frac{e^{-iKe^{i\phi}(t-t')}}{(Ke^{i\phi} - k_1)(Ke^{i\phi} - k_2)} \, iKe^{i\phi} \, d\phi \, .$$

But this integral vanishes as $K \to \infty$ by Jordan's lemma (Section 6.8). Therefore

$$G(t, t') = \frac{e^{-\gamma(t-t')} \sin\left[\sqrt{\omega_0^2 - \gamma^2}(t - t')\right]}{\sqrt{\omega_0^2 - \gamma^2}} \qquad t > t' \, . \tag{7.34}$$

Now if $t < t'$, the above argument fails because the integrals involved in estimating R grow exponentially. In this case, however, we choose a contour that closes in the upper half-plane. But then the integrand in I of Eq. (7.32) has no singularities inside the contour, so

$$G(t, t') = 0 \, , \qquad t < t' \, .$$

Thus we may summarize by saying

$$G(t, t') = \theta(t - t') \frac{e^{-\gamma(t-t')} \sin\left[\sqrt{\omega_0^2 - \gamma^2}\,(t - t')\right]}{\sqrt{\omega_0^2 - \gamma^2}}, \qquad (7.35a)$$

and writing the general solution as

$$x(t) = Ax_1(t) + Bx_2(t) + \int_{t_0}^{t} \frac{e^{-\gamma(t-t')} \sin\left[\sqrt{\omega_0^2 - \gamma^2}(t - t')\right] F(t')\, dt'}{\sqrt{\omega_0^2 - \gamma^2}}, \qquad (7.35b)$$

where t_0 is the time at which the initial conditions are applied (i. e., $F(t')$ may be taken to be zero at times prior to t_0). Note that the term involving the integral vanishes at $t = t_0$, as does its first derivative with respect to t. Thus A and B are determined from the initial conditions, $x(t_0) = x_0$, $\dot{x}(t_0) = \dot{x}_0$, just as they would be if there were no inhomogeneous term present. We anticipated this result in referring to the kernel of the integral as $G(t, t')$ at the beginning of this section.

Finally, we leave it to the reader to show that

$$\left[\frac{d^2}{dt^2} + 2\gamma\frac{d}{dt} + \omega_0^2\right] G(t, t') = \delta(t - t'), \qquad (7.36)$$

just as we expect.

As an example, suppose that the forcing term is

$$F(t) = F_0 e^{-\alpha t}$$

starting at $t = 0$. The system is assumed to be at rest in its equilibrium position at $t = 0$, so that $A = 0 = B$ in Eq. (7.35b). Thus

$$x(t) = F_0 e^{-\gamma t} \int_0^t \frac{1}{\sqrt{\omega_0^2 - \gamma^2}} \sin\left[\sqrt{\omega_0^2 - \gamma^2}(t - t')\right] e^{(\gamma - \alpha)t'}\, dt'.$$

All the integrals are straightforward, and we obtain

$$x(t) = \frac{F_0}{\sqrt{\omega_0^2 - \gamma^2}} \frac{\sin\left[\sqrt{\omega_0^2 - \gamma^2}\,t - \delta\right]}{\sqrt{\omega_0^2 + \alpha^2 - 2\alpha\gamma}} e^{-\gamma t} + \frac{F_0}{\omega_0^2 + \alpha^2 - 2\alpha\gamma} e^{-\alpha t},$$

where $\tan\delta = \sqrt{\omega_0^2 - \gamma^2}/(\alpha - \gamma)$ with δ in the first or second quadrant. Note that the boundary conditions $x(0) = 0$, $\dot{x}(0) = 0$ are satisfied. It is also easy to check that the $x(t)$ found in this way actually does satisfy Eq. (7.25).

If we let the damping go to zero, we find that

$$x(t) = \frac{F_0}{\omega_0} \frac{\sin(\omega_0 t - \delta)}{\sqrt{\omega_0^2 + \alpha^2}} + \frac{F_0}{\omega_0^2 + \alpha^2} e^{-\alpha t}.$$

After a long time has elapsed and the force $F(t)$ has become very small, we obtain pure oscillatory motion. Thus, in the limit of no damping and of long time, we get simply

$$x(t) = \frac{F_0}{\omega_0} \frac{\sin(\omega_0 t - \delta)}{\sqrt{\omega_0^2 + \alpha^2}}.$$

From this result we can compute the final energy of the system. The system had initially zero energy, so the final energy is equal to the energy transferred to the system. Now

$$E = \tfrac{1}{2}\dot{x}^2 + \tfrac{1}{2}\omega_0^2 x^2 ,$$

for a particle of unit mass. Thus

$$E = \frac{F_0^2}{2(\omega_0^2 + \alpha^2)} .$$

According to Section 5.7,

$$E = \frac{1}{2}\left|\int_{-\infty}^{\infty} e^{-i\omega_0 t} F(t)\right|^2 = \frac{1}{2} F_0^2 \left|\int_0^{\infty} e^{-i\omega_0 t} e^{-\alpha t} \, dt\right|^2 = \frac{F_0^2}{2(\omega_0^2 + \alpha^2)} ,$$

which agrees with our result.

In looking at Eq. (7.35a), one is struck by the fact that $G(t, t')$ bears a close resemblance to the solutions of the homogeneous equation

$$\frac{d^2x}{dt^2} + 2\gamma \frac{dx}{dt} + \omega_0^2 x = 0 . \tag{7.37}$$

In fact, considered as a function of t, $G(t, t')$ for $t > t'$ is a linear combination of the two linearly independent solutions of Eq. (7.37) given in Eq. (7.30). (The coefficients of this linear combination depend, of course, on t'.) For this case,

$$G(t, t') = A(t')e^{-\gamma t} \sin\left[\sqrt{\omega_0^2 - \gamma^2}\, t\right] + B(t')e^{-\gamma t} \cos\left[\sqrt{\omega_0^2 - \gamma^2}\, t\right] ,$$

where

$$A(t') = \frac{e^{\gamma t'} \cos\left[\sqrt{\omega_0^2 - \gamma^2}\, t'\right]}{\sqrt{\omega_0^2 - \gamma^2}} , \qquad B(t') = -\frac{e^{\gamma t'} \sin\left[\sqrt{\omega_0^2 - \gamma^2}\, t'\right]}{\sqrt{\omega_0^2 - \gamma^2}} .$$

The reason for this is easily seen by looking at Eq. (7.36).

Everywhere, except at $t = t'$, $G(t, t')$ must satisfy Eq. (7.37), since the δ-function vanishes except at $t = t'$. Therefore, for $t > t'$, $G(t, t')$ is some linear combination of the two solutions to Eq. (7.37) and similarly for $t < t'$.

To put the matter in a less specialized setting, let us consider the most general second-order linear differential operator

$$L \equiv f_0(t) \frac{d^2}{dt^2} + f_1(t) \frac{d}{dt} + f_2(t) .$$

Let $x_1(t)$ and $x_2(t)$ be two linearly independent solutions to

$$Lx(t) = 0 .$$

We wish to solve

$$LG(t, t') = f_0(t) \frac{d^2G(t, t')}{dt^2} + f_1(t) \frac{dG(t, t')}{dt} + f_2(t)G(t, t') = \delta(t - t') . \tag{7.38}$$

For $t > t'$, we write

$$G(t, t') = a_1 x_1(t) + a_2 x_2(t) , \qquad (7.39a)$$

and for $t < t'$,

$$G(t, t') = b_1 x_1(t) + b_2 x_2(t) . \qquad (7.39b)$$

Now let us try to determine $a_1, a_2, b_1,$ and b_2. At $t = t'$, $G(t, t')$ must be continuous; if it were not, dG/dt would contain a δ-function and therefore d^2G/dt^2 would contain the *derivative* of a δ-function. However, on the right-hand side of Eq. (7.38) there is just a δ-function, so we conclude that $G(t, t')$ is continuous at $t = t'$. However, dG/dt will not be continuous at $t = t'$, and from Eq.(7.38) we can determine the value of

$$\left[\frac{dG(t, t')}{dt} \right]_{t=t'+\epsilon} - \left[\frac{dG(t, t')}{dt} \right]_{t=t'-\epsilon}$$

by integrating both sides of Eq. (7.38) from $t = t' - \epsilon$ to $t = t' + \epsilon$. On the right-hand side, the δ-function yields 1, so

$$\int_{t'-\epsilon}^{t'+\epsilon} f_0(t) \frac{d^2G(t, t')}{dt^2} \, dt + \int_{t'-\epsilon}^{t'+\epsilon} f_1(t) \frac{dG(t, t')}{dt} \, dt + \int_{t'-\epsilon}^{t'+\epsilon} f_2(t) G(t, t') \, dt = 1 .$$

Let us assume that $f_0, f_1,$ and f_2 are continuous throughout the region of definition of the Green's function. Then since ϵ is very small, these functions will vary negligibly in the region of integration, and we can replace them by their values at $t = t'$:

$$f_0(t') \int_{t'-\epsilon}^{t'+\epsilon} \frac{d^2G(t, t')}{dt^2} \, dt + f_1(t') \int_{t'-\epsilon}^{t'+\epsilon} \frac{dG(t, t')}{dt} \, dt + f_2(t') \int_{t'-\epsilon}^{t'+\epsilon} G(t, t') \, dt = 1.$$

Since G is continuous at $t = t'$, and since the domain of integration can be made arbitrarily small, the last term on the left of this equation vanishes. Doing the remaining two integrals, we get

$$f_0(t') \left\{ \left[\frac{dG(t, t')}{dt} \right]_{t=t'+\epsilon} - \left[\frac{dG(t, t')}{dt} \right]_{t=t'-\epsilon} \right\}$$
$$+ f_1(t') [G(t' + \epsilon, t') - G(t' - \epsilon, t')] = 1.$$

Since $G(t, t')$ is continuous at $t = t'$, the second term on the left-hand side vanishes and we are left with

$$\left[\frac{dG(t, t')}{dt} \right]_{t=t'+\epsilon} - \left[\frac{dG(t, t')}{dt} \right]_{t=t'-\epsilon} = \frac{1}{f_0(t')} . \qquad (7.40)$$

Using this relation and the fact that $G(t, t')$ is continuous at $t = t'$, we can obtain useful information about the coefficients $a_1, a_2, b_1,$ and b_2 in Eqs. (7.39a) and (7.39b).

From continuity at $t = t'$, we get

$$a_1 x_1(t') + a_2 x_2(t') = b_1 x_1(t') + b_2 x_2(t') ,$$

while from Eq. (7.40), we obtain

$$a_1 \dot{x}_1(t') + a_2 \dot{x}_2(t') - [b_1 \dot{x}_1(t') + b_2 \dot{x}_2(t')] = 1/f_0(t') \, .$$

Combining terms, we find the following set of equations for the differences $(a_1 - b_1)$ and $(a_2 - b_2)$:

$$(a_1 - b_1) x_1(t') + (a_2 - b_2) x_2(t') = 0 \, ,$$
$$(a_1 - b_1) \dot{x}_1(t') + (a_2 - b_2) \dot{x}_2(t') = 1/f_0(t') \, .$$

The solutions are

$$a_1 - b_1 = -\frac{x_2(t')}{f_0(t') \, W(t')} \, , \qquad a_2 - b_2 = \frac{x_1(t')}{f_0(t') \, W(t')} \, ,$$

where $W(t')$ is the *Wronskian* of x_1 and x_2, defined by

$$W(t') = x_1(t') \dot{x}_2(t') - \dot{x}_1(t') x_2(t')$$
$$= \begin{vmatrix} x_1(t') & x_2(t') \\ \dot{x}_1(t') & \dot{x}_2(t') \end{vmatrix} .$$

In this determinant form, the Wronskian generalizes to differential equations of any order. Putting the above result into Eqs. (7.39a, b) we see that $G(t, t')$ may be written as

$$G(t, t') = b_1 x_1(t) + b_2 x_2(t) - \frac{x_1(t) x_2(t') - x_2(t) x_1(t')}{f_0(t') \, W(t')} \, , \qquad t > t'$$
$$\tag{7.41a}$$
$$G(t, t') = b_1 x_1(t) + b_2 x_2(t) \, , \qquad t < t' \, .$$

It is left as an exercise (Problem 6) to show that $f_0(t') W(t')$ never vanishes. The two remaining constants, b_1 and b_2, can now be chosen to satisfy the appropriate boundary conditions. The form which the Green's function finally takes is strongly dependent on the type of boundary conditions involved. If the boundary conditions are of the single point variety typical of classical mechanics, then we shall require that $b_1 = 0 = b_2$ in Eq. (7.41a). If we do this, the Green's function is given by

$$G(t, t') = -\theta(t - t') \frac{x_1(t) x_2(t') - x_2(t) x_1(t')}{f_0(t') \, W(t')} \, , \tag{7.41b}$$

and the solution in terms of the Green's function is

$$x(t) = A x_1(t) + B x_2(t) + \int_{t_0}^{t} G(t, t') F(t') \, dt' \, . \tag{7.41c}$$

The term involving the integral vanishes at $t = t_0$ and so does its derivative with respect to t. Thus, when we apply the one-point boundary conditions, $x(t_0) = x_0$, $\dot{x}(t_0) = \dot{x}_0$, the constants A and B in Eq. (7.41c) are determined just as though the integral term were not present.

However, if the boundary conditions are of the two-point type, say

$$x(t_0) = x_0, \quad x(t_1) = x_1 \, ,$$

then we write

$$x(t) = Ax_1(t) + Bx_2(t) + \int_{t_0}^{t_1} G(t, t')F(t') \, dt' \,. \tag{7.42}$$

Then it would seem reasonable to choose b_1 and b_2 in Eq. (7.41a) so that $G(t_0, t') = 0 = G(t_1, t')$ and therefore A and B of Eq. (7.42) are determined by the boundary condition, just as though the integral term were not present.

To illustrate this case and also to demonstrate a simple calculation of a Green's function by our new method, let us consider

$$L = \frac{d^2}{dt^2} + \omega_0^2 \,.$$

We already know that for one-point (classical mechanical) boundary conditions, the Green's function is

$$G(t, t') = \theta(t - t') \frac{\sin [\omega_0(t - t')]}{\omega_0} \,,$$

which is readily obtained by letting $\gamma = 0$ in Eq. (7.35a). Now let us use another method and apply a two-point boundary condition. We may choose

$$x_1(t) = \sin \omega_0 t \,, \qquad x_2(t) = \cos \omega_0 t \,,$$

so that

$$W(t') = x_1(t)\dot{x}_2(t) - \dot{x}_1(t)x_2(t) = -\omega_0 \,.$$

Since $f_0 = 1$, we obtain from Eq. (7.41a)

$$G(t, t') = b_1 \sin \omega_0 t + b_2 \cos \omega_0 t + \frac{\sin \omega_0(t - t')}{\omega_0} \,, \qquad t > t' \,, \tag{7.43a}$$

$$G(t, t') = b_1 \sin \omega_0 t + b_2 \cos \omega_0 t \,, \qquad t < t' \,. \tag{7.43b}$$

For convenience, let us choose the endpoints to be $t_0 = 0$ and $t_1 = 1$. Then applying the condition $G(t_0, t') \equiv G(0, t') = 0$ to Eq. (7.43b), we get $b_2 = 0$. Similarly, applying the condition $G(t_1, t') \equiv G(1, t') = 0$ to Eq. (7.43a), we find that

$$b_1 \sin \omega_0 + \frac{1}{\omega_0} \sin \omega_0(1 - t') = 0 \,,$$

so that

$$b_1 = \frac{1}{\omega_0} \cot \omega_0 \sin \omega_0 t' - \frac{1}{\omega_0} \cos \omega_0 t' \,.$$

With b_1 and b_2 evaluated, Eqs. (7.43a) and (7.43b) become

$$G(t, t') = \frac{1}{\omega_0} [\cot \omega_0 \sin \omega_0 t' - \cos \omega_0 t'] \sin \omega_0 t \qquad t > t' \,, \tag{7.44a}$$

$$G(t, t') = \frac{1}{\omega_0} [\cot \omega_0 \sin \omega_0 t' - \cos \omega_0 t'] \sin \omega_0 t \qquad t < t' \,. \tag{7.44b}$$

Note how different this result is from that found for the case of one-point boundary conditions. It is interesting to note that if we let $\omega_0 \to 0$, we recover the function $G_3(t, t')$ of Eq. (7.11') for the Green's function of d^2/dt^2 with two-point boundary conditions.

Note that when $\omega_0 = n\pi$ $(n = 1, 2, \cdots)$ in Eqs. (7.44a) and (7.44b), the function $G(t, t')$ becomes infinite and our method fails! This is because, for $\omega_0 = n\pi$,

$$L = \frac{d^2}{dt^2} + (n\pi)^2$$

has an eigenfunction with zero eigenvalue, namely, $\sin(n\pi t)$, which satisfies the boundary condition that it vanish at both $t = 0$ and $t = 1$. In this case the eigenfunction expansion of Eq. (7.18') does not work because of a zero eigenvalue in the denominator of the expression for $G(t, t')$. And then, of course, there is *no unique* solution to the equation

$$Lx = F;$$

we can add an arbitrary multiple of $\sin(n\pi t)$ to any solution and thus get another perfectly acceptable solution.

An analysis identical to the one given here can be carried out for the general nth order linear differential operator, again with the restriction $f_0(t) \neq 0$ and with the proviso ruling out zero eigenvalues.

As was pointed out at the end of Section 7.1, the use of Green's functions is by no means restricted to solving differential equations with inhomogeneous terms which are independent of x. One of the most important applications occurs when the inhomogeneous term itself depends on the unknown function $x(t)$. For example, the differential equation

$$Lx = f(t, x)$$

can be rewritten as an integral equation of the form

$$x(t) = \xi(t) + \int G(t, t')f[t', x(t')]\,dt' ,$$

where $\xi(t)$ is a linear combination of the solutions to the homogeneous equation,

$$Lx = 0 ,$$

which satisfies the boundary conditions, and $G(t, t')$ is the Green's function belonging to L which satisfies its own appropriate boundary conditions. For example, for a simple harmonic oscillator, perturbed by some nonharmonic force of the form $\phi(t)x(t)$ or $[x(t)]^2$, we have

$$x(t) = x_0 \cos \omega_0 t + \frac{\dot{x}_0}{\omega_0} \sin \omega_0 t + \int_0^t \frac{1}{\omega_0} \sin \omega_0(t - t')f[t', x(t')]\,dt' ,$$

for the one-point boundary conditions $x(0) = x_0$, $\dot{x}(0) = \dot{x}_0$. A perturbation of the form $\phi(t)x(t)$ indicates that the "spring constant" of the harmonic oscillator is not constant in time, but instead has the form $k = k_0 + \phi(t)$.

Similarly, if the force were not perfectly harmonic, a term of the form $[x(t)]^2$ might be necessary to achieve an accurate representation of the force; this is often the case for the forces which bind solids, where small terms proportional to the square of the displacement play an important role. In the next chapter, we shall discuss methods by which such integral equations can be solved.

7.4 GREEN'S FUNCTIONS IN THREE DIMENSIONS

The method described at the end of the last chapter for obtaining Green's functions in one dimension is not generally suited for three dimensional problems. Since three dimensions corresponds to the real world, it is not surprising that the problems are harder in this case. However, there is a particularly important operator in three dimensions which yields readily to the Fourier transform method described at the beginning of the last section. The operator in question is

$$H_0 = \nabla^2 + \lambda ,$$

where ∇^2 is the familiar Laplacian operator discussed in Chapter 1. We shall employ the Fourier transform method to solve

$$H_0 \phi(\mathbf{r}) = F(\mathbf{r}) , \tag{7.45}$$

assuming that $\phi(\mathbf{r})$ and $F(\mathbf{r})$ may be Fourier transformed. Let

$$\hat{F}(\mathbf{k}) = \frac{1}{(2\pi)^{3/2}} \int e^{-i\mathbf{k}\cdot\mathbf{r}} F(\mathbf{r}) d^3\mathbf{r} , \tag{7.46a}$$

$$\hat{\phi}(\mathbf{k}) = \frac{1}{(2\pi)^{3/2}} \int e^{-i\mathbf{k}\cdot\mathbf{r}} \phi(\mathbf{r}) d^3\mathbf{r} , \tag{7.46b}$$

then from Eq. (7.45),

$$\frac{1}{(2\pi)^{3/2}} \int e^{-i\mathbf{k}\cdot\mathbf{r}} \nabla^2 \phi(\mathbf{r}) d^3\mathbf{r} + \lambda\hat{\phi}(\mathbf{k}) = \hat{F}(\mathbf{k}) . \tag{7.47}$$

Now we use Green's theorem, which states that

$$\int_V (F\nabla^2 G - G\nabla^2 F) d^3\mathbf{r} = \int_S (F\nabla G - G\nabla F)\cdot\mathbf{n}\, dS ,$$

where S is the surface enclosing the volume V, and $\mathbf{n}$ is the unit vector normal to S, pointing outward. Thus we conclude that

$$\frac{1}{(2\pi)^{3/2}} \int_V e^{-i\mathbf{k}\cdot\mathbf{r}} \nabla^2 \phi(\mathbf{r}) d^3\mathbf{r} = \frac{1}{(2\pi)^{3/2}} \int_V \phi(\mathbf{r}) \nabla^2 e^{-i\mathbf{k}\cdot\mathbf{r}} d^3\mathbf{r}$$

$$+ \frac{1}{(2\pi)^{3/2}} \int_S [e^{-i\mathbf{k}\cdot\mathbf{r}}\nabla\phi(\mathbf{r}) - \phi(\mathbf{r})\nabla e^{-i\mathbf{k}\cdot\mathbf{r}}]\cdot\mathbf{n}\, dS . \tag{7.48}$$

The region of integration is the entire three-dimensional space, so in evaluating the surface integral, let us take the surface to be a sphere of radius R and take the limit as $R \to \infty$. In this case, $\mathbf{n}$ is just a unit vector in the radial direction, so the surface term is

$$\frac{1}{(2\pi)^{3/2}} \int_S [e^{-i\mathbf{k}\cdot\mathbf{r}}\nabla\psi(\mathbf{r}) - \psi(\mathbf{r})\nabla e^{-i\mathbf{k}\cdot\mathbf{r}}]\cdot\mathbf{n}\, dS$$

$$= \frac{1}{(2\pi)^{3/2}} \lim_{R\to\infty} R^2 \left\{ \int\int \left[e^{-i\mathbf{k}\cdot\mathbf{r}}\frac{d\psi}{dr} - \psi\frac{d}{dr}e^{-i\mathbf{k}\cdot\mathbf{r}} \right] d\Omega \right\}_{r=R}, \qquad (7.48')$$

where $d\Omega = \sin\theta\, d\theta\, d\phi$. If $\psi(\mathbf{r})$ tends to zero sufficiently rapidly as $|\mathbf{r}| \to \infty$ (roughly, if ψ vanishes faster than $1/r$), then the surface term will vanish, so Eq. (7.48) reduces to

$$\frac{1}{(2\pi)^{3/2}} \int_V e^{-i\mathbf{k}\cdot\mathbf{r}}\nabla^2\psi(\mathbf{r})d^3\mathbf{r} = -k^2\hat{\psi}(\mathbf{k}) ,$$

and Eq. (7.47) becomes

$$(-k^2 + \lambda)\hat{\psi}(\mathbf{k}) = \hat{F}(\mathbf{k}) . \qquad (7.49)$$

There are now two cases to be distinguished: $\lambda \geq 0$ and $\lambda < 0$. Let us consider the latter case first, and write $\lambda = -\kappa^2$. Then $(-k^2 - \kappa^2)$ never vanishes, so

$$\hat{\psi}(\mathbf{k}) = -\frac{\hat{F}(\mathbf{k})}{k^2 + \kappa^2} , \qquad (7.50)$$

and by the Fourier integral theorem,

$$\psi(\mathbf{r}) = \xi(\mathbf{r}) - \frac{1}{(2\pi)^{3/2}} \int \frac{\hat{F}(\mathbf{k})}{k^2 + \kappa^2} e^{i\mathbf{k}\cdot\mathbf{r}}d^3\mathbf{k} ,$$

where $\xi(\mathbf{r})$ represents an arbitrary linear combination of solutions of the homogeneous equation

$$H_0\psi(\mathbf{r}) = (\nabla^2 - \kappa^2)\psi(\mathbf{r}) = 0 .$$

Using Eq. (7.45a), we get

$$\psi(\mathbf{r}) = \xi(\mathbf{r}) + \int G(\mathbf{r}, \mathbf{r}')F(\mathbf{r}')d^3\mathbf{r}' \qquad (7.51a)$$

with

$$G(\mathbf{r}, \mathbf{r}') = -\frac{1}{(2\pi)^3} \int \frac{e^{i\mathbf{k}\cdot(\mathbf{r}-\mathbf{r}')}}{k^2 + \kappa^2} d^3\mathbf{k} . \qquad (7.51b)$$

Using the result of Eq. (6.51) we obtain

$$G(\mathbf{r}, \mathbf{r}') = -\frac{1}{4\pi}\frac{e^{-\kappa|\mathbf{r}-\mathbf{r}'|}}{|\mathbf{r} - \mathbf{r}'|} . \qquad (7.52)$$

To complete the solution, we need only determine $\xi(\mathbf{r})$ in Eq. (7.51a). In most physical problems we want $\psi(\mathbf{r})$ to remain bounded as $|\mathbf{r}|$ becomes very large. Let us see if we can solve

$$H_0\psi(\mathbf{r}) = (\nabla^2 - \kappa^2)\psi(\mathbf{r}) = 0 \qquad (7.53)$$

subject to the requirement that $\phi(\mathbf{r})$ be bounded as $|\mathbf{r}| \to \infty$. Clearly, the solutions to Eq. (7.53) are just

$$\phi(\mathbf{r}) = e^{-\kappa_1 x} e^{-\kappa_2 y} e^{-\kappa_3 z}, \qquad \kappa^2 = \kappa_1^2 + \kappa_2^2 + \kappa_3^2. \tag{7.54}$$

But all these solutions "blow up" as $|\mathbf{r}|$ becomes large, except in the directions in which $\kappa_1 x$, $\kappa_2 y$, and $\kappa_3 z$ are positive. Thus there are no acceptable solutions to the homogeneous equation, and we may write the final result as

$$\psi(\mathbf{r}) = -\frac{1}{4\pi} \int \frac{e^{-\kappa|\mathbf{r}-\mathbf{r}'|}}{|\mathbf{r}-\mathbf{r}'|} F(\mathbf{r}') d^3\mathbf{r}'. \tag{7.55}$$

If $F(\mathbf{r}')$ decreases sufficiently rapidly as $|\mathbf{r}'| \to \infty$ (for example, if $F(\mathbf{r}')$ vanishes when $|\mathbf{r}'| > R$ for some R), then we see that as $|\mathbf{r}| \to \infty$,

$$\psi(\mathbf{r}) \to C \frac{e^{-\kappa r}}{r}.$$

In this case our neglect of surface terms in Eq. (7.48) was justified, since $\psi(\mathbf{r})$ drops off exponentially for large values of $|\mathbf{r}|$.

An interesting application of Eq. (7.55) occurs in electromagnetic theory, the electromagnetic potential, $\phi(\mathbf{r})$ is related to the charge distribution, $\rho(\mathbf{r})$, by Poisson's equation:

$$\nabla^2 \phi(\mathbf{r}) = -4\pi\rho(\mathbf{r}).$$

Equation (7.55), in the limit $\kappa = 0$, tells us that

$$\phi(\mathbf{r}) = \int \frac{\rho(\mathbf{r}')}{|\mathbf{r}-\mathbf{r}'|} d^3\mathbf{r}',$$

which leads to the familiar multipole expansion for $\phi(\mathbf{r})$. For $|\mathbf{r}|$ large enough, $\phi(\mathbf{r}) \to Q/r$, where

$$Q = \int \rho(\mathbf{r}') d^3\mathbf{r}'.$$

This result is sensible, since at large enough distances any charge distribution should look like a point charge.

Another important application of Eq. (7.55) is to Schrödinger's equation,

$$\left(\nabla^2 + \frac{2mE}{\hbar^2} \right) \psi(\mathbf{r}) = \frac{2m}{\hbar^2} V(\mathbf{r})\psi(\mathbf{r}). \tag{7.56}$$

For bound states in an attractive potential $[V(\mathbf{r}) \leq 0]$, E is negative. Hence, writing $(-2mE/\hbar^2) \equiv \kappa^2$, we get from Eq. (7.56), using Eq. (7.55),

$$\psi(\mathbf{r}) = -\frac{m}{2\pi\hbar^2} \int \frac{e^{-\kappa|\mathbf{r}-\mathbf{r}'|}}{|\mathbf{r}-\mathbf{r}'|} V(\mathbf{r}')\psi(\mathbf{r}') d^3\mathbf{r}'. \tag{7.57}$$

Thus the linear, differential eigenvalue problem has been transformed into a linear, integral eigenvalue problem. Because of the complexity of the Green's function, it is often preferable to write equations like this in "momentum space," i.e., to write instead an integral equation for the Fourier transform of

$\phi(\mathbf{r})$. Such an equation is given straightaway by Eq. (7.50). For Schrödinger's equation,

$$F(\mathbf{r}) = \frac{2m}{\hbar^2} V(\mathbf{r})\phi(\mathbf{r}) ,$$

and using Eq. (7.46a) and the convolution theorem [see Eq. (5.65)], we get

$$\hat{F}(\mathbf{k}) = \frac{2m}{(2\pi)^{3/2}\hbar^2} \int \hat{V}(\mathbf{k} - \mathbf{p})\hat{\phi}(\mathbf{p}) \, d^3\mathbf{p} ,$$

so Eq. (7.50) becomes

$$\hat{\phi}(\mathbf{k}) = -\frac{2m}{(2\pi)^{3/2}\hbar^2} \int \frac{\hat{V}(\mathbf{k} - \mathbf{p})}{k^2 + \kappa^2} \hat{\phi}(\mathbf{p}) d^3\mathbf{p} , \tag{7.57'}$$

which, of course, could also have been obtained by taking the Fourier transform of both sides of Eq. (7.57) and making use of the convolution theorem [Eq. (5.65)] twice.

As a specific example, suppose that $V(\mathbf{r})$ is given by the Yukawa potential

$$V(\mathbf{r}) = -g^2 \frac{e^{-\mu r}}{r} . \tag{7.58}$$

A straightforward integration shows that

$$\hat{V}(\mathbf{q}) = -\left(\frac{2}{\pi}\right)^{1/2} g^2 \frac{1}{q^2 + \mu^2} , \tag{7.58'}$$

so for this case Schrödinger's integral equation is

$$\hat{\phi}(\mathbf{k}) = \frac{mg^2}{\pi^2\hbar^2} \int \frac{\hat{\phi}(\mathbf{p})}{(k^2 + \kappa^2)[(\mathbf{k} - \mathbf{p})^2 + \mu^2]} \, d^3\mathbf{p} . \tag{7.59}$$

In this form it is more convenient to regard κ as fixed and g^2 to be determined as an eigenvalue; that is, it is easier to ask what potential strengths can produce a given binding energy, $\hbar^2\kappa^2/2m$, rather than what binding energies will be produced by a given potential strength, g^2. For a central potential, the wave functions have the angular dependence of the spherical harmonics. Therefore

$$\hat{\phi}(\mathbf{k}) = \phi_l(k) Y_{lm}(\theta_k, \phi_k) , \tag{7.60}$$

and it is a simple matter to obtain a collection of integral equations, one for each $\phi_l(k)$. For example, when $l = 0$, Y_{lm} is a constant. If we substitute Eq. (7.60) into both sides of Eq. (7.59), the angular integration is straightforward, and we get as our equation for $\phi_0(k)$,

$$\phi_0(k) = \frac{mg^2}{\pi^2\hbar^2} \int_0^\infty \frac{1}{k(k^2 + \kappa^2)} \ln\left[\frac{(k + p)^2 + \mu^2}{(k - p)^2 + \mu^2}\right] \phi_0(p)p \, dp . \tag{7.61}$$

One-dimensional integral equations of this kind can be solved by using techniques that will be developed in the next two chapters. Just to assure himself that this equation really does have something in common with Schrödinger's equation, the reader who enjoys doing arduous integrations can substitute the values

$$\phi_0(p) = \frac{C}{\left(p^2 + \dfrac{1}{a_0^2}\right)^2}, \qquad E_0 = -\frac{\hbar^2}{2ma_0^2}, \qquad k^2 = -\frac{2mE_0}{\hbar^2} = +\frac{1}{a_0^2} \qquad (7.62)$$

(where $a_0 = \hbar^2/mg^2$ is the Bohr radius of the hydrogen atom) into Eq. (7.61). Upon doing the integration and letting $\mu \to 0$ *afterward*, he will find that this $\phi_0(p)$ is in fact a solution to Eq. (7.61). [*Hint*: Integrate by parts once to get rid of the log term and then do a contour integral.] This is as it should be, since $\phi_0(p)$, as given in Eq. (7.62), is proportional to the Fourier transform of the ground state wave function of the hydrogen atom, and E_0 is the corresponding ground state energy. Note in passing that Eq. (7.61) tells us that for a Yukawa potential (and also for a Coulomb potential),

$$\phi_0(k) \sim 1/k^4$$

for k very large, as may be seen by expanding the log term in Eq. (7.61). This is true for any $l = 0$ state.

Before the reader objects that there is nothing new in all this, since everyone knows that there exist exact solutions for all the bound states of hydrogen, let us point out that the Coulomb potential is one of the very few potentials which can be dealt with in closed form. Many potentials of interest in physics do not have closed-form solutions, so other techniques, such as the ones being developed here, must be employed.

Having disposed of the case $\lambda < 0$, let us now look at the more subtle case, $\lambda \geq 0$. Now the quantity $(-k^2 + \lambda)$ in Eq. (7.49) has a zero for $k = \pm\sqrt{\lambda}$, so we cannot invert it as it stands. We shall first give a prescription for avoiding this difficulty and discuss its legitimacy later. The idea is to assume that $\sqrt{\lambda}$ is the sum of a positive real number and an imaginary number, so that

$$\lambda = (q \pm i\epsilon)^2, \qquad \epsilon > 0 . \qquad (7.63)$$

The use of ϵ expresses the hope that when we are finished we can let ϵ tend to zero and obtain a well-behaved result. Thus, Eq. (7.49) yields

$$\hat{\phi}_\pm(\mathbf{k}) = -\frac{\hat{F}(\mathbf{k})}{k^2 - (q \pm i\epsilon)^2} , \qquad (7.64)$$

and proceeding just as before, we arrive at

$$\psi_\pm(\mathbf{r}) = \xi(\mathbf{r}) + \int G_\pm(\mathbf{r}, \mathbf{r}')F(\mathbf{r})d^3\mathbf{r}' , \qquad (7.65)$$

with

$$G_\pm(\mathbf{r}, \mathbf{r}') = -\frac{1}{(2\pi)^3} \int \frac{e^{i\mathbf{k}\cdot(\mathbf{r}-\mathbf{r}')}}{k^2 - (q \pm i\epsilon)^2} d^3\mathbf{k} .$$

Because of the imaginary part which we have inserted, this integral has no poles on the path of integration, so we may proceed just as in the $\lambda < 0$ case.

Doing the angular integration and extending the k integral to $-\infty$ as we did in obtaining Eq. (7.52), we obtain

$$G_{\pm}(\mathbf{r}, \mathbf{r}') = -\frac{1}{8\pi^2 i |\mathbf{r} - \mathbf{r}'|} \int_{-\infty}^{\infty} \left[\frac{e^{ik|\mathbf{r}-\mathbf{r}'|}}{(k - q \mp i\epsilon)(k + q \pm i\epsilon)} \right.$$
$$\left. - \frac{e^{-ik|\mathbf{r}-\mathbf{r}'|}}{(k - q \mp i\epsilon)(k + q \pm i\epsilon)} \right] k \, dk \, .$$

There are two integrals in question. We consider first

$$J_{\pm} = \int_{-\infty}^{\infty} k \, \frac{e^{ik|\mathbf{r}-\mathbf{r}'|}}{(k - q \mp i\epsilon)(k + q \pm i\epsilon)} \, dk \, .$$

By arguments used before in similar circumstances, we can evaluate this integral by contour integration, closing the contour in the upper half-plane. Again, the contribution from the semicircle vanishes just as in the $\lambda < 0$ case, so that, by the residue theorem,

$$J_{\pm} = 2\pi i \frac{(\pm q + i\epsilon) e^{i(\pm q + i\epsilon)|\mathbf{r}-\mathbf{r}'|}}{2(\pm q + i\epsilon)}$$
$$= \pi i e^{\pm iq|\mathbf{r}-\mathbf{r}'|} e^{-\epsilon|\mathbf{r}-\mathbf{r}'|} \, .$$

Likewise,

$$K_{\pm} = \int_{-\infty}^{\infty} k \frac{e^{-ik|\mathbf{r}-\mathbf{r}'|}}{(k - q \pm i\epsilon)(k + q \pm i\epsilon)} \, dk = -\pi i e^{\pm iq|\mathbf{r}-\mathbf{r}'|} e^{-\epsilon|\mathbf{r}-\mathbf{r}'|} \, .$$

Hence

$$G_{\pm}(\mathbf{r}, \mathbf{r}') = -\frac{1}{4\pi} \frac{e^{\pm iq|\mathbf{r}-\mathbf{r}'|}}{|\mathbf{r} - \mathbf{r}'|} e^{-\epsilon|\mathbf{r}-\mathbf{r}'|} \, . \tag{7.66}$$

Returning to Eq. (7.65), we find that

$$\psi_{\pm}(\mathbf{r}) = \xi(\mathbf{r}) - \frac{1}{4\pi} \int \frac{e^{i(\pm q + i\epsilon)|\mathbf{r}-\mathbf{r}'|}}{|\mathbf{r} - \mathbf{r}'|} F(\mathbf{r}') d^3\mathbf{r}' \, .$$

Thus the choice of positive or negative imaginary part in Eq. (7.63) has a profound effect on the solution. In one case, as $|\mathbf{r}| \to \infty$,

$$\psi_{+}(\mathbf{r}) \to \xi(\mathbf{r}) + C \frac{e^{iqr}}{r} \, ,$$

whereas, in the other case,

$$\psi_{-}(\mathbf{r}) \to \xi(\mathbf{r}) + C \frac{e^{-iqr}}{r} \, .$$

In both these cases, C may depend on θ and ϕ, but not on r. Thus, in cases where the boundary condition can be put in the form of a restriction on the behavior of the solutions at large distances (such as in quantum mechanical scattering problems), the choice of $\lambda = (q + i\epsilon)^2$ or $\lambda = (q - i\epsilon)^2$ corresponds to the application of a particular boundary condition at all points of a two-dimensional surface.

Now we must examine the possibilities for $\xi(\mathbf{r})$, the appropriate solution of the homogeneous equation

$$(\nabla^2 + q^2)\phi(\mathbf{r}) = 0 .$$

This equation has as its solution $e^{i\mathbf{q}\cdot\mathbf{r}}$, where $\mathbf{q}$ is a vector whose magnitude is q and whose direction is arbitary. Thus the complete solution reads

$$\phi_{\pm}(\mathbf{r}) = \frac{A}{(2\pi)^{3/2}} e^{i\mathbf{q}\cdot\mathbf{r}} - \frac{1}{4\pi} \int \frac{e^{i(\pm q + i\epsilon)|\mathbf{r}-\mathbf{r'}|}}{|\mathbf{r} - \mathbf{r'}|} F(\mathbf{r'})d^3\mathbf{r'} . \tag{7.67}$$

The constant A and the direction of $\mathbf{q}$ are determined by the initial conditions.

A particularly important example is again provided by Schrödinger's equation, which we write in the form

$$\left(\nabla^2 + \frac{2mE}{\hbar^2}\right)\phi(\mathbf{r}) = \frac{2m}{\hbar^2} V(\mathbf{r})\phi(\mathbf{r}) .$$

If we look at the so-called *scattering case* $(E \geq 0)$, then we have precisely the situation envisioned in deriving Eq. (7.67). We find immediately the following *integral equation* for the wave function:

$$\phi_{\pm}(\mathbf{r}) = \frac{A}{(2\pi)^{3/2}} e^{i\mathbf{q}_i\cdot\mathbf{r}} - \frac{m}{2\pi\hbar^2} \int \frac{e^{\pm i q_i|\mathbf{r}-\mathbf{r'}|}}{|\mathbf{r} - \mathbf{r'}|} V(\mathbf{r'})\phi_{\pm}(\mathbf{r'})d^3\mathbf{r'} . \tag{7.68}$$

where $q_i = \sqrt{2mE/\hbar^2}$. This equation is called the Lippmann-Schwinger equation; it is the starting point for most modern studies of quantum-mechanical scattering phenomena. We have dropped the ϵ in anticipation of the fact that the limit $\epsilon \rightarrow 0$ will pose no difficulties. We shall return to this point later.

The physical picture here is that of a plane wave traveling in the direction $\mathbf{q}_i$, with energy $\hbar^2 q_i^2/2m$, incident on a scattering center represented by $V(\mathbf{r})$. The intensity is determined by A, but is largely irrelevant to the physics of the problem. At large distances, we expect to find not only the incident wave, but also an outgoing spherical wave due to the scattering. In this case the boundary condition demands that we have an asymptotic behavior of the type

$$\phi_{+}(\mathbf{r}) = \frac{A}{(2\pi)^{3/2}} e^{i\mathbf{q}_i\cdot\mathbf{r}} + C\frac{e^{iq_i r}}{r} .$$

That this is the appropriate solution which contains *outgoing* spherical waves can be seen by remembering that Schrödinger's time-dependent equation is

$$H\Psi = i\hbar \frac{\partial\Psi}{\partial t} .$$

If H is time independent,

$$\Psi(\mathbf{r}, t) = \phi(\mathbf{r})e^{-iEt/\hbar} = \phi(\mathbf{r})e^{-i\omega t} ,$$

where $\omega = E/\hbar$ and $\phi(\mathbf{r})$ satisfies Schrödinger's time-independent equation,

$$H\phi(\mathbf{r}) = E\phi(\mathbf{r}) .$$

Thus the *asymptotic* solution to the time-dependent equation is

$$\Psi_+(\mathbf{r}, t) = \frac{A}{(2\pi)^{3/2}} e^{i(\mathbf{q}_i \cdot \mathbf{r} - \omega t)} + C \frac{e^{i(q_i r - \omega t)}}{r} , \qquad (7.69)$$

where $\omega = \hbar q_i^2/2m$. For the phase to remain constant as t increases, r must increase; thus Eq. (7.69) describes an *outgoing* wave.

Conversely, the asymptotic form

$$\phi_-(\mathbf{r}) = \frac{A}{(2\pi)^{3/2}} e^{i\mathbf{q}_i \cdot \mathbf{r}} + C \frac{e^{-iq_i r}}{r}$$

corresponds to an incoming spherical wave. This boundary condition is also relevant in quantum mechanics when discussing final states of scattering processes. Since it involves no extra difficulty to do so, we shall discuss both conditions together.

It is interesting to look a bit more closely at the asymptotic form of Eq. (7.68). If we write

$$|\mathbf{r} - \mathbf{r}'| = \sqrt{r^2 - 2\mathbf{r}\cdot\mathbf{r}' + r'^2} = r\left[1 - \frac{2\mathbf{r}\cdot\mathbf{r}'}{r^2} + \frac{r'^2}{r^2}\right]^{1/2} ,$$

and assume that r is very large, then a binomial expansion yields

$$|\mathbf{r} - \mathbf{r}'| = r - \mathbf{n}\cdot\mathbf{r}' + \mathcal{O}(1/r);$$

$\mathcal{O}(1/r)$ represents terms which vanish at least as fast as $1/r$ for large r, and $\mathbf{n}$ is a unit vector in the radial direction. Thus for large r, Eq. (7.68) becomes

$$\phi_\pm(\mathbf{r}) \rightarrow \frac{A}{(2\pi)^{3/2}} e^{i\mathbf{q}_i \cdot \mathbf{r}} - \frac{m}{2\pi\hbar^2} \frac{e^{\pm iq_i r}}{r} \int e^{\mp iq_i \mathbf{n} \cdot \mathbf{r}'} V(\mathbf{r}')\phi_\pm(\mathbf{r}')d^3\mathbf{r}' .$$

Setting $\mathbf{q}_f = q_i\mathbf{n}$, we have

$$\phi_\pm(\mathbf{r}) = \frac{A}{(2\pi)^{3/2}}\left[e^{i\mathbf{q}_i \cdot \mathbf{r}} + f_\pm^s(\mathbf{q}_f) \frac{e^{\pm iq_i r}}{r}\right], \qquad (7.70)$$

where

$$f_\pm^s(\mathbf{q}_f) = -\frac{(2\pi)^{1/2}m}{A\hbar^2} \int e^{\mp i\mathbf{q}_f \cdot \mathbf{r}'} V(\mathbf{r}')\phi_\pm(\mathbf{r}')d^3\mathbf{r}'; \qquad (7.71)$$

$f_\pm^s(\mathbf{q}_f)$ is called the scattering amplitude. It measures the ratio of the flux of scattered particles to that of incident particles. It is clearly independent of A, since $\phi(\mathbf{r})$ will be proportional to A. Since $\phi(\mathbf{r})$ and A have the same dimensions, we see from Eq. (7.70) that $f_\pm^s(\mathbf{q}_f)$ must have the dimensions of length. The quantity $f_\pm^s(\mathbf{q}_f)$ is of great importance in quantum mechanics, since its modulus squared is what is measured in scattering experiments. We shall soon obtain an integral equation for this important quantity. For the moment, we merely remark that since $f_\pm^s(\mathbf{q}_f)$ is, apart from constant factors, just the Fourier transform of $V(\mathbf{r})\psi(\mathbf{r})$, we can use the convolution theorem to obtain

$$f_{\pm}^s(\mathbf{q}_f) = -\frac{(2\pi)^{1/2}m}{A\hbar^2} \int \hat{V}(\pm\mathbf{q}_f - \mathbf{p})\hat{\phi}(\mathbf{p})d^3\mathbf{p} \ . \tag{7.72}$$

The fact that $f_{\pm}^s(\mathbf{q}_f)$ is simply related to the Fourier transform of $\psi(\mathbf{r})$ suggests that it may be useful to obtain an integral equation for $\hat{\phi}(\mathbf{p})$ just as we did in Eq. (7.57′) for the bound state $(\lambda < 0)$ case. The only difference is that we now have an inhomogeneous term. By looking at Eq. (7.68), we see that this must be the Fourier transform of $[A/(2\pi)^{3/2}]e^{i\mathbf{q}_i \cdot \mathbf{r}}$, which is

$$\frac{A}{(2\pi)^3} \int e^{i\mathbf{q}_i \cdot \mathbf{r}} e^{-i\mathbf{k} \cdot \mathbf{r}} d^3\mathbf{r} = A\delta(\mathbf{q}_i - \mathbf{k}) \ .$$

(This representation of the δ-function was introduced in Chapter 5, Eq. 5.63.) Now proceeding exactly as we did in obtaining Eq. (7.57′), we find that

$$\hat{\phi}_{\pm}(\mathbf{k}) = A\delta(\mathbf{q}_i - \mathbf{k}) - \frac{2m}{(2\pi)^{3/2}\hbar^2} \int \frac{\hat{V}(\mathbf{k} - \mathbf{p})}{k^2 - (q_i \pm i\epsilon)^2} \hat{\phi}_{\pm}(\mathbf{p})d^3\mathbf{q} \ . \tag{7.73}$$

This is the momentum-space version of the Lippmann-Schwinger equation. Equation (7.72) suggests that we define a new function $f_{\pm}(\mathbf{q})$ by

$$f_{\pm}(\mathbf{q}) = -\frac{(2\pi)^{1/2}m}{A\hbar^2} \int \hat{V}(\mathbf{q} - \mathbf{p})\hat{\phi}_{\pm}(\mathbf{p})d^3\mathbf{p} \ . \tag{7.74}$$

Multiplying both sides of Eq. (7.73) by

$$-\frac{(2\pi)^{1/2}m}{A\hbar^2} \hat{V}(\mathbf{q} - \mathbf{k}) \ ,$$

and integrating over all $\mathbf{k}$-space, we obtain

$$f_{\pm}(\mathbf{q}) = -\frac{(2\pi)^{1/2}m}{\hbar^2} \hat{V}(\mathbf{q} - \mathbf{q}_i) - \frac{2m}{(2\pi)^{3/2}\hbar^2} \int \hat{V}(\mathbf{q} - \mathbf{k}) \frac{f_{\pm}(\mathbf{k})}{k^2 - (q_i \pm i\epsilon)^2} d^3\mathbf{k} \ . \tag{7.75}$$

Comparing Eqs. (7.72) and (7.74), we see that the scattering amplitude is given simply by

$$f_{\pm}^s(\mathbf{q}_f) = f_{\pm}(\pm \mathbf{q}_f) \ ,$$

where

$$\mathbf{q}_f = q_i\mathbf{n} = \sqrt{2mE/\hbar^2}\,\mathbf{n} \ .$$

The function $f_{\pm}$ has physical significance only at a particular value of $\mathbf{q}$; when we evaluate $f_{\pm}$ at this particular value, we often say that we evaluate $f_{\pm}$ "on the energy shell."

It is interesting to see what Eq. (7.75) looks like for the Yukawa potential of Eq. (7.58), whose Fourier transform is given by Eq. (7.58′). Putting this into Eq. (7.75), we get

$$f_{\pm}(\mathbf{q}) = \frac{2mg^2}{\hbar^2} \frac{1}{(\mathbf{q} - \mathbf{q}_i)^2 + \mu^2} + \frac{mg^2}{\pi^2\hbar^2} \int \frac{f_{\pm}(\mathbf{k})d^3\mathbf{k}}{[(\mathbf{q} - \mathbf{k})^2 + \mu^2][k^2 - (q_i \pm i\epsilon)^2]} \ . \tag{7.76}$$

The first term of this equation for $f_\pm$ [generally, the first term of Eq. (7.75)] is called the *Born approximation* to the scattering amplitude when evaluated at $\mathbf{q} = \pm\mathbf{q}_f$. It is not unreasonable to imagine that if the potential is weak (say, g^2 is small), then this might be a good approximation for the scattering amplitude. We shall see later in what sense this is actually the case. If we let $g^2 = e^2$, where e is the electronic charge, and set $\mu = 0$, then the Born approximation to the scattering amplitude for a Coulomb potential is

$$f^s = \frac{2me^2}{\hbar^2}\frac{1}{(\mathbf{q}_f - \mathbf{q}_i)^2} .$$

Since $|\mathbf{q}_i| = |\mathbf{q}_f|$, we may write this as

$$f^s = \frac{me^2}{\hbar^2 q_i^2}\frac{1}{1 - \cos\theta} ,$$

where θ is the *scattering angle*, i.e., the angle between the incident direction of the plane wave, $\mathbf{q}_i$, and the direction of the outgoing particle, $\mathbf{q}_f$. Writing $1 - \cos\theta = 2\sin^2(\theta/2)$, we have

$$f^s = \frac{me^2}{2\hbar^2 q_i^2}\frac{1}{\sin^2(\theta/2)} ,$$

and therefore

$$|f^s|^2 = \left(\frac{e^2}{2mv_i^2}\right)^2 \cdot \frac{1}{\sin^4(\theta/2)} , \tag{7.77}$$

since $\hbar^2 q_i^2/m = mv_i^2$, where v_i is the velocity of the incident particle. Equation (7.77) gives the relative probability of finding a particle scattered through an angle θ. It is the famous Rutherford differential cross section, first derived by Lord Rutherford from classical mechanics.

7.5 RADIAL GREEN'S FUNCTIONS

In the last section we saw how Schrödinger's momentum-space integral equation could be reduced to a one-variable integral equation by factoring out the known angular dependence of the solutions given by the spherical harmonics. This suggests that a similar reduction could be carried out at the very outset starting from Schrödinger's differential equation in position space. This can, in fact, be done, and the manner in which the Green's function is handled in this case demonstrates the relationship between the last two sections.

Writing Schrödinger's equation as

$$-\frac{\hbar^2}{2m}\nabla^2\psi(\mathbf{r}) + V(r)\psi(\mathbf{r}) = E\psi(\mathbf{r}) ,$$

where $V(r)$ depends only on the magnitude of $\mathbf{r}$, we look for solutions of the form

$$\psi(\mathbf{r}) = \phi_l(r) Y_{lm}(\theta, \phi) .$$

Now, according to Section 5.8, the spherical harmonics are eigenfunctions of

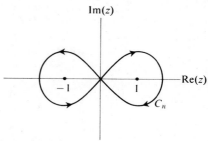

Fig. 7.5 The contour C_j for the evaluation of the spherical Bessel function.

Fig. 7.6 The contour C_n for the evaluation of the spherical Neumann function.

the angular part of ∇^2 with eigenvalues $l(l+1)$. Thus $\phi_l(r)$ satisfies

$$\frac{d^2\phi_l}{dr^2} + \frac{2}{r}\frac{d\phi_l}{dr} + \frac{2mE}{\hbar^2}\phi_l(r) - \frac{l(l+1)}{r^2}\phi_l(r) = \frac{2m}{\hbar^2}V(r)\phi_l(r) \ . \qquad (7.78)$$

Let us consider the homogeneous equation

$$\frac{d^2\phi_l}{dr^2} + \frac{2}{r}\frac{d\phi_l}{dr} + \left[\frac{2mE}{\hbar^2} - \frac{l(l+1)}{r^2}\right]\phi_l(r) = 0 \ . \qquad (7.79)$$

If we make the change of variable

$$x = [2mE/\hbar^2]^{1/2}r \ , \qquad (7.80)$$

the equation for ϕ_l becomes

$$\frac{d^2\phi_l}{dx^2} + \frac{2}{x}\frac{d\phi_l}{dx} + \left[1 - \frac{l(l+1)}{x^2}\right]\phi_l(x) = 0 \ . \qquad (7.81)$$

When x tends to zero, a solution to Eq. (7.81) can tend to either x^l or x^{-l-1}. The reader should find it instructive to verify this. The regular solution which behaves like x^l near $x = 0$ is called the *spherical Bessel function* of order l, and the solution which blows up like x^{-l-1} is called the *spherical Neumann function* of order l.

Power series solutions to equations of the form of Eq. (7.81) are well known. However, we shall not proceed in this manner; instead, we shall write two linearly independent solutions in the form of complex *integral representations*. In particular, we claim that

$$j_l(x) = \frac{1}{2\pi}\frac{(-2)^l l!}{x^{l+1}}\oint_{C_j}\frac{e^{-ixz}}{(z+1)^{l+1}(z-1)^{l+1}}dz \qquad (7.82)$$

is a solution to Eq. (7.81), when C_j is any contour enclosing the poles at $z = \pm 1$ in the manner shown in Fig. 7.5. Another solution is given by taking a different contour, C_n, shown in Fig. 7.6. We write

$$n_l(x) = \frac{1}{2\pi i}\frac{(-2)^l l!}{x^{l+1}}\oint_{C_n}\frac{e^{-ixz}}{(z+1)^{l+1}(z-1)^{l+1}}dz \ . \qquad (7.83)$$

We adopt this method in order to demonstrate the power of complex variable techniques in the domain of differential equations. It is an interesting exercise to derive these integral representations starting with power series solutions corresponding to the two different types of behavior near the origin; however, at this point we content ourselves with showing that the integral representations above do indeed satisfy Eq. (7.81).

To show this, let us compute the first two derivatives of

$$f_l(x) = \frac{C_l}{x^{l+1}} \oint \frac{e^{-ixz}}{(z+1)^{l+1}(z-1)^{l+1}} \, dz \; ,$$

where the contour is any closed curve containing at least one of the points $z = \pm 1$. Clearly, if it contains neither $z = +1$ nor $z = -1$, then by the Cauchy theorem, $f_l(x) \equiv 0$. We shall now show that such an $f_l(x)$ satisfies Eq. (7.81). For the first derivative we have, omitting the constant C_l,

$$f_l'(x) = -\frac{(l+1)}{x^{l+2}} \oint \frac{e^{-ixz}}{(z^2-1)^{l+1}} \, dz - \frac{i}{x^{l+1}} \oint \frac{ze^{-ixz}}{(z^2-1)^{l+1}} \, dz \; .$$

Similarly,

$$f_l''(x) = \frac{(l+1)(l+2)}{x^{l+3}} \oint \frac{e^{-ixz} \, dz}{(z^2-1)^{l+1}} + \frac{2i(l+1)}{x^{l+2}} \oint \frac{ze^{-ixz} \, dz}{(z^2-1)^{l+1}}$$
$$- \frac{1}{x^{l+1}} \oint \frac{z^2 e^{-ixz} \, dz}{(z^2-1)^{l+1}} \; .$$

Now we form the quantity

$$q_l(x) = f_l''(x) + \frac{2}{x} f_l'(x) + \left[1 - \frac{l(l+1)}{x^2} \right] f_l(x) \; .$$

To show that $f_l(x)$ satisfies Eq. (7.81), we now need only show that $q_l(x) = 0$. Using the expressions for $f_l'(x)$ and $f_l''(x)$, we get

$$q_l(x) = \frac{2il}{x^{l+2}} \oint \frac{ze^{-ixz}}{(z^2-1)^{l+1}} \, dz - \frac{1}{x^{l+1}} \oint \frac{e^{-ixz}}{(z^2-1)^l} \, dz \; .$$

But

$$\frac{2lze^{-ixz}}{(z^2-1)^{l+1}} = -\frac{d}{dz}\left[\frac{e^{-ixz}}{(z^2-1)^l} \right] - ix \frac{e^{-ixz}}{(z^2-1)^l} \; ,$$

so

$$q_l(x) = -\frac{i}{x^{l+2}} \oint \frac{d}{dz}\left[\frac{e^{-ixz}}{(z^2-1)^l} \right] dz = 0 \; ,$$

since the integral of an exact derivative around a closed contour vanishes.

Hence $f_l(x)$ is a solution to Eq. (7.81) for any closed contour containing a singularity. We have taken the two contours of Figs. 7.5 and 7.6 to conform to the conventional definitions. This is also the reason for our particular choice of constants multiplying the integrals in Eqs. (7.82) and (7.83). Naturally,

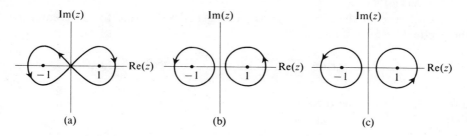

Fig. 7.7 The pinching of the contour of Figure 7-5 to obtain two contours for the evaluation of the spherical Bessel function.

the shape of the contour does not matter; Cauchy's theorem tells us that only the singularities which it encloses are relevant. For example, we have chosen for C_j a circular contour, as shown in Fig. 7.5, which contains both $z = 1$ and $z = -1$. But we can just as well pinch this contour as shown in Fig. 7.7(a), then separate the contour into two parts as shown in Fig. 7.7(b), and finally deform it into the form of *two* circular contours as shown in Fig. 7.7(c), each traced out in a counterclockwise direction, one about $z = -1$, and the other about $z = +1$. Similarly, the figure-eight contour defining $n_l(x)$ can be turned into two circular contours, the one about $z = -1$ being traced out counterclockwise, the one about $z = +1$ being traced out *clockwise*. Thus the function defined by

$$h_l^{(1)}(x) \equiv j_l(x) + in_l(x) , \qquad (7.84a)$$

has the representation

$$h_l^{(1)}(x) = \frac{1}{\pi} \frac{(-2)^l l!}{x^{l+1}} \oint_{C_1} \frac{e^{-ixz}}{(z^2 - 1)^{l+1}} dz , \qquad (7.84b)$$

where C_1 is a contour encircling only $z = -1$, in the counterclockwise direction. [Remember that we defined $n_l(x)$ with an extra factor of i^{-1} relative to $j_l(x)$.] Similarly,

$$h_l^{(2)}(x) \equiv j_l(x) - in_l(x) \qquad (7.85a)$$

has the representation

$$h_l^{(2)}(x) = \frac{1}{\pi} \frac{(-2)^l l!}{x^{l+1}} \oint_{C_2} \frac{e^{-ixz}}{(z^2 - 1)^{l+1}} dz , \qquad (7.85b)$$

where C_2 is a contour encircling only $z = 1$ in the counterclockwise sense. $h_l^{(1)}(x)$ and $h_l^{(2)}(x)$ are called the *spherical Hankel functions* of the first and second kind, respectively. Had we so desired, we could equally well have chosen $h_l^{(1)}(x)$ and $h_l^{(2)}(x)$ to be our basic solutions rather than $j_l(x)$ and $n_l(x)$.

We can now obtain the properties of $j_l(x)$ and $n_l(x)$ from the integral representations in a very simple way. These properties will in turn lead us quickly to the desired Green's function for Eq. (7.81). First of all, let us obtain explicit formulas for the two functions. Using Leibnitz's rule for differentiating the product of two functions,

$$\frac{d^n}{dx^n}[f(x)g(x)] = \sum_{m=0}^{n} \frac{n!}{m!\,(n-m)!}\left[\frac{d^{n-m}}{dx^{n-m}}f(x)\right]\frac{d^m}{dx^m}g(x) ,$$

along with the residue theorem for a pole of order $l+1$, [Eq. (6.17)], we find that

$$j_l(x) = \frac{i(-2)^l l!}{l!\,x^{l+1}} \sum_{m=0}^{l} \frac{l!}{m!\,(l-m)!} \left\{ \left[\frac{d^{l-m}}{dz^{l-m}} e^{-ixz} \frac{d^m}{dz^m}\left(\frac{1}{z+1}\right)^{l+1}\right]_{z=1} \right.$$
$$\left. + \left[\frac{d^{l-m}}{dz^{l-m}} e^{-ixz} \frac{d^m}{dz^m}\left(\frac{1}{z-1}\right)^{l+1}\right]_{z=-1} \right\} .$$

The expression for $n_l(x)$ differs from the above only by a factor of i^{-1} and the presence of a minus sign in front of the term coming from the pole at $z = +1$, since this pole is encircled in a clockwise direction in the case of $n_l(x)$. The derivatives are elementary, and we find that

$$j_l(x) = \frac{i(-2)^l}{x^{l+1}} \sum_{m=0}^{l} \frac{l!}{m!\,(l-m)!} (-ix)^{l-m}(-1)^m \frac{(l+m)!}{l!}\left[\frac{e^{-ix}}{2^{l+m+1}} + \frac{e^{ix}}{(-2)^{l+m+1}}\right]$$
$$= \sum_{m=0}^{l} \frac{(l+m)!}{m!\,(l-m)!} \frac{1}{2^m} \frac{1}{x^{m+1}} i^{l-m+1}\left[\frac{(-1)^{-(l-m+1)}e^{ix} + e^{-ix}}{2}\right] ,$$

where we have several times made use of the fact that $(-1)^m = (-1)^{-m}$. Writing $(-1) = e^{i\pi}$, $i = e^{i\pi/2}$, we get finally

$$j_l(x) = \sum_{m=0}^{l} \frac{(l+m)!}{m!\,(l-m)!} \frac{1}{2^m} \frac{\cos\left(x - \dfrac{l-m+1}{2}\pi\right)}{x^{m+1}} . \tag{7.86a}$$

Changing the sign of e^{-ix} in the previous expression and dividing by i, we get

$$n_l(x) = \sum_{m=0}^{l} \frac{(l+m)!}{m!\,(l-m)!} \frac{1}{2^m} \frac{\sin\left(x - \dfrac{l-m+1}{2}\pi\right)}{x^{m+1}} . \tag{7.86b}$$

According to our definitions of the spherical Hankel functions, we have immediately

$$h_l^{(1)}(x) = \sum_{m=0}^{l} \frac{(l+m)!}{m!\,(l-m)!} \frac{1}{2^m} \frac{\exp\left(i\left[x - \dfrac{l-m+1}{2}\pi\right]\right)}{x^{m+1}} , \tag{7.86c}$$

$$h_l^{(2)}(x) = \sum_{m=0}^{l} \frac{(l+m)!}{m!\,(l-m)!} \frac{1}{2^m} \frac{\exp\left(-i\left[x - \dfrac{l-m+1}{2}\pi\right]\right)}{x^{m+1}} . \tag{7.86d}$$

Thus, after a few simple manipulations, we have explicit expressions for all the spherical Bessel functions and spherical Hankel functions. Let us now examine their asymptotic behavior. First of all, it is clear that as x tends toward infinity, the dominant term in each sum will be $m = 0$, so

$$j_l(x) \xrightarrow[x \to \infty]{} \frac{\cos\left(x - \frac{l+1}{2}\pi\right)}{x}, \tag{7.87a}$$

$$n_l(x) \xrightarrow[x \to \infty]{} \frac{\sin\left(x - \frac{l+1}{2}\pi\right)}{x}, \tag{7.87b}$$

$$h_l^{(1)}(x) \xrightarrow[x \to \infty]{} \frac{\exp\left(i\left[x - \frac{l+1}{2}\pi\right]\right)}{x}, \tag{7.87c}$$

$$h_l^{(2)}(x) \xrightarrow[x \to \infty]{} \frac{\exp\left(-i\left[x - \frac{l+1}{2}\pi\right]\right)}{x}. \tag{7.87d}$$

As $x \to 0$, the term $m = l$ in the sum for $n_l(x)$ dominates, and we find that

$$n_l(x) \xrightarrow[x \to 0]{} \frac{(2l)!}{2^l l!} \frac{\sin(x - \pi/2)}{x^{l+1}}.$$

Thus

$$n_l(x) \xrightarrow[x \to 0]{} -\frac{(2l)!}{2^l l!} \frac{1}{x^{l+1}}, \tag{7.88a}$$

since $\sin(x - \pi/2) = -\cos x$, which tends toward -1 as x tends toward zero.

Now, at first glance it would appear reasonable to do the same thing for $j_l(x)$. If we proceed in this manner, we are rapidly led to

$$j_l(x) \xrightarrow[x \to 0]{} \frac{(2l)!}{2^l l!} \frac{\cos(x - \pi/2)}{x^{l+1}}.$$

But $\cos(x - \pi/2) = \sin x$, and since $\sin x$ varies like x as x tends to zero, we find that $j_l(x)$ appears to vary like x^{-l}. Before we conclude that this is the limiting behavior, we must check the term $m = l - 1$ in the sum for $j_l(x)$. For x very small this term varies like

$$\frac{(2l-1)!}{(l-1)!\,2^{l-1}} \frac{\cos(x - \pi)}{x^l} = -\frac{(2l-1)!}{(l-1)!\,2^{l-1}} \frac{1}{x^l}.$$

However,

$$\frac{(2l-1)!}{(l-1)!\,2^{l-1}} = \frac{(2l)!}{l!\,2^l},$$

so this term $(m = l - 1)$ exactly cancels the leading contribution from the term $m = l$. That this should be the case is really not surprising, since we have seen earlier that the two solutions to Eq. (7.91) vary like either x^{-l-1} or x^l. We have seen that $n_l(x)$ varies like x^{-l-1}, so we suspect that if all is well, $j_l(x)$ should vary like x^l for small x. Hence the expression Eq. (7.86a) for $j_l(x)$ is rather misleading as far as small x behavior is concerned. This is not to say that Eq. (7.86a) is incorrect, but merely that when x becomes small there must be a great deal of cancellation (the cancellation increases rapidly with l) among the various terms contributing to $j_l(x)$, which ultimately produces the desired x^l behavior for small x.

To see that $j_l(x)$ actually does vary like x^l for small x let us return to the integral representation, Eq. (7.82), and make the change of variable $\xi = xz$. Then

$$ j_l(x) = \frac{1}{2\pi} \frac{(-2)^l l!}{x^{l+2}} \oint_{C_j} \frac{e^{-i\xi}}{(\xi^2/x^2 - 1)^{l+1}} \, d\xi \, , $$

where C_j is any counterclockwise contour enclosing the singularities at $\xi = \pm x$. We rewrite this as

$$ j_l(x) = \frac{1}{2\pi} (-2)^l l! \, x^l \oint_{C_j} \frac{e^{-i\xi}}{\xi^{2l+2}} \left[1 - \frac{x^2}{\xi^2} \right]^{-l-1} d\xi \, . $$

But in any closed region outside the circle of radius $|\xi| = x$, the quantity in square brackets has a uniformly convergent power series:

$$ \left[1 - \frac{x^2}{\xi^2} \right]^{-l-1} = 1 + (l + 1) \frac{x^2}{\xi^2} + \frac{1}{2} (l + 1)(l + 2) \frac{x^4}{\xi^4} + \cdots $$

$$ = \sum_{m=0}^{\infty} \frac{(l + m)!}{m! \, l!} \frac{x^{2m}}{\xi^{2m}} \, . $$

Since we are free to do so, let us choose C_j to be a circle lying outside the disc $\xi = x$. Because of uniform convergence, we may interchange summation and integration to obtain

$$ j_l(x) = \frac{1}{2\pi} (-2)^l l! \, x^l \left[\oint_{C_j} \frac{e^{-i\xi}}{\xi^{2l+2}} \, d\xi + (l + 1)x^2 \oint_{C_j} \frac{e^{-i\xi}}{\xi^{2l+4}} \, d\xi + \cdots \right] $$

$$ = i(-2)^l l! \, x^l \left[\frac{(-i)^{2l+1}}{(2l + 1)!} + (l + 1) \frac{(-i)^{2l+3}}{(2l + 3)!} x^2 + \cdots \right] $$

by a simple application of the residue calculus. Thus

$$ j_l(x) = \frac{2^l l!}{(2l + 1)!} \left[x^l - \frac{x^{l+2}}{2(2l + 3)} + \cdots \right]. \tag{7.88b} $$

The leading term is proportional to x^l, as we had anticipated. We leave it to the interested reader to show that if one keeps all terms in the expansion of

$[1 - x^2/\xi^2]^{-l-1}$, then

$$j_l(x) = 2^l x^l \sum_{m=0}^{\infty} (-1)^m \frac{(l+m)! \, x^{2m}}{m!(2l+2m+1)!} \, .$$

$$= \frac{\sqrt{\pi}}{2} \sum_{m=0}^{\infty} (-1)^m \frac{(x/2)^{2m+l}}{m! \, \Gamma(l+m+3/2)} \, , \qquad (7.88b')$$

where we have used Eq. (6.54) as the definition of $\Gamma(x)$. It follows readily from Eq. (6.54) [see, for example, the derivation of Eq. (6.56)] that

$$\Gamma(n+3/2) = \sqrt{\pi} \, \frac{(2n+1)!}{2^{2n+1} \, n!} \, ,$$

which result has been used in obtaining Eq. (7.88b').

If the reader will glance back at Eq. (6.69), he will note a rather strong similarity between the above expression for $j_l(x)$ and the expression for $J_n(x)$ given there. For integral values of m and n, we know that $(m+n)! = \Gamma(m+n+1)$, and once this substitution is made, it is apparent that Eq. (6.69) generalizes to non-integral values of n. Then using Eq. (7.88b'), it takes only a few steps to show that

$$j_l(x) = \sqrt{\frac{\pi}{2x}} \, J_{l+1/2}(x) \, .$$

This is why the functions $j_l(x)$ are called spherical *Bessel* functions; they are closely related to the Bessel functions of half-integral order.

With exact expressions and all the asymptotic information for the various solutions to Eq. (7.81), we are finally ready to determine the Green's function for Eq. (7.79). Let us take the two linearly independent solutions of Eq. (7.81) to be $j_l(x)$ and $n_l(x)$. The corresponding solutions to Eq. (7.79) are $j_l(kr)$ and $n_l(kr)$, where we assume first that $E \geq 0$ and define, according to Eq. (7.80),

$$k \equiv \sqrt{2mE/\hbar^2} \, .$$

Thus, according to Eq. (7.41), the Green's function for Eq. (7.79) is

$$g_l(r, r') = b_1 j_l(kr) + b_2 n_l(kr) - \frac{1}{W(r')} \, [j_l(kr) n_l(kr') - j_l(kr') n_l(kr)] \qquad (7.89a)$$

if $r > r'$, and

$$g(r, r') = b_1 j_l(kr) + b_2 n_l(kr) \qquad (7.89b)$$

if $r < r'$. $W(r')$ is the Wronskian, given by

$$W(r') = j_l(kr') \frac{d}{dr'} n_l(kr') - n_l(kr') \frac{d}{dr'} j_l(kr') \, .$$

In the terminology of Section 7.3 [Eq. (7.38)], $f_0(r) = 1$, $f_1(r) = 2/r$, $f_2(r) = k^2 - l(l+1)/r^2$. We saw in Section 7.3 that W satisfies the equation

$$\frac{dW}{dr'} = -\frac{f_1(r')}{f_0(r')} \, W \, .$$

Substituting for f_0 and f_1, we find that

$$\frac{dW}{dr'} = -\frac{2}{r'} W ,$$

from which we conclude that $W(r') = C(1/r'^2)$.

Now we must determine C, which depends on the particular normalization of the functions. Since we know the asymptotic form of j_l and n_l at large distances, we can use this knowledge to determine $W(r')$ for large r', and hence C. Using Eqs. (7.87a) and (7.87b), we have

$$W(r') \xrightarrow[r' \to \infty]{} \frac{1}{kr'^2} ,$$

from which we conclude that $C = 1/k$. Of course, the identical result could be obtained by using the expressions for small r'. Thus, quite generally,

$$W(r') = 1/kr'^2 ,$$

and Eqs. (7.89a) and (7.89b) become

$$g_l(r, r') = b_1 j_l(kr) + b_2 n_l(kr) - kr'^2 [j_l(kr) n_l(kr') - j_l(kr') n_l(kr)] \quad \text{(7.90a)}$$

for $r > r'$, and

$$g_l(r, r') = b_1 j_l(kr) + b_2 n_l(kr) \quad \text{(7.90b)}$$

for $r < r'$. Now we do not want the solutions to Schrödinger's equation to be singular at the origin, so for $r < r'$, $g_l(r, r')$ must have no singularity at $r = 0$. However, $n_l(kr)$ has a singularity of the type $(1/r)^{l+1}$ at $r = 0$, so we must exclude the term in n_l from the solution. Hence we take $b_2 = 0$. For large r, a possible boundary condition is to require that the solution have the form e^{ikr}/r, as we did in the last section. But this is the asymptotic form of the function $h_l^{(1)}$, so let us choose b_1 so as to ensure this behavior for $r > r'$. If we take

$$b_1 = -ikr'^2 h_l^{(1)}(kr') ,$$

then for $r > r'$ we have, using Eq. (7.90a) with $b_2 = 0$ and Eq. (7.84a),

$$g_l(r, r') = -ikr'^2 h_l^{(1)}(kr) j_l(kr') .$$

For $r < r'$, this value for b_1 leads to the result

$$g_l(r, r') = -ikr'^2 j_l(kr) h_l^{(1)}(kr') .$$

This completes the specification of g_l. Note that $g_l(r, r')$ is continuous at $r = r'$, although, of course, its derivatives are not. One often introduces the notation $r_> \equiv$ larger of (r, r') and $r_< \equiv$ smaller of (r, r'). Using this convention, we have the following simple expression for g_l:

$$g_l(r, r') = -ikr'^2 j_l(kr_<) h_l^{(1)}(kr_>) . \quad \text{(7.91)}$$

Now, if we write Schrödinger's equation as

$$\frac{d^2\phi_l}{dr^2} + \frac{2}{r}\frac{d\phi_l}{dr} + \left[k^2 - \frac{l(l+1)}{r^2} \right] \phi_l(r) = \frac{2m}{\hbar^2} V(r)\phi_l(r) ,$$

then by our previous work we can immediately transform this into the integral equation

$$\phi_l(r) = A j_l(kr) + \frac{2m}{\hbar^2} \int_0^\infty g_l(r, r') V(r') \phi_l(r') \, dr' \, . \tag{7.92}$$

Or, more explicitly,

$$\phi_l(r) = A j_l(kr) - \frac{2mki}{\hbar^2} \int_0^\infty j_l(kr_<) h_l^{(1)}(kr_>) V(r') \phi_l(r') r'^2 \, dr' \, . \tag{7.93}$$

We have added an arbitrary multiple of $j_l(kr)$, that solution of the homogeneous equation which is regular at the origin.

In our study of Schrödinger's equation, we have considered only the case $E \geq 0$, but it is easy to remedy this by defining

$$\kappa^2 \equiv -2mE/\hbar^2$$

and writing Schrödinger's equation as

$$\frac{d^2\phi_l}{dr^2} + \frac{2}{r} \frac{d\phi_l}{dr} + \left[-\kappa^2 - \frac{l(l+1)}{r^2} \right] \phi_l(r) = \frac{2m}{\hbar^2} V(r) \phi_l(r) \, .$$

If we now choose the square root of $-\kappa^2$ with *positive* imaginary part, then the solutions to the zero-order equation are $j_l(i\kappa r)$ and $n_l(i\kappa r)$. In this case, $h_l^{(1)}(i\kappa r)$ has just the type of behavior at large distances that we want in a bound state problem, namely, exponential decrease. All other solutions grow exponentially at large distances, so our integral equation becomes

$$\phi_l(r) = \frac{2m\kappa}{\hbar^2} \int_0^\infty j_l(i\kappa r_<) h_l^{(1)}(i\kappa r_>) V(r') \phi_l(r') r'^2 \, dr' \, . \tag{7.94}$$

There is no inhomogeneous term present because there is no solution to the equation

$$\frac{d^2\phi_l}{dr^2} + \frac{2}{r} \frac{d\phi_l}{dr} + \left[-\kappa^2 - \frac{l(l+1)}{r^2} \right] \phi_l(r) = 0,$$

which satisfies the boundary conditions of regularity at $r = 0$ and exponential decrease at large distances.

It is interesting to compare these one-dimensional integral equations, for example Eq. (7.94), with the three-dimensional results of the last section. In the bound state case, we found in Section 7.4, Eq. (7.57), that

$$\psi(\mathbf{r}) = -\frac{m}{2\pi\hbar^2} \int \frac{e^{-\kappa|\mathbf{r}-\mathbf{r}'|}}{|\mathbf{r} - \mathbf{r}'|} V(\mathbf{r}') \psi(\mathbf{r}') \, d^3r' \, . \tag{7.57}$$

Since the Green's function depends only on $|\mathbf{r} - \mathbf{r}'|$, we can consider it as a function of r, r', and x, where x is the cosine of the angle between $\mathbf{r}$ and $\mathbf{r}'$. It is natural to expand it in a series of Legendre polynomials in x. To this end, we define

$$g_l(r, r') \equiv \frac{1}{2} \int_{-1}^1 \frac{e^{-\kappa|\mathbf{r}-\mathbf{r}'|}}{|\mathbf{r} - \mathbf{r}'|} P_l(x) \, dx \, . \tag{7.95}$$

Then

$$\frac{e^{-\kappa|\mathbf{r}-\mathbf{r}'|}}{|\mathbf{r}-\mathbf{r}'|} = \sum_{l=0}^{\infty} (2l+1)g_l(r,r')P_l(x) ,\qquad (7.96)$$

where we have used the fact [Eq. (5.37), Theorem 5.3] that

$$\int_{-1}^{1} P_l(x)P_{l'}(x)\, dx = \frac{2}{2l+1}\,\delta_{ll'} .$$

We now insert Eq. (7.96) into Eq. (7.57) to get

$$\phi(\mathbf{r}) = -\frac{m}{2\pi\hbar^2}\int \sum_{l=0}^{\infty} (2l+1)g_l(r,r')P_l(x)V(r')\phi(\mathbf{r}')\, d^3r' .$$

Next we use the addition theorem for spherical harmonics, Eq. (5.83), which tells us that if x is the cosine of the angle between $\mathbf{r}$ and $\mathbf{r}'$ and if the orientation of $\mathbf{r}$ is specified by (θ, ϕ) and that of $\mathbf{r}'$ is specified by (θ', ϕ'), then

$$P_l(x) = \frac{4\pi}{2l+1}\sum_{m=-l}^{l} Y_{lm}(\theta,\phi)Y_{lm}^*(\theta',\phi') .$$

Thus

$$\phi(\mathbf{r}) = -\frac{2m}{\hbar^2}\int \sum_{l=0}^{\infty}\sum_{m=-l}^{l} g_l(r,r')Y_{lm}(\theta,\phi)Y_{lm}^*(\theta',\phi')V(r')\phi(\mathbf{r}')\, d^3r' .\qquad (7.97)$$

We now look for solutions of the form

$$\psi(\mathbf{r}) = \phi_l(r)Y_{lm}(\theta,\phi) .$$

Inserting this into Eq. (7.97) and using the completeness and orthonormality of the spherical harmonics, we get

$$\phi_l(r) = -\frac{2m}{\hbar^2}\int_0^{\infty} g_l(r,r')V(r')\phi_l(r')r'^2\, dr' ,$$

since $V(r')$ depends only on the magnitude of $\mathbf{r}'$.

It is possible to show that $g_l(r,r')$, as defined by Eq. (7.95), is equal to $-\kappa j_l(i\kappa r_<)h_l^{(1)}(i\kappa r_>)$, so that the two approaches agree completely. This result follows from the relation

$$\frac{e^{ik|\mathbf{r}-\mathbf{r}'|}}{|\mathbf{r}-\mathbf{r}'|} = ik\sum_{l=0}^{\infty} (2l+1)j_l(kr_<)h_l^{(1)}(kr_>)P_l(x)\qquad (7.98)$$

and Eq. (7.95). This is a very useful relationship in mathematical physics, but it would not be instructive to carry out an independent demonstration of it here. [One could, of course, regard the work of this section as a derivation of Eq. (7.98).] We content ourselves with showing that for $l=0$, $g_l(r,r')$ as defined by Eq. (7.95) is indeed equal to $-\kappa j_l(i\kappa r_<)h_l^{(1)}(i\kappa r_>)$. To do this, we must evaluate

$$g_0(r,r') = \tfrac{1}{2}\int_{-1}^{1} \frac{e^{-\kappa|\mathbf{r}-\mathbf{r}'|}}{|\mathbf{r}-\mathbf{r}'|} P_0(x)\, dx .$$

We write

$$u = |\mathbf{r} - \mathbf{r}'| = (r^2 + r'^2 - 2rr'\cos\theta)^{1/2} = (r^2 + r'^2 - 2rr'x)^{1/2} .$$

Thus

$$du = -\frac{rr'\,dx}{u} , \qquad dx = -\frac{u\,du}{rr'} .$$

Making use of this change of variable, we find that

$$g_0(r, r') = \frac{1}{2rr'} \int_{|r-r'|}^{|r+r'|} e^{-\kappa u}\,du = -\frac{1}{2rr'\kappa} \left[e^{-\kappa|r+r'|} - e^{-\kappa|r-r'|} \right] .$$

In terms of the variables $r_>$ and $r_<$, this is

$$
\begin{aligned}
g_0(r, r') &= -\frac{1}{2\kappa} \frac{e^{-\kappa(r_>+r_<)} - e^{-\kappa(r_>-r_<)}}{r_> r_<} \\
&= \kappa \frac{e^{-\kappa r_>}}{\kappa r_>} \left[\frac{e^{\kappa r_<} - e^{-\kappa r_<}}{\kappa r_<} \right] \\
&= \kappa \left[\frac{e^{-\kappa r_>}}{\kappa r_>} \right] \left[\frac{\sinh(\kappa r_<)}{\kappa r_<} \right] .
\end{aligned}
$$

But by Eqs. (7.86a) and (7.86c),

$$j_0(i\kappa r_<) = \frac{\sin(i\kappa r_<)}{i\kappa r_<} \equiv \frac{\sinh(\kappa r_<)}{\kappa r_<} , \qquad h_0^{(1)}(i\kappa r_>) = -\frac{e^{-\kappa r_>}}{\kappa r_>} ,$$

so

$$g_0(r, r') = -\kappa j_0(i\kappa r_<) h_0^{(1)}(i\kappa r_>) .$$

Thus there is a nice relationship between the techniques of Sections 7.3 and 7.4 whenever the potential in Schrödinger's equation is spherically symmetric. Depending on the type of problem, the three-dimensional approach or the one-dimensional approach may be more useful. Both of them have been used extensively in quantum theoretical studies of scattering processes.

At this juncture, it is perhaps worthwhile to emphasize again the importance of boundary conditions in determining the form of a Green's function. In the work of this section we have reduced ∇^2 to a one-dimensional operator by factoring out its angular dependence and have thereby seen how to apply in a straightforward way the boundary conditions appropriate to the scattering problem. The "$i\epsilon$-prescription" used in Section 7.4 is a very convenient shorthand device for achieving the same end. Its great practical utility more than justifies its use, but it is good to remember that it is in one sense a "trick." In considering a general three-dimensional operator it is often impossible to find such a prescription, and one is in trouble unless the operator in question can be brought to an effective one-dimensional form, where the methods of Section 7.3 can be used.

In this context, however, it should also be pointed out that whenever one can obtain an object which satisfies

$$\mathscr{O} G(x, x') = \delta(x - x') ,$$

then if one also has the solutions to $\mathscr{O}\phi = 0$, the general solution to

$$\mathscr{O}\phi(x) = F(x)$$

can be written as

$$\phi(x) = \xi(x) + \int G(x, x')F(x')\, dx' \;.$$

However, there is an important difference between this formal solution and the very similar equations written in previous sections. There we imagined that the coefficients of the solutions to $\mathscr{O}\phi = 0$ appearing in $\xi(x)$ were *independent of* $F(x)$, the inhomogeneous term. In fact, strictly speaking, this is what we meant by a Green's function; it was a function which enabled us to solve a given operator equation in such a way that the coefficients occurring in $\xi(x)$ could be determined without having to think about the inhomogeneous term of the operator equation. However, if all we know about $G(x, x')$ is that it satisfies $\mathscr{O}G(x, x') = \delta(x - x')$, then it will, in general, be the case that the coefficients in $\xi(x)$ will depend on F. This is not surprising, since to any solution of $\mathscr{O}G(x, x') = \delta(x - x')$ we can add an arbitrary linear combination of solutions to $\mathscr{O}\phi(x) = 0$, so the equation $\mathscr{O}G(x, x') = \delta(x - x')$ does not uniquely specify the function $G(x, x')$; that is, one must specify definite boundary conditions for $G(x, x')$.

For example, suppose that for some reason the only function satisfying

$$(\nabla^2 + k^2)G(\mathbf{r}, \mathbf{r}') = \delta(\mathbf{r} - \mathbf{r}')$$

which was known to us was the function

$$G_-(\mathbf{r}, \mathbf{r}') = -\frac{1}{4\pi} \frac{e^{-ik|\mathbf{r}-\mathbf{r}'|}}{|\mathbf{r} - \mathbf{r}'|} \;. \tag{7.99a}$$

Then we could certainly write Schrödinger's equation,

$$(\nabla^2 + k^2)\phi(x) = \frac{2m}{\hbar^2} V(x)\phi(x) \;,$$

as

$$\phi(\mathbf{r}) = \xi(\mathbf{r}) - \frac{m}{2\pi\hbar^2} \int G_-(\mathbf{r}, \mathbf{r}')V(\mathbf{r}')\phi(\mathbf{r}')d^3r' \;. \tag{7.99b}$$

But if we want the function $\phi(\mathbf{r})$ to behave at large values of $|\mathbf{r}|$ like

$$\phi(\mathbf{r}) \sim e^{i\mathbf{k}\cdot\mathbf{r}} + f(\theta, \phi)\frac{e^{+ikr}}{r} \;,$$

that is, if we want the potential to produce only *outgoing* spherical waves, then the function $\xi(r)$ needed to satisfy the boundary conditions would not be simply $e^{i\mathbf{k}\cdot\mathbf{r}}$ (then we would have just *incoming* spherical waves), but rather $e^{i\mathbf{k}\cdot\mathbf{r}}$ *plus* a complicated linear combination of solutions to the homogeneous equation,

$$(\nabla^2 + k^2)\phi(\mathbf{r}) = 0 \;,$$

whose coefficients would depend on $V(\mathbf{r})$. For this purpose, it would be convenient to take the solutions to be of the form

$$\phi_{lm}(\mathbf{r}) = j_l(kr) Y_{lm}(\theta, \phi) ,$$

where we reject solutions depending on $n_l(kr)$ because they are singular at the origin. (Note that $e^{i\mathbf{k}\cdot\mathbf{r}}$ is a particular linear combination of these $\phi_{lm}(\mathbf{r})$. What are the coefficients of this linear combination? See Problem 7.14.) The reader should show (Problem 7.15) that if we take

$$\xi(\mathbf{r}) = \frac{A}{(2\pi)^{3/2}} e^{i\mathbf{k}\cdot\mathbf{r}} - \frac{4imk}{\hbar^2} \sum_{l=0}^{\infty} \sum_{m=-l}^{l} j_l(kr) Y_{lm}(\theta, \phi)$$

$$\times \int Y_{lm}^*(\theta', \phi') j_l(kr') V(\mathbf{r}') \psi(\mathbf{r}') \, d\mathbf{r}' ,$$

then Eq. (7.99b) reduces to the familiar result

$$\psi(\mathbf{r}) = \frac{A}{(2\pi)^{3/2}} e^{i\mathbf{k}\cdot\mathbf{r}} - \frac{m}{2\pi\hbar^2} \int \frac{e^{ik|\mathbf{r}-\mathbf{r}'|}}{|\mathbf{r} - \mathbf{r}'|} V(\mathbf{r}') \psi(\mathbf{r}') \, d\mathbf{r}' .$$

This is just the result of Eq. (7.68) with the proper sign in the exponential to guarantee *outgoing* spherical waves. (Naturally, we could also view the above situation in terms of adding an appropriate linear combination of terms to the "incoming spherical wave Green's function" of Eq. (7.99a) in order to turn it into the desired "outgoing spherical wave Green's function.")

Thus we see that even if one starts with a Green's function satisfying very inconvenient boundary conditions, it is possible to utilize the freedom in the choice of $\xi(r)$ (or equivalently the freedom to add solutions of the homogeneous equation to $G(x, x')$) to overcome this difficulty. It should be clear, however, that in three dimensions this procedure would, in general, present very serious practical difficulties. Fortunately, many of the most important operators of physics are sufficiently simple in form so that it is a relatively straightforward matter to obtain for them Green's functions which satisfy physically useful boundary conditions. However, it is also often the case that even for simple operators the boundary conditions in three (or even two) dimensions are so complicated that the determination of the Green's function becomes virtually impossible. The following section is devoted to such a problem.

7.6 AN APPLICATION TO THE THEORY OF DIFFRACTION

In many problems of practical interest in physics, the boundary conditions are quite complicated from a mathematical point of view, even though the physical situation may be comparatively simple; this means that the appropriate operator equation is made difficult by the form of the boundary condition, rather than by the complexity of the operator itself. This is typically the case in electromagnetic theory where the presence of conducting surfaces—often not even "perfectly conducting" surfaces—makes the solution of many realistic problems extremely difficult, even after the most convenient geometrical configurations have been chosen. However, because of the relatively simple form of the *operator*, it is often possible to solve the Green's function equation,

$$LG(\mathbf{r}, \boldsymbol{\rho}) = \delta^3(\mathbf{r} - \boldsymbol{\rho}) , \qquad (7.100)$$

subject to some simple boundary condition. This would be the case in electromagnetic theory, for example, where $L = \nabla^2 + k^2$; if we then ask for the outgoing spherical wave solution, we get the Green's function of Eq. (7.66).

It is thus natural to ask the question: Can a solution to Eq. (7.100) help us obtain a solution to the equation,

$$L\phi = \phi , \qquad (7.101)$$

where ϕ must satisfy much more complicated boundary conditions than those imposed on $G(\mathbf{r}, \boldsymbol{\rho})$ in Eq. (7.100)?

To answer this question, let us first make the assumption that the operator L has the form

$$\nabla \cdot [f(\mathbf{r})\nabla] + g(\mathbf{r}) , \qquad (7.102)$$

which is sufficiently general for many physical applications. Now, if ϕ is any solution of Eq. (7.101), and if $G(\mathbf{r}, \boldsymbol{\rho})$ satisfies Eq. (7.100), then

$$\phi(\boldsymbol{\rho}) = \int_V \phi(\mathbf{r})G(\mathbf{r}, \boldsymbol{\rho})d^3\mathbf{r} + \int_V [\phi(\mathbf{r})LG(\mathbf{r}, \boldsymbol{\rho}) - G(\mathbf{r}, \boldsymbol{\rho})L\phi(\mathbf{r})] d^3\mathbf{r} , \qquad (7.103)$$

where V is the volume throughout which we want the solution. Using the specific form of L [Eq. (7.102)], we can rewrite Eq. (7.103) as

$$\phi(\boldsymbol{\rho}) = \int_V \phi(\mathbf{r})G(\mathbf{r}, \boldsymbol{\rho})d^3\mathbf{r} + \int_V [\phi(\mathbf{r})\nabla \cdot f(\mathbf{r})\nabla G(\mathbf{r}, \boldsymbol{\rho}) - G(\mathbf{r}, \boldsymbol{\rho})\nabla \cdot f(\mathbf{r})\nabla\phi(\mathbf{r})]d^3\mathbf{r} .$$

From the properties of the del operator, we find that

$$\phi(\boldsymbol{\rho}) = \int_V \phi(\mathbf{r})G(\mathbf{r}, \boldsymbol{\rho})d^3\mathbf{r} + \int_V \nabla \cdot [\phi(\mathbf{r})f(\mathbf{r})\nabla G(\mathbf{r}, \boldsymbol{\rho}) - G(\mathbf{r}, \boldsymbol{\rho})f(\mathbf{r})\nabla\phi(\mathbf{r})] d^3\mathbf{r} .$$

By Gauss's theorem, this last expression can be written as an integral over the surface S which encloses V. Denoting the outward normal to S by $\mathbf{n}$, we have

$$\phi(\boldsymbol{\rho}) = \int_V \phi(\mathbf{r})G(\mathbf{r}, \boldsymbol{\rho})d^3\mathbf{r} + \int_S f(\mathbf{r})[\phi(\mathbf{r})\nabla G(\mathbf{r}, \boldsymbol{\rho}) - G(\mathbf{r}, \boldsymbol{\rho})\nabla\phi(\mathbf{r})] \cdot \mathbf{n} \, dS .$$
$$(7.104)$$

Since $\phi(\mathbf{r})$, $f(\mathbf{r})$ and $G(\mathbf{r}, \boldsymbol{\rho})$ are presumed known, all that is required for the evaluation of the integrals is the value of ϕ and its normal derivative *on the surface S*.

It must be emphasized, however, that the situation is really more complicated than Eq. (7.104) suggests because $\phi(\mathbf{r})$ and its normal derivative are not *both* arbitrary on S. As a boundary condition we might have $\phi(\mathbf{r})$ specified on S *or* $\nabla\phi(\mathbf{r}) \cdot \mathbf{n}$ specified on S, or even a combination of $\phi(\mathbf{r})$ and $\nabla\phi(\mathbf{r}) \cdot \mathbf{n}$ specified, *but not both separately*. This is a familiar situation from one-dimensional problems, where for second-order equations we specify the value of the function at the endpoints, not both the value of the function and its first derivative at both endpoints.

In many circumstances, this difficulty can be overcome by making use of the freedom of choice of $G(\mathbf{r}, \boldsymbol{\rho})$ which arises from the fact that to any solution of Eq. (7.100) we can add an arbitrary multiple of any solution of $L\xi(\mathbf{r}) = 0$. If, for example, we can find a $G(\mathbf{r}, \boldsymbol{\rho})$ which satisfies Eq. (7.100) and also vanishes when $\mathbf{r}$ is on the surface, S, then Eq. (7.104) takes the form

$$\psi(\boldsymbol{\rho}) = \int_V \phi(\mathbf{r})G(\mathbf{r}, \boldsymbol{\rho})d^3\mathbf{r} + \int_S f(\mathbf{r})\psi(\mathbf{r})\boldsymbol{\nabla}G(\mathbf{r}, \boldsymbol{\rho})\cdot\mathbf{n}\,dS\,.$$

Thus, if the boundary condition involves a specification of $\psi(\mathbf{r})$ on S the problem is formally solved. This is a very common problem in electrostatics [$f(\mathbf{r}) \equiv 1$, $g(\mathbf{r}) \equiv 0$ in Eq. (7.102)], where numerous special techniques are available for the solution of Eq. (7.100) subject to the requirement that $G(\mathbf{r}, \boldsymbol{\rho})$ vanish on S. For a discussion of some of these methods, the reader is referred to Jackson's excellent book, *Classical Electrodynamics*. Notice that Eq. (7.100) is, apart from factors of 4π, just Poisson's equation for the potential due to a point charge at $\boldsymbol{\rho}$. Thus the above technique applied to electrostatics boils down to just the replacement of Poisson's equation for an arbitrary charge distribution and some complicated restriction on the potential at certain boundaries by Poisson's equation for a point charge and a simple boundary condition. (Note that if the shape of S is complicated even the boundary condition that $G(\mathbf{r}, \boldsymbol{\rho})$ vanish for $\mathbf{r}$ on S may in fact not be so "simple"!)

However, situations can also arise in which even the *specification* of boundary conditions becomes difficult. Nevertheless, on the basis of physical considerations one may be able to get an idea of what to expect for $\psi(\mathbf{r})$ and its normal derivative on the boundary of some region.

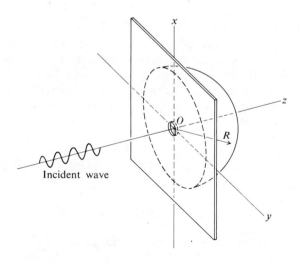

Fig. 7.8 A schematic illustration of the diffraction problem.

A beautiful example of such a situation, and one of the most important applications of Eq. (7.104), is the study of the diffraction of waves by a boundary. From a rigorous mathematical point of view, the theory of diffraction is one of the most complicated topics in classical physics. It involves solving Maxwell's equations in the presence of an awkward boundary, such as a barrier with a hole in it, and only under very special circumstances can an exact solution be obtained. However, in the freewheeling spirit of this chapter, let us try to use some physical ideas along with Eq. (7.104) to study this problem.

We envision a plane wave $e^{i\mathbf{k}_i \cdot \mathbf{r}}$ incident from the left on a flat boundary which contains an aperture, as in Fig. 7.8. The aperture is centered at the origin of the coordinate system; the screen lies in the xy-plane. Everywhere in space except on the screen the function describing the wave must satisfy the wave equation,

$$\nabla^2 \psi + k_i^2 \psi = 0 \,.$$

We are interested in the solution to the right of the screen, so let us take as our volume a hemisphere of large radius centered at the origin, whose flat bottom lies infinitesimally close to the screen.

Now what can we say about the nature of the solution on the boundary? Certainly we would expect the solution at large distances from the scattering center (the aperture) to look like an outgoing spherical wave. Thus, near the curved part of the hemisphere, the wave should have the form

$$\psi(\mathbf{r}) \sim f(\theta, \phi) \frac{e^{ik_i r}}{r} \,. \tag{7.105}$$

Thus the appropriate Green's function for the wave equation in that region is

$$G(\mathbf{r}, \boldsymbol{\rho}) = -\frac{1}{4\pi} \frac{e^{ik_i |\mathbf{r} - \boldsymbol{\rho}|}}{|\mathbf{r} - \boldsymbol{\rho}|} \,, \tag{7.106}$$

which will, according to previous arguments, yield outgoing spherical waves in Eq. (7.104). What about the flat bottom surface of the hemisphere? Here we make the physically reasonable guess that on the back of the "opaque" screen (opposite from the side on which the incident wave is falling) the solution should be identically zero. In the aperture, we take the incoming wave itself as a first approximation:

$$\psi(\mathbf{r}) = e^{i\mathbf{k}_i \cdot \mathbf{r}} \,.$$

We now use these physical assumptions to write Eq. (7.104) in the form appropriate to this case. We have

$$\psi(\boldsymbol{\rho}) = \int_{ap} [e^{i\mathbf{k}_i \cdot \mathbf{r}} \nabla G(\mathbf{r}, \boldsymbol{\rho}) - G(\mathbf{r}, \boldsymbol{\rho}) \nabla e^{i\mathbf{k}_i \cdot \mathbf{r}}] \cdot \mathbf{n} \, dS$$
$$+ \int f(\theta, \phi) \left[\frac{e^{ik_i r}}{r} \frac{\partial}{\partial r} G(\mathbf{r}, \boldsymbol{\rho}) - G(\mathbf{r}, \boldsymbol{\rho}) \frac{\partial}{\partial r} \frac{e^{ik_i r}}{r} \right]_{r=R} R^2 \, d\Omega \,. \tag{7.107}$$

In the first integral, $\mathbf{n}$ is a unit vector in the negative z-direction (an *outward* normal), and the integral ranges over the entire aperture. The second integral is an angular integration over the curved surface of the hemisphere. The derivatives in the second integral are radial derivatives, since the outward normal is in the radial direction for a spherical surface. R is the radius of the hemisphere, and may be taken to be arbitrarily large. We want to show that this second term vanishes as $R \to \infty$. It is not sufficient to say that the solution drops off like $1/r$ at large distances, since there is a factor of r^2 in the volume element. However, using the value of $G(\mathbf{r}, \boldsymbol{\rho})$ given in Eq. (7.106), it is a simple matter to show that the second integral in Eq. (7.107) falls off like $1/R$. Thus this term vanishes as we make the radius of the hemisphere large, and

$$\phi(\boldsymbol{\rho}) = \int_{\text{ap}} [e^{i\mathbf{k}_i \cdot \mathbf{r}} \nabla G(\mathbf{r}, \boldsymbol{\rho}) - G(\mathbf{r}, \boldsymbol{\rho}) \nabla e^{i\mathbf{k}_i \cdot \mathbf{r}}] \cdot \mathbf{n} \, dS . \qquad (7.108)$$

To simplify the work, let us assume that $\mathbf{k}_i$ is in the z-direction, which means that the wave is incident perpendicular to the screen. Now $\mathbf{n}$ is in the negative z-direction, and $\mathbf{k}_i \cdot \mathbf{r} = 0$, because the surface over which we integrate is in the xy-plane. Therefore, Eq. (7.108) reduces to

$$\phi(\boldsymbol{\rho}) = \int_{\text{ap}} \left[ik_i G(\mathbf{r}, \boldsymbol{\rho}) - \frac{\partial}{\partial z} G(\mathbf{r}, \boldsymbol{\rho}) \right] dS . \qquad (7.109)$$

Even in this form the integration represents a formidable problem, so we shall simplify life further by considering $|\boldsymbol{\rho}|$ to be large compared to a typical screen dimension. Then we can use the asymptotic form of $G(\mathbf{r}, \boldsymbol{\rho})$ discussed in Section 7.4:

$$-\frac{1}{4\pi} \frac{e^{ik_i|\mathbf{r} - \boldsymbol{\rho}|}}{|\mathbf{r} - \boldsymbol{\rho}|} \xrightarrow[|\boldsymbol{\rho}| \to \infty]{} -\frac{1}{4\pi} \frac{e^{ik_i\rho}}{\rho} e^{-i\mathbf{k}_f \cdot \mathbf{r}} , \qquad (7.110)$$

where $\mathbf{k}_f$ is a vector whose magnitude is k_i and whose direction is given by (θ, ϕ)—the same angles specifying the orientation of $\boldsymbol{\rho}$. Using the fact that

$$(\mathbf{k}_f)_z = |\mathbf{k}_f| \cos \theta = k_i \cos \theta ,$$

and inserting Eq. (7.110) into Eq. (7.109), we get

$$\phi(\boldsymbol{\rho}) = -\frac{ik_i}{4\pi} \frac{e^{ik_i\rho}}{\rho} (1 + \cos \theta) \int_{\text{ap}} e^{-i\mathbf{k}_f \cdot \mathbf{r}} \, dS . \qquad (7.111)$$

This is the general expression for the diffraction of a wave by an aperture in the region whose distance from the origin is much larger than the size of the aperture. The precise form of the solution depends, of course, on the geometrical details. However, several important results follow immediately from the general result of Eq. (7.111).

First, it can be shown that if the wavelength λ of the radiation is small compared to the aperture dimensions, there is very intense radiation in the forward direction. In this direction, $\theta = 0$, and $\mathbf{k}_f \cdot \mathbf{r} = 0$, because $\mathbf{k}_f$ is perpendicular to the screen, on which $\theta = \pi/2$. Therefore

$$[\phi(\boldsymbol{\rho})]_{\text{forward}} = -\frac{ik_i A}{2\pi} \frac{e^{ik_i\rho}}{\rho}, \tag{7.112}$$

where A is the area of the aperture. Since $k_i = 2\pi/\lambda$, we see that

$$[\phi(\boldsymbol{\rho})]_{\text{forward}} = \phi(\rho, \theta = 0, \phi) = -i\frac{A}{\lambda} \frac{e^{ik_i\rho}}{\rho}.$$

If we denote the number of photons per square centimeter per second falling on the screen by I_0, then the number of photons per second at a distance $|\boldsymbol{\rho}| = R$ coming into the solid angle $d\Omega$ about some direction (θ, ϕ) is given by

$$I(\theta, \phi) = I_0 |\phi(R, \theta, \phi)|^2 R^2 d\Omega.$$

For $\theta = 0$ this is

$$I(0, \phi) = (I_0 A)(A/\lambda^2) d\Omega,$$

which is very large if $\lambda^2 \ll A$. Note that $I_0 A$ is just the number of photons per second falling on the aperture. If λ is much smaller than a typical aperture dimension then it is possible to evaluate the total intensity of diffracted radiation by integrating $I(\theta, \phi)$ over all solid angle, using Eq. (7.111) for $\phi(R, \theta, \phi)$. This integration yields precisely $I_0 A$, i.e., the number of diffracted photons per second arriving on the hemisphere is exactly equal to the number of photons per second falling on the screen, in the short wavelength limit.

It will also become apparent in the following examples that $\phi(\rho, \pi/2, \phi)$ —the solution on the screen—and its normal derivative are very small in absolute value compared to $|\phi(\rho, 0, \phi)|$. Thus the boundary condition on the screen is approximately, although not exactly, satisfied in this case.

Let us now see what $\phi(\boldsymbol{\rho})$ looks like for some simple aperture shapes. The easiest case is that of a rectangular aperture with sides a and b, centered about the origin. Then

$$\phi(\boldsymbol{\rho}) = -\frac{ik_i}{4\pi}(1 + \cos\theta)\frac{e^{ik_i\rho}}{\rho}\int_{-a/2}^{a/2} e^{ik_x x}\, dx \int_{-b/2}^{b/2} e^{ik_y y}\, dy$$

$$= -\frac{ik_i}{\pi}(1 + \cos\theta)\frac{\sin(k_x a/2)\sin(k_y b/2)}{k_x k_y}\frac{e^{ik_i\rho}}{\rho}.$$

This has the form of Eq. (7.112) in the forward direction ($\theta = 0$) since

$$k_x = k_i \sin\theta \cos\phi$$

and

$$k_y = k_i \sin\theta \sin\phi.$$

It is also of interest to consider $\phi(\boldsymbol{\rho})$ on the screen (at $\theta = \pi/2$). We find that

$$\phi(\rho, \theta = \pi/2, \phi) = -\frac{i}{\pi k_i}\frac{\sin[(k_i a/2)\cos\phi]\sin[(k_i b/2)\sin\phi]}{\sin\phi\cos\phi}\frac{e^{ik_i\rho}}{\rho}.$$

If λ is small, k_i is large, so $\phi(\rho, \theta = \pi/2, \phi)$ is small on the screen, as we said above. The derivative normal to the screen is also very small when $\theta = \pi/2$. Thus the boundary conditions on the screen are approximately satisfied, at least for large ρ.

A particularly convenient arrangement is a circular aperture. Denoting a point in the aperture by $(r, \theta_r = \pi/2, \phi_r)$ and $\mathbf{k}_f$ by (k_i, θ, ϕ), we have

$$\phi(\boldsymbol{\rho}) = -\frac{ik_i}{4\pi} \frac{e^{ik_i\rho}}{\rho} (1 + \cos \theta) \int_0^R r \, dr \int_0^{2\pi} d\phi_r e^{-ik_i r \sin \theta \cos (\phi_r - \phi)} \;,$$

where R is the radius of the aperture. Here we have used the fact that if α is the angle between two vectors whose directions are specified by (θ, ϕ) and (θ_r, ϕ_r), then

$$\cos \alpha = \cos \theta \cos \theta_r + \sin \theta \sin \theta_r \cos (\phi_r - \phi) \;.$$

Because of the rotational symmetry about the z-axis, the final result cannot depend on ϕ, so by changing variables to $x = k_i r \sin \theta$, we get

$$\phi(\boldsymbol{\rho}) = -\frac{i}{2k_i} \frac{e^{ik_i\rho}}{\rho} \frac{(1 + \cos \theta)}{\sin^2 \theta} \int_0^{k_i R \sin \theta} x \, dx \left[\frac{1}{2\pi} \int_0^{2\pi} e^{-ix \cos \beta} \, d\beta \right] .$$

The term in brackets is easily transformed into the integral representation of the Bessel function of order zero, (Section 6.9). Thus

$$\phi(\boldsymbol{\rho}) = -\frac{i}{2k_i} \frac{(1 + \cos \theta)}{\sin^2 \theta} \int_0^{k_i R \sin \theta} x J_0(x) \, dx \, \frac{e^{ik_i\rho}}{\rho} \;.$$

Using Eq. (6.69), which gives an infinite series for the Bessel functions of integral order, the reader can show that

$$x J_0(x) = \frac{d}{dx} \left[x J_1(x) \right] \;,$$

so finally

$$\phi(\boldsymbol{\rho}) = -\frac{iR}{2} \frac{(1 + \cos \theta)}{\sin \theta} J_1(k_i R \sin \theta) \frac{e^{ik_i\rho}}{\rho} \;. \tag{7.113}$$

This agrees with the general result of Eq. (7.112) when $\theta = 0$, for, as can be seen from Eq. (6.69), $J_1(x) \to x/2$ as $x \to 0$. Since $J_1(x) \sim 1/\sqrt{x}$ for large x, we can see that when $\theta = \pi/2$, $\phi(\boldsymbol{\rho})$ and its derivative normal to the screen are very small if the wavelength is small compared to R. Once again, the boundary conditions on the screen are approximately satisfied. The Bessel functions are oscillatory, so if we put a screen behind the circular aperture at a distance that is large compared to the radius of the aperture, the radiation falling on it will give rise to circular rings, starting with an intense central bright ring, then a dark ring as the Bessel function passes through its first zero, and so forth. Figure 7.9 shows the quantity

$$|\phi(\rho, \theta, \phi)|^2 \rho^2 \;,$$

Fig. 7.9 The intensity of diffracted radiation in arbitrary units as a function of angle. The curve does not reach $\theta = 0$ until $I = 256$. This curve corresponds to a circular aperture with $kR = 16$ in Eq. (7.113). Essentially all the intensity is concentrated in the first peak.

which is proportional to the intensity; it is also independent of ϕ because of the symmetry about the z-axis. The intensity pattern of Fig. 7.9 has been verified experimentally.

It is interesting to ask the question, "What would we find if instead of having radiation fall on a screen containing a hole, we let it fall on a small screen exactly the size of the hole?" A screen of this type is called the screen *complementary* to the one we have been considering; a screen plus its complement form a completely opaque barrier. To solve this problem we use the configuration of Fig. 7.8 except that the "screen" is now transparent and the "aperture" is now opaque. In order that the boundary conditions in the xy-plane be consistent with our previous treatment, we take ψ_c to be given simply by $e^{i\mathbf{k}_i \cdot \mathbf{r}}$ in the transparent part, and identically equal to zero behind the opaque part. On the curved hemispherical surface we expect at large distances to find a scattered spherical wave superimposed on the incident plane wave:

$$\psi_c(\mathbf{r}) \sim e^{i\mathbf{k}_i \cdot \mathbf{r}} + F(\theta, \phi)e^{ik_ir}/r \ .$$

From Eq. (7.104) we have for the "complementary solution," $\psi_c(\boldsymbol{\rho})$,

$$\psi_c(\boldsymbol{\rho}) = \int_{xy-ap} [e^{i\mathbf{k}_i \cdot \mathbf{r}}\nabla G(\mathbf{r}, \boldsymbol{\rho}) - G(\mathbf{r}, \boldsymbol{\rho})\nabla e^{i\mathbf{k}_i \cdot \mathbf{r}}] \cdot \mathbf{n} \, dS$$

$$+ \int_{hemisphere} [e^{i\mathbf{k}_i \cdot \mathbf{r}}\nabla G(\mathbf{r}, \boldsymbol{\rho}) - G(\mathbf{r}, \boldsymbol{\rho})\nabla e^{i\mathbf{k}_i \cdot \mathbf{r}}] \cdot \mathbf{n} \, dS$$

$$+ \int_{hemisphere} F(\theta, \phi)\left[\frac{e^{ik_ir}}{r}\nabla G(\mathbf{r}, \boldsymbol{\rho}) - G(\mathbf{r}, \boldsymbol{\rho})\nabla\frac{e^{ik_ir}}{r}\right] \cdot \mathbf{n} \, dS \ , \quad (7.114)$$

where we have used our assumptions about the behavior of ψ on the boundaries. In Eq. (7.114) the subscript $xy - ap$ means that the integral goes over the entire xy-plane, minus the aperture. Now, we have seen before that the last term of

Eq. (7.114) vanishes when the radius of the hemisphere becomes very large. Thus

$$\phi_c(\boldsymbol{\rho}) = \int_{xy-ap} [e^{i\mathbf{k}_i \cdot \mathbf{r}} \nabla G(\mathbf{r}, \boldsymbol{\rho}) - G(\mathbf{r}, \boldsymbol{\rho}) \nabla e^{i\mathbf{k}_i \cdot \mathbf{r}}] \cdot \mathbf{n} \, dS$$

$$+ \int_{hemisphere} [e^{i\mathbf{k}_i \cdot \mathbf{r}} \nabla G(\mathbf{r}, \boldsymbol{\rho}) - G(\mathbf{r}, \boldsymbol{\rho}) \nabla e^{i\mathbf{k}_i \cdot \mathbf{r}}] \cdot \mathbf{n} \, dS . \qquad (7.115)$$

If we now compare this result with Eq. (7.108) for $\phi(\boldsymbol{\rho})$, we see that the sum $\phi(\boldsymbol{\rho}) + \phi_c(\boldsymbol{\rho})$ obeys the simple relation

$$\phi(\boldsymbol{\rho}) + \phi_c(\boldsymbol{\rho}) = \int_S [e^{i\mathbf{k}_i \cdot \mathbf{r}} \nabla G(\mathbf{r}, \boldsymbol{\rho}) - G(\mathbf{r}, \boldsymbol{\rho}) \nabla e^{i\mathbf{k}_i \cdot \mathbf{r}}] \cdot \mathbf{n} \, dS , \qquad (7.116)$$

where S denotes, as before, the *entire* closed surface. Now using Green's theorem and remembering that $e^{i\mathbf{k}_i \cdot \mathbf{r}}$ is a solution of the wave equation, we see that

$$\phi(\boldsymbol{\rho}) + \phi_c(\boldsymbol{\rho}) = e^{i\mathbf{k}_i \cdot \boldsymbol{\rho}} . \qquad (7.117)$$

This beautifully simple result is known in optics as *Babinet's principle* or *the principle of complementary screens*.

If we use Eq. (7.111) for $\phi(\boldsymbol{\rho})$ at distances that are large compared to the dimensions of the screen, then

$$\phi_c(\boldsymbol{\rho}) = e^{i\mathbf{k}_i \cdot \boldsymbol{\rho}} + f(\theta, \phi) \frac{e^{ik_i\rho}}{\rho} , \qquad (7.118a)$$

where

$$f(\theta, \phi) = \frac{ik_i}{4\pi} (1 + \cos \theta) \int_{ap} e^{-i\mathbf{k}_f \cdot \mathbf{r}} \, dS . \qquad (7.118b)$$

Equations (7.118a) and (7.118b) are of the same form as the results which we found in our study of the Lippmann-Schwinger equation. In the latter case, $f(\theta, \phi)$, the scattering amplitude, was given in terms of the potential and the wave function. Here we obtain $f(\theta, \phi)$ in terms of a boundary condition.

According to Eq. (7.113), the scattering of a plane wave by a circular, opaque obstacle is described by the function

$$f(\theta, \phi) = \frac{iR}{2} \frac{1 + \cos \theta}{\sin \theta} J_1(k_i R \sin \theta) , \qquad (7.119)$$

where R is the radius of the obstacle and $k_i = 2\pi/\lambda$, as before. Several interesting attempts have been made to understand in terms of diffraction the quantum-mechanical scattering of short wavelength (high energy) nuclear projectiles (α-particles, for example) from nuclei. For reasonable values of the nuclear radius, scattering amplitudes given by Eq. (7.119) match the experimental results quite closely. They show a strong forward maximum and an oscillatory behavior away from the forward peak very similar to the pattern shown in Fig. 7-8. This provides a nice illustration of the wave aspect of particles.

7.7 TIME-DEPENDENT GREEN'S FUNCTIONS: FIRST ORDER

In the past few sections we have concentrated our attention of the application of Green's function techniques to the solution of certain partial differential equations in which the time did not play an essential role. In this section we begin looking at problems where the evolution of some system in time (as well as in space) is important.

Consider an equation such as

$$H\psi + \frac{\partial \psi}{\partial \tau} = 0 , \qquad (7.120)$$

where τ is a time variable, and H is an operator, *independent of time* which is assumed to possess a complete set of eigenfunctions. There are numerous equations of this type, and their application extends into all domains of physics. A familiar example is the heat equation,

$$\nabla^2 T = \frac{c}{k} \frac{\partial T}{\partial t} ,$$

where T is the temperature, c is the specific heat per unit volume, and k is the heat conductivity. If we call $H = -\nabla^2$ and $\tau = kt/c$, then this has precisely the form of Eq. (7.120). Schrödinger's time-dependent equation is also of this form, namely,

$$\mathscr{H}\psi = i\hbar \frac{\partial \psi}{\partial t} ,$$

where $\mathscr{H}$ is the total Hamiltonian of the system described by the wave function ψ. For example, for a free particle,

$$\mathscr{H} = -\frac{\hbar^2}{2m} \nabla^2 ,$$

so Schrödinger's equation is

$$-\nabla^2 \psi = \frac{2mi}{\hbar} \frac{\partial \psi}{\partial t} .$$

Thus if we set $H = -\nabla^2$ and $\tau = (i\hbar/2m)t$, the equation has exactly the same form as the heat equation. Another equation of this type is the diffusion equation which reads

$$\nabla^2 \rho = \frac{1}{a^2} \frac{\partial \rho}{\partial t} ,$$

where ρ is the density of the diffusing material, and a is the diffusion constant. Here again the identification $H = -\nabla^2$ and $\tau = a^2 t$ brings the equation to the basic form of Eq. (7.120).

Since we assume that H has a complete orthonormal set of eigenfunctions,

$$H\phi_m = \lambda_m \phi_m ,$$

we can expand the solution to Eq. (7.120) in terms of them;

$$\psi(\mathbf{r}, \tau) = \sum_m A_m(\tau)\phi_m(\mathbf{r}) .$$

Since $\psi(\mathbf{r}, \tau)$ depends on τ, so will the functions $A_m(\tau)$. Now

$$H\psi = H\left[\sum_m A_m(\tau)\phi_m(\mathbf{r}) \right] = \sum_m A_m(\tau) H\phi_m(\mathbf{r})$$

$$= \sum_m \lambda_m A_m(\tau)\phi_m(\mathbf{r}) .$$

Also,

$$\frac{\partial\psi}{\partial\tau} = \sum_m \frac{\partial A_m(\tau)}{\partial\tau} \phi_m(\mathbf{r}) .$$

Thus Eq. (7.120) becomes

$$\sum_m \left[\lambda_m A_m(\tau) + \frac{dA_m(\tau)}{d\tau} \right]\phi_m(\mathbf{r}) = 0 .$$

Since the $\phi_m(\mathbf{r})$ are complete and orthonormal, we conclude immediately that

$$\frac{dA_m(\tau)}{d\tau} + \lambda_m A_m(\tau) = 0$$

for all m. The solution for $A_m(\tau)$ is simply

$$A_m(\tau) = A_m(0)e^{-\lambda_m\tau} ,$$

and thus we obtain

$$\psi(\mathbf{r}, \tau) = \sum_m A_m(0)\phi_m(\mathbf{r})e^{-\lambda_m\tau} .$$

Now, to complete the solution to a partial differential equation which is of first order in the time derivative, we need to specify the boundary condition at $\tau = 0$. Assuming that we know $\psi(\mathbf{r}, 0)$ (for example, in the case of the heat equation, if the initial temperature distribution $T(\mathbf{r}, 0)$ is known), we may write

$$\psi(\mathbf{r}, 0) = \sum_m A_m(0)\phi_m(\mathbf{r}) .$$

Using the fact that the ϕ_m form a complete orthonormal set, we have

$$A_n(0) = \int \phi_n^*(\mathbf{r})\psi(\mathbf{r}, 0) \, d^3\mathbf{r} .$$

Thus

$$\psi(\mathbf{r}, \tau) = \sum_m e^{-\lambda_m\tau}\phi_m(\mathbf{r}) \int \phi_m^*(\mathbf{r}')\psi(\mathbf{r}', 0) \, d^3\mathbf{r}' ,$$

or

$$\psi(\mathbf{r}, \tau) = \int G_1(\mathbf{r}, \mathbf{r}', \tau)\psi(\mathbf{r}', 0) \, d^3\mathbf{r}' , \qquad (7.121a)$$

where

$$G_1(\mathbf{r}, \mathbf{r}', \tau) = \sum_m \phi_m(\mathbf{r})\phi_m^*(\mathbf{r}')e^{-\lambda_m\tau} . \qquad (7.121b)$$

Note that

$$G_1(\mathbf{r}, \mathbf{r}', 0) = \sum_m \phi_m(\mathbf{r})\phi_m^*(\mathbf{r}') = \delta^3(\mathbf{r} - \mathbf{r}') , \qquad (7.122)$$

as it must, of course, because of Eq. (7.121a). Also,

$$\left(H + \frac{\partial}{\partial\tau}\right)G_1(\mathbf{r}, \mathbf{r}', \tau) = 0 . \qquad (7.123)$$

Thus $\phi(\mathbf{r}, \tau)$, as given by Eq. (7.121a), is indeed a solution which satisfies the prescribed boundary condition.

We have put a subscript 1 on our function $G_1(\mathbf{r}, \mathbf{r}', \tau)$ to denote that it arises from an equation which is first order in time. We will refer loosely to G_1 as a Green's function, although it does not satisfy

$$\left[H + \frac{\partial}{\partial\tau}\right]G(\mathbf{r}, \mathbf{r}', \tau) = \delta^3(\mathbf{r} - \mathbf{r}')\delta(\tau) . \qquad (7.124)$$

We will soon see, however, that G_1 is closely related to a function which *is* a Green's function in this usual sense.

Since G_1 does not satisfy Eq. (7.124), but, rather, Eq. (7.123), G_1 is itself a solution to Eq. (7.120). In fact, if $\phi(\mathbf{r}, 0) = \delta(\mathbf{r} - \mathbf{r}_0)$, then Eq. (7.121a) yields immediately

$$\phi(\mathbf{r}, \tau) = G_1(\mathbf{r}, \mathbf{r}_0, \tau)$$

for $\tau \geq 0$. Thus G_1 is a solution of Eq. (7.120) for a very special initial condition: the so-called "point source" initial condition. This fact leads to a simple physical interpretation of the Green's function which we shall discuss shortly.

Needless to say, our choice of initial time was completely arbitrary. We could equally well have chosen the initial time to be τ', and then we would have

$$\phi(\mathbf{r}, \tau) = \int G_1(\mathbf{r}, \mathbf{r}', \tau, \tau')\phi(\mathbf{r}', \tau') \, d^3\mathbf{r}' , \qquad (7.125a)$$

where

$$G_1(\mathbf{r}, \mathbf{r}', \tau, \tau') = \sum_m \phi_m(\mathbf{r})\phi_m^*(\mathbf{r}')e^{-\lambda_m(\tau-\tau')} . \qquad (7.125b)$$

In other words, $G_1(\mathbf{r}, \mathbf{r}', \tau, \tau')$ *propagates* the function ϕ in time from τ' to $\tau > \tau'$; for this reason, G_1 is often referred to as a *propagator*. This manner of speaking suggests that if we propagate ϕ from τ_0 to τ_1 and then from τ_1 to τ_2, we should get the same result as if we propagate directly from τ_0 to τ_2.

Mathematically, we write

$$\phi(\mathbf{r}, \tau_1) = \int G_1(\mathbf{r}, \mathbf{r}'', \tau_1, \tau_0)\phi(\mathbf{r}'', \tau_0) \, d^3\mathbf{r}''$$

$$\phi(\mathbf{r}, \tau_2) = \int G_1(\mathbf{r}, \mathbf{r}', \tau_2, \tau_1)\phi(\mathbf{r}', \tau_1) \, d^3\mathbf{r}'$$

$$= \int\int G_1(\mathbf{r}, \mathbf{r}', \tau_2, \tau_1)G_1(\mathbf{r}', \mathbf{r}'', \tau_1, \tau_0)\phi(\mathbf{r}'', \tau_0) \, d^3\mathbf{r}' \, d^3\mathbf{r}'' \ .$$

Using Eq. (7.125b), we find that

$$\int G_1(\mathbf{r}, \mathbf{r}', \tau_2, \tau_1)G_1(\mathbf{r}', \mathbf{r}'', \tau_1, \tau_0) \, d^3\mathbf{r}'$$

$$= \int \sum_m \phi_m(\mathbf{r})\phi_m^*(\mathbf{r}')e^{-\lambda_m(\tau_2-\tau_1)} \sum_n \phi_n(\mathbf{r}')\phi_n^*(\mathbf{r}'')e^{-\lambda_n(\tau_1-\tau_0)} \, d^3\mathbf{r}' \ .$$

Since

$$\int \phi_m^*(\mathbf{r}')\phi_n(\mathbf{r}') \, d^3\mathbf{r}' = \delta_{mn} \ ,$$

we obtain immediately

$$\int G_1(\mathbf{r}, \mathbf{r}', \tau_2, \tau_1)G_1(\mathbf{r}', \mathbf{r}'', \tau_1, \tau_0) \, d^3\mathbf{r}'$$

$$= \sum_m \phi_m(\mathbf{r})\phi_m^*(\mathbf{r}'')e^{-\lambda_m(\tau_2-\tau_1)}e^{-\lambda_m(\tau_1-\tau_0)}$$

$$= \sum_m \phi_m(\mathbf{r})\phi_m^*(\mathbf{r}'')e^{-\lambda_m(\tau_2-\tau_0)}$$

$$= G_1(\mathbf{r}, \mathbf{r}'', \tau_2, \tau_0) \ .$$

Thus, as we expected,

$$\phi(\mathbf{r}, \tau_2) = \int G_1(\mathbf{r}, \mathbf{r}'', \tau_2, \tau_0)\phi(\mathbf{r}'', \tau_0) \, d^3\mathbf{r}'' \ .$$

This idea of compounding propagations is a very important notion in physics; we restate the result below:

$$G_1(\mathbf{r}, \mathbf{r}'', \tau_2, \tau_0) = \int G_1(\mathbf{r}, \mathbf{r}', \tau_2, \tau_1)G_1(\mathbf{r}', \mathbf{r}'', \tau_1, \tau_0) \, d^3\mathbf{r}' \ .$$

Let us now determine the Green's function for an equation of the diffusion or heat conduction type. We work in one dimension for convenience, in the interval $-L/2 \leq x \leq L/2$, and impose periodic boundary conditions, $\phi(L/2, \tau) = \phi(-L/2, \tau)$. As mentioned above, the operator H is simply $-d^2/dx^2$ in this case, so we want to solve

$$-\frac{d^2\phi_m}{dx^2} = \lambda_m\phi_m(x) \ .$$

This equation has as its solution

$$\phi_m(x) = \frac{1}{\sqrt{L}} e^{i\sqrt{\lambda_m}x},$$

where $\lambda_m = (2\pi m/L)^2$, in order to satisfy the boundary condition, and m is any integer. Thus if we call $k_m = 2\pi m/L$, we get for $G_1(x, x', \tau)$, using Eq. (7.121b),

$$G_1(x, x', \tau) = \sum_{m=-\infty}^{\infty} \frac{1}{L} e^{ik_m(x-x')} e^{-k_m^2\tau}. \tag{7.126}$$

Now suppose that we want to obtain the Green's function on the *infinite* line. Let us employ the same type of limiting procedure used in making the transition from Fourier series to Fourier integrals in Section 5.7. In Eq. (7.126), as L becomes larger and larger, k_m changes only very slightly as we go from one value of m to the next in the sum. In fact, k_m changes by $2\pi/L$ each time m is incremented by one unit. Let us therefore set $2\pi/L = \Delta k_m$ and write

$$G_1(x, x', \tau) = \frac{1}{2\pi} \sum_{m=-\infty}^{\infty} \Delta k_m e^{ik_m(x-x')} e^{-k_m^2\tau}.$$

In this form we see that our expression is exactly what one finds when one discusses the Riemann integral of some function; we break the interval of integration in question up into small subintervals Δ_i and evaluate the function at some point x_i in each interval. Then

$$\sum_i \Delta_i f(x_i) \to \int f(x)\, dx.$$

In this spirit, as $L \to \infty$, we have for G_1 just

$$G_1(x, x', \tau) = \frac{1}{2\pi} \int_{-\infty}^{\infty} e^{ik(x-x')} e^{-k^2\tau}\, dk. \tag{7.127}$$

It is not difficult to evaluate this integral. We note that

$$ik(x - x') - k^2\tau = -\tau \left[k - \frac{i(x - x')}{2\tau} \right]^2 - \frac{(x - x')^2}{4\tau},$$

so that

$$G_1(x, x', \tau) = \frac{1}{2\pi} e^{-(x-x')^2/4\tau} \int_{-\infty}^{\infty} e^{-\tau(k-i\delta)^2}\, dk,$$

where $\delta = (x - x')/2\tau$. To evaluate this integral, we consider the integrand to be a function of a complex variable z, and investigate the contour integral along the curve C shown in Fig. 7.10. Thus

$$I = \int_C e^{-\tau(z-i\delta)^2}\, dz = 0.$$

Fig. 7.10 The curve C used to evaluate the function $G_1(x, x', \tau)$. X is to be considered as being arbitrarily large.

since there are no singularities inside the contour. On Γ_1, $z = x$, and on Γ_3, $z = x + i\delta$. Thus

$$
I = 0 = \int_{-X}^{X} e^{-\tau (x - i\delta)^2} \, dx + \int_{\Gamma_2} e^{-\tau (z - i\delta)^2} \, dz
$$
$$
+ \int_{X}^{-X} e^{-\tau x^2} \, dx + \int_{\Gamma_4} e^{-\tau (z - i\delta)^2} \, dz \ .
$$

Now on Γ_2, $z = X + iy$, where X can become arbitrarily large. Hence

$$
\int_{\Gamma_2} e^{-\tau (z - i\delta)^2} \, dz = i \int_0^\delta e^{-\tau [X + i (y - \delta)]^2} \, dy
$$
$$
= ie^{-\tau X^2} \int_0^\delta e^{\tau (y - \delta)^2} e^{-2iX\tau (y - \delta)} \, dy \ .
$$

Clearly, the integral on y yields a finite number since we integrate a bounded function over a finite interval. Thus as $X \to \infty$, the integral along Γ_2 vanishes because of the factor $e^{-X^2\tau}$. The same argument eliminates the integral along Γ_4. Thus

$$
\int_{-\infty}^{\infty} e^{-\tau (x - i\delta)^2} \, dx = \int_{-\infty}^{\infty} e^{-\tau x^2} \, dx = \sqrt{\frac{\pi}{\tau}} \ ,
$$

where this last integral can be evaluated by real integral techniques, (or see Eq. 6.56). (It should be remarked that, although we have tacitly assumed that τ is real in this calculation, it is a simple matter [see Problem 31 (l) of Chapter 6] to show that the result is valid even when τ is pure imaginary.) Thus, finally,

$$
G_1(x, x', \tau) = \frac{1}{\sqrt{4\pi\tau}} e^{-(x - x')^2/4\tau} \ . \tag{7.128}
$$

Note that $G_1(x, x', \tau)$ is a symmetric function of x and x'. As τ tends to zero,

$$
\lim_{\tau \to 0} G(x, x', \tau) = \lim_{\tau \to 0} \frac{1}{\sqrt{4\pi\tau}} e^{-(x - x')^2/4\tau} \ ,
$$

which is just one of the representations of the δ-function discussed in Section 5.3. Thus

$$
\lim_{\tau \to 0} G(x, x', \tau) = \delta(x - x') \ ,
$$

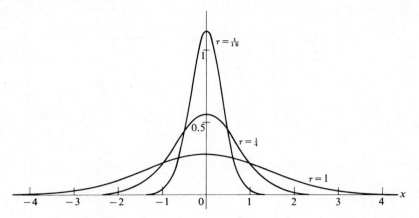

Fig. 7.11 The Green's function $G(x, x', \tau)$ as a function of x (centered at $x' = 0$ for convenience) for several values of τ.

in agreement with the general result of Eq. (7.122). As the time, τ, increases from zero, $G_1(x, x', \tau)$ looks like the familiar Gaussian, centered about $x = x'$ with half width equal to $\sqrt{2\tau}$. For small τ, the Gaussian is tall and narrow; as τ increases, the Gaussian broadens out and its height decreases, as shown in Fig. 7.11. However, the area under these Gaussians remains constant, since we see that

$$\int_{-\infty}^{\infty} G_1(x, x') \, dx = \frac{1}{\sqrt{4\pi\tau}} \int_{-\infty}^{\infty} e^{-(x-x')^2/4\tau} \, dx = 1 \, ,$$

independent of τ and x'. In terms of the diffusion equation, this means that the total quantity of diffusing gas (the integral of the density over all space) is constant, since

$$\phi(x, \tau) = \int_{-\infty}^{\infty} G_1(x, x', \tau)\phi(x', 0) \, dx'$$

implies that

$$\int_{-\infty}^{\infty} \phi(x, \tau) \, dx = \int_{-\infty}^{\infty} \phi(x', 0) \, dx' \, , \qquad (7.129)$$

by the result above. In the diffusion equation, $\phi(x, \tau)$ is the density of the diffusing gas, so

$$\int_{-\infty}^{\infty} \phi(x, \tau) \, dx$$

is the total amount of diffusing gas. Equation (7.129) states that this quantity is constant in time.

In terms of this Green's function we can write the solution to the diffusion or heat equation at a later time in terms of the initial distribution:

$$\phi(x, \tau) = \frac{1}{\sqrt{4\pi\tau}} \int_{-\infty}^{\infty} e^{-(x-x')^2/4\tau} \phi(x', 0) \, dx' \; . \tag{7.130}$$

This equation has a simple physical interpretation: At $\tau = 0$, each element of space has an amount of diffusing material (or heat) equal to $\phi(x', 0) \, dx'$. The effect of this source at a later time at a point x is obtained by multiplying by the Green's function, which describes how the material (or heat) diffuses away from the point x'. The density (or temperature) at time τ at the point x is obtained by linear superposition of the effects at x due to all sources at the different points x'—that is, by integrating over the source.

Now suppose that we want to solve an equation of the form

$$H\phi + \frac{\partial \phi}{\partial \tau} = F(\mathbf{r}, \tau) \; . \tag{7.131}$$

We would like to find a Green's function such that

$$\phi(\mathbf{r}, \tau) = \phi_0(\mathbf{r}, \tau) + \int G(\mathbf{r}, \mathbf{r}', \tau, \tau') F(\mathbf{r}', \tau') \, d^3r \, d\tau' \; , \tag{7.132}$$

where $\phi_0(\mathbf{r}, \tau)$ is a solution of the homogeneous equation. In the case of the heat equation or the diffusion equation, we might have a source of heat or a source of diffusing material which continuously varies in time described by the function $F(\mathbf{r}, \tau)$. In Schrödinger's equation, $F(\mathbf{r}, \tau)$ might represent a perturbation of some sort, such as an electromagnetic wave incident on a quantum mechanical system.

What is the relationship between the function $G_1(\mathbf{r}, \mathbf{r}', \tau, \tau')$ discussed above and a Green's function of the type required in Eq. (7.132)? First of all, the function $G(\mathbf{r}, \mathbf{r}', \tau, \tau')$ in Eq. (7.132) must satisfy

$$\left(H + \frac{\partial}{\partial \tau}\right) G(\mathbf{r}, \mathbf{r}', \tau, \tau') = \delta^3(\mathbf{r} - \mathbf{r}')\delta(\tau - \tau') \; , \tag{7.133}$$

whereas G_1 satisfies

$$\left(H + \frac{\partial}{\partial \tau}\right) G_1(\mathbf{r}, \mathbf{r}', \tau, \tau') = 0 \; . \tag{7.133'}$$

Now G_1 has one particularly interesting property which was emphasized above, namely,

$$\lim_{\tau \to \tau'} G_1(\mathbf{r}, \mathbf{r}', \tau, \tau') = \delta^3(\mathbf{r} - \mathbf{r}') \; , \tag{7.134}$$

according to Eq. (7.122). This suggests that if we can introduce a discontinuity in G_1 at $\tau = \tau'$, we may be able to satisfy Eq. (7.133). Since G must satisfy Eq. (7.134) everywhere except at $\mathbf{r} = \mathbf{r}'$, $\tau = \tau'$, it seems reasonable to try the modification

$$G(\mathbf{r}, \mathbf{r}', \tau, \tau') = G_1(\mathbf{r}, \mathbf{r}', \tau, \tau')\theta(\tau - \tau'); \tag{7.135}$$

that is, for $\tau > \tau'$, $G(\mathbf{r}, \mathbf{r}', \tau, \tau')$ is just equal to $G_1(\mathbf{r}, \mathbf{r}', \tau, \tau')$, but for $\tau < \tau'$, $G(\mathbf{r}, \mathbf{r}', \tau, \tau') = 0$. We now compute

$$\left(H + \frac{\partial}{\partial\tau}\right)G(\mathbf{r}, \mathbf{r}', \tau, \tau')$$

$$= H[G_1(\mathbf{r}, \mathbf{r}', \tau, \tau')\theta(\tau - \tau')] + \frac{\partial}{\partial\tau}[G_1(\mathbf{r}, \mathbf{r}', \tau, \tau')\theta(\tau - \tau')]$$

$$= \theta(\tau - \tau')HG_1(\mathbf{r}, \mathbf{r}', \tau, \tau') + \theta(\tau - \tau')\frac{\partial}{\partial\tau}G_1(\mathbf{r}, \mathbf{r}', \tau, \tau')$$

$$+ G_1(\mathbf{r}, \mathbf{r}', \tau, \tau')\frac{\partial}{\partial\tau}\theta(\tau - \tau')$$

$$= \theta(\tau - \tau')\left[H + \frac{\partial}{\partial\tau}\right]G_1(\mathbf{r}, \mathbf{r}', \tau, \tau') + G_1(\mathbf{r}, \mathbf{r}', \tau, \tau')\delta(\tau - \tau'),$$

since by Eq. (7.22),

$$\frac{\partial}{\partial\tau}\theta(\tau - \tau') = \delta(\tau - \tau').$$

Using Eq. (7.133'), we then have

$$\left(H + \frac{\partial}{\partial\tau}\right)G(\mathbf{r}, \mathbf{r}', \tau, \tau') = G_1(\mathbf{r}, \mathbf{r}', \tau, \tau')\delta(\tau - \tau').$$

But since $\delta(\tau - \tau')$ is zero except at $\tau = \tau'$, we are only interested in $G_1(\mathbf{r}, \mathbf{r}', \tau, \tau')$ at $\tau = \tau'$, which by Eq. (7.134) is just $\delta^3(\mathbf{r} - \mathbf{r}')$. Thus we have the desired result,

$$\left(H + \frac{\partial}{\partial\tau}\right)G(\mathbf{r}, \mathbf{r}', \tau, \tau') = \delta^3(\mathbf{r} - \mathbf{r}')\delta(\tau - \tau').$$

Using Eq. (7.135), we see that the solution to Eq. (7.131) is given by

$$\psi(\mathbf{r}, \tau) = \psi_0(\mathbf{r}, \tau) + \int d^3r' \int_{-\infty}^{\tau} d\tau' \, G_1(\mathbf{r}, \mathbf{r}', \tau, \tau')F(\mathbf{r}', \tau'). \tag{7.136}$$

The object G_1 is seen to be very nearly a Green's function, in our original sense of the word. Since $F(\mathbf{r}, \tau)$ represents the effect of a known source of heat or diffusing material, once G_1 has been determined we need only evaluate the integrals in question.

A different situation arises in quantum mechanics, where Schrödinger's time-dependent equation has the form

$$\left(H + \frac{\partial}{\partial\tau}\right)\Psi(\mathbf{r}, \tau) = -\frac{2m}{\hbar^2}U(\mathbf{r}, \tau)\Psi(\mathbf{r}, \tau);$$

in the simplest case H might be given by $H = -\nabla^2$ and $\tau = i\hbar t/2m$. Thus we obtain from Eq. (7.136) Schrödinger's time-dependent integral equation

$$\Psi(\mathbf{r}, \tau) = \Psi_0(\mathbf{r}, \tau) - \frac{2m}{\hbar^2} \int d^3r' \int_{-i\infty}^{\tau} d\tau'\, G(\mathbf{r}, \mathbf{r}', \tau, \tau')\, U(\mathbf{r}', \tau')\Psi(\mathbf{r}', \tau') ,$$

$$(7.137)$$

where the integral is along the imaginary axis, since $\tau = i\hbar t/2m$ is pure imaginary.

When $U(\mathbf{r}, \tau)$ represents a perturbation like an oscillating electromagnetic field, Eq. (7.137) leads to the theory of transition probabilities and the "Fermi Golden Rule."

We can also use Eq. (7.137) to obtain a different perspective on the work of previous sections. Suppose that $U(\mathbf{r}, \tau)$ is a static (time-independent) potential. Then we would expect to see Eq. (7.137) reduce to the Lippmann-Schwinger equation (7.68). However, rather than simply replacing $U(\mathbf{r}, \tau)$ by $V(\mathbf{r})$, let us imagine that in the very remote past $U(\mathbf{r}, \tau)$ was "turned off" and that we slowly allowed $U(\mathbf{r}, \tau)$ to be "turned on." We may express this by writing

$$U(\mathbf{r}, \tau) = V(\mathbf{r})e^{\epsilon' t} = V(\mathbf{r})e^{-i\epsilon\tau}; \qquad (7.138)$$

by making the real quantity $\epsilon' = \hbar\epsilon/2m$ small enough, we can approximate a static potential arbitrarily well. Clearly, this should have no effect on any physically realistic scattering problem. If we take $H = -\nabla^2$, as we have done before in discussing scattering, then by direct analogy with Eq. (7.127)

$$G_1(\mathbf{r}, \mathbf{r}', \tau, \tau') = (1/(2\pi)^3) \int dk_x\, dk_y\, dk_z$$

$$\times \exp\{i[k_x(x - x') + k_y(y - y') + k_z(z - z')]\}$$

$$\times \exp[-(k_x^2 + k_y^2 + k_z^2)(\tau - \tau')]$$

where we imagine that we have put our system in a large rectangular box and afterwards let the sides become arbitrarily large. In spherical coordinates, this result appears as

$$G_1(\mathbf{r}, \mathbf{r}', \tau, \tau') = \frac{1}{(2\pi)^3} \int e^{i\mathbf{k}\cdot(\mathbf{r}-\mathbf{r}')} e^{-k^2(\tau-\tau')}\, d^3k . \qquad (7.139)$$

Putting Eq. (7.139) and Eq. (7.138) for $U(\mathbf{r}, \tau)$ into Eq. (7.137), we get

$$\Psi(\mathbf{r}, \tau) = \Psi_0(\mathbf{r}, \tau)$$

$$- (2m/\hbar^2(2\pi)^3) \int d^3r' \int d^3k \int_{-i\infty}^{\tau} d\tau'\, e^{i\mathbf{k}\cdot(\mathbf{r}-\mathbf{r}')}$$

$$\times e^{-k^2(\tau-\tau')} V(\mathbf{r}')e^{-i\epsilon\tau'}\Psi(\mathbf{r}', \tau') \qquad (7.140)$$

with

$$\Psi_0(\mathbf{r}, \tau) = Ce^{i\mathbf{k}_i\cdot\mathbf{r}}e^{-k_i^2\tau} ,$$

where k_i is the wave number of the incident wave. Let us look for a solution of the form

$$\Psi(\mathbf{r}, \tau) = \phi(\mathbf{r})e^{-k_i^2\tau} .$$

With this substitution, Eq. (7.140) becomes

$$\phi(\mathbf{r})e^{-k_i^2\tau} = Ce^{i\mathbf{k}_i\cdot\mathbf{r}}e^{-k_i^2\tau}$$
$$- \frac{2m}{\hbar^2}\int d^3\mathbf{r}'\, \frac{1}{(2\pi)^3}\int d^3\mathbf{k}\,e^{i\mathbf{k}\cdot(\mathbf{r}-\mathbf{r}')}\,V(\mathbf{r}')\phi(\mathbf{r}')$$
$$\times e^{-k^2\tau}\int_{-i\infty}^{\tau} e^{(k^2-k_i^2-i\epsilon)\tau'}\,d\tau' \tag{7.141}$$

Now,

$$\int_{-i\infty}^{\tau} e^{(k^2-k_i^2-i\epsilon)\tau'}\,d\tau' = \frac{e^{(k^2-k_i^2-i\epsilon)\tau}}{(k^2 - k_i^2 - i\epsilon)} ; \tag{7.142}$$

the lower limit of integration gives a vanishing contribution because the perturbation was switched on adiabatically via the term $\exp(-i\epsilon\tau)$. Putting Eq. (7.142) into Eq. (7.141) and canceling a common factor of $\exp(-k_i^2\tau)$, we get

$$\phi(\mathbf{r}) = Ce^{i\mathbf{k}_i\cdot\mathbf{r}} - \frac{2m}{\hbar^2}\int d^3\mathbf{r}'\,V(\mathbf{r}')\phi(\mathbf{r}')\,\frac{1}{(2\pi)^3}$$
$$\times \int \frac{e^{i\mathbf{k}\cdot(\mathbf{r}-\mathbf{r}')}}{(k^2 - k_i^2 - i\epsilon)}\,e^{-i\epsilon\tau}\,d^3\mathbf{k} . \tag{7.143}$$

The integral

$$I(\mathbf{r}, \mathbf{r}') = -\frac{1}{(2\pi)^3}\int \frac{e^{i\mathbf{k}\cdot(\mathbf{r}-\mathbf{r}')}}{(k^2 - k_i^2 - i\epsilon)}\,d^3\mathbf{k}$$

is precisely the *outgoing spherical wave* Green's function $G_+(\mathbf{r}, \mathbf{r}')$ obtained for the operator $-\nabla^2 - k_i^2$ in Section 7.4 (Eq. 7.66). Thus

$$I(\mathbf{r}, \mathbf{r}') = -\frac{1}{4\pi}\,\frac{\exp[i(k_i + i\epsilon/2k_i)|\mathbf{r} - \mathbf{r}'|]}{|\mathbf{r} - \mathbf{r}'|} .$$

We now let $\epsilon \to 0$ and find that

$$\phi(\mathbf{r}) = Ce^{i\mathbf{k}_i\cdot\mathbf{r}} - \frac{m}{2\pi\hbar^2}\int \frac{e^{ik_i|\mathbf{r}-\mathbf{r}'|}}{|\mathbf{r} - \mathbf{r}'|}\,V(\mathbf{r}')\phi(\mathbf{r}')\,d^3\mathbf{r}' ,$$

which agrees with the Lippmann-Schwinger equation for ϕ_+ which we derived earlier, Eq. (7.68). Thus in the limit of a static potential, the time-dependent formalism goes over to the form we should expect, with the prescription we used earlier for avoiding singularities being automatically provided. We now see that this prescription can be thought of as arising from the physically reasonable assumption that at sufficiently remote times in the past there is no interaction, just a free particle.

7.8 THE WAVE EQUATION

As a final example of the Green's function technique, we investigate the Lorentz-invariant, time-dependent wave equation. This is the basic equation of electro-dynamics, and its properties have been exhaustively analyzed.

The homogeneous wave equation is

$$\Box^2\psi \equiv \nabla^2\psi - \frac{1}{c^2}\frac{\partial^2\psi}{\partial t^2} = 0 \; . \tag{7.144}$$

For the sake of generality, we write this in the form

$$H\psi + \frac{\partial^2\psi}{\partial\tau^2} = 0 \; , \tag{7.145}$$

where, in this case, $\tau = ct$ and $H = -\nabla^2$. For the moment, let us imagine that H is a general linear operator with a complete orthonormal set of eigenfunctions ϕ_n which satisfy

$$H\phi_n = \lambda_n\phi_n \; . \tag{7.146}$$

Then we look for a solution of Eq. (7.145) in the form

$$\psi(\mathbf{r}, \tau) = \sum_n A_n(\tau)\phi_n(\mathbf{r}) \; . \tag{7.147}$$

Using Eq. (7.146) and Eq. (7.147), we find

$$H\psi + \frac{\partial^2\psi}{\partial\tau^2} = \sum_n (A_n\lambda_n + \ddot{A}_n)\phi_n = 0 \; . \tag{7.148}$$

Since the eigenfunctions of H form a complete orthonormal set, we conclude from Eq. (7.148) that

$$\ddot{A}_n(\tau) + \lambda_n A_n(\tau) = 0 \; .$$

Hence

$$A_n(\tau) = a_n e^{i\sqrt{\lambda_n}\tau} + b_n e^{-i\sqrt{\lambda_n}\tau} \; ,$$

and

$$\psi(\mathbf{r}, \tau) = \sum_n (a_n e^{i\sqrt{\lambda_n}\tau} + b_n e^{-i\sqrt{\lambda_n}\tau})\phi_n(\mathbf{r}) \; . \tag{7.149}$$

The constants a_n and b_n must be determined from the boundary conditions, which we assume to be of the familiar type; that is, $\psi(\mathbf{r}, 0)$ and $\dot{\psi}(\mathbf{r}, 0)$ are specified. Then

$$\psi(\mathbf{r}, 0) = \sum_n (a_n + b_n)\phi_n(\mathbf{r}) \; ,$$

$$\dot{\psi}(\mathbf{r}, 0) = i\sum_n \sqrt{\lambda_n}(a_n - b_n)\phi_n(\mathbf{r}) \; .$$

We find that

$$a_n + b_n = \int \phi_n^*(\mathbf{r}')\psi(\mathbf{r}', 0)\, d^3\mathbf{r}' \,,$$

$$a_n - b_n = -\frac{i}{\sqrt{\lambda_n}} \int \phi_n^*(\mathbf{r}')\dot{\psi}(\mathbf{r}', 0)\, d^3\mathbf{r}' \,,$$

so

$$a_n = \tfrac{1}{2}\left[\int \phi_n^*(\mathbf{r}')\psi(\mathbf{r}', 0)\, d^3\mathbf{r}' + \frac{1}{i\sqrt{\lambda_n}} \int \phi_n^*(\mathbf{r}')\dot{\psi}(\mathbf{r}', 0)\, d^3\mathbf{r}' \right],$$

$$b_n = \tfrac{1}{2}\left[\int \phi_n^*(\mathbf{r}')\psi(\mathbf{r}', 0)\, d^3\mathbf{r}' - \frac{1}{i\sqrt{\lambda_n}} \int \phi_n^*(\mathbf{r}')\dot{\psi}(\mathbf{r}', 0)\, d^3\mathbf{r}' \right].$$

Inserting these values for a_n and b_n into Eq. (7.149), we get

$$\psi(\mathbf{r}, \tau) = \int \sum_n \cos(\sqrt{\lambda_n}\tau)\phi_n(\mathbf{r})\phi_n^*(\mathbf{r}')\psi(\mathbf{r}', 0)\, d^3\mathbf{r}'$$

$$+ \int \sum_n \sin(\sqrt{\lambda_n}\tau)\frac{1}{\sqrt{\lambda_n}}\phi_n(\mathbf{r})\phi_n^*(\mathbf{r}')\dot{\psi}(\mathbf{r}', 0)\, d^3\mathbf{r}' \,.$$

In keeping with the notation of the previous section, let us write this as

$$\psi(\mathbf{r}, \tau) = \int G_2(\mathbf{r}, \mathbf{r}', \tau)\psi(\mathbf{r}', 0)\, d^3\mathbf{r}' + \int \tilde{G}_2(\mathbf{r}, \mathbf{r}', \tau)\dot{\psi}(\mathbf{r}', 0)\, d^3\mathbf{r}' \,, \qquad (7.150)$$

where

$$G_2(\mathbf{r}, \mathbf{r}', \tau) = \sum_n \cos(\sqrt{\lambda_n}\tau)\phi_n(\mathbf{r})\phi_n^*(\mathbf{r}') \,, \qquad (7.151a)$$

$$\tilde{G}_2(\mathbf{r}, \mathbf{r}', \tau) = \sum_n \frac{\sin\sqrt{\lambda_n}\tau}{\sqrt{\lambda_n}}\phi_n(\mathbf{r})\phi_n^*(\mathbf{r}') \,. \qquad (7.151b)$$

Since the wave equation is second order in time, two boundary conditions have been required to determine the constants of integration. Hence we have obtained two Green's functions, one which acts on $\psi(\mathbf{r}, 0)$, the other which acts on $\dot{\psi}(\mathbf{r}, 0)$. For the first-order (in time) heat or diffusion equation, only one boundary condition is needed, and hence we found only one Green's function which acted on $\psi(\mathbf{r}, 0)$. Just as the Green's function obtained in the last section satisfied the heat equation, so both of our Green's functions, G_2 and $\tilde{G}_2$, satisfy the wave equation;

$$\Box^2 G_2(\mathbf{r}, \mathbf{r}', \tau) = 0 \,, \qquad \Box^2 \tilde{G}_2(\mathbf{r}, \mathbf{r}', \tau) = 0 \,.$$

Thus $\psi(\mathbf{r}, \tau)$ satisfies the wave equation. Note also that

$$G_2(\mathbf{r}, \mathbf{r}', \tau) = \frac{d}{d\tau}\tilde{G}_2(\mathbf{r}, \mathbf{r}'. \tau) \,,$$

so that if we can calculate $\tilde{G}_2$, then G_2 can be obtained directly from it. The boundary conditions are clearly satisfied by the solution given in Eq. (7.150) since

$$G_2(\mathbf{r}, \mathbf{r}', 0) = \sum_n \phi_n(\mathbf{r})\phi_n^*(\mathbf{r}') = \delta^3(\mathbf{r} - \mathbf{r}') \, . \tag{7.152}$$

With these general results in mind, let us return to the specific case of the wave equation, and start by considering a region defined by a rectangular parallelepiped with sides L_1, L_2, and L_3 in the x, y- and z-directions, respectively. If we have periodic boundary conditions, the eigenfunctions of $H = -\nabla^2$ may be written as

$$\phi_{n_1 n_2 n_3}(\mathbf{r}) = \frac{1}{\sqrt{L_1 L_2 L_3}} e^{ik_x x} e^{ik_y y} e^{ik_z z} \, ,$$

where

$$k_x = \frac{2\pi n_1}{L_1}, \qquad k_y = \frac{2\pi n_2}{L_2}, \qquad k_z = \frac{2\pi n_3}{L_3},$$

and the eigenvalues are given simply by

$$\lambda_{n_1 n_2 n_3} = k_x^2 + k_y^2 + k_z^2 \, .$$

Let us now write $\tilde{G}_2$ in terms of these quantities. According to Eq. (7.151b),

$$\tilde{G}_2(\mathbf{r}, \mathbf{r}', \tau) = \frac{1}{L_1 L_2 L_3} \sum_{n_1, n_2, n_3}^{\infty} \frac{\sin \sqrt{k_x^2 + k_y^2 + k_z^2}\,\tau}{\sqrt{k_x^2 + k_y^2 + k_z^2}} e^{ik_x(x-x')} e^{ik_y(y-y')} e^{ik_z(z-z')} \, .$$

Now we can move to the limit in which the box becomes arbitrarily large, as we did before. Then

$$\frac{1}{L_1} \sum_{n_1=-\infty}^{\infty} \to \frac{1}{2\pi} \int_{-\infty}^{\infty} dk_x$$

and similarly for the sums on n_2 and n_3. Hence, in the limit of very large dimensions,

$$\tilde{G}_2(\mathbf{r}, \mathbf{r}', \tau) = \frac{1}{(2\pi)^3} \int_{-\infty}^{\infty} dk_x \int_{-\infty}^{\infty} dk_y \int_{-\infty}^{\infty} dk_z \frac{\sin k\tau}{k} e^{i\mathbf{k} \cdot (\mathbf{r}-\mathbf{r}')} \, ,$$

where $\mathbf{k} = k_x \mathbf{i} + k_y \mathbf{j} + k_z \mathbf{k}$ and $k^2 = k_x^2 + k_y^2 + k_z^2$. It will clearly be advantageous to evaluate this integral by using spherical coordinates. Setting $\mathbf{r} - \mathbf{r}' \equiv \boldsymbol{\rho}$, we get

$$\tilde{G}_2(\mathbf{r}, \mathbf{r}', \tau) = \frac{1}{(2\pi)^3} \int_0^{\infty} dk \cdot k^2 \sin k\tau \cdot \frac{1}{k} \int_0^{\pi} \sin \theta_k \, d\theta_k \int_0^{2\pi} d\phi_k e^{i\mathbf{k} \cdot \boldsymbol{\rho}} \, .$$

Since the integral is independent of the direction of $\boldsymbol{\rho}$, let us for convenience choose $\boldsymbol{\rho}$ to be in the z-direction. Then $\mathbf{k} \cdot \boldsymbol{\rho} = k\rho \cos \theta_k$, and making the change of variable $x = \cos \theta_k$, we have

$$\tilde{G}_2(\mathbf{r}, \mathbf{r}', \tau) = \frac{1}{(2\pi)^3} \int_0^\infty dk \cdot k \sin k\tau \int_{-1}^1 dx \int_0^{2\pi} d\phi_k e^{ik\rho x}$$

$$= \frac{1}{2\pi^2 \rho} \int_0^\infty \sin k\tau \sin k\rho \, dk$$

$$= \frac{1}{4\pi^2 \rho} \int_{-\infty}^\infty \sin k\tau \sin k\rho \, dk$$

$$= \frac{1}{8\pi^2 \rho} \int_{-\infty}^\infty [\cos k(\rho - \tau) - \cos k(\rho + \tau)] \, dk .$$

Since

$$\delta(x) = \frac{1}{2\pi} \int_{-\infty}^\infty \cos xy \, dy$$

(this follows immediately from Eq. 5.63), we get finally

$$\tilde{G}_2(\mathbf{r}, \mathbf{r}', \tau) = \frac{1}{4\pi\rho} [\delta(\rho - \tau) - \delta(\rho + \tau)] .$$

In terms of the original variables, this is

$$\tilde{G}_2(\mathbf{r}, \mathbf{r}', t) = \frac{1}{4\pi|\mathbf{r} - \mathbf{r}'|} [\delta(|\mathbf{r} - \mathbf{r}'| - ct) - \delta(|\mathbf{r} - \mathbf{r}'| + ct)] . \quad (7.153)$$

Clearly, our choice of $t = 0$ as the initial time was arbitrary. The reader can check that if we choose t' as the initial time, then

$$\psi(\mathbf{r}, t) = \int G_2(\mathbf{r}, \mathbf{r}', t, t') \psi(\mathbf{r}', t') \, d^3r'$$

$$+ \int \tilde{G}_2(\mathbf{r}, \mathbf{r}', t, t') \dot{\psi}(\mathbf{r}', t') \, d^3r' , \quad (7.154)$$

where

$$\tilde{G}_2(\mathbf{r}, \mathbf{r}', t, t') = \sum_n \frac{\sin [\sqrt{\lambda_n} c(t - t')]}{\sqrt{\lambda_n}} \phi_n(\mathbf{r}) \phi_n^*(\mathbf{r}') , \quad (7.155a)$$

and

$$G_2(\mathbf{r}, \mathbf{r}', t, t') = \sum_n \cos [\sqrt{\lambda_n} c(t - t')] \phi_n(\mathbf{r}) \phi_n^*(\mathbf{r}')$$

$$= \frac{1}{c} \frac{d}{dt} \tilde{G}_2(\mathbf{r}, \mathbf{r}', t, t') , \quad (7.155b)$$

For the case of the wave equation, $H = -\nabla^2$, $\tilde{G}_2$ is given by

$$\tilde{G}_2(\mathbf{r}, \mathbf{r}', t, t') = \frac{1}{4\pi|\mathbf{r} - \mathbf{r}'|} \{\delta[|\mathbf{r} - \mathbf{r}'| - c(t - t')]$$

$$- \delta[|\mathbf{r} - \mathbf{r}'| + c(t - t')]\} . \quad (7.156)$$

This gives the solution to the homogeneous wave equation, once the boundary conditions are specified.

However, just as in the case of the first-order equation studied in the last section, the inhomogeneous equation is very important. In classical electrodynamics, for example, Eq. (7.144) corresponds to a situation where no sources or currents are present. However, in general, one is interested in cases where there are currents and charges present. Thus, typically, we would like to be able to solve

$$\Box^2\psi \equiv \nabla^2\psi - \frac{1}{c^2}\frac{\partial^2\psi}{\partial t^2} = \frac{4\pi}{c}j(\mathbf{r}, t) , \tag{7.157}$$

or, in general,

$$H\psi + \frac{\partial^2\psi}{\partial\tau^2} = J(\mathbf{r}, \tau) . \tag{7.158}$$

Now, to solve Eq. (7.158), we need a Green's function $G(\mathbf{r}, \mathbf{r}', \tau, \tau')$ which satisfies

$$\left(H + \frac{\partial^2}{\partial\tau^2}\right)G(\mathbf{r}, \mathbf{r}', \tau, \tau') = \delta^3(\mathbf{r} - \mathbf{r}')\delta(\tau - \tau') .$$

Neither G_2 nor $\tilde{G}_2$ has this property; in fact, letting $\mathscr{G}$ stand for either G_2 or $\tilde{G}_2$,

$$\left(H + \frac{\partial^2}{\partial\tau^2}\right)\mathscr{G} = 0 . \tag{7.159}$$

However, let us be guided by our experience in the previous section and look for G in the form

$$G_R(\mathbf{r}, \mathbf{r}', \tau, \tau') = \mathscr{G}(\mathbf{r}, \mathbf{r}', \tau, \tau')\theta(\tau - \tau') .$$

We have

$$\left(H + \frac{\partial^2}{\partial\tau^2}\right)G_R(\mathbf{r}, \mathbf{r}', \tau, \tau')$$

$$= \theta(\tau - \tau')H\mathscr{G} + \frac{\partial^2}{\partial\tau^2}[\mathscr{G}\theta(\tau - \tau')]$$

$$= \theta(\tau - \tau')\left(H + \frac{\partial^2}{\partial\tau^2}\right)\mathscr{G} + 2\dot{\theta}(\tau - \tau')\dot{\mathscr{G}} + \mathscr{G}\ddot{\theta}(\tau - \tau') ,$$

where a dot indicates differentiation with respect to τ. By Eq. (7.159), this is just

$$\left(H + \frac{\partial^2}{\partial\tau^2}\right)G_R = 2\dot{\theta}(\tau - \tau')\dot{\mathscr{G}} + \mathscr{G}\ddot{\theta}(\tau - \tau') .$$

But $\dot{\theta}(\tau - \tau') = \delta(\tau - \tau')$, so

$$\left(H + \frac{\partial^2}{\partial\tau^2}\right)G_R(\mathbf{r}, \mathbf{r}', \tau, \tau')$$

$$= 2\delta(\tau - \tau')\dot{\mathscr{G}}(\mathbf{r}, \mathbf{r}', \tau, \tau') + \dot{\delta}(\tau - \tau')\mathscr{G}(\mathbf{r}, \mathbf{r}', \tau, \tau') ,$$

From the results of Section 7.2,

$$\delta(\tau - \tau')\, \dot{\mathscr{G}}(\mathbf{r}, \mathbf{r}', \tau, \tau') = [\,\dot{\mathscr{G}}(\mathbf{r}, \mathbf{r}', \tau, \tau')]_{\tau'=\tau}\,\delta(\tau - \tau')\ ,$$

$$\dot{\delta}(\tau - \tau')\, \mathscr{G}(\mathbf{r}, \mathbf{r}', \tau, \tau') = -[\,\dot{\mathscr{G}}(\mathbf{r}, \mathbf{r}', \tau, \tau')]_{\tau'=\tau}\,\delta(\tau - \tau')\ .$$

Thus

$$\left(H + \frac{\partial^2}{\partial \tau^2}\right) G_R(\mathbf{r}, \mathbf{r}', \tau, \tau') = \delta(\tau - \tau')[\,\dot{\mathscr{G}}(\mathbf{r}, \mathbf{r}', \tau, \tau')]_{\tau'=\tau}\ . \qquad (7.160)$$

If $\mathscr{G} = G_2$, the right-hand side of Eq. (7.160) vanishes by Eq. (7.155b), but if $\mathscr{G} = \tilde{G}_2$, then according to Eq. (7.155a) we get

$$\left(H + \frac{\partial^2}{\partial \tau^2}\right) G_R(\mathbf{r}, \mathbf{r}', \tau, \tau') = \delta(\tau - \tau')\delta^3(\mathbf{r} - \mathbf{r}')\ ,$$

which is the desired form. Hence the Green's function for the homogeneous equation is

$$G_R(\mathbf{r}, \mathbf{r}', \tau, \tau') = \theta(\tau - \tau')\tilde{G}_2(\mathbf{r}, \mathbf{r}', \tau, \tau')\ , \qquad (7.161)$$

and the solution to Eq. (7.158) can be written as

$$\psi_R(\mathbf{r}, \tau) = \psi_0(\mathbf{r}, \tau) + \int d^3r' \int_{-\infty}^{\tau} d\tau'\, \tilde{G}_2(\mathbf{r}, \mathbf{r}', \tau, \tau')J(\mathbf{r}', \tau')\ , \qquad (7.162)$$

where $\psi_0(\mathbf{r}, \tau)$ is a solution of the homogeneous equation.

Now for the special case of the wave equation, $\tilde{G}_2$ is given by Eq. (7.156); therefore, since G_R vanishes for $\tau < \tau'$, we may write

$$G_R(\mathbf{r}, \mathbf{r}', \tau, \tau') = \frac{1}{4\pi|\mathbf{r} - \mathbf{r}'|}\,\delta(|\mathbf{r} - \mathbf{r}'| - (\tau - \tau'))\theta(\tau - \tau')\ ,$$

for when $\tau > \tau'$ the argument of the second δ-function in Eq. (7.156) is always nonzero. Since $\delta(|\mathbf{r} - \mathbf{r}'| - (\tau - \tau'))$ has zero argument only when $\tau > \tau'$, we may drop the factor $\theta(\tau - \tau')$ from G_R so that finally

$$G_R(\mathbf{r}, \mathbf{r}', \tau, \tau') = \frac{1}{4\pi|\mathbf{r} - \mathbf{r}'|}\,\delta(|\mathbf{r} - \mathbf{r}'| - (\tau - \tau'))\ . \qquad (7.163)$$

Thus the solution to the wave equation is

$$\psi_R(\mathbf{r}, \tau) = \psi_0(\mathbf{r}, \tau)$$

$$+ \frac{1}{4\pi} \int d^3r' \int_{-\infty}^{\infty} d\tau'\, \frac{1}{|\mathbf{r} - \mathbf{r}'|}\,\delta(|\mathbf{r} - \mathbf{r}'| - (\tau - \tau'))J(\mathbf{r}', \tau')\ .$$

The τ integration can be done immediately, giving

$$\psi_R(\mathbf{r}, \tau) = \psi_0(\mathbf{r}, \tau) + \frac{1}{4\pi} \int \frac{[J(\mathbf{r}', \tau')]_{\text{ret}}}{|\mathbf{r} - \mathbf{r}'|}\, d^3r'$$

where the bracket [ ]$_{\text{ret}}$ means that the time τ' is to be evaluated at the *retarded* time

$$\tau' = \tau - |\mathbf{r} - \mathbf{r}'| .$$

Writing this in terms of the time t, we have

$$\psi_R(\mathbf{r}, t) = \psi_0(\mathbf{r}, t) + \frac{1}{4\pi} \int \frac{[J(\mathbf{r}', t')]_{\text{ret}}}{|\mathbf{r} - \mathbf{r}'|} d^3\mathbf{r}' , \qquad (7.164)$$

where in the bracket

$$t' = t - \frac{|\mathbf{r} - \mathbf{r}'|}{c} .$$

This is one of the most beautiful results in electromagnetic theory. It tells us that an observer at the field point $\mathbf{r}$ is affected at a given time t only by what a source at $\mathbf{r}'$ was doing at an earlier time t'; furthermore, this earlier time t' precedes the present time t by just the amount of time it takes a wave to travel from the source point $\mathbf{r}'$ to the field point $\mathbf{r}$, namely, $|\mathbf{r} - \mathbf{r}'|/c$. In general, an effect at one point in space-time is due to all disturbances throughout space which preceded the effect by exactly the amount of time necessary for the disturbances to propagate from their points of origin to the point where their effects are felt. ψ_R is referred to as the *retarded* solution to the inhomogeneous wave equation and G_R is called the *retarded* Green's function: hence the subscript R.

This is by no means the only Green's function that we could have defined. For example, we could write

$$G_A(\mathbf{r}, \mathbf{r}', \tau, \tau') = -\theta(\tau' - \tau)_2\tilde{G}(\mathbf{r}, \mathbf{r}', \tau, \tau') .$$

We leave it to the reader to show that this is also a Green's function for the inhomogeneous wave equation (called the *advanced* Green's function), and to show that the solution obtained from G_A corresponds to the effects of disturbances propagating back from the future to the present.

PROBLEMS

1. Show that the Green's functions of Eqs. (7.9′) and (7.11′) satisfy

$$\frac{d^2G(x, x')}{dx^2} = \delta(x - x') .$$

2. Show that

$$\frac{d\delta(x)}{dx} = -\delta(x) \frac{d}{dx}$$

when both elements of the equation are considered to operate on a function in an integrand; i.e., we really mean

$$\int_{-a}^{b} \frac{d\delta(x)}{dx} f(x) \, dx = -\int_{-a}^{b} \delta(x) \frac{df}{dx} \, dx$$

for any $f(x)$ with a continuous derivative.

3. Show that if H is a real, Hermitian operator (that is, $H = H^*$, $H = H^\dagger$) then the Green's function for the inhomogeneous equation

$$H\phi(x) = f(x)$$

is symmetric, that is, $G(x, x') = G(x', x)$.

[*Hint*: Show that the eigenfunctions of a real, Hermitian operator can always be chosen to be real.]

4. Show that the Green's function of Eq. (7.35) satisfies Eq. (7.36).

5. In Section 6.9 we discussed those solutions of Bessel's equation,

$$x^2 \frac{d^2 J_n}{dx^2} + x \frac{dJ_n}{dx} + (x^2 - n^2)J_n = 0 \,,$$

which were finite at the origin. In particular, we chose a normalization such that for small x

$$J_n(x) \cong \frac{1}{n!}\left(\frac{x}{2}\right)^n .$$

There is, of course, another set of solutions, usually denoted by $N_n(x)$, which are irregular at the origin. They are conventionally normalized so that

$$N_0(x) \cong \frac{2}{\pi}\ln x \,, \qquad N_n(x) \sim -\frac{1}{\pi}\left(\frac{2}{x}\right)^n (n - 1)!$$

(Note that for small values of x these $N_n(x)$ do indeed satisfy Bessel's equation.)

Consider the inhomogeneous Bessel's equation (for $n \geq 1$)

$$x^2 \frac{d^2 u}{dx^2} + x \frac{du}{dx} + (x^2 - n^2)u = f(x)$$

on the interval $[0, 1]$ with boundary condition $u(0) = 0 = u(1)$. Show that $u(x)$ is given by

$$u(x) = \int_0^1 G(x, x')f(x')\, dx \,,$$

where

$$G(x, x') = -\frac{\pi}{2x' J_n(1)} J_n(x_<)[J_n(x_>)N_n(1) - N_n(x_>)J_n(1)] \,.$$

As usual, $x_>$ is the greater of x and x', and $x_<$ is the lesser of x and x'.

6. Prove that the Wronskian of a second-order linear differential operator never vanishes. Do this by first proving that $W(x)$ cannot be identically equal to zero (because if it were, u_1 and u_2 would be linearly dependent, contrary to assumption). Then, differentiating $W(x)$ and using the fact that u_1 and u_2 are solutions to

$$f_0(x) \frac{d^2 u}{dx^2} + f_1(x) \frac{du}{dx} + f_2(x)u = 0 \,,$$

prove that

$$\frac{dW}{dx} = -\frac{f_1}{f_0} W \,.$$

Integrate this and show that if $f_0(x)$ and $f_1(x)$ are continuous and if $f_0(x)$ never vanishes, then $W(x)$ *never* vanishes.

7. Prove that for *any* linear differential operator of the form

$$f_0(x) \frac{d^n}{dx^n} + f_1(x) \frac{d^{n-1}}{dx^{n-1}} + \cdots + f_n(x) \, ,$$

we have

$$\frac{dW}{dx} = -\frac{f_1}{f_0} W \, ,$$

where W is defined by

$$W(x) = \begin{vmatrix} u_1(x) & u_2(x) & \cdots & u_n(x) \\ u_1^{(1)}(x) & u_2^{(1)}(x) & \cdots & u_n^{(1)}(x) \\ u_1^{(n-1)}(x) & u_2^{(n-1)}(x) & \cdots & u_n^{(n-1)}(x) \end{vmatrix} \, ,$$

$u_1(x), u_2(x), \cdots, u_n(x)$ are the linearly independent solutions of the equations and $u^{(m)}$ denotes the mth derivative of u. Thus $W(x)$ is given by

$$W(x) = C \exp\left[-\int \frac{f_1(x)}{f_0(x)} \, dx \right] .$$

8. Show that the Green's function for the differential operator

$$f_0(x) \frac{d^n}{dx^n} + f_1(x) \frac{d^{n-1}}{dx^{n-1}} + \cdots + f_n(x)$$

is given by

$$G(x, x') = \sum_{m=1}^{n} a_m(x') u_m(x) + \frac{N(x, x')}{f_0(x') W(x')} \theta(x - x') \, ,$$

where $W(x')$ is defined as in the previous problem and

$$N(x, x') = \begin{vmatrix} u_1(x') & u_2(x') & \cdots & u_n(x') \\ u_1^{(1)}(x') & u_2^{(1)}(x') & & u_n^{(1)}(x') \\ \cdot & \cdot & & \cdot \\ \cdot & \cdot & & \cdot \\ \cdot & \cdot & & \cdot \\ u_1^{(n-2)}(x') & u_2^{(n-2)}(x') & & u_n^{(n-2)}(x') \\ u_1(x) & u_2(x) & \cdots & u_n(x) \end{vmatrix} .$$

The $a_m(x')$ are determined by the boundary condition which the Green's function must satisfy. As in Problem 7, $u_1, u_2, \cdots, u_n$ are the n linearly independent solutions of the homogeneous equation.

9. Using the results of the previous problem, find the Green's function for the general third-order linear differential operator,

$$\frac{d^3}{dx^3} + a_2 \frac{d^2}{dx^2} + a_2 \frac{d}{dx} + a_3$$

in terms of the roots, r_1, r_2 and r_3 of the characteristic polynomial

$$z^3 + a_1 z^2 + a_2 z + a_3 = 0 \, .$$

Assume that the Green's function and its first two derivatives vanish at $x = 0$.

10. Schrödinger's equation in one dimension is

$$-\frac{h^2}{2m} \frac{d^2\psi}{dx^2} + V(x)\psi(x) = E\psi(x) \, .$$

Using the methods discussed in Section 7.4, derive a Lippmann-Schwinger integral equation for $\phi(x)$,

a) for the case $E < 0$,   b) for the case $E \geq 0$.

In case (b) you will find separate equations for $\psi_+(x)$ and $\psi_-(x)$ corresponding to different types of boundary conditions at infinity. Discuss the meaning of $\psi_+(x)$ and $\psi_-(x)$.

11. Solve Problem 10 by using the method of Section 7.3. What is the appropriate statement of boundary conditions to specify the Green's function completely in this case?

12. a) By making the change of variable $\phi_l(x) = f_l(x)/\sqrt{x}$ in Eq. (7.81), show that the following equation is obtained for $f_l(x)$:

$$x^2 f_l''(x) + x f_l'(x) + [x^2 - (l + 1/2)^2] f_l(x) = 0.$$

b) Using the results of Section 6.9, show that

$$j_l(x) \propto \frac{1}{\sqrt{x}} J_{l+1/2}(x),$$

where J denotes a Bessel function [see the discussion following Eq. (7.88b')].

13. a) Show that the Green's function

$$G(t, t') = \frac{1}{2\omega_0 i} e^{i\omega_0 |t - t'|}$$

satisfies

$$\left(\frac{d^2}{dt^2} + \omega_0^2\right) G(t, t') = \delta(t - t').$$

This Green's function was used in Problem 7.10 to convert Schrödinger's differential equation into the Lippmann-Schwinger integral equation.

b) Show that a general solution to the equation

$$\ddot{X}(t) + \omega_0^2 X(t) = F(t)$$

can be written in terms of the function $G(t, t')$ above as

$$X(t) = A \cos \omega_0 t + B \sin \omega_0 t + \int_{-\infty}^{\infty} G(t, t') F(t') \, dt',$$

where A and B are to be determined in terms of the boundary conditions. For classical mechanical one-point boundary conditions, they will clearly depend on F. Show that if we require $x(0) = x_0$ and $\dot{x}(0) = 0$, then the equation reduces to the familiar result

$$X(t) = x_0 \cos \omega_0 t + \frac{1}{\omega_0} \int_0^t \sin \omega_0 (t - t') F(t') \, dt'.$$

Clearly, for one-point boundary conditions, it is easier to start with $(1/\omega_0) \times \theta(t - t') \sin \omega_0 (t - t')$ as Green's function, but it is not necessary to do so.

14. Show from Eq. (7.98) that

$$e^{i\mathbf{k} \cdot \mathbf{r}} = \sum_{l=0}^{\infty} i^l (2l + 1) j_l(kr) P_l (\cos \theta),$$

where θ is the angle between $\mathbf{k}$ and $\mathbf{r}$.

[*Hint*: Consider Eq. (7.98) in the limit $|\mathbf{r}'| \to \infty$.]

15. Making use of Eqs. (7.98), (7.86), (7.84a) and (5.83), show that if we choose

$$\xi(\mathbf{r}) = \frac{A}{(2\pi)^{3/2}} e^{i\mathbf{k}\cdot\mathbf{r}}$$

$$- \frac{4imk}{\hbar^2} \sum_{l=0}^{\infty} \sum_{m=-\infty}^{\infty} j_l(kr) Y_{lm}(\theta, \phi) \int j_l(kr') Y_{lm}^*(\theta', \phi') V(\mathbf{r}') \psi(\mathbf{r}')\, d\mathbf{r}',$$

then the equation

$$\psi(\mathbf{r}) = \xi(\mathbf{r}) - \frac{m}{2\pi\hbar^2} \int \frac{e^{-ik|\mathbf{r}-\mathbf{r}'|}}{|\mathbf{r}-\mathbf{r}'|} V(\mathbf{r}')\psi(\mathbf{r}')\, d\mathbf{r}'$$

reduces to

$$\psi(\mathbf{r}) = \frac{A}{(2\pi)^{3/2}} e^{i\mathbf{k}\cdot\mathbf{r}} - \frac{m}{2\pi\hbar^2} \int \frac{e^{+ik|\mathbf{r}-\mathbf{r}'|}}{|\mathbf{r}-\mathbf{r}'|} V(\mathbf{r}')\psi(\mathbf{r}')\, d\mathbf{r}'.$$

Note that $\xi(\mathbf{r})$ is a linear superposition of solutions to $(\nabla^2 + k^2)\phi = 0$.

16. In obtaining the Lippmann-Schwinger bound-state equation by the Fourier transform method, it almost appears that we applied *no* boundary conditions at all (no "$i\epsilon$-prescription" was necessary) and yet we got a uniquely determined Green's function. Show that this is not actually the case, i.e., that we really did insert a boundary condition. How was this done? Relate your discussion to the work in Section 7.5.

17. Consider a thin ring of radius R. Initially, at $t = 0$, there is a temperature distribution $T(\phi, 0)$ around the ring, where ϕ is the appropriate angular coordinate. Using the Green's function method, find the temperature at later times. Explain any decisions you make concerning boundary conditions. Suppose that the ring is initially heated in a very small region around $\phi = \phi_0$, so that the form $T(\phi, 0) = T_0\delta(\phi - \phi_0)$ is a reasonable boundary condition. Find the temperature at later times, $t > 0$. What is the value of the uniform temperature which the ring finally attains? How is the rate of approach to equilibrium affected by increasing the radius of the ring?

18. a) Consider a one-dimensional rod of length L. Let one end, at $x = 0$, be held at zero temperature and the other end, at $x = L$, be held at temperature T_0. If the initial temperature distribution is $T(x, 0)$, show that the temperature at subsequent times is given by

$$T(x, t) = T_0 x/L + \int_0^L G_1(x, x', t)\, \tilde{T}(x', 0)\, dx',$$

where

$$\tilde{T}(x, 0) = T(x, 0) - T_0 x/L$$

and

$$G_1(x, x', t) = \frac{2}{L} \sum_{m=1}^{\infty} \sin \frac{m\pi x}{L} \sin \frac{m\pi x'}{L} e^{(-k/c)(m\pi/L)^2 t}.$$

[*Hint*: Note that $\tilde{T}(x, t) = T(x, t) - T_0 x/L$ also satisfies the heat equation. What are the boundary conditions satisfied by $\tilde{T}(x, t)$?]

b) Using the result of part (a), find the Green's function which will enable one to solve the equation

$$\nabla^2 T = \frac{c}{k} \frac{\partial T}{\partial t}$$

on the infinite half-line $[0, \infty]$ when $T(x, 0)$ is given some prescribed functional value.

19. a) Using the results of the previous problem (or any other method), find in terms of a Green's function the solution to the heat equation for a one-dimensional rod whose ends at $x = -L/2$ and $x = L/2$ are kept at temperatures T_1 and T_2 respectively.

b) Find an expression for the Green's function of part (a) in the limit $L \rightarrow \infty$, that is, for the infinite line. Compare this expression with the result found in Section 7.7 for periodic boundary conditions.

20. Using the eigenfunction expansion method, show that the potential energy in a two-dimensional, charge-free region bounded by circles of radii R_1 and R_2 is given by

$$V(r, \theta) = \int_0^{2\pi} G_1(\theta, \theta', r) V(R_1, \theta') \, d\theta' + \int_0^{2\pi} G_2(\theta, \theta', r) V(R_2, \theta') \, d\theta' \,,$$

where $V(R_1, \theta)$ is the known value of the potential on the first surface as a function of θ, and $V(R_2, \theta)$ is its value on the second surface. Find the eigenfunction expansion of G_1 and G_2, using the fact that $\partial^2/\partial\theta^2$ is an Hermitian operator if one imposes periodic boundary conditions on $[0, 2\pi]$. Why do we require such conditions in this problem? Does the limit $V(R_1, \theta) = \text{const}$, $V(R_2, \theta) = \text{const}$ give the result you would expect? Show that $G_1(\theta, \theta', R_1) = \delta(\theta - \theta')$ and $G_2(\theta, \theta', R_2) = \delta(\theta - \theta')$.

21. a) Determine the Green's function, $G_1(x, y, x', y', t)$, for the homogeneous heat equation for the entire xy-plane (i.e., the two-dimensional Green's function for an infinite space).

b) Assume that at $t = 0$ the temperature is a constant T_0 inside a square of side $2a$, centered at the origin, and zero outside this square. Determine the temperature distribution throughout the plane for all later times t in terms of the error function:

$$\text{erf}(x) = \frac{2}{\sqrt{\pi}} \int_0^x e^{-u^2} \, du \,.$$

22. Show that the Green's function for the two-dimensional Laplacian over the entire two-dimensional space is

$$G(x, y; x', y') = + \frac{1}{2\pi} \log{[(x - x')^2 + (y - y')^2]^{1/2}} \,.$$

[*Hint*: One can always add a constant to the Green's function and it will still satisfy $\nabla^2 G = \delta(x - x')\delta(y - y')$.]

23. Show that if the wave function ψ of a particle satisfies Schrödinger's equation,

$$H\psi = ih \frac{\partial \psi}{\partial t} \,.$$

where H is a self-adjoint operator, and if

$$\int \phi^*(\mathbf{r}, 0)\phi(\mathbf{r}, 0)\, d^3r = 1 \qquad (1)$$

at $t = 0$, then at any subsequent time t, we will also have

$$\int \phi^*(\mathbf{r}, t)\phi(\mathbf{r}, t)d^3r = 1 . \qquad (2)$$

Since in quantum mechanics $|\phi|^2$ is the probability density, $|\phi|^2 d^3r$ gives the probability of finding the particle in the volume element d^3r, and Eqs. (1) and (2) are a statement of the conservation of total probability. That is, if the total probability of finding the particle *someplace* is initially equal to unity [Eq. (1)], it remains equal to unity at all later times. Clearly, the interpretation of $|\phi|^2$ as a probability density would not make sense if this were not the case. Note that such an interpretation would not hold for solutions to the heat (or diffusion) equation.

24. Use Green's theorem to obtain Eq. (7.117) from Eq. (7.116).

25. a) Show that the function

$$G'(\mathbf{r}, \mathbf{r}', \tau, \tau') = -\, G_1(\mathbf{r}, \mathbf{r}', \tau, \tau')\theta(\tau' - \tau)$$

 is a Green's function for Eq. (7.131), where G_1 satisfies Eqs. (7.134) and (7.135).

 b) This means that we can write a time-dependent Schrödinger integral equation as

$$\phi(\mathbf{r}, t) = \phi_0(\mathbf{r}, t) - \frac{2m}{\hbar^2} \int d^3r' \int_\tau^{i\infty} G'(\mathbf{r}, \mathbf{r}', \tau, \tau')\, U(\mathbf{r}', \tau')\phi(\mathbf{r}', \tau')\, d\tau'$$

 in the notation of Eq. (7.137). Show that U is a static potential which is "turned off" at remote *future* times, that is,

$$U(\mathbf{r}, \tau) = V(\mathbf{r})e^{-\epsilon' t} = V(\mathbf{r})e^{i\epsilon\tau},$$

 then we obtain in the limit $\epsilon \to 0$ the Lippmann-Schwinger equation with an *incoming* spherical wave boundary condition solution.

26. a) Note that Eq. (7.125b) does not make sense if $\tau' > \tau$ (assuming, as will usually be the case, that $\lambda_m \to +\infty$ as $m \to \infty$) and τ and τ' are real. This is also reflected in the discussion following Eq. (7.128), where we are tacitly assuming that $\tau \to 0$ from "the positive side of zero" (see Section 5.3). Thus the Green's function

$$G(\mathbf{r}, \mathbf{r}', \tau, \tau') = -\, \theta(\tau' - \tau)G_1(\mathbf{r}, \mathbf{r}', \tau, \tau')$$

 obtained in the previous problem, although it formally seems to satisfy

$$\left(H + \frac{\partial}{\partial\tau}\right)G = \delta^3(\mathbf{r} - \mathbf{r}')\delta(\tau - \tau') ,$$

 is *not* an acceptable Green's function. Show that if one derives $G(\mathbf{r}, \mathbf{r}', \tau, \tau')$ for the case of the diffusion (or heat) equation by using the Fourier transform method, one obtains *only*

$$G(\mathbf{r}, \mathbf{r}', \tau, \tau') = \theta(\tau - \tau')G_1(\mathbf{r}, \mathbf{r}', \tau, \tau') ,$$

 where G_1 is given by Eq. (7.139).

 b) For the case of Schrödinger's equation for a free particle, the expontial in Eq. (7.125b) is oscillatory because τ is imaginary. In this case, show that the Fourier transform method yields two Green's functions:

$$G_+(\mathbf{r}, \mathbf{r}', t, t') = \theta(t - t')G_1(\mathbf{r}, \mathbf{r}', t, t')$$

and

$$G_-(\mathbf{r}, \mathbf{r}', t, t') = -\theta(t' - t)G_1(\mathbf{r}, \mathbf{r}', t, t'),$$

depending on whether one uses $+i\epsilon$ or $-i\epsilon$ to avoid the singularity arising in the Fourier transform method for this case. In the above equation for G_+ and G_-, G_1 is given by Eq. (7.139) with $\tau = iht/2m$.

27. a) Show that the function

$$G_A(\mathbf{r}, \mathbf{r}', \tau, \tau') = -\theta(\tau' - \tau)\tilde{G}_2(\mathbf{r}, \mathbf{r}', \tau, \tau')$$

is indeed a Green's function for the operator

$$\theta = H + \frac{\partial^2}{\partial \tau^2}$$

if $\tilde{G}_2$ satisfies Eqs. (7.152) and (7.157).

   b) For the case of the wave equation, find an expression for $G_A(\mathbf{r}, \mathbf{r}', \tau, \tau')$ analogous to the one for G_R given in Eq. (7.163).
   c) Find a solution to $\theta\psi(\mathbf{r}, \tau) = J(\mathbf{r}, \tau)$ in terms of G_A. Interpret the solution by analogy with Eq. (7.164).
   d) Show that

$$G_A + G_R = \frac{1}{2\pi}\delta(s^2),$$

where s^2 is the Lorentz-invariant scalar product:

$$s^2 \equiv (\mathbf{r} - \mathbf{r}')^2 - (\tau - \tau')^2 = (x - x')^2 + (y - y')^2 + (z - z')^2 - c^2(t - t')^2.$$

28. Using the Fourier transform method (in *four dimensions*) obtain the Green's functions for the wave equation. Show that one obtains G_R [of Eq. (7.163)] or G_A (of the previous problem) depending on how one chooses to avoid a singularity which arises in the Fourier transform method (see a similar discussion in Section 7.4, (Eq. (7.63) *et seq.*)

29. Consider the time-dependent inhomogeneous Klein-Gordon equation:

$$\left[-\nabla^2 + \frac{1}{c^2}\frac{\partial^2}{\partial t^2} + \kappa^2\right]\psi(\mathbf{r}, t) = \rho(\mathbf{r}, t).$$

   a) Show that by using the Fourier transform method one obtains the following two integral expressions for the Green's functions G_R and G_A:

$$G_R(\mathbf{r}, t, \mathbf{r}', t') = \frac{c}{8\pi^2 Ri}\frac{d}{dR}\int_{-\infty}^{\infty}\frac{e^{i(R/c)\sqrt{q^2-\kappa^2c^2}}}{\sqrt{q^2 - \kappa^2c^2}}e^{-iq(t-t')}\,dq,$$

$$G_A(\mathbf{r}, t, \mathbf{r}', t') = -\frac{c}{8\pi^2 Ri}\frac{d}{dR}\int_{-\infty}^{\infty}\frac{e^{-i(R/c)\sqrt{q^2-\kappa^2c^2}}}{\sqrt{q^2 - \kappa^2c^2}}e^{-iq(t-t')}\,dq,$$

where $R = |\mathbf{r} - \mathbf{r}'|$. The two expressions correspond to two possible ways of avoiding a singularity which occurs in doing the Fourier transform integrals corresponding to the space variables. In the first integral, $\sqrt{q^2 - \kappa^2c^2}$ has *positive* imaginary part when $|q| < \kappa c$; in the second integral $\sqrt{q^2 - \kappa^2c^2}$ has *negative* imaginary part when $|q| < \kappa c$.

b) Show that $G_R = 0$ when $R/c > (t - t')$ and that $G_A = 0$ when $R/c + (t - t') > 0$. [*Hint*: If the integral for G_R is considered as an integral in the complex plane, then the plane is cut from $-\kappa c$ to $+\kappa c$ and the integral in question runs along the *top* of the cut. For G_A, the integral runs along the bottom of the cut.]

Fig. 7.12

c) When $R/c < (t - t')$, show that the integral occurring in G_R can be reduced to the contour integral shown in Fig. 7.12. Hence show that

$$G_R = -\frac{c}{4\pi^2 R}\frac{d}{dR}\left[\int_{-\kappa c}^{\cdot \kappa c}\frac{1}{\sqrt{\kappa^2 c^2 - q^2}}\cosh\left[\frac{R}{c}\sqrt{\kappa^2 c^2 - q^2}\right]\right.$$
$$\left.\times e^{-iq(t-t')}\,dq\,\theta(T - R)\right],$$

and, similarly,

$$G_A = -\frac{c}{4\pi^2 R}\frac{d}{dR}\left[\int_{-\kappa c}^{\cdot \kappa c}\frac{1}{\sqrt{\kappa^2 c^2 - q^2}}\cosh\left[\frac{R}{c}\sqrt{\kappa^2 c^2 - q^2}\right]\right.$$
$$\left.\times e^{-iq(t-t')}\,dq\,\theta(-T - R)\right],$$

where $\theta(x)$ equals 1 if $x > 0$ and equals zero if $x < 0$. Also, $T = c(t - t')$.

d) Making the change of variable $q = \kappa c \sin\theta$ and using some symmetry considerations, show that

$$G_R = -\frac{c}{8\pi^2 R}\frac{d}{dR}\left[\int_{-\pi}^{\pi}\cosh\,(\kappa R\cos\theta)e^{-i\kappa T\sin\theta}\,d\theta\,\theta(T - R)\right],$$

$$G_A = -\frac{c}{8\pi^2 R}\frac{d}{dR}\left[\int_{-\pi}^{\pi}\cosh\,(\kappa R\cos\theta)e^{-i\kappa T\sin\theta}\,d\theta\,\theta(-T - R)\right].$$

[*Hint*: Note that the limits of integration are $\pm\pi$, *not* $\pm\pi/2$.]

e) Show that this can be written as

$$G_R = -\frac{c}{8\pi^2 Ri}\frac{d}{dR}\left[\oint_C \frac{1}{z}\cosh\left[\frac{1}{2}\kappa R\left(z + \frac{1}{z}\right)\right]e^{-\kappa T(z-1/z)/2}dz\,\theta(T - R)\right],$$

with a similar expression for G_A. Here C is a counterclockwise contour around the *unit* circle.

f) By making two variable changes (in two different integrals), show that one obtains

$$G_R = -\frac{c}{8\pi^2 Ri}\frac{d}{dR}\left[\oint\frac{1}{\xi}\exp\left[-\frac{\kappa}{2}\sqrt{T^2 - R^2}\left(\xi - \frac{1}{\xi}\right)\right]d\xi\,\theta(T - R)\right].$$

Using the integral representation of the Bessel function [Eq. (6.65) and the sentence following this equation], show that this reduces to

$$G_R = -\frac{c}{4\pi R}\frac{d}{dR}[J_0(\kappa\sqrt{T^2 - R^2})\theta(T - R)].$$

Also,

$$G_A = -\frac{c}{4\pi R}\frac{d}{dR}[J_0(\kappa\sqrt{T^2 - R^2})\theta(-T - R)] \, .$$

[Here we have used the fact that $J_0(x) = J_0(-x)$, which is clear from Eq. (6.66).]

g) (We're almost done!) Carry out the differentiation using Eq. (7.22) to show that

$$G_R = \frac{c}{4\pi R}\delta(R - T) - \frac{\kappa c}{4\pi\sqrt{T^2 - R^2}}J_1(\kappa\sqrt{T^2 - R^2})\theta(T - R) \, ,$$

$$G_A = \frac{c}{4\pi R}\delta(R + T) - \frac{\kappa c}{4\pi\sqrt{T^2 - R^2}}J_1(\kappa\sqrt{T^2 - R^2})\theta(-T - R) \, .$$

Note that as $\kappa \to 0$, G_R goes over into the result of Eq. (7.163), apart from a factor of c which you should be able to explain (*Note*: $\delta(ax) = \delta(x)/|a|$). Also, note that $G_A + G_R$ can be written as

$$G_R + G_A = \frac{c}{2\pi}\delta(T^2 - R^2) - \frac{\kappa c}{4\pi\sqrt{T^2 - R^2}}J_1(\kappa\sqrt{T^2 - R^2})\theta(T^2 - R^2) \, ,$$

which is a function only of the Lorentz invariant $s^2 = R^2 - T^2 = (x - x')^2 + (y - y')^2 + (z - z')^2 - c^2(t - t')^2$.

FURTHER READINGS

CARSLAW, H. S., and J. C. JAEGER, *Conduction of Heat in Solids*, Second Edition. New York: Oxford University Press, 1959.

COURANT, R., and D. HILBERT, *Methods of Mathematical Physics* Vol. II. New York: Interscience, 1962.

DETTMAN, J., *Mathematical Methods in Physics and Engineering*. New York: McGraw-Hill, 1962.

FRIEDMAN, B., *Principles and Techniques of Applied Mathematics*. New York: Wiley, 1956.

JACKSON, J. D., *Classical Electrodynamics*. New York: Wiley, 1962.

LANCZOS, C., *Linear Differential Operations*. Princeton, N. J.: D. Van Nostrand, 1961.

MORSE, P. M. and H. FESHBACH, *Methods of Theoretical Physics*, Vol. I. New York: McGraw-Hill, 1953.

SOMMERFELD, A., *Partial Differential Equations in Physics*. New York: Academic Press, 1949.

CHAPTER 8

INTRODUCTION TO INTEGRAL EQUATIONS

INTRODUCTION

In the last chapter, we saw that by introducing the concept of a Green's function we were led in a natural way to reformulate certain problems in terms of integral equations rather than differential equations. In this chapter and the next, we shall study integral equations as a subject in their own right, independent of the particular physical origin of these equations. We shall find that the relevant mathematical setting for this study is in infinite-dimensional vector spaces; within this framework, we shall concentrate primarily, although not exclusively, on Hilbert space. A particularly interesting question, in light of the work in Chapters 3 and 4, is: What is the relationship between the results of finite-dimensional and infinite-dimensional vector space theory? We will see that there is a very close relationship and that in many important cases one can solve infinite-dimensional problems by finite-dimensional techniques. However, there are also important and interesting differences which have many consequences for physics.

This chapter is devoted to a study of several special types of integral equations which can be solved rather easily. We will also take this opportunity to introduce, in a more precise manner than in Chapter 5, some of the key concepts in the theory of infinite-dimensional vector spaces.

8.1 ITERATIVE TECHNIQUES—LINEAR INTEGRAL OPERATORS

In Chapter 7 we encountered several different integral equations of the form

$$f(x) = g(x) + \int_a^b k(x, y) f(y) \, dy , \qquad (8.1)$$

where $g(x)$ and $k(x, y)$ are given functions. Equations of this form are known as *integral equations of the second kind*. If $g(x)$ is not identically zero, the equation is said to be inhomogeneous; if $g(x)$ vanishes everywhere, the equation is called homogeneous. If on the left-hand side of Eq. (8.1) we replace $f(x)$ by zero, the resulting equation is an *integral equation of the first kind*. An example of such an equation is

$$g(x) = \frac{1}{\sqrt{2\pi}} \int_{-\infty}^{\infty} e^{ixy} f(y) \, dy ,$$

where $g(x)$ is a known function and $f(y)$ is to be determined. For this particular case, we know from the theory of Fourier transforms that the solution is given by

$$f(y) = \frac{1}{\sqrt{2\pi}} \int_{-\infty}^{\infty} e^{-iyx} g(x)\, dx \,,$$

but, in general, little is known about these equations and we will not discuss them further.

An important special case of Eq. (8.1) is the *Volterra* integral equation, which has the general form

$$f(x) = g(x) + \int_{a}^{x} \bar{k}(x, y)\, f(y)\, dy \,. \tag{8.2}$$

Equation (8.1) reduces to this form if the function $k(x, y)$ vanishes when $y > x$. A generalization of Eq. (8.2), which one might encounter, for example, in Newtonian mechanics, has the form

$$f(x) = g(x) + \int_{a}^{x} h(x, y, f(y))\, dy \,. \tag{8.3}$$

Here the unknown function f may occur linearly, as in Eq. (8.2), or nonlinearly, depending on the form of $h(x, y, f(y))$. In this chapter we will discuss primarily linear integral equations, although in Section 8.4 we will look briefly at some of the simpler aspects of nonlinear equations.

Let us now rewrite Eq. (8.1) in the form

$$f = g + Kf \,, \tag{8.4}$$

where K is an operator defined by

$$Kf \equiv \int_{a}^{b} k(x, y)\, f(y)\, dy \,. \tag{8.5}$$

Evidently K is linear, since

$$\begin{aligned}
K(f_1 + f_2) &= \int_{a}^{b} k(x, y)[f_1(y) + f_2(y)]\, dy \\
&= \int_{a}^{b} k(x, y) f_1(y)\, dy + \int_{a}^{b} k(x, y) f_2(y)\, dy \\
&= Kf_1 + Kf_2 \,.
\end{aligned}$$

Therefore we may consider f and g as elements in some vector space, say V, and K as a linear operator which maps V into itself. The operator K, defined by Eq. (8.5), is called an *integral operator*, and $k(x, y)$ is called the *kernel* of the operator.

Equation (8.4) can now be stated as

$$(I - K)f = g \,, \tag{8.6}$$

where I is the identity operator. In this form the problem looks very much like the matrix equations discussed in Chapters 3 and 4. If we can compute $(I - K)^{-1}$, the problem is formally solved, since

$$f = (I - K)^{-1} g \tag{8.7}$$

(provided, of course, that the inverse operator is well defined). Note that although K may be an integral operator in Eq. (8.7), I is not an integral operator unless we want to use the δ-function:

$$If = \int_{-\infty}^{\infty} \delta(x - y) f(y) \, dy .$$

The most fortunate situation would be if K were in some sense a "small" operator, so that we could try to write

$$(I - K)^{-1} = I + K + K^2 + \cdots \tag{8.8}$$

by analogy with the power series for $(1 - x)^{-1}$ for small x. Since we have already required that K acting on *any* element of V produce another element of V, K^n is defined simply by successive applications of K: $K^2 = KK$, $K^3 = KK^2$, etc. This restriction on K is not trivial because it sometimes happens that reasonable-looking operators acting on V produce objects which are not in V. For example, consider the space $L_2[0, 1]$ of square-integrable functions of one variable defined on $[0, 1]$, and let the operator d/dx act on this space. Clearly, $f(x) = \sqrt{x}$ belongs to $L_2[0, 1]$, but

$$\frac{d}{dx}[f(x)] = \tfrac{1}{2}x^{-1/2}$$

does not. Thus d/dx does not transform every element of the space $L_2[0, 1]$ into another element of the same space, and cannot therefore be an admissible operator for our purposes. In fact, the assumption that a set of operators always transforms elements in a given space into elements of the *same* vector space has some strong consequences, as we shall point out later.

Suppose now that the right-hand side of Eq. (8.8) "converges." (We use quotation marks around "converges" because we have not yet given a careful definition of convergence for operators.) Then the operator to which it converges is the inverse of $(I - K)$, because multiplying $I + K + K^2 + K^3 + \cdots$ on either side by $(I - K)$ gives I. Thus we are led to speculate that the series

$$f = g + Kg + K^2g + K^3g + \cdots , \tag{8.9}$$

when it converges, is the solution to Eq. (8.4). The series in Eq. (8.9) is called the *Neumann series* by mathematicians, and the *Born series* by physicists, since it was Max Born who first utilized the basic iterative idea in quantum mechanics (although he was motivated by rather different considerations than the ones described here).

Let us now begin to investigate the circumstances under which the series of Eq. (8.9) converges. If K is an integral operator of the type defined by Eq. (8.5), then Eq. (8.9) can be written as

$$f(x) = g(x) + \int_a^b k(x, x')g(x') \, dx'$$
$$+ \int_a^b dx' \int_a^b dx'' \, k(x, x')k(x', x'')g(x'') + \cdots . \tag{8.10}$$

We are, of course, assuming that $g(x) \not\equiv 0$; otherwise the series of Eq. (8.9) or (8.10) degenerates into the result $f(x) \equiv 0$, which is always a possible (but uninteresting) solution when $g(x) \equiv 0$. We require that $|k(x, y)|$ be *bounded* when x and y lie in $[a, b]$:

$$\max_{x, y \in a, b} |k(x, y)| = M, \tag{8.11}$$

where M is some finite number. We further assume that the integral

$$\int_a^b |g(x)| \, dx \tag{8.12}$$

exists and is equal to a finite constant C. Then we may write

$$f(x) = g_0(x) + g_1(x) + g_2(x) + g_3(x) + \cdots, \tag{8.13}$$

where $g_0(x) \equiv g(x)$ and

$$g_n(x) = \int_a^b k(x, y) g_{n-1}(y) \, dy.$$

We next want to show that, with the given assumptions about $k(x, y)$ and $g(x)$,

$$|g_n(x)| \le CM[M(b - a)]^{n-1} \tag{8.14}$$

for $n \ge 1$. For $n = 1$,

$$|g_1(x)| \le \int_a^b |k(x, y) g(y)| \, dy \le \int_a^b |k(x, y)| \cdot |g(y)| \, dy.$$

But $|k(x, y)| \le M$, so

$$|g_1(x)| \le M \int_a^b |g(y)| \, dy = MC.$$

Thus Eq. (8.14) is satisfied for $n = 1$. We now assume it to be true for $n = m - 1$ and then prove that it is true for $n = m$. This will establish the general result by induction. For $g_m(x)$, we have

$$|g_m(x)| \le \int_a^b |k(x, y)| \cdot |g_{m-1}(y)| \, dy \le MC[M(b - a)]^{m-2} \int_a^b |k(x, y)| \, dy$$
$$\le MC[M(b - a)]^{m-1},$$

which is the desired result. Thus the mth term in the series of Eq. (8.13) is *dominated* by $MC[M(b - a)]^{m-1}$, that is, it is less in absolute magnitude than $MC[M(b - a)]^{m-1}$, for all x. Therefore

$$\left| f(x) - \sum_{n=0}^N g_n(x) \right| \le |g_{N+1}(x)| + |g_{N+2}(x)| + \cdots$$

$$\le MC \sum_{m=N}^\infty [M(b - a)]^m$$

$$\le MC[M(b - a)]^N \sum_{m=0}^\infty [M(b - a)]^m.$$

If $M(b - a) < 1$, this last sum converges, so we can write

$$|f(x) - \sum_{n=0}^{N} g_n(x)| \leq \frac{MC[M(b - a)]^N}{1 - M(b - a)}$$

for *all* x. Since $M(b - a) < 1$, the right-hand side of this equation can be made as small as we please by choosing N sufficiently large. Thus as N tends to infinity, $\sum_{n=0}^{N} g_n(x)$ converges uniformly to a function $f(x)$. The reader can easily show that if $k(x, y)$ is continuous in x for all y and if $g(x)$ is continuous, then each $g_n(x)$ will be continuous, and the uniformly convergent sum will also be continuous. Since the series $f = g + Kg + K^2g + \cdots$ is uniformly convergent, we can calculate $(I - K)f$ by integrating term by term. We obtain

$$(I - K)f = g_0 + g_1 + g_2 + g_3 + \cdots - K(g_0 + g_1 + g_2 + \cdots) .$$

But $Kg_n = g_{n+1}$; therefore

$$(I - K)f = g_0 \equiv g ,$$

so the Neumann series does indeed give a solution to the problem.

We may summarize by saying that if $M < (b - a)^{-1}$, then the Neumann series of Eqs. (8.9) or (8.10) converges to the solution of Eq. (8.1). This in no way implies that M *must* be less than $(b - a)^{-1}$ for the Neumann series to converge. It is easy to construct kernels for which $M \geq (b - a)^{-1}$ but for which the Neumann series nevertheless converges. For example, the reader should calculate the Neumann series for

$$k(x, y) = \xi(x)\eta(y) ,$$

where

$$\int_a^b \xi(x)\eta(x) \, dx = 0 .$$

Another large class of kernels for which the restriction $M < (b - a)^{-1}$ is unnecessary is the Volterra class, i.e., equations of the form of Eq. (8.2). For this case, if we write

$$f(x) = \tilde{g}_0(x) + \tilde{g}_1(x) + \tilde{g}_2(x) + \cdots ,$$

where again $\tilde{g}_0(x) \equiv g(x)$ and

$$\tilde{g}_n(x) \equiv \int_a^x k(x, y)\tilde{g}_{n-1}(y) \, dy ,$$

then we can show that

$$|\tilde{g}_n(x)| \leq MC[M(x - a)]^{n-1}/(n - 1)!$$

for $n \geq 1$, if $a \leq x \leq b$. Just as before, this is true for $n = 1$. Assuming it to be true for $n = m - 1$, we get

$$\tilde{g}_m(x) \leq \int_a^x |k(x, y)| \cdot |\tilde{g}_{m-1}(y)| \, dy$$

$$\leq MCM^{m-2} \int_a^x |k(x, y)| \, (y - a)^{m-2} \, dy/(m - 2)! .$$

Since $|k(x, y)| \leq M$, we have

$$|g_m(x)| \leq MC[M(x - a)]^{m-1}/(m - 1)! \,,$$

as required. Thus for $x \in [a, b]$, the nth term of the Neumann series is dominated by

$$MC[M(b - a)]^{n-1}/(n - 1)! \,,$$

so that the Neumann series is dominated by a series which converges for *all* values of $M(b - a)$. Hence the Neumann series *always* provides a solution to equations of the Volterra type.

8.2 NORMS OF OPERATORS

It may have occurred to the reader that the discussion of the previous section suffers from one serious limitation, namely, the requirement $M < (b - a)^{-1}$. In the case considered in Section 8.1, if the interval of integration is infinite, this requirement reduces to $M < 0$. But M is by definition positive, so no kernel can satisfy this requirement. However, to estimate a function by replacing it everywhere by its maximum value is a very crude approximation for infinite intervals. What we would like to be able to show is that we can replace

$$\max |k(x, y)| < (b - a)^{-1}$$

by a less restrictive requirement on $k(x, y)$. To do so we must first examine in some detail the problem of defining the magnitude of a linear *operator*.

In Hilbert space, we defined the norm of a *vector f* by

$$||f|| \equiv (f, f)^{1/2} \,,$$

where $(,)$ is an inner product on the Hilbert space to which f belongs (see Definition 4.1). However, the concept of the norm of a vector is much more general; the existence of a norm is associated only with a definition of length, not of angle. There are many vector spaces on which one cannot define an inner product, but where nevertheless a length, or metric, can be defined. We can generalize the concept of norm to this wider class of spaces as follows.

Definition 8.1. A *norm* on a vector space, V, is a relation which assigns to any element, f, of V a real number denoted by $||f||$ such that
a) $||f + g|| \leq ||f|| + ||g||$, for all $f, g \in V$;
b) $||f|| = 0$ if and only if $f \equiv 0$;
c) $||af|| = |a| \cdot ||f||$ for any scalar a belonging to the field over which V is defined.

A vector space on which a norm can be defined is called a *normed vector space*. We have already studied one such space in some detail, namely, Hilbert space, where the norm of a vector can be derived from the existence of the inner product. Because of the axioms satisfied by the inner product (Definition 4.1), the norm defined in this way will have all the properties required by Definition 8.1.

Once a norm has been defined on a vector space, questions concerning the convergence of sequences of vectors can be considered.

Definition 8.2. A sequence of vectors $\{f_n\}$ in a normed vector space, V, is said to *converge in norm* to $f \in V$ if $||f_n - f|| \to 0$ as $n \to \infty$.

This generalizes to an arbitrary normed space the notion of mean convergence introduced in Section 5.2 for Hilbert space.

Definition 8.3. A sequence of vectors $\{f_n\}$ in a normed vector space V is called a *Cauchy sequence* if, given any $\epsilon > 0$, there exists a number N such that $||f_n - f_m|| < \epsilon$ whenever $m > N$ and $n > N$.

The most important property of a Cauchy sequence is that we need make no reference to a limit function. With this in mind, we make a final definition.

Definition 8.4. A normed vector space is said to be *complete* if every Cauchy sequence in the space tends to a vector which lies in the space.

A well-known vector space which is normed but not complete is the vector space of rational numbers with the usual Euclidean norm (absolute value). For example, the sequence $\{s_n\}$ where

$$s_n = \sum_{m=1}^{n} \frac{1}{m^2}$$

is a Cauchy sequence of rationals whose limit, $\pi^2/6$, is irrational.

Complete, normed vector spaces are called *Banach spaces*, after the Polish mathematician who played the key role in developing the theory of these spaces. A familiar Banach space is the space of continuous functions on the interval $[a, b]$, which we denote by $C[a, b]$. A norm for this space is

$$||f(x)|| = \max_{x \in [a, b]} |f(x)| .$$

By the triangle inequality for real numbers,

$$|f(x) + g(x)| \leq |f(x)| + |g(x)|$$

for any x. Thus, in particular,

$$\max_{x \in [a, b]} |f(x) + g(x)| \leq \max_{x \in [a, b]} |f(x)| + \max_{x \in [a, b]} |g(x)| ,$$

or

$$||f + g|| \leq ||f|| + ||g|| .$$

The other two requirements of Definition 8.1 are trivially satisfied. Clearly, $C[a, b]$ is a vector space, since the sum of two continuous functions is a continuous function. Finally, and most important, with a norm defined in this way $C[a, b]$ is a *complete* space, because the limit of a uniformly convergent sequence of continuous functions is continuous (see Problem 8.1). Thus $C[a, b]$ is a Banach space.

Another important family of Banach spaces are the so-called L_p spaces, defined to be the vector spaces of functions, $f(x)$, which satisfy

$$\int_D |f(x)|^p \, dx < \infty \, ,$$

where D is some subset (not necessarily finite) of the real line. A norm for this space is given by (see Problems 8.2 and 8.3)

$$\|f\| = \left[\int_D |f(x)|^p \, dx \right]^{1/p}$$

and it can be shown (Generalized Riesz-Fisher theorem) that the space L_p is complete with this norm, and is thus a Banach space. We see, in particular, that the space, L_2, of square-integrable functions which we considered in Chapter 5 is a Banach space as well as being a Hilbert space. In fact, *any* Hilbert space is a Banach space since it is a complete inner-product space whose norm is automatically provided by the inner product.

Now that we have fixed the structure of Banach spaces, it is appropriate to consider how the space is changed by linear transformations. Throughout this chapter we shall limit the discussion to *bounded* linear transformations.

Definition 8.5. A transformation K on a normed linear vector space V is said to be a *bounded, linear transformation* if
a) $K(f + g) = Kf + Kg$ for all $f, g \in V$;
b) $K(af) = aKf$ for all $f \in V$ and all scalars a in the field over which V is defined;
c) there exists a constant M such that $\|Kf\| \leq M\|f\|$ for all $f \in V$.

Definition 8.6. Let V be a normed vector space, and K a bounded transformation on V. The *smallest M* satisfying $\|Kf\| \leq M\|f\|$ for all $f \in V$ is called the *norm* of K, which we will write as $\|K\|$. Note that we are using the same notation for the norm of an operator as for the norm of a function. To avoid confusion, vectors will always be written in lower case letters, operators in upper case letters.

It is not hard to see that $\|K\|$ as defined above is indeed a norm; for example

$$\|(K_1 + K_2)f\| = \|K_1 f + K_2 f\| \leq \|K_1 f\| + \|K_2 f\|$$

since $K_1 f$ and $K_2 f$ are elements of V. Applying Definition 8.6, we have, for all f,

$$\|(K_1 + K_2)f\| \leq \|K_1\| \, \|f\| + \|K_2\| \, \|f\|$$
$$\leq [\|K_1\| + \|K_2\|]\|f\| \, .$$

But $\|K_1 + K_2\|$ is the smallest M satisfying $\|(K_1 + K_2) f\| \leq M\|f\|$ for all f, so we have immediately

$$\|K_1 + K_2\| \leq \|K_1\| + \|K_2\| \, .$$

The other properties of the norm of the operator follow similarly from the normed structure of the underlying vector space V. This leads to the conclusion that the set of all bounded linear transformations of a Banach space is a normed linear vector space—in fact, a Banach space, since the space can be shown to be complete. Now, what about the norm of the product of two bounded linear transformations on V?

$$||(K_1 K_2)f|| = ||K_1(K_2 f)|| \le ||K_1||\,||K_2 f|| \le ||K_1||\,||K_2||\,||f||$$

for all f, so that $||K_1 K_2|| \le ||K_1||\,||K_2||$. In particular, this implies that

$$||K^n|| \le ||K||^n .\qquad (8.15)$$

The assumption that K is a bounded transformation has one particularly useful consequence. Consider a sequence of vectors, f_n, in V which converges in norm to some element $f \in V$, that is,

$$||f_n - f|| \to 0$$

as $n \to \infty$. It is natural to inquire whether or not the related sequence $\{Kf_n\}$ converges to Kf. To show that it does, consider the expression

$$||Kf_n - Kf|| = ||K(f_n - f)|| \le ||K||\,||f_n - f|| ;$$

since $||K||$ is finite and $f_n \to f$ in norm, it follows that $Kf_n \to Kf$ in norm. This is called the *continuity property* of bounded linear transformations.

The introduction of an operator norm gives us a particularly powerful means of discussing the convergence of operator sequences.

Definition 8.7. We say that a sequence of operators, K_n, *converges in norm* to an operator, K, if $||K_n - K|| \to 0$ as $n \to \infty$.

There are, of course, other possible ways in which we could have defined the convergence of a sequence of operators. For example, we could say that $\{K_n\}$ converges to K if, for all $f \in B$,

$$||K_n f|| \to ||Kf|| .\qquad (8.16)$$

This is certainly an acceptable way to define the convergence of operators, but it is *not* equivalent to convergence in norm.

To illustrate the difference between these two types of convergence in a Hilbert space, and also to introduce a particularly useful type of operator, we consider the so-called projection operators, P_n, which are defined for any orthonormal set of vectors, $\{\phi_i\}$, by

$$P_n f \equiv \sum_{i=1}^{n} (\phi_i, f)\phi_i .\qquad (8.17)$$

We say that P_n is the projection operator onto the subspace of H spanned by the first n elements of the set $\{\phi_i\}$. It is clear from the definition of Eq. (8.17) that P_n is an Hermitian operator, since

$$(f, P_n g) = (P_n f, g)\qquad (8.18)$$

for all $f, g \in H$. Also, P_n is idempotent:

$$P_n^2 = P_n .\qquad(8.19)$$

(This last property is obvious geometrically, since after once projecting a function into a subspace of H, subsequent applications of the same projection leave the function unaffected.)

The operator norm of P_n satisfies

$$||P_n|| \leq 1 .$$

To show this, we consider

$$||P_n f|| = (P_n f, P_n f)^{1/2} = (f, P_n f)^{1/2} = [\sum_{i=1}^{n} (f, \phi_n)(\phi_n, f)]^{1/2} .$$

But by Bessel's inequality [Eq. (5.9)], we get immediately

$$||P_n f|| \leq ||f||$$

for all f. Hence $||P_n|| \leq 1$. The same proof may be applied to the operator $(I - P_n)$ to show that

$$||I - P_n|| \leq 1 ;$$

we now observe that both of the inequalities on the norms of P_n and $I - P_n$ can be converted into strict equalities by noting, for example, that there is always at least one f for which $||P_n f|| = ||f||$. In fact, whenever $f = \phi_1, \phi_2, \cdots, \phi_n$ we will have $||P_n f|| = ||f||$. Thus, $||P_n|| \geq 1$, and combining this with our previous result $(||P_n|| \leq 1)$, we conclude that

$$||P_n|| = 1 .\qquad(8.20)$$

Similarly,

$$||I - P_n|| = 1 .\qquad(8.21)$$

The completeness of an orthonormal set $\{\phi_i\}$ as given in Definition 5.6 may be stated according to Eq. (5.10) in terms of projection operators as

$$\lim_{n \to \infty} (f, P_n f) = (f, f)$$

for all $f \in H$. Now using Eqs. (8.18) and (8.19), we have

$$||P_n f|| = (P_n f, P_n f)^{1/2} = (f, P_n^2 f)^{1/2} = (f, P_n f)^{1/2} ,$$

so

$$\lim_{n \to \infty} ||P_n f|| = (f, f)^{1/2} = ||If|| .$$

Thus P_n converges to I in the sense suggested by Eq. (8.16). Using a common terminology (albeit a somewhat misleading one), we may say that the sequence of operators $\{P_n\}$ *converges strongly* to I. If we think of the vectors as "points" in the vector space, then operators are analogous to functions; in this sense strong convergence of sequences of operators is analogous to the pointwise convergence of sequences of functions.

What about convergence in norm? For the sequence $\{P_n\}$ to converge to I in norm, given any ϵ, there must exist an N such that

$$||(P_n - I)f|| \leq \epsilon||f|| \tag{8.22}$$

whenever $n \geq N$, *for all* $f \in H$, that is, N is independent of f. Thus convergence in norm of operators is analogous to uniform convergence of a sequence of functions. But Eq. (8.22) cannot be satisfied, for, given any N, it is always possible to pick some function $h \in H$, in particular, $h = \phi_{N+1}$, such that

$$(P_N - I)h = (P_N - I)\phi_{N+1} = -\phi_{N+1} .$$

Then

$$||(P_N - I)h|| = ||h|| ,$$

so the sequence $\{P_n\}$ does *not* converge in norm to I. We see that convergence in norm is a *stronger* requirement than is strong convergence. In the sections that follow, when there can be no ambiguity, we shall often refer to convergence in norm simply as "convergence."

8.3 ITERATIVE TECHNIQUES IN A BANACH SPACE

Now that we have a method for specifying the magnitude of a linear operator, we can give a brief but complete account of the general iterative technique. Our discussion in this section will contain the results of Section 8.1 as a special case, but will also apply to infinite intervals and to operators more general than those of the integral type. We consider the operator equation

$$f = g + Kf$$

as an equation on a Banach space, B, with $g \in B$ and K a bounded linear transformation on B. We impose on the operator K, the restriction

$$||K|| < 1 , \tag{8.23}$$

which is analogous to the requirement $M(b - a) < 1$ of Section 8.1.

We want to show that the sequence of partial sums $\{f_n\}$, where

$$f_n = \sum_{m=0}^{n} K^m g ,$$

is a Cauchy sequence. Consider

$$||f_\nu - f_\mu|| = ||\sum_{m=\mu+1}^{\nu} K^m g|| \leq \sum_{m=\mu+1}^{\nu} ||K^m g|| \leq \sum_{m=\mu+1}^{\nu} ||K^m|| \, ||g|| ,$$

where we have taken $\nu > \mu$ for convenience. According to Eq. (8.15) $||K^m|| \leq ||K||^m$ so

$$||f_\nu - f_\mu|| \leq ||g|| \sum_{m=\mu+1}^{\nu} ||K||^m = ||g|| \, ||K||^{\mu+1} \sum_{m=0}^{\nu-\mu-1} ||K||^m .$$

But

$$\sum_{m=0}^{\nu-\mu-1} ||K||^m \leq \sum_{m=0}^{\infty} ||K||^m = (1 - ||K||)^{-1} ,$$

where we have summed the geometric series. Thus finally,

$$||f_\nu - f_\mu|| \leq ||g|| \, ||K||^{\mu+1}(1 - ||K||)^{-1} . \tag{8.24}$$

Since $||K|| < 1$, $(1 - ||K||)^{-1}$ is a finite number. Hence Eq. (8.24) tells us that it is possible to choose μ large enough so that $||f_\nu - f_\mu||$ is smaller than any preassigned number. Therefore $\{f_n\}$ is a Cauchy sequence, and, since the space B is complete (by definition),

$$f_n \to f ,$$

where f is an element of B. Now, by the continuity property of bounded linear operators,

$$Kf_n \to Kf$$

in norm. But Kf_n is given by

$$Kf_n = K \sum_{m=0}^{n} K^m g = \sum_{m=1}^{n+1} K^m g = \sum_{m=0}^{n+1} K^m g - g = f_{n+1} - g .$$

Hence

$$(f_{n+1} - g) \to Kf$$

in norm. But $f_{n+1} \to f$ in norm, so

$$f = g + Kf .$$

Thus f is a solution of the basic equation. It is also the only solution, for suppose that

$$f_1 = g + Kf_1 , \qquad f_2 = g + Kf_2 .$$

Then

$$f_1 - f_2 = K(f_1 - f_2) ,$$

and therefore

$$||f_1 - f_2|| = ||K(f_1 - f_2)|| \leq ||K|| \cdot ||f_1 - f_2|| .$$

Since $||K|| < 1$, this means that $||f_1 - f_2|| = 0$, so the solution we have found is unique.

Thus when $||K|| < 1$ it is always possible to solve Eq. (8.4). It is worth emphasizing that this does not mean that for $||K|| \geq 1$ the Neumann series must diverge. We have only shown that it *necessarily* converges for $||K|| < 1$. Clearly, the smaller $||K||$, the more rapidly the series will converge. If $||K||$ is sufficiently small, even one or two terms of the Neumann series may be adequate for the purpose at hand. This is often the case in physical problems.

A particularly important application of these results is to the space L_2 of square-integrable functions. Consider the integral operator K defined by

$$Kf = \int k(x, y) f(y) \, dy ,$$

acting on this space. If $k(x, y)$ is square-integrable as a function of two variables, so that

$$\int dx \int dy \, |k(x, y)|^2 < \infty \, , \tag{8.25}$$

then we can show that K is a transformation which maps every element of L_2 into an element of L_2. From Schwartz's inequality,

$$\left[\left| \int k(x, y) f(y) \, dy \right| \right]^2 \le \int |k(x, y)|^2 \, dy \cdot \int |f(y)|^2 \, dy \, ,$$

or

$$|Kf|^2 \le \int |k(x, y)|^2 \, dy \cdot ||f||^2 \, .$$

Therefore

$$||Kf||^2 = \int |Kf|^2 \, dx \le ||f||^2 \int dx \int dy \, |k(x, y)|^2 \, . \tag{8.26}$$

But this last integral is finite by Eq. (8.25), so $||Kf||$ is finite, as we asserted above.

Equation (8.26) also gives a useful estimate for the norm of K. From it we conclude that

$$||Kf|| \le \left[\int dx \int dy \, |k(x, y)|^2 \right]^{1/2} ||f|| \, ,$$

for all $f \in L_2$, and hence

$$||K|| \le \left[\int dx \int dy \, |k(x, y)|^2 \right]^{1/2} \, .$$

In particular, if

$$\int dx \int dy |k(x, y)|^2 < 1 \, ,$$

then $||K|| < 1$, and the above theory applies.

The integral form of Schrödinger's equation furnishes a good example of square-integrable kernels. According to Eqs. (7.57) and (7.68),

$$\psi(\mathbf{r}) = \xi(\mathbf{r}) + \int G_0(\mathbf{r}, \mathbf{r}', E) V(\mathbf{r}') \psi(\mathbf{r}') \, d\mathbf{r}' \, , \tag{8.27}$$

where

$$G_0(\mathbf{r}, \mathbf{r}', E) = -\frac{m}{2\pi\hbar^2} \frac{e^{iq|\mathbf{r}-\mathbf{r}'|}}{|\mathbf{r} - \mathbf{r}'|} \, ; \tag{8.28}$$

here $\xi(\mathbf{r}) \equiv 0$ for the bound state case $(E < 0)$, and

$$\xi(\mathbf{r}) = \frac{A}{(2\pi)^{3/2}} e^{i\mathbf{q} \cdot \mathbf{r}}$$

for the scattering case $(E \geq 0)$. Also, q is defined by

$$q = |\mathbf{q}| = \sqrt{2mE/\hbar^2} \ ,$$

and when $E < 0$ we take q with *positive* imaginary part. It will be convenient in what follows to consider q to be a complex number with positive imaginary part. Now the kernel of the above equation is

$$k(\mathbf{r}, \mathbf{r}', E) = G_0(\mathbf{r}, \mathbf{r}', E) V(\mathbf{r}') \ ,$$

so

$$||K||^2 \leq \int d\mathbf{r} \int d\mathbf{r}' \, |k(\mathbf{r}, \mathbf{r}', E)|^2 = \int d\mathbf{r} \int d\mathbf{r}' \, |G_0(\mathbf{r}, \mathbf{r}', E) V(\mathbf{r}')|^2 \ .$$

Using Eq. (8.28) for $G_0(\mathbf{r}, \mathbf{r}', E)$ and writing $q = \operatorname{Re} q + i \operatorname{Im} q$, we get

$$||K||^2 \leq \left(\frac{m}{2\pi\hbar^2}\right)^2 \int d\mathbf{r} \int d\mathbf{r}' \, \frac{e^{-2 \operatorname{Im} q |\mathbf{r}-\mathbf{r}'|}}{|\mathbf{r} - \mathbf{r}'|^2} | V(\mathbf{r}')|^2 \ .$$

If we change variables by setting $\mathbf{r} = \boldsymbol{\rho} + \mathbf{r}'$, the integral can be handled easily. The result is

$$||K||^2 \leq \frac{m^2}{2\pi\hbar^4 \operatorname{Im} q} \int |V(\mathbf{r})|^2 \, d\mathbf{r} \ , \tag{8.29}$$

which is finite *except* when $\operatorname{Im} q = 0$. But unfortunately this corresponds to the most interesting case, $E > 0$. This is when we are in the scattering region and would hope to be able to iterate Schrödinger's integral equation, at least under some conditions.

The reason that we encounter this difficulty is simply that we have failed to take adequate account of the physical situation. If $E > 0$, we are really interested in obtaining the scattering amplitude, $f(\theta, \phi)$, as was emphasized in Section 7.4. In terms of the wave function, $\psi(\mathbf{r})$, of Eq. (8.27),

$$f(\theta, \phi) = -\frac{m}{2\pi\hbar^2} \int e^{-i\mathbf{k}_f \cdot \mathbf{r}} V(\mathbf{r})\psi(\mathbf{r}) \, d\mathbf{r} \ .$$

From this expression, it is clear that we need only know $\psi(\mathbf{r})$ in those regions of space where the magnitude (strength) of $V(\mathbf{r})$ is significant, i.e., three-dimensional space should be weighted in importance by the function $V(\mathbf{r})$. With this in mind, we can write the above expression for $f(\theta, \phi)$ as

$$f(\theta, \phi) = -\frac{m}{2\pi\hbar^2} (\psi_{\text{free}}, \psi)_\rho \ ,$$

where $\psi_{\text{free}} = e^{i\mathbf{k}_f \cdot \mathbf{r}}$ and the inner product $(,)_\rho$ is taken with respect to the weight function $V(\mathbf{r})$:

$$(f, g)_\rho \equiv \int f^*(\mathbf{r})g(\mathbf{r}) \, d\rho (\mathbf{r}) \ , \tag{8.30a}$$

where $\rho(\mathbf{r})$ is defined by

$$d\rho (\mathbf{r}) \equiv V(\mathbf{r})r^2 \sin \theta \, dr \, d\theta \, d\phi \ . \tag{8.30b}$$

Clearly, for this to be an inner product in the sense of Definition 4.1, $V(\mathbf{r})$ must not change sign as $\mathbf{r}$ varies. We will assume that this is the case; if it is not, the necessary modifications should be obvious to the reader. In this notation we may rewrite Eq. (8.27) as

$$\psi(\mathbf{r}) = \xi(\mathbf{r}) + \int G_0(\mathbf{r}, \mathbf{r}', E)\psi(\mathbf{r}')\, d\rho\, (\mathbf{r}')\,, \tag{8.31}$$

which we would like to consider as an integral equation on the Hilbert space whose inner product is given by Eq. (8.30a). This will be legitimate if $||\xi|| < \infty$, which will be the case if

$$\int d\rho\, (\mathbf{r}) = \int V(\mathbf{r})d\mathbf{r} < \infty\,,$$

since $|\xi(\mathbf{r})| = |Ae^{i\mathbf{k}_i \cdot \mathbf{r}}|$ is a constant. For most reasonable potentials $||\xi||$ is finite, although for the Coulomb potential $||\xi||$ is infinite. To be more precise, $||\xi||$ will be finite if $V(\mathbf{r})$ falls off faster than $1/r^3$ at large distances and is less singular than $1/r^3$ at the origin. For Eq. (8.31) to be an acceptable equation in Hilbert space, the norm of the integral operator in Eq. (8.31) must be finite. Denoting the integral operator whose kernel is $G_0(\mathbf{r}, \mathbf{r}', E)$ by K, we have

$$||K||^2 \leq \int d\rho\, (\mathbf{r}) \int d\rho\, (\mathbf{r}')\, |G_0(\mathbf{r}, \mathbf{r}', E)|^2$$

$$= \left(\frac{m}{2\pi\hbar^2}\right)^2 \int d\mathbf{r} \int d\mathbf{r}'\, V(\mathbf{r})\, V(\mathbf{r}')\, \frac{e^{-2\,\mathrm{Im}\,q|\mathbf{r}-\mathbf{r}'|}}{|\mathbf{r} - \mathbf{r}'|^2}\,.$$

It is a relatively simple matter to evaluate this integral for the *central* potentials which typically occur in practice. The reason for this is that the integrand then depends only on $|\mathbf{r}|$, $|\mathbf{r}'|$, and $|\mathbf{r} - \mathbf{r}'|$, which form sides of a triangle. The integration over the angles which give the orientation of the triangle in space gives just $8\pi^2$. Writing $s = r + r'$, $t = r - r'$ and $u = |\mathbf{r} - \mathbf{r}'|$, one can easily show that for kernels which depend only on s, t, and u the volume element $d\mathbf{r}\, d\mathbf{r}'$ reduces to just $\pi^2(s^2 - t^2)u\, ds\, dt\, du$. The integration limits are defined by the inequalities $-u < t < u < s$. Thus

$$||K||^2 \leq \left(\frac{m}{2\hbar^2}\right)^2 \int_0^\infty ds \int_0^s du \int_{-u}^u dt\, (s^2 - t^2)\frac{e^{-2u\,\mathrm{Im}\,q}}{u}\, V(r)\, V(r')\,.$$

If, for example, $V(r)$ is the Yukawa potential, $V(r) = g^2 e^{-\mu r}/r$, then since $s = r + r'$ and $rr' = (s^2 - t^2)/4$, we get

$$||K||^2 \leq \frac{m^2 g^4}{\hbar^4} \int_0^\infty ds\, e^{-\mu s} \int_0^s \frac{du}{u}\, e^{-2u\,\mathrm{Im}\,q} \int_{-u}^u dt\,.$$

Doing the integrations, we find that

$$||K|| \leq \left[\frac{2}{1 + 2\,\mathrm{Im}\,(q/\mu)}\right]^{1/2} \frac{mg^2}{\mu\hbar^2}\,. \tag{8.32a}$$

Thus when $E > 0$ (that is, $\mathrm{Im}\,q = 0$),

$$||K|| \leq \sqrt{2}\,\frac{mg^2}{\mu\hbar^2}\,. \tag{8.32b}$$

Hence if the potential is weak enough, i.e., if g is small enough so $||K|| < 1$, we can iterate Schrödinger's integral equation. The iteration will converge in the weighted norm provided by Eq. (8.30a).

In the interest of not deceiving the reader, it should be emphasized that although the iteration is certain to converge if $V(\mathbf{r})$ is not too strong (and not too singular), it is, nevertheless, extremely difficult to perform the integrations involved in computing the successive terms of the series. If the reader has any doubts on this score, he is invited to try evaluating the first term in the iteration of Eq. (8.27) when $V(\mathbf{r})$ is given by some simple potential like the Yukawa potential. As we shall see, there are other methods of solution available which are often easier to employ than the method presented here. However, the Neumann series is a very important theoretical tool for developing other more practical methods of solution.

8.4 ITERATIVE TECHNIQUES FOR NONLINEAR EQUATIONS

Before leaving the subject of iterative solutions of integral equations, it is worthwhile contrasting the simple situation which prevails in the linear case with the more complicated features which arise in the nonlinear case. We shall see that the power of the iterative procedure is sharply reduced by nonlinearity, even when we restrict our attention to equations analogous to the Volterra equation discussed in Section 8.1.

Let us consider an equation of the form

$$f(x) = g(x) + \int_a^x h(x, y, f(y))\, dy , \qquad a \le x \le b . \tag{8.33}$$

We would like to develop an iterative procedure similar to the one we just employed to handle the linear case. However, since, in general, $f(y)$ does not occur linearly under the integration sign in Eq. (8.33), we shall proceed as follows. Set $f_0(x) \equiv g(x)$ and then by induction define

$$f_n(x) \equiv g(x) + \int_a^x h(x, y, f_{n-1}(y))\, dy . \tag{8.34}$$

The reader can easily verify that in the linear case, that is, $h(x, y, f(y)) = k(x, y) f(y)$, $f_n(x)$ is given by

$$f_n(x) = \sum_{m=0}^{n} K^m g ,$$

where K is defined by Eq. (8.5). With this in mind, the basic idea is very simple. We start with $f_0(x) \equiv g(x)$ as a zeroth-order approximation to $f(x)$ and insert this approximation into Eq. (8.34) to obtain a first approximation, $f_1(x)$. Continuing this process, we would hope to generate a sequence which converges eventually to the solution to Eq. (8.33). One might expect that just as in the case of the Volterra linear integral equation, this process will always converge if $h(x, y, f(y))$ is bounded in the domain $a \le x \le b$, $a \le y \le b$. However, we must also remember that h depends on a third variable, namely, f itself.

Therefore we shall make the additional assumption that for (x, y) in the square $a \leq x \leq b, a \leq y \leq b$,

$$|h(x, y, f(y))| \leq M \tag{8.35}$$

whenever

$$|f(y) - g(y)| \leq \Delta , \tag{8.36}$$

where Δ is some given positive number and $y \in [a, b]$. These assumptions will at least enable us to start the iterative procedure.

Setting $f_0(x) = g(x)$, we obtain

$$f_1(x) \equiv g(x) + \int_a^x h(x, y, f_0(y)) \, dy$$

$$= g(x) + \int_a^x h(x, y, g(y)) \, dy ,$$

from which we may deduce that

$$|f_1(x) - g(x)| = |f_1(x) - f_0(x)| \leq M(x - a) , \tag{8.37}$$

since $|f_0(y) - g(y)| = 0 < \Delta$. But to continue one step further, we need to know that $|f_1(y) - g(y)| \leq \Delta$. Equation (8.37) tells us that this will be the case if $|y - a| \leq \Delta/M$. Thus, to get any further, we must restrict the variables so that

$$a \leq x \leq (\Delta/M) + a , \qquad a \leq y \leq (\Delta/M) + a . \tag{8.38}$$

Clearly, if $(\Delta/M) + a \geq b$, this is no restriction at all. Thus we can calculate

$$f_2(x) \equiv g(x) + \int_a^x h(x, y, f_1(y)) \, dy .$$

Since $a \leq x \leq (\Delta/M) + a$, we have $|f_1(x) - g(x)| \leq \Delta$, and

$$|f_2(x) - g(x)| \leq M(x - a) \leq \Delta ;$$

this will be true for all further iterations. However, we also hope to show, in analogy with the linear case, that f_n and f_{n-1} get very close to each other when n becomes sufficiently large. Hence we need to calculate the difference between successive approximations. Let us look first at $|f_2(x) - f_1(x)|$. We find that

$$|f_2(x) - f_1(x)| = \left| \int_a^x [h(x, y, f_1(y)) - h(x, y, f_0(y))] \, dy \right| . \tag{8.39}$$

For linear integral equations, it is relatively easy to estimate the difference occurring under the integral in Eq. (8.39), because

$$h(x, y, f(y)) = k(x, y) f(y) .$$

But in the nonlinear case it is necessary to put further restrictions on the function h in the region defined by Eq. (8.38). By analogy with the linear case, we require that there exist some finite number, N, such that

$$|h(x, y, \phi(y)) - h(x, y, \varphi(y))| \leq N|\phi(y) - \varphi(y)| \tag{8.40}$$

whenever $|\phi(y) - g(y)| \leq \Delta$ and $|\psi(y) - g(y)| \leq \Delta$. This requirement is called the *Lipschitz condition*.

Returning now to Eq. (8.39), we see that since $|f_1(y) - g(y)| \leq \Delta$ and $|f_0(y) - g(y)| = 0 < \Delta$, we can use the Lipschitz condition to get

$$|f_2(x) - f_1(x)| \leq N \int_a^x |f_1(y) - f_0(y)| \, dy \, .$$

But $|f_1(y) - f_0(y)| = |f_1(y) - g(y)| \leq \Delta$, so

$$|f_2(x) - f_1(x)| \leq N\Delta(x - a) \, .$$

Continuing to the next step,

$$|f_3(x) - f_2(x)| \leq \Delta N^2(x - a)^2/2! \, ,$$

since $|f_2(x) - g(x)| \leq \Delta$. In general,

$$|f_n(x) - g(x)| \leq \Delta \tag{8.41}$$

and

$$|f_n(x) - f_{n-1}(x)| \leq \Delta N^{n-1}(x - a)^{n-1}/(n - 1)! \, . \tag{8.42}$$

In view of Eq. (8.38), Eq. (8.42) can be written as

$$|f_n(x) - f_{n-1}(x)| \leq \Delta(\Delta N/M)^{n-1}/(n - 1)! \, . \tag{8.43}$$

Thus for all $x \in [a, (\Delta/M) + a]$, $|f_n(x) - f_{n-1}(x)| \to 0$ uniformly as $n \to \infty$.

Just as in the linear case, we expect that $f_n(x)$ should tend to the solution of Eq. (8.33). To see this, we write $f_\nu(x)$ in the form

$$f_\nu(x) = f_0(x) + \sum_{n=1}^{\nu} [f_n(x) - f_{n-1}(x)] \, .$$

According to Eq. (8.43), each term of this sum is dominated by

$$\Delta(\Delta N/M)^{n-1}/(n - 1)! \quad \text{for} \quad x \in [a, (\Delta/M) + a] \, .$$

Thus as ν goes to infinity, $f_\nu(x)$ tends uniformly toward some function, say, $f(x)$. We now show that $f(x)$ satisfies Eq. (8.33). We write

$$f_\nu(x) = g(x) + \int_a^x h(x, y, f_{\nu-1}(y)) \, dy$$

$$= g(x) + \int_a^x h(x, y, f(y)) \, dy + \int_a^x [h(x, y, f_{\nu-1}(y)) - h(x, y, f(y))] \, dy \, .$$

Taking the limit $\nu \to \infty$ on both sides of this equation, we obtain

$$f(x) = g(x) + \int_a^x h(x, y, f(y)) \, dy + \lim_{\nu \to \infty} R_\nu \, ,$$

where

$$R_\nu = \int_a^x [h(x, y, f_{\nu-1}(y)) - h(x, y, f(y))] \, dy \, .$$

Since $|f(y) - g(y)| < \Delta$ because of Eqs. (8.41) and (8.43), we can use the Lipschitz condition to get

$$|R_\nu| \leq N \int_a^x |f_{\nu-1}(y) - f(y)| \, dy$$

$$\leq N\Delta \sum_{n=\nu}^{\infty} \frac{N^{n-1}}{(n-1)!} \int_a^x (y-a)^{n-1} \, dy$$

$$\leq \Delta \sum_{n=\nu}^{\infty} \frac{N^n (x-a)^n}{n!} \leq \Delta \sum_{n=\nu}^{\infty} \left(\frac{N\Delta}{M}\right)^n \frac{1}{n!} \, ,$$

which tends to zero as $\nu \to \infty$. Thus

$$f(x) = g(x) + \int_a^x h(x, y, f(y)) \, dy \, ,$$

and $f(x)$ is indeed the desired solution to Eq. (8.33).

We have therefore obtained an iterative solution in an interval, the length of which will generally depend on specific properties of $h(x, y, f(y))$. In the linear Volterra case, we were able to exhibit a convergent iterative series for *all* values of x, so we see that nonlinearity has a very serious effect on the iterative technique. The appropriate *region* of convergence is controlled by Δ/M, while the *rate* of convergence depends on the size of N, the constant in the Lipschitz condition [Eq. (8.40)].

As an example of nonlinear perturbation theory, we consider a problem from classical mechanics. Suppose that a particle is bound by a slightly anharmonic spring, with potential energy

$$V(x) = \tfrac{1}{2}kx^2 + \tfrac{1}{3}ax^3 \, ,$$

where a is a small constant. The equation of motion is

$$m\ddot{x} + kx + ax^2 = 0 \, , \qquad \text{or} \qquad \ddot{x} + \omega_0^2 x = -\epsilon x^2 \, ,$$

where $\omega_0^2 = k/m$ and $\epsilon = a/m > 0$.

According to Eq. (7.35) (with $\gamma = 0$) the Green's function for the operator $d^2/dt^2 + \omega_0^2$ with one-point boundary conditions is

$$G(t, t') = \frac{1}{\omega_0} \sin [\omega_0(t - t')]\theta(t - t') \, .$$

Assuming that the boundary condition is applied at $t = 0$ and has the form $x(0) = x_0 > 0$, $\dot{x}(0) = 0$, we get

$$x(t) = x_0 \cos \omega_0 t - \frac{\epsilon}{\omega_0} \int_0^t \sin \omega_0(t - t') x^2(t') \, dt' \, .$$

In keeping with the previous discussion, let us inquire under what conditions we can obtain an iterative solution for $x(t)$ if we require that

$$|x(t) - x_0 \cos \omega_0 t| < x_0 \, . \tag{8.44}$$

For this particular problem, we have also

$$h(t, t', x(t')) = -(\epsilon/\omega_0) \sin \omega_0(t - t')x^2(t') .$$

Thus

$$|h(t, t', x(t'))| \leq (\epsilon/\omega_0)x^2(t') ,$$

which may be written as

$$|h(t, t', x(t'))| \leq (\epsilon/\omega_0)[x(t') - x_0 \cos \omega_0 t' + x_0 \cos \omega_0 t']^2$$
$$\leq (\epsilon/\omega_0)[|x(t') - x_0 \cos \omega_0 t'| + x_0|\cos \omega_0 t'|]^2 .$$

Using Eq. (8.44), we obtain immediately

$$|h(t, t', x(t'))| < 4\epsilon x_0^2/\omega_0 , \tag{8.45}$$

for all t and t' whenever $|x(t') - x_0 \cos \omega_0 t'| \leq x_0$.

Similarly, we may estimate the quantity

$$|h(t, t', x(t')) - h(t, t', \xi(t'))|$$

which appears in the Lipschitz condition. We have

$$|h(t, t', x(t')) - h(t, t', \xi(t'))| \leq (\epsilon/\omega_0)|x(t') + \xi(t')| \, |x(t') - \xi(t')| ,$$

which may be rewritten as

$$|h(t, t', x(t')) - h(t, t', \xi(t'))|$$
$$\leq (\epsilon/\omega_0)|x(t') - x_0 \cos \omega_0 t' + \xi(t') - x_0 \cos \omega_0 t' + 2x_0 \cos \omega_0 t'| \cdot$$
$$|x(t') - \xi(t')| .$$

Using Eq. (8.44) again, we have

$$|h(t, t', x(t')) - h(t, t', \xi(t'))| \leq (4\epsilon x_0/\omega_0)|x(t') - \xi(t')| \tag{8.46}$$

for all t and t' whenever $|x(t') - x_0 \cos \omega_0 t'| \leq x_0$ and $|\xi(t') - x_0 \cos \omega_0 t'| \leq x_0$. Thus the quantities Δ, M, and N are given by

$$\Delta = x_0 , \tag{8.47a}$$

$$M = 4\epsilon x_0^2/\omega_0 , \tag{8.47b}$$

$$N = 4\epsilon x_0/\omega_0 . \tag{8.47c}$$

The above estimates involve no restrictions on t, but the previous discussion of the iterative method in the nonlinear case tells us that the iterative solution will be valid only in the interval $0 \leq t \leq \Delta/M$ or $0 \leq \omega_0 t \leq 1/(4\delta)$, where $\delta = \epsilon x_0/\omega_0^2$, and δ is the parameter in which we are attempting to expand $x(t)$. Hence we see that if δ is small, the expansion will converge for a large range of times.

With these results in hand, we begin the iterative procedure by setting

$$x_0(t) = x_0 \cos \omega_0 t . \tag{8.48}$$

By our previous work,

$$x_1(t) = x_0 \cos \omega_0 t - (\epsilon/\omega_0) \int_0^t \sin \omega_0(t - t')x_0^2(t') \, dt' .$$

Using Eq. (8.48) for $x_0(t')$, we get

$$x_1(t) = x_0 \left[\cos \omega_0 t + \delta(\tfrac{1}{6} \cos 2\omega_0 t + \tfrac{1}{3} \cos \omega_0 t - \tfrac{1}{2}) \right] . \qquad (8.49)$$

Note that $x_1(t)$ satisfies the boundary conditions at $t = 0$.

The main effect of the perturbation in first approximation is a slight change in the amplitude of the dominant harmonic ($\cos \omega_0 t$) and the addition of a second harmonic term ($\cos 2\omega_0 t$) with small amplitude (assuming that δ is small). By looking at $x_1(t)$ alone, it is not clear why the restriction $0 \leq \omega_0 t \leq 1/(4\delta)$ is necessary, since the size of the first-order correction is on the average independent of t. To see the reason for this restriction we look at $x_2(t)$. A few integrations show that

$$\begin{aligned}
x_2(t) = x_0[&\cos \omega_0 t + \delta(\tfrac{1}{6} \cos 2\omega_0 t + \tfrac{1}{3} \cos \omega_0 t - \tfrac{1}{2}) \\
&+ \delta^2(\tfrac{1}{48} \cos 3\omega_0 t + \tfrac{1}{9} \cos 2\omega_0 t + \tfrac{29}{144} \cos \omega_0 t - \tfrac{1}{3}) \\
&+ \delta^3(\tfrac{1}{1080} \cos 4\omega_0 t + \tfrac{1}{144} \cos 3\omega_0 t - \tfrac{1}{27} \cos 2\omega_0 t + \tfrac{753}{2160} \cos \omega_0 t - \tfrac{23}{72}) \\
&+ \omega_0 t(\tfrac{5}{12}\delta^2 \sin \omega_0 t + \tfrac{5}{36}\delta^3 \sin \omega_0 t)] .
\end{aligned} \qquad (8.50)$$

This iterate has the same general form as $x_1(t)$ expect for the appearance of terms linear in $\omega_0 t$. Thus for t large, both $|x_2(t) - x_1(t)|$ and $|x_2(t) - x_0(t)|$ are dominated by terms proportional to t. These terms will remain bounded only if we restrict the range of t.

It should be noted that $x_2(t)$, although it contains terms of order δ^3, is complete only through terms of order δ^2; there are further terms of order δ^3 which will make their appearance in $x_3(t)$, along with terms of still higher order. (In general, there will be terms proportional to $\delta^{(2^n-1)}$ in the nth iterate.) It is also interesting to note that if we define

$$\omega_1 \equiv \omega_0 [1 - \tfrac{5}{6}\delta^2]^{1/2} , \qquad (8.51)$$

and replace ω_0 by ω_1 in $\cos \omega_0 t$, then through order δ^2, $x_2(t)$ can be written as in Eq. (8.50), but with the omission of the term linear in t and proportional to δ^2. This follows from the fact that through order δ^2

$$\cos \omega_0 t + \tfrac{5}{12}\delta^2\omega_0 t \sin \omega_0 t \simeq \cos \omega_1 t ,$$

where ω_1 is given by Eq. (8.51). Thus, by redefining the frequency, it is possible to eliminate terms proportional to t, at least through order δ^2. It can be shown (see Problem 8.15) that a similar elimination can be achieved for all terms through order δ^3.

8.5 SEPARABLE KERNELS

We have now seen in some detail how to solve linear equations involving operators of small norm. However, it is clear, particularly from the example discussed at the end of Section 8.3, that there are many interesting problems which involve operators of finite, but not necessarily small, norm. We must therefore develop techniques of more general applicability.

We might hope that it will prove possible to treat operators on infinite-dimensional spaces in the same way that we treated operators on finite-dimensional spaces (Chapters 3 and 4). There we could simply take an operator, A, and turn it into a finite-dimensional matrix by computing its inner product between the finite number of vectors which constitute an orthonormal basis for the space. However, on infinite-dimensional spaces there must be an infinite number of vectors in any basis, so this procedure would lead us to infinite-dimensional matrices, and we have said nothing about such objects in previous chapters. (Even the problem of multiplying two infinite-dimensional matrices is not a trivial one because of convergence questions.)

On the other hand, we know that if we write a function, f, in terms of an orthonormal basis, $\{\phi_n\}$, of Hilbert space by computing the expansion coefficients, $a_n = (\phi_n, f)$, we can associate the infinite collection of a_n with an infinite column vector, and, more important, as n becomes large, say $n > N$, the elements a_n with $n > N$ become *small* (Bessel's inequality). Thus any function in Hilbert space can be approximated arbitrarily closely by a *finite* linear combination,

$$f \equiv \sum_{n=1}^{N} a_n \phi_n .$$

This encourages us to believe that perhaps the same situation will prevail for linear operators; namely, if we start computing the matrix elements of an operator, A, between the elements of an infinite orthonormal basis, then after we have computed enough matrix elements, A_{mn}, the elements will start to become small, just as did the a_n in the case of vectors. Thus we might hope that we can stop completely when we get to a large $N \times N$ array and just forget about the elements A_{mn}, with m or n greater than N. The value of N would, of course, have to depend on the degree of precision which one wanted in a given problem, but we imagine that any degree of precision can be obtained by this method.

If this were possible, the problem would come down to simple matrix diagonalization or inversion, which we can carry out by employing the methods of Chapters 3 and 4. We shall see that there is a rather large class of operators for which such an approach will work. It is the purpose of the subsequent sections of this chapter and also of the following chapter to present in some detail the theory of such operators.

It is best, however, to start with a type of operator for which no approximation is necessary in the reduction to a simple matrix. This is the class of operators of *finite rank*, so called because they are directly reducible to finite-dimensional matrices (and hence, by the discussion in Section 3.10, to matrices of finite rank).

To illustrate what we have in mind, let us consider a separable kernel, i.e., one which has the form

$$k_s(x, y) = \lambda \phi(x) \psi^*(y) , \tag{8.52}$$

where for the sake of simplicity we shall assume that ϕ and ψ are functions in Hilbert space. If

$$\int |k_s(x, y)|^2 \, dx \, dy < 1 , \tag{8.53}$$

then we know from our work in the previous section that the Neumann series converges. Let us look at this series. The iterative solution to the equation

$$f(x) = g(x) + \int k_s(x, y) f(y) \, dy \tag{8.54}$$

is

$$f(x) = g(x) + \int dy_1 \, k_s(x, y_1) g(y_1) + \int dy_1 \int dy_2 \, k_s(x, y_1) k_s(y_1, y_2) g(y_2) + \cdots$$

Since $k_s(x, y)$ is square integrable as a function of two variables, $\phi(x)$ and $\psi(y)$ must be square integrable as functions of a single variable. Thus if $g(x)$ is square integrable, then all the integrals in the iteration are well defined, and thus

$$f(x) = g(x) + \lambda \int dy_1 \, \phi(x) \psi^*(y_1) g(y_1)$$
$$+ \lambda^2 \int dy_1 \int dy_2 \, \phi(x) \psi^*(y_1) \phi(y_1) \psi^*(y_2) g(y_2) + \cdots$$

Let us set

$$\int \psi^*(y) \phi(y) \, dy = (\psi, \phi) \, .$$

Then $f(x)$ can be written as

$$f(x) = g(x) + \lambda \phi(x)(\psi, g) + \lambda^2 \phi(x)(\psi, \phi)(\psi, g)$$
$$+ \lambda^3 \phi(x)(\psi, \phi)^2(\psi, g) + \cdots \tag{8.55}$$
$$= g(x) + \lambda \phi(x)(\psi, g) \sum_{n=0}^{\infty} \lambda^n (\psi, \phi)^n \, .$$

If $|\lambda(\psi, \phi)| < 1$, the series of Eq. (8.55) converges. In fact, $|\lambda(\psi, \phi)|$ *is* less than unity. To prove this, note that Eq. (8.53) implies

$$|\lambda|^2 \int |\phi(x)|^2 \, dx \int |\psi(y)|^2 \, dy < 1 \, . \tag{8.56}$$

But by Schwartz's inequality,

$$|(\psi, \phi)| \leq [(\phi, \phi)(\psi, \psi)]^{1/2} \, .$$

Thus, by Eq. (8.56),

$$|\lambda(\psi, \phi)| \leq [|\lambda|^2(\phi, \phi)(\psi, \psi)]^{1/2} < 1 \, ,$$

and we can sum the geometric series in Eq. (8.55) directly:

$$f(x) = g(x) + \lambda \frac{(\psi, g)}{1 - \lambda(\psi, \phi)} \phi(x) \, . \tag{8.57}$$

Although we derived this simple result in the framework of the Neumann series, its closed form suggests that it might be more general. That this is indeed the case may be seen by writing Eq. (8.54) as

$$f(x) = g(x) + \lambda \int \phi(x) \psi^*(y) f(y) \, dy$$
$$= g(x) + \lambda \phi(x)(\psi, f) \, . \tag{8.58}$$

If we take the inner product of both sides of Eq. (8.58) with ϕ, we get

$$(\phi, f) = (\phi, g) + \lambda(\phi, \phi)(\phi, f) . \tag{8.59}$$

Thus

$$(\phi, f) = \frac{(\phi, g)}{1 - \lambda(\phi, \phi)} , \tag{8.60}$$

and

$$f(x) = g(x) + \lambda \frac{(\phi, g)}{1 - \lambda(\phi, \phi)} \phi(x) \tag{8.61}$$

for all values of λ, *except* $\lambda = 1/(\phi, \phi)$. Thus right at the boundary of the domain of validity of the Neumann series, we seem to run into ambiguities. The reason for this may be most easily seen by considering the case where $g(x) = 0$. Then our equation becomes simply

$$f(x) = \int k_s(x, y) f(y) \, dy = \lambda \phi(x)(\phi, f) , \tag{8.62}$$

which is an eigenvalue problem of the usual type. Equation (8.62) implies that

$$(\phi, f) = \lambda(\phi, \phi)(\phi, f) ,$$

which has a nonzero solution for (ϕ, f) if and only if

$$\lambda = 1/(\phi, \phi) ,$$

in which case (ϕ, f) can be any constant. Thus the eigenvalue problem has as its solution

$$f(x) = A\phi(x) ,$$

where A is arbitrary. To fix A, a normalization condition is necessary, just as in the finite-dimensional case. The interesting result is that the condition for the existence of an eigensolution is the same condition under which we saw that a solution of the inhomogeneous equation given by Eq. (8.61) did not exist. But this result is familiar from finite-dimensional theory, where we know that if the homogeneous equation has a solution, then the inhomogeneous term of the inhomogeneous equation must be subject to certain conditions in order that a solution should exist. We see immediately from Eq. (8.61) that we must require $(\phi, g) = 0$ to compensate for the vanishing denominator. Thus in Eq. (8.59) we find that (ϕ, f) is arbitrary, so the solution to Eq. (8.54), given by Eq. (8.58), becomes

$$f(x) = g(x) + B\phi(x) ,$$

where B is an arbitrary constant. Substituting this result into Eq. (8.54), we see that it is indeed a solution for any B when $\lambda(\phi, \phi) = 1$, that is, when $\phi(x)$ is an eigenvector of the integral operator K_s whose kernel is $k_s(x, y)$. This looks very much like the finite-dimensional Theorem 4.27; the resemblance is complete if we note that $(\phi, g) = 0$ means that g is orthogonal to the solution of

$$K_s^\dagger \phi = \lambda^* \int k_s(y, x)\, \phi(y)\, dy = \phi$$

when $\lambda = 1/(\phi, \phi)$.

Thus there is a close relation between this simple infinite-dimensional example and the finite-dimensional case. More interesting, however, is the hint that the divergence of the Neumann series is somehow related to the occurrence of a solution to the homogeneous equation.

Because separable kernels lead to integral equations with extremely simple closed-form solutions, physicists have naturally attempted to make use of them in practical problems. One example of their utility is found in the study of nuclear forces. For many years physicists have tried to determine the form of nucleon-nucleon potentials, and in doing so were forced to discard practically every sacred classical concept of what a potential should be. As mentioned in Chapter 1, the requirement of central potentials had to be abandoned, and it also had to be admitted that nuclear forces might depend on the intrinsic spin of the nuclear particles. It was natural that eventually even the requirement of *locality* would come into doubt.

By a *local potential*, we mean one whose action at a point depends only on what is happening at that point. Thus Schrödinger's equation is traditionally written with a local potential:

$$-\frac{\hbar^2}{2m} \nabla^2 \psi(\mathbf{r}) + V(\mathbf{r})\psi(\mathbf{r}) = E\phi(\mathbf{r}) \, . \tag{8.63}$$

However, it cannot be ruled out a priori that in quantum mechanics the potential may be an operator which acts in a nonlocal manner. For example, we could imagine writing Schrödinger's equation as

$$-\frac{\hbar^2}{2m} \nabla^2 \psi + \int U(\mathbf{r}, \mathbf{r}')\psi(\mathbf{r}')\, d\mathbf{r}' = E\phi(\mathbf{r}') \, . \tag{8.64}$$

We see from this equation that the effect of the potential operating on ϕ does not depend just on the value of ϕ at one point $\mathbf{r}$, as is the case in Eq. (8.63), but on the integral over some region of space weighted by the potential function $U(\mathbf{r}, \mathbf{r}')$. Note that if we want the Hamiltonian of Eq. (8.64) to be Hermitian, we must require that

$$U(\mathbf{r}, \mathbf{r}') = U(\mathbf{r}', \mathbf{r})^* \, , \tag{8.65}$$

The Green's function technique developed in Chapter 7 can readily be applied to Eq. (8.64). Proceeding in the manner described in Section 7.4, we find that $\psi(\mathbf{r})$ is given by the integral equation

$$\psi(\mathbf{r}) = \frac{A}{(2\pi)^{3/2}} e^{i\mathbf{q}_i \cdot \mathbf{r}} - \frac{m}{2\pi\hbar^2} \iint \frac{e^{iq_i|\mathbf{r}-\mathbf{r}'|}}{|\mathbf{r}-\mathbf{r}'|} U(\mathbf{r}', \mathbf{r}'')\psi(\mathbf{r}'')\, d\mathbf{r}'\, d\mathbf{r}'' \, , \tag{8.66}$$

where $\mathbf{q}_i$, m, $\hbar$, and A have the same significance as in Section 7.4. Note the similarity between this equation and Eq. (7.68). As was mentioned in Section

7.4, one of the most interesting physical quantities is the scattering amplitude $f^s(\mathbf{q}_f)$, which is defined in terms of the amplitude of the outgoing scattered wave. If we proceed as in Section 7.4, it is a simple matter to show that $f^s(\mathbf{q}_f)$ is given by

$$f^s(\mathbf{q}_f) = f(\mathbf{q}_f) , \qquad (8.67a)$$

where f satisfies the integral equation

$$f(\mathbf{k}) = -\frac{4\pi^2 m}{\hbar^2} \hat{U}(\mathbf{k}, \mathbf{q}_i) - \frac{2m}{\hbar^2} \int \hat{U}(\mathbf{k}, \mathbf{q}) \frac{1}{q^2 - (q_i + i\epsilon)^2} f(\mathbf{q}) \, d\mathbf{q} , \qquad (8.67b)$$

where $\hat{U}(\mathbf{k}, \mathbf{q})$ is the Fourier transform of $U(\mathbf{r}, \mathbf{r}')$, that is,

$$\hat{U}(\mathbf{k}, \mathbf{q}) = \frac{1}{(2\pi)^3} \int\int e^{i\mathbf{q}\cdot\mathbf{r}'} e^{i\mathbf{k}\cdot\mathbf{r}} \hat{U}(\mathbf{r}, \mathbf{r}') \, d\mathbf{r} \, d\mathbf{r}' .$$

In Eqs. (8.67a) and (8.67b), $\mathbf{q}_i$ represents the incident direction of the particle and $\mathbf{q}_f$ represents its final direction. The magnitudes of $\mathbf{q}_i$ and $\mathbf{q}_f$ are equal and given by

$$|\mathbf{q}_i| = |\mathbf{q}_f| = \left[\frac{2mE}{\hbar^2}\right]^{1/2} .$$

Once we have $f(\mathbf{k})$, all the quantities of interest in the scattering process can be determined. For a general $U(\mathbf{k}, \mathbf{q})$ there is not much we can say about this function $f(\mathbf{k})$, but if we take U to be of the *separable* form, that is,

$$U(\mathbf{r}, \mathbf{r}') = -g^2 v(\mathbf{r}) v(\mathbf{r}') , \qquad (8.68)$$

then we can make progress. Here $v(\mathbf{r})$ is a real-valued function, in order to insure that U is Hermitian. Using this form for U and denoting the Fourier transform of $v(\mathbf{r})$ by $\hat{v}(\mathbf{k})$, we bring Eq. (8.67b) to the form

$$f(\mathbf{k}) = \frac{4\pi^2 m g^2}{\hbar^2} \hat{v}(\mathbf{q}_i) \hat{v}(\mathbf{k}) + \frac{2m g^2}{\hbar^2} \int \hat{v}(\mathbf{k}) \frac{\hat{v}(\mathbf{q})}{q^2 - (q_i + i\epsilon)^2} f(\mathbf{q}) \, d\mathbf{q} ,$$

or

$$f(\mathbf{k}) = \pi\tau \hat{v}(\mathbf{q}_i) \hat{v}(\mathbf{k}) + \frac{\tau}{2\pi} \int \hat{v}(\mathbf{k}) \frac{\hat{v}(\mathbf{q})}{q^2 - (q_i + i\epsilon)^2} f(\mathbf{q}) \, d\mathbf{q} , \qquad (8.69)$$

where we have set $4\pi m g^2/\hbar^2 \equiv \tau$. But Eq. (8.69) has precisely the form of Eq. (8.54) if we make the identifications

$$x \to \mathbf{k} , \qquad y \to \mathbf{q} , \qquad g(x) \to \pi\tau \hat{v}(\mathbf{q}_i) \hat{v}(\mathbf{k}) , \qquad \phi(x) \to \hat{v}(\mathbf{k}) ,$$

$$\phi^*(y) \to \frac{\hat{v}(\mathbf{q})}{q^2 - (q_i + i\epsilon)^2} ,$$

and set $\lambda = \tau/2\pi$. Of course, the volume of integration is three-dimensional, but in Eq. (8.54) one need not be so literal-minded as to associate x and y with one-dimensional vectors and dy with a one-dimensional volume. The solution to Eq. (8.69) is given immediately by Eq. (8.61). We find that

$$f(\mathbf{k}) = \pi\tau\hat{v}(\mathbf{q}_i)\hat{v}(\mathbf{k}) + \lambda \frac{\displaystyle\int \frac{\hat{v}(\mathbf{q})}{q^2 - (q_i + i\epsilon)^2}[\pi\tau\hat{v}(\mathbf{q}_i)\hat{v}(\mathbf{q})]\,d\mathbf{q}}{1 - \lambda \displaystyle\int \frac{\hat{v}(\mathbf{q})}{q^2 - (q_i + i\epsilon)^2}\hat{v}(\mathbf{q})\,d\mathbf{q}}\hat{v}(\mathbf{k})\ ,$$

which can be written as

$$\begin{aligned}f(\mathbf{k}) &= \pi\tau\hat{v}(\mathbf{q}_i)\hat{v}(\mathbf{k})[1 + \lambda I/(1 - \lambda I)]\\ &= \pi\tau\hat{v}(\mathbf{q}_i)\hat{v}(\mathbf{k})/(1 - \lambda I)\ ,\end{aligned}$$

where we define

$$I \equiv \int \frac{\hat{v}(\mathbf{q})\hat{v}(\mathbf{q})}{q^2 - (q_i + i\epsilon)^2}\,d\mathbf{q}\ .$$

According to the definition of $f^s(\mathbf{q}_f)$, we see that

$$f^s(\mathbf{q}_f) = \frac{\pi\tau\hat{v}(\mathbf{q}_i)\hat{v}(\mathbf{q}_f)}{1 - \tau I/2\pi}\ . \tag{8.70}$$

Thus given any function $v(\mathbf{r})$ [or $v(\mathbf{q})$] the problem is solved. One obvious choice for $v(\mathbf{r})$ is a simple Yukawa potential, $v(\mathbf{r}) = e^{-\mu r}/r$, with the corresponding Fourier transform given by Eq. (7.58'):

$$\hat{v}(\mathbf{q}) = \left(\frac{2}{\pi}\right)^{1/2}\frac{1}{q^2 + \mu^2}\ . \tag{8.71}$$

Since this depends only on q^2, we see that $f^s(\mathbf{q}_f)$ will depend only on the magnitude of $\mathbf{q}_f$ (and of $\mathbf{q}_i$). We can therefore consider f^s to be a function of E alone, and not of the scattering angle. For this choice of $\hat{v}(\mathbf{q})$, the integral I can be readily computed by the contour integral techniques of Chapter 6. One finds that

$$I = -\frac{2\pi}{\mu}\frac{1}{(q_i + i\mu)^2}\ , \tag{8.72}$$

where we have let ϵ go to zero after performing the integration. Putting Eqs. (8.71) and (8.72) into Eq. (8.70), we find that

$$f^s(E) = \frac{2\tau}{(q_i^2 + \mu^2)^2 + \dfrac{\tau}{\mu}(q_i - i\mu)^2}\ . \tag{8.73}$$

If we make the definitions

$$a_0 \equiv \frac{2}{\mu}\left(1 - \frac{\mu^3}{\tau}\right)^{-1}\ ,\qquad r_0 \equiv \frac{1}{\mu}\left(1 + \frac{2\mu^3}{\tau}\right)\ ,$$

then

$$f^s(E) = \left[-\frac{1}{a_0} + \frac{1}{2}r_0 q_i^2 + \frac{1}{2\tau}q_i^4 - iq_i\right]^{-1}\ . \tag{8.74}$$

We see that f^s has no angular dependence; i.e., it represents pure s-wave $(l = 0)$ scattering.

It can be shown that for any well-behaved short-range *local* potential, the low energy ($\mathbf{q}_i$ small) behavior of the s-wave scattering amplitude is

$$f^s = \left[-\frac{1}{a_0} + \frac{1}{2} r_0 q_i^2 + \cdots - iq_i \right]^{-1} ,$$

where a_0 and r_0 can be calculated from the specific form of the local potential. (See, for example, Blatt and Weisskopf, *Theoretical Nuclear Physics*.) This is known as the effective range form of f^s; a_0 and r_0 are called the *scattering length* and the *effective range* respectively. Thus we see that it is possible to find a non-local potential, which can be handled in closed form, whose associated scattering amplitude looks just like the low energy scattering amplitude for a local potential. We leave it as an exercise for the reader to show that the above potential can also give rise to a bound state (i.e., a negative eigenvalue of Schrödinger's equation) if g is sufficiently large.

Because of the possibility of accommodating a bound deuteron and also because it gives rise to a scattering amplitude of the effective range type, the separable potential of Eq. (8.68) (and its generalization to spin-dependent forces) has often been used to analyze the low energy properties of the nucleon-nucleon system. In recent years, potentials of this type have also been used in theoretical studies of three-particle systems, where their simple form is very useful in obtaining tractable expressions for three-particle scattering amplitudes and bound state wave functions.

8.6 GENERAL KERNELS OF FINITE RANK

Now that we have seen how the separable kernel leads to a closed-form solution to an integral equation, it is not difficult to generalize to kernels of *finite rank*. The only complication is that instead of being able to reduce the vector space equation to a single scalar equation as we did for separable kernels, for kernels of finite rank we will reduce the vector space equation to a *system* of scalar equations. These equations can be written in the form of a finite-dimensional *matrix* equation, which is why such kernels are said to be of finite rank (see Section 3.10).

We define a *kernel of finite rank* to be of the form

$$K_F f \equiv \sum_{n=1}^{N} \phi_n (\psi_n, f) , \tag{8.75}$$

where f is any vector in the Banach space, B, on which K_F acts. The inner product used here need not be that appropriate to a Hilbert space; all we mean by (ψ_n, f) is a *linear functional*, denoted symbolically by (ψ_n, f), which takes any $f \in B$ into a scalar. The set of all linear functionals on a Banach space, B, is also a Banach space, often referred to as the *dual space* of B. In the case of a Hilbert space, this space of linear functionals is isomorphic to the Hilbert space itself. For the space L_p, the Banach space of linear functionals can be identified isomorphically with the space L_q, where $1/p + 1/q = 1$.

It can readily be shown (see Problem 8.21) that if $f \in L_p$, and $g \in L_q$ and if $1/p + 1/q = 1$, then

$$(g, f) = \int g^* f \, dx$$

exists, and it is in terms of this relation that we shall interpret Eq. (8.75). If the reader wishes, he can view Eq. (8.75) as an equation in Hilbert space, where the symbol $(\ ,\ )$ has its usual interpretation as an inner product. However, it is by no means necessary to do so; the results which we will obtain below are more general.

Since we have already seen that the finite-dimensional Theorem 4.27 holds for separable kernels, it will be interesting to see if it also holds in this more general case. We therefore want to consider the adjoint transformation, $K_F^\dagger$, which is defined by

$$K_F^\dagger \tilde{f} = \sum_{n=1}^{N} \psi_n (\phi_n, \tilde{f}) \ . \tag{8.76}$$

In the light of our previous discussion of Banach spaces, it is clear that if K_F acts on the space L_p, transforming $f \in L_p$ into $K_F f \in L_p$, then $K_F^\dagger$ acts on the space L_q ($1/p + 1/q = 1$), transforming $\tilde{f} \in L_q$ into $K_F^\dagger \tilde{f} \in L_q$. We may remark at this point that seemingly more general forms for K_F such as, for example,

$$K_F' f \equiv \sum_{m,\,n=1}^{N} k_{mn} \phi_m (\psi_n, f) \ ,$$

where k_{mn} is a collection of constants, are included in our definition of Eq. (8.75) since ϕ_m and ψ_n are not assumed to be normalized in any particular way and N, the range of the sum, is completely arbitrary.

We now consider, in the spirit of Theorem 4.27, the two equations

$$f - \lambda K f = g \tag{8.77}$$

and

$$\tilde{h} - \lambda^* K^\dagger \tilde{h} = 0 \ , \tag{8.78}$$

where f and g are vectors in B and $\tilde{h}$ is a vector in the dual space of B. Using the definitions of Eqs. (8.75) and (8.76) respectively, we get

$$f = g + \lambda \sum_{n=1}^{N} \phi_n (\psi_n, f) \tag{8.79}$$

and

$$\tilde{h} - \lambda^* \sum_{n=1}^{N} \psi_n (\phi_n, \tilde{h}) = 0 \ . \tag{8.80}$$

Equation (8.79) tells us that we need to determine only the collection of constants,

$$a_n \equiv (\psi_n, f) \ ,$$

to obtain a solution. Using Eq. (8.79), we find that

$$(\psi_m, f) = (\psi_m, g) + \lambda \sum_{n=1}^{N} (\psi_m, \phi_n)(\psi_n, f) .$$

Setting

$$\alpha_{mn} \equiv (\psi_m, \phi_n) , \qquad b_m \equiv (\psi_m, g) , \tag{8.81}$$

this becomes

$$a_m - \lambda \sum_{n=1}^{N} \alpha_{mn} a_n = b_m .$$

It is convenient to write this in matrix notation as

$$(I - \lambda A)a = b , \tag{8.82}$$

where

$$[A]_{mn} = \alpha_{mn} , \qquad [a]_n = a_n , \qquad [b]_n = b_n .$$

Similarly, if we set $\bar{a}_n = (\phi_n, \bar{h})$, the homogeneous adjoint equation is

$$\bar{a}_m - \lambda^* \sum_{n=1}^{N} (\phi_m, \psi_n)\bar{a}_n = 0 ,$$

which, according to Eq. (8.81), may be written as

$$\bar{a}_m - \lambda^* \sum_{n=1}^{N} \alpha_{nm}^* \bar{a}_n = 0 .$$

In matrix notation, this is just

$$(I - \lambda A)^\dagger \bar{a} = 0 , \tag{8.83}$$

where $[\bar{a}]_n = \bar{a}_n$. Thus our basic equations, Eqs. (8.77) and (8.78), have been transformed into the matrix equations, Eqs. (8.82) and (8.83).

But Eqs. (8.82) and (8.83) are in just the form required by Theorem 4.27. We conclude, therefore, that Eq. (8.82) has a solution if and only if

$$(b, \bar{a}) = 0 = \sum_{n=1}^{N} b_n^* \bar{a}_n \tag{8.84}$$

for all $\bar{a}$ which are solutions of the homogeneous adjoint equation. Similarly, Eq. (8.77) will have solutions only under these conditions. Using the above definitions of b_n and $\bar{a}_n$, this becomes

$$\sum_{n=1}^{N} (g, \psi_n)(\phi_n, \bar{h}) = 0 .$$

But by our definition of $K^\dagger$ [Eq. (8.76)], this is just

$$(g, K^\dagger \bar{h}) = 0 .$$

If $\bar{h} \not\equiv 0$, $\lambda^* K^\dagger \bar{h} = \bar{h}$, by Eq. (8.78), so a solution to Eq. (8.77) exists if we require that

$$(g, \bar{h}) = 0 \tag{8.85}$$

for all $\bar{h}$ satisfying Eq. (8.78). Note that if Eq. (8.83) has no solution then $[I - \lambda A]^{-1}$ exists and Eq. (8.82) has a *unique* solution. Thus, if Eq. (8.78) has no solution, then Eq. (8.77) has a unique solution. We have, therefore, the following result:

Theorem 8.1. If K_F is a linear transformation of finite rank, then the equation

$$f = g + \lambda K_F f$$

has a solution if and only if $(g, \bar{h}_i) = 0$ for all i, where $\bar{h}_i$ satisfies the homogeneous adjoint equation

$$\lambda^* K_F^\dagger \bar{h}_i = \bar{h}_i .$$

If the homogeneous adjoint equation has no solutions then the solution to the inhomogeneous equation is unique.

By an identical argument, the same result holds for $K_F^\dagger$.

Corollary. If K_F is a linear operator of finite rank, then the equation

$$\tilde{f} = \tilde{g} + \lambda^* K_F^\dagger \tilde{f}$$

has a solution if and only if $(\tilde{g}, h_i) = 0$, where h_i is any solution of the homogeneous equation

$$\lambda K_F h_i = h_i .$$

If the homogeneous equation has no solution, then the solution to the inhomogeneous adjoint equation is unique.

The next corollary is an immediate consequence of the finite-dimensional Theorem 4.26.

Corollary. The equations

$$\lambda K_F h_i = h_i \qquad \text{and} \qquad \lambda^* K_F^\dagger \bar{h}_i = \bar{h}_i$$

have the same number of linearly independent solutions.

Theorem 8.1 and its two corollaries are often referred to as the Fredholm alternative ("alternative" because it expresses on option—*either* the inhomogeneous linear equation, $(I - \lambda K)f = g$, has a unique solution *or* the homogeneous adjoint equation possesses at least one solution). They represent an extension of the theorems of Section 4.8 to an infinite-dimensional space, but only for operators of a rather special type. However, in the next section we shall see that this result can be extended to a much broader class of operators.

Before extending these results, let us remark that if a unique solution to Eq. (8.77) exists, then we can find it explicitly by using Eqs. (8.79) and (8.82).

Equation (8.82) tells us that

$$a = (I - \lambda A)^{-1}b \, ,$$

or, in component form

$$a_n \equiv (\psi_n, f) \equiv \sum_{m=1}^{N} [(I - \lambda A)^{-1}]_{nm} b_m$$

$$= \sum_{m=1}^{N} [(I - \lambda A)^{-1}]_{nm} (\psi_m, g) \, .$$

Putting this result into Eq. (8.79), we find that

$$f = g + \lambda \sum_{n=1}^{N} \sum_{m=1}^{N} \phi_n [(I - \lambda A)^{-1}]_{nm} (\psi_m, g) \, , \tag{8.86}$$

which gives us the desired solution if the equation

$$\lambda^* K_F^\dagger \bar{h} = \bar{h}$$

has no solutions, or, equivalently, if the equation

$$(I - \lambda A)^\dagger \bar{a} = 0$$

has no solutions. Thus the problem of solving Eq. (8.77) reduces to calculating the inverse of a given matrix of scalars. Equation (8.86) may be thought of as defining a new operator, G_{K_F}, which is the inverse of $(I - \lambda K_F)$. According to Eq. (8.86), we write

$$G_{K_F} \equiv I + \lambda R_{K_F} = (I - \lambda K_F)^{-1} \, , \tag{8.87}$$

where

$$R_{K_F} f \equiv \sum_{n=1}^{N} \sum_{m=1}^{N} [(I - \lambda A)^{-1}]_{mn} \phi_m (\psi_n, f) \, ; \tag{8.88}$$

R_{K_F} is called the *resolvent* operator corresponding to K_F. It is clearly also an operator of finite rank. It exists whenever $(I - \lambda A)^{-1}$ exists, that is, whenever

$$\det (I - \lambda A) \neq 0 \, .$$

Since $\det (I - \lambda A)$ is a polynomial of degree N in λ, and therefore has N (not necessarily distinct) roots, we see that R_{K_F} is a *meromorphic function* of λ—that is, it is analytic everywhere except for a finite number of poles. At these poles, R_{K_F} fails to exist, and we have a solution to the equation

$$\lambda K_F h = h \, ,$$

or, equivalently, to the equation

$$\lambda^* K_F^\dagger \bar{h} = \bar{h} \, .$$

It is a worthwhile exercise to check that

$$(I - \lambda K_F)(I + \lambda R_{K_F}) = (I + \lambda R_{K_F})(I - \lambda K_F) = I \, .$$

As an example of a kernel of finite rank, consider the equation

$$f(x) = x + \lambda \int_0^\pi \frac{\sin (x + x')}{\pi} f(x') \, dx'$$

$$= x + \lambda \frac{\sin x}{\sqrt{\pi}} \int_0^\pi \frac{\cos x'}{\sqrt{\pi}} f(x') \, dx' + \lambda \frac{\cos x}{\sqrt{\pi}} \int_0^\pi \frac{\sin x'}{\sqrt{\pi}} f(x') \, dx' . \quad (8.89)$$

Calling

$$a_1 = \frac{1}{\sqrt{\pi}} \int_0^\pi \cos x' f(x') \, dx' , \qquad a_2 = \frac{1}{\sqrt{\pi}} \int_0^\pi \sin x' f(x') \, dx' ,$$

and

$$b_1 = \frac{1}{\sqrt{\pi}} \int_0^\pi x \cos x \, dx , \qquad b_2 = \frac{1}{\sqrt{\pi}} \int_0^\pi x \sin x \, dx ,$$

We find that Eq. (8.89) may be transformed to

$$a_1 = b_1 + \lambda \frac{1}{\pi} \int_0^\pi \cos^2 x \, dx \, a_2 , \qquad a_2 = b_2 + \lambda \frac{1}{\pi} \int_0^\pi \sin^2 x \, dx \, a_1 .$$

Thus in matrix notation

$$a = b + \lambda M a \qquad \text{or} \qquad (I - \lambda M)a = b ,$$

where

$$M = \begin{bmatrix} 0 & \frac{1}{2} \\ \frac{1}{2} & 0 \end{bmatrix} , \qquad a = \begin{bmatrix} a_1 \\ a_2 \end{bmatrix} , \qquad b = \begin{bmatrix} b_1 \\ b_2 \end{bmatrix} = \frac{1}{\sqrt{\pi}} \begin{bmatrix} -2 \\ \pi \end{bmatrix} .$$

The inverse matrix $(I - \lambda M)^{-1}$ is

$$\begin{bmatrix} 1 & -\lambda/2 \\ -\lambda/2 & 1 \end{bmatrix}^{-1} = \frac{1}{1 - \lambda^2/4} \begin{bmatrix} 1 & \lambda/2 \\ \lambda/2 & 1 \end{bmatrix} .$$

Hence

$$a = (I - \lambda M)^{-1}b = \frac{1}{1 - \lambda^2/4} \begin{bmatrix} 1 & \lambda/2 \\ \lambda/2 & 1 \end{bmatrix} \frac{1}{\sqrt{\pi}} \begin{bmatrix} -2 \\ \pi \end{bmatrix} ,$$

so

$$a_1 = \frac{2}{\sqrt{\pi}} \frac{(\pi\lambda - 4)}{4 - \lambda^2} , \qquad a_2 = \frac{4}{\sqrt{\pi}} \frac{\pi - \lambda}{4 - \lambda^2} .$$

Thus

$$f(x) = x + 2\lambda \frac{(\lambda - 4/\pi)}{4 - \lambda^2} \sin x + 4\lambda \frac{(1 - \lambda/\pi)}{4 - \lambda^2} \cos x . \qquad (8.90)$$

Clearly, when $\lambda = \pm 2$, this solution becomes infinite, corresponding to the existence of solutions to the homogeneous equation for these values.

The Neumann series for $f(x)$ is

$$f(x) = x + \frac{\lambda}{\pi} \int_0^\pi dx' \sin (x + x')x'$$

$$+ \frac{\lambda^2}{\pi^2} \int_0^\pi dx' \int_0^\pi dx'' \sin (x + x') \sin (x' + x'')x'' + \cdots .$$

According to our previously developed convergence criteria, this series will certainly converge when

$$\frac{|\lambda|}{\pi} \left[\int_0^\pi \int_0^\pi \sin^2 (x + x') \, dx \, dx' \right]^{1/2} < 1 .$$

Performing the integrations, we find the requirement that $\lambda < \sqrt{2}$. The first few terms of the Neumann series, written out explicitly, are

$$f(x) = x + \lambda[\cos x - (2/\pi) \sin x] + \lambda^2[(1/2) \sin x - (1/\pi) \cos x] + \cdots \quad (8.91)$$

This result agrees with the first few terms in the power series expansion of Eq. (8.90). Since the power series converges whenever $\lambda < 2$, it is clear that the Neumann series must also converge if $\lambda < 2$. Thus we see that the estimate on the norm of an integral operator given by the integrated square of its kernel provides only a lower bound on the radius of convergence of the Neumann series. In fact, even if we knew the exact norm of the operator, the requirement $||K|| < 1$ only tells us that the Neumann series *will* converge if $||K|| < 1$, not that it will *fail* to converge if $||K|| > 1$.

When $\lambda = \pm 2$, the two eigenvectors of

$$f(x) = \lambda \int_0^\pi \frac{\sin (x + x')}{\pi} f(x') \, dx'$$

turn out to be $f_+(x) = A_+ (\sin x + \cos x)$ and $f_-(x) = A_- (\sin x - \cos x)$, corresponding respectively to $\lambda_+ = 2$ and $\lambda_- = -2$. If we normalize them to unity, we find that

$$f_+(x) = \sqrt{\frac{2}{\pi}} \sin \left(x + \frac{\pi}{4} \right) , \qquad f_-(x) = \sqrt{\frac{2}{\pi}} \sin \left(x - \frac{\pi}{4} \right) .$$

Note that these two solutions are orthogonal, as they should be, since $k(x, y) = (1/\pi) \sin (x + y)$ is a real symmetric kernel.

Figure 8.1 shows, for the case $\lambda = 1$, the exact solution compared to the iterates:

$$f_0(x) = x ,$$
$$f_1(x) = x + \lambda[\cos x - (2/\pi) \sin x] ,$$
$$f_2(x) = x + \lambda[\cos x - (2/\pi) \sin x] + \lambda^2[(1/2) \sin x - (1/\pi) \cos x] .$$

It is seen that $f_2(x)$ is a very good approximation to the exact solution, even though $||K_F|| \cong \frac{1}{2}$ when $\lambda = 1$.

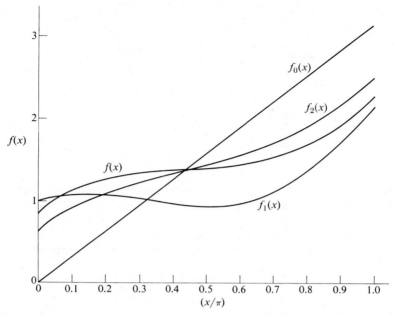

Fig. 8.1 The exact solution, $f(x)$, to Eq. (8.79) of the text, compared with the first three Neumann iterates, $f_0(x)$, $f_1(x)$, and $f_2(x)$.

8.7 COMPLETELY CONTINUOUS OPERATORS

Although the kernels of finite rank which we have discussed thus far lead to integral equations which can be solved in closed form, they are seldom *directly* relevant to physical problems. The integral equations which arise in physics (for example, in Schrödinger's integral equation and its relativistic generalizations) usually have kernels, $k(x, y)$, in which the x- and y-dependence cannot be unravelled into sums of the form of Eq. (8.75).

The reason that we have nevertheless spent so much time talking about these transformations of finite rank is explained by the following theorem.

Theorem 8.2. Any linear transformation of Hilbert space whose kernel is continuous and square integrable as a function of two variables can be approximated arbitrarily closely in norm by a linear transformation of finite rank.

Proof. The simplest case is when the functions in the Hilbert space are defined on a finite interval. Then the two-dimensional Weierstrass theorem tells us that $k(x, y)$ can be approximated *uniformly* by a polynomial; in other words, given any δ there exists a polynomial $P_N(x, y)$, where N depends on δ such that

$$|k(x, y) - P_N(x, y)| < \delta$$

for all x, y. Note that a kernel in polynomial form is a kernel of finite rank since

$$P_N(x, y) = \sum_{m,\,n=0}^{N} C_{mn} x^m y^n$$

for all x, y. Hence

$$\int_a^b dx \int_a^b dy \, |k(x, y) - P_N(x, y)| \le [\delta(b - a)]^2 \,.$$

Thus we can find an N which will provide a δ to make

$$||K - K_N|| < \epsilon$$

for any preassigned ϵ, where K_N is the transformation whose kernel is $P_N(x, y)$. Now if the Hilbert space is defined over an infinite interval, we need only truncate the kernel by setting it equal to zero for all x, y which lie outside some set, B, of finite area. Call this kernel k_B and the related linear transformation K_B. Then if we let $C(B)$ denote the complement of B in the xy-plane,

$$\int_{-\infty}^{\infty} dx \int_{-\infty}^{\infty} dy \, |k(x, y) - k_B(x, y)|^2 = \int dx \int_{C(B)} dy \, |k(x, y)|^2 \,.$$

But $k(x, y)$ is square integrable, so it must be possible to choose a set of points outside of which the integral of $|k|^2$ is arbitrarily small. Thus we can choose B so that

$$||K - K_B|| < \epsilon/2 \,.$$

But by previous reasoning, we can find a polynomial kernel $k_N(x, y)$ with related linear transformation K_N such that

$$||K_B - K_N|| < \epsilon/2 \,.$$

Thus

$$||K - K_N|| \le ||K - K_B|| + ||K_B - K_N|| < \epsilon$$

for a suitable choice of N, which is what we wanted to show.

This theorem can easily be weakened to include the case of piecewise continuous kernels. Furthermore, the theorem can be extended to the class of square-integrable kernels with no continuity or boundedness requirements on $k(x, y)$ other than those implied by square integrability. The only difficulty in this more general case will be the fact that the kernel can become infinite at some points. For example, in the space $L_2[0, 1]$, the linear operator whose kernel is

$$k(x, y) = 1/\sqrt{x + y} \tag{8.92}$$

is an admissible operator because $k(x, y)$ is square integrable. However, at the point $x = 0$, $y = 0$ the kernel becomes infinite. This difficulty is easily overcome. We truncate the kernel by setting it equal to zero whenever $|k(x, y)| \ge$

L; where L is a number which may be made as large as we please. The truncated kernel, $k_L(x, y)$, can be approximated in the manner of Theorem 8.2. However, since $k(x, y)$ is square integrable, it must be possible to choose L sufficiently large so that we make negligible error in using $k_L(x, y)$ instead of $k(x, y)$; that is, the number

$$I_L = \int dx \int dy \, |k(x, y) - k_L(x, y)|^2$$

can be made as small as we please. I_L can be written as

$$I_L = \iint\limits_{\mathscr{D}_L} |k(x, y)|^2 \, dx \, dy \,,$$

where $\mathscr{D}_L$ is the set of points on which $|k(x, y)| \geq L$. Now clearly it must be possible to choose L sufficiently large so that the area of $\mathscr{D}_L$ is as small as we please [otherwise $k(x, y)$ would not be square integrable]. Also, it is clear that I_L must be finite for any $\mathscr{D}_L$ or again $k(x, y)$ would not be square integrable. There remains only the possibility that although the area of $\mathscr{D}_L$ is as small as we please, the integral of $|k(x, y)|^2$ over this arbitrarily small set is finite. Now it is possible to imagine objects which are singular in just such a way that their integral over an arbitrarily small set is finite; the δ-function, for example, has this property. However, in the Lebesgue theory of integration (and also in the Riemann theory) such objects are excluded from the class of admissible *functions*, and therefore we exclude them from the vector space of square-integrable functions. The kernel mentioned above [Eq. (8.92)], although singular at the origin, still has the property that the integral of $|k(x, y)|^2$ over a region of arbitrarily small area containing the origin tends toward zero as the area of the region tends toward zero. Thus *Theorem 8.2 can be extended to the space of square-integrable functions.*

Because of the practical importance of square-integrable kernels (see, for example, Section 8.3) this result is extremely useful, and in Chapter 9 we will develop its consequences in considerable detail. However, for many purposes it is best to concentrate not on the property of finite rank approximation, but rather on a more subtle property which can be inferred from it (and which is, in fact, equivalent to it). It is with this in mind that we introduce the concept of a *completely continuous* operator.

Definition 8.8. A linear operator on a normed vector space is said to be *completely continuous* if it transforms *any* bounded sequence of vectors (i.e., vectors whose norms are all less than some fixed constant) into a sequence containing a subsequence which converges in norm.

The use of the terminology *completely continuous* is fairly clear from the definition. An *ordinary* continuous (i.e., bounded) transformation maintains the status quo regarding convergent sequences; if $\{f_n\}$ converges, so does $\{Kf_n\}$ if K is continuous. But a *completely* continuous transform *forces* sequences to converge, even though they may not have converged originally. For the definition of complete continuity to be at all interesting, it must be possible to choose an infinite sequence of vectors which has a subsequence that does not converge. In a finite-dimensional space, it is impossible to find such a sequence because of the existence of the Bolzano-Weierstrass theorem* for real numbers. Thus the definition is empty on a finite-dimensional space; or if one likes, one may say that on a finite-dimensional vector space all operators are completely continuous.

Let us obtain some of the simpler properties of such transformations. Obviously, the sum of any finite number of completely continuous transformations is completely continuous. We can also show that the product of a completely continuous transformation and a bounded transformation is completely continuous. Suppose that K is completely continuous and let B be a bounded transformation. Consider KB acting on $\{f_n\}$, where $||f_n|| < C$ for all n. Then K acts on the sequence $\{Bf_n\}$, which is bounded because B is a bounded operator. Since K is completely continuous, there must be a subsequence of $\{KBf_n\}$ which converges in norm to an element of the space, so KB is completely continuous. Now consider BK acting on $\{f_n\}$. Since K is completely continuous, $\{Kf_n\}$ possesses a subsequence which converges in norm. Since B is bounded, it is continuous, so $\{BKf_n\}$ has a trivially related convergent subsequence.

We now show that the class of such transformations is not empty. Consider the space of square-integrable functions and take the separable transformation K_s with kernel

$$k_s(x, y) = \phi(x)\psi^*(y) ,$$

along with any sequence $\{f_n\}$, $||f_n|| < C$ for all n. Now

$$K_s f_n = \phi(x)(\psi, f_n) .$$

Since $|(\psi, f_n)| \le ||\psi|| \cdot ||f_n||$, the sequence of complex numbers (ψ, f_n) is bounded in the complex plane and therefore possesses a convergent subsequence (Bolzano-Weierstrass theorem). Call the limit of this subsequence l, and consider

$$||K_s f_{n_k} - l\phi|| = ||\phi[(\psi, f_{n_k}) - l]|| \le ||\phi|| \cdot |(\psi, f_{n_k}) - l| ,$$

where n_k $(k = 1, 2, 3, \cdots)$ defines the convergent subsequence. Since $|(\psi, f_{n_k}) - l|$ tends toward zero as n_k increases, we have

$$K_s f_{n_k} \to l\phi$$

in the norm of the space, so K_s is completely continuous. Hence any operator of finite rank is completely continuous, since it is a finite sum of separable operators.

Of course, there are also many operators which are not completely continuous. Consider $D_x = -i d/dx$ acting on the space of square-integrable functions on $[0, 1]$. We know that $\{f_n = e^{inx}\}$ is a bounded sequence, but $\{Df_n =$

---

* For our purposes, the Bolzano-Weierstrass theorem may be stated as follows: From every bounded sequence of points in n-dimensional Euclidean space, it is possible to select a convergent subsequence.

ne^{inx}} does not contain a convergent subsequence. In fact, even the identity operator is not completely continuous.

A particularly interesting property of the class of completely continuous operators is that the limit of any sequence of completely continuous operators is itself a completely continuous operator.

Theorem 8.3. If $||K_i - K|| \to 0$ as $i \to \infty$, and if K_i is a completely continuous transformation for all i, then K is also completely continuous.

Proof. Let $\{f_n\}$ be any bounded sequence of functions. Then we can select a subsequence, $\{f_{n_1}^{(1)}\}$, such that $\{K_1 f_{n_1}^{(1)}\}$ converges in norm, since K_1 is completely continuous. Now consider the bounded sequence $\{f_{n_1}^{(1)}\}$. From this we can select a subsequence, $\{f_{n_2}^{(2)}\}$, such that $\{K_2 f_{n_2}^{(2)}\}$ converges in norm. Clearly, $\{K_1 f_{n_2}^{(2)}\}$ will still converge in norm. We can continue this process indefinitely, thus obtaining finally a sequence $\{\phi_m\}$ such that $\{K_i \phi_m\}$ converges in norm for all K_i. Now consider

$$K\phi_n - K\phi_m = K\phi_n - K_i\phi_n + K_i\phi_n - K_i\phi_m + K_i\phi_m - K\phi_m .$$

By the triangle inequality, we find that

$$||K\phi_n - K\phi_m|| \le ||K\phi_n - K_i\phi_n|| + ||K_i\phi_n - K_i\phi_m|| + ||K_i\phi_m - K\phi_m||$$
$$\le ||K - K_i|| \cdot ||\phi_n|| + ||K_i\phi_n - K_i\phi_m|| + ||K - K_i|| \cdot ||\phi_m|| .$$

Since the ϕ_n are bounded,

$$||K\phi_n - K\phi_m|| \le C||K - K_i|| + ||K_i\phi_n - K_i\phi_m|| .$$

Because $||K - K_i|| \to 0$, we can pick some i sufficiently large so that

$$||K - K_i|| < \epsilon/(2C) .$$

Then when $m, n > N$ the second term on the right above can be made smaller than $\epsilon/2$. Thus for $m, n > N$, we have

$$||K\phi_n - K\phi_m|| < \epsilon .$$

Hence the sequence $\{K\phi_n\}$ is convergent, and the proof is complete.

As we remarked above, any transformation with a square-integrable kernel can be approximated arbitrarily closely in norm by a kernel of finite rank. Hence such transformations are completely continuous. This theorem underlines the fact that the projection operators, P_n, defined in Section 8.2 do not converge in norm to I, the identity operator. If they did, then since P_n is of finite rank and hence completely continuous, Theorem 8.3 would say that the identity operator is completely continuous, which it is not.

The above results show that any operator which can be approximated in norm by a sequence of operators of finite rank is completely continuous. We now want to show that the converse is also true, namely, any completely continuous operator can be approximated in norm arbitrarily closely by a sequence of operators of finite rank. In order that we may make use of a complete orthonormal basis, we will prove this result only in Hilbert space.

Patterning our work on the techniques of Chapter 5, let us imagine that we are dealing with an integral transformation whose kernel is $k(x, y)$. Let $\{\phi_n\}$ be an orthonormal basis in L_2. We write

$$k(x, y) = \sum_{n, m=1}^{\infty} (\phi_n \phi_m^*, k) \, \phi_n(x) \, \phi_m^*(y) \,,$$

in the sense of mean convergence. Here we make use of the fact that the collection of all products $\phi_n(x) \phi_m(y)$ [or $\phi_n(x) \phi_m^*(y)$] forms a complete orthonormal basis for the Hilbert space of square-integrable functions of two variables to which $k(x, y)$ belongs. By truncating the sum at some large N, we obtain a kernel of finite rank

$$k_N(x, y) = \sum_{n, m=1}^{N} (\phi_n \phi_m^*, k) \, \phi_n(x) \, \phi_m^*(y) \,.$$

One would hope, on the basis of experience with Fourier series, that this will approximate $k(x, y)$ arbitrarily closely in norm for N sufficiently large. The related transformation K_N is defined by

$$K_N f = \sum_{n, m=1}^{N} \phi_n(x) \, (\phi_n \phi_m^*, k) \, (\phi_m, f) \,. \tag{8.93}$$

We can abbreviate this by writing K_N as (see Problem 8.26)

$$K_N = P_N K P_N \,,$$

where P_N is the projection operator defined by

$$P_N f \equiv \sum_{n=1}^{N} (\phi_n, f) \phi_n \,. \tag{8.94}$$

With the above discussion as background, we now state the final theorem of this chapter in completely generality.

Theorem 8.4. Let $\{\phi_n\}$ be an orthonormal basis* for a Hilbert space H, and let K be a completely continuous operator on H. If we denote by P_N the operator that projects onto the subspace of H spanned by $\{\phi_1, \phi_2, \cdots, \phi_N\}$ and define $K_N \equiv P_N K P_N$, then the operator K_N tends in norm to K as N tends to infinity.

Proof. Consider

$$K - K_N = K - P_N K P_N = K - P_N K + P_N K - P_N K P_N$$
$$= (I - P_N) K + P_N K (I - P_N) \,. \tag{8.95}$$

---

* We are assuming here the existence of a *countable* basis for H. A Hilbert space with this property is called a *separable* Hilbert space; most, but not all, spaces which occur in physics are of this type. The proof of Theorem 8.4 can be extended to nonseparable Hilbert spaces.

If it were true that P_N tended toward I in operator norm, then the triangle inequality applied to Eq. (8.95) would complete the proof, which would then hold for *any bounded* operator. However, as we have already seen, this is *not* the case. The result will be proved by contradiction. The basic idea is that if the theorem is *not* true, then there must exist some real number a, such that for each n we can find a vector f_n, which satisfies

$$||(K - K_n)f_n|| > a||f_n|| , \qquad (8.96)$$

where a is independent of n and $a > 0$. If there were no such number a, then according to Definition 8.7, K_n would tend toward K in norm. If we divide both sides of Eq. (8.96) by $||f_n||$, we may say that if the theorem is *not* true then there exists a sequence of functions $\{f_n : ||f_n|| = 1\}$ such that

$$||(K - K_n)f_n|| > a \qquad (8.97)$$

for all n. Assuming that K is completely continuous, we will show that Eq. (8.97) does not hold, so the theorem must be true. It is important to appreciate the fact that it is *not* enough to show that for any fixed $f \in H$, $||(K - K_n)f|| \to 0$. The triangle inequality applied to Eq. (8.95) would prove this.

We begin our proof by using the triangle inequality together with the relation $||P_N|| \le 1$, to obtain from Eq. (8.95)

$$||(K - K_N)f_N|| \le ||(I - P_N)Kf_N|| + ||P_N K(I - P_N)f_N||$$
$$\le ||(I - P_N)Kf_N|| + ||K(I - P_N)f_N|| . \qquad (8.98)$$

We must now show that both $||(I - P_N)Kf_N||$ and $||K(I - P_N)f_N||$ become small as N increases. It is at this point that the complete continuity of K becomes of central importance. It enables us to choose from the sequence $\{f_N\}$ a subsequence $\{\tilde{g}_n\}$ such that $\{K\tilde{g}_n\}$ converges to a limit, say $\xi \in H$. Consider also the sequence $\{(I - P_n)\tilde{g}_n\}$, which is a bounded sequence since $||I - P_n|| = 1$ and $||\tilde{g}_n|| = 1$. Because K is completely continuous, we can choose a subsequence $\{(I - P_m)g_m\}$, such that $\{K(I - P_m)g_m\}$ converges to a limit, say $\eta \in H$. Note that $\{Kg_m\}$ will converge to ξ since $\{K\tilde{g}_n\}$ converges to ξ and $\{g_m\}$ is a subsequence of $\{\tilde{g}_n\}$. In order to avoid confusion over notation, let us remind the reader that each g_m is equal to some element of our original collection $\{f_N\}$.

The meat of the proof is now behind us; only a few estimates of $||(I - P_m)Kg_m||$ and $||K(I - P_m)g_m||$ remain to be made. Consider first $||(I - P_m)Kg_m||$. We write

$$(I - P_m)Kg_m \equiv (I - P_m)(Kg_m - \xi) + (I - P_m)\xi ,$$

where ξ is a fixed vector, and using the triangle inequality, we find that

$$||(I - P_m)Kg_m|| \le ||(I - P_m)(Kg_m - \xi)|| + ||(I - P_m)\xi||$$
$$\le ||Kg_m - \xi|| + ||\xi - P_m\xi|| ,$$

since $||I - P_m|| = 1$. But by construction, Kg_m tends in norm toward ξ, and since ξ is fixed, $P_m\xi$ tends toward ξ in norm. Thus

$$||(I - P_m)Kg_m|| \to 0 \qquad (8.99)$$

as $m \to \infty$.

Finally, we discuss $||K(I - P_m)g_m||$. By construction, as $m \to \infty$, $K(I - P_m)g_m$ tends in norm toward η. We will show that $||\eta|| = 0$. Consider

$$||\eta||^2 = (\eta, \eta) = \lim_{m \to \infty} (\eta, K(I - P_m)g_m) = \lim_{m \to \infty} ((I - P_m)K^\dagger \eta, g_m) ,$$

where we have used that fact that P_m is self-adjoint (regarding the second equality in the above equation; see Problem 8.21a). But

$$|((I - P_m)K^\dagger \eta, g_m)| \leq ||(I - P_m)K^\dagger \eta|| \, ||g_m|| ,$$

by Schwartz's inequality, so using $||g_m|| = 1$, we have

$$||\eta||^2 \leq \lim_{m \to \infty} ||(I - P_m)K^\dagger \eta|| .$$

Since $K^\dagger \eta$ is a fixed vector, $||(I - P_m)K^\dagger \eta|| \to 0$ as $m \to \infty$, so $||\eta|| = 0$. Thus η is the zero vector, and since $K(I - P_m)g_m$ tends in norm toward η, we may write

$$||K(I - P_m)g_m|| \to 0 \tag{8.100}$$

as $m \to \infty$. Putting the results of Eqs. (8.99) and (8.100) into Eq. (8.98), we see that

$$||(K - K_m)g_m|| \to 0$$

as $m \to \infty$. Since the g_m form a subset of our original collection of f_N, *all* of which were assumed to satisfy $||(K - K_N)f_N|| > a$, where a is strictly positive, we see that we have reached the desired contradiction. Thus the theorem is proved.

This theorem suggests a very attractive method for solving equations involving completely continuous transformations. We just split any such transformation into a "small" operator plus an operator of finite rank. The former will yield to simple iterative techniques while the latter can be handled as an ordinary matrix, as we have seen before. In practice, many problems in physics and engineering must be handled in this way, since the operators are neither "small" enough for a simple Born approximation to be valid, nor simple enough to fall into the finite-rank category. The main problem that remains is to develop a method whereby the two processes, iteration and finite-rank approximation, can be combined. It is to this matter that Chapter 9 is primarily devoted.

PROBLEMS

1. Prove that the space C of continuous functions on $[a, b]$ with norm given by

$$||f|| = \max_{a \leq x \leq b} |f(x)|$$

for $f \in C$ is a Banach space, i. e., show that it is complete with respect to the above norm.

2. *Hölder's Inequality*

   a) Show that the function $f(z) = z^\alpha - \alpha z - \beta$ takes on a maximum value at $z = 1$ if $\alpha < 1$ and that if $\beta = 1 - \alpha$, then this maximum value is zero. Thus $z^\alpha \leq \alpha z + \beta$ with $\alpha < 1$, $\beta = 1 - \alpha$.

   b) By making use of the change of variables $z = x/y$, show that $x^\alpha y^\beta \leq \alpha x + \beta y$, where again $\alpha \leq 1$ and $\beta = 1 - \alpha$.

   c) Suppose now that $|f(x)|^p$ and $|g(x)|^q$ are integrable functions with $1/p + 1/q = 1$. Use the result of part (b) to show that

   $$|fg| \leq \frac{1}{p}|f|^p + \frac{1}{q}|g|^q,$$

   so that $|fg|$ is also integrable.

   d) Show that if $|f(x)|^p$ and $|g(x)|^q$ are integrable, then

   $$\left|\int f(x)g(x)\,dx\right| \leq \left[\int |f(x)|^p\,dx\right]^{1/p}\left[\int |g(x)|^q\,dx\right]^{1/q}.$$

   Hint: Apply part (c) to the functions

   $$F(x) = f(x)/\left[\int |f(x)|^p\,dx\right]^{1/p} \quad \text{and} \quad G(x) = g(x)/\left[\int |g(x)|^q\,dx\right]^{1/q}.$$

   This result generalizes Schwartz's inequality of Hilbert space and is known as Hölder's inequality.

3. *Minkowski's Inequality*

   a) Show that $|f(x) + g(x)|^p \leq 2^p[|f(x)|^p + |g(x)|^p]$, and hence that if f and g belong to L_p (the space of p-integrable functions), then so does $f + g$. Thus L_p is indeed a vector space.

   b) Show that for $p > 1$,

   $$\int |f(x) + g(x)|^p\,dx \leq \int |f(x)|\,|f(x) + g(x)|^{p-1}\,dx + \int |g(x)|\,|f(x) + g(x)|^{p-1}\,dx,$$

   and that $|f + g|^{p-1}$ belongs to L_q if f and g belong to L_p, where $1/p + 1/q = 1$.

   c) Apply Hölder's inequality (see Problem 8.2) to each of the two integrals on the right-hand side of the inequality in part (b), and hence show that

   $$\left[\int |f(x) + g(x)|^p\,dx\right]^{1/p} \leq \left[\int |f(x)|^p\,dx\right]^{1/p} + \left[\int |g(x)|^p\,dx\right]^{1/p}.$$

   This is Minkowski's inequality. We see therefore that $[\int |f(x)|^p\,dx]^{1/p}$ does indeed define a norm for the space L_p; Minkowski's inequality is just a statement of the triangle inequality which is the essential ingredient in the definition of a norm.

4. Solve the equations

   a) $f(x) = 1 + \lambda \int_0^\infty e^{-(x+y)} f(y)\,dy$ b) $f(x) = 1 + \lambda \int_0^x f(y)\,dy$

   by iteration. For what values of λ will the iterations converge?

5. Multiplying both sides of Eq. (8.27) by $V^{1/2}(\mathbf{r})$ [assume $V(\mathbf{r})$ to be strictly positive], show that if we define

$$\tilde{\phi}(\mathbf{r}) = V^{1/2}(\mathbf{r})\phi(\mathbf{r}), \qquad \tilde{\xi}(\mathbf{r}) = V^{1/2}(\mathbf{r})\xi(\mathbf{r})$$

and

$$\tilde{k}(\mathbf{r}, \mathbf{r}', E) = V^{1/2}(\mathbf{r})G_0(\mathbf{r}, \mathbf{r}', E)V^{1/2}(\mathbf{r}') ,$$

then

$$\tilde{\phi}(\mathbf{r}) = \tilde{\xi}(\mathbf{r}) + \int \tilde{k}(\mathbf{r}, \mathbf{r}', E)\tilde{\phi}(\mathbf{r}')\, d\mathbf{r}' .$$

Calling $\tilde{K}$ the integral operator whose kernel is $\tilde{k}(\mathbf{r}, \mathbf{r}', E)$, show that the norm of $\tilde{K}$ is the same as the norm of the kernel of Eq. (8.27) obtained by the weight-function method. Show also that if we iterate the equation for $\tilde{\phi}(\mathbf{r})$, the object $V^{1/2}(\mathbf{r})$ never actually appears in the calculation—the ordinary Born series for $\phi(\mathbf{r})$ is duplicated, apart from a multiplicative factor of $V^{1/2}(\mathbf{r})$.

6. Estimate the norm of the kernel of the Lippmann-Schwinger equation when $V(\mathbf{r}) = V_0 e^{-\mu r}$. For what values of V_0 will the Born series converge according to this estimate.

7. a) Suppose that we have an attractive δ-function potential in one dimension, $V(x) = -V_0\delta(x)$. Using the result of Problem 7.10, show that this potential will support one and only one bound state, no matter how large V_0 may be. Determine the binding energy and wave function of this state.

   b) Suppose that particles of positive energy E are incident on a δ-function potential, $V(x) = V_0\delta(x)$, in one dimension. What fraction of the particles is transmitted through the potential barrier and what fraction is reflected?

8. a) Using the result of Problem 7.10, show that if we have a potential $V(x)$ in one dimension which vanishes outside the interval $[-a/2, a/2]$, then, if we denote the wave function in the region $[-\infty, -a/2]$ by $\psi_1(x)$, the wave function in the region $[-a/2, a/2]$ by $\psi_2(x)$ and the wave function in $[a/2, \infty]$ by $\psi_3(x)$, then, calling $E = \hbar^2 k^2/2m$ where $E > 0$ is the energy of the particle and m is its mass,

$$\psi_1(x) = e^{ikx} - \frac{im}{\hbar^2 k} e^{-ikx} \int_{-a/2}^{a/2} e^{ikx'} V(x')\psi_2(x')\, dx' ,$$

$$\psi_3(x) = e^{ikx}\left[1 - \frac{im}{\hbar^2 k} \int_{-a/2}^{a/2} e^{-ikx'} V(x')\,\psi_2(x')\, dx' \right],$$

and

$$\psi_2(x) = e^{ikx} - \frac{im}{\hbar^2 k} \int_{-a/2}^{a/2} e^{ik|x-x'|} V(x')\psi_2(x')\, dx' .$$

Thus we see that in order to determine the wave function in the region where the potential doesn't act, we need only know the wave function in the region where the potential does act.

   b) In part (a) above, assume $V(x) = V_0 =$ constant in the region of interest. Then

$$\psi_2(x) = e^{ikx} - \frac{imV_0}{\hbar^2 k} \int_{-a/2}^{a/2} e^{ik|x-x'|}\psi_2(x')\, dx' .$$

Show that the nth term in the iteration of this equation is less than $(mV_0 a/\hbar^2 k)^{n-1}$ in magnitude; so the iteration will converge if $(mV_0 a/\hbar^2 k) < 1$. Since $\hbar k =$

$p = mv$, this is equivalent to $V_0 a/hv < 1$. This result also holds for three-dimensional problems, although it is much more difficult to prove in that case. Note that the Hilbert space techniques used in the text give estimates for the convergence of the Born series in the three-dimensional case which are independent of the energy of the particle, whereas the result $V_0 a/hv < 1$ says that for *any* potential strength the Born series will converge if the energy of the particle is *sufficiently large*.

9. Using the weight-function method, show that in one dimension the iteration of the Lippmann-Schwinger equation will converge if

$$\frac{1}{hv} \int_{-\infty}^{\infty} V(x) \, dx < 1 ,$$

where $V(x)$ is the potential. Note that if the range of $V(x)$ is a, then

$$\int_{-\infty}^{\infty} V(x) \, dx = \bar{V} a ,$$

where $\bar{V}$ is a mean potential strength. Thus this result is a simple generalization of the result of Problem 8(b). In that problem, the basic physical ideas are clearer, since there we can sharply delineate a region in which the potential acts and a region in which it does not act. The weight function becomes necessary because of the fact that most practical potentials have a nonvanishing magnitude at *all* points of space, although at *most* points the magnitude is small.

10. In Problem 8(a), assume that $V(x) = V_0 = \text{const}$, with V_0 small in the sense of Problem 8(b). Calculate ψ_1 and ψ_3 using the lowest-order approximation to ψ_2. What is the transmission probability in this approximation? What is the probability of reflection? Note that these two probabilities do not add up to 1. Why not? (For exact answers, see L. I. Schiff, *Quantum Mechanics*, McGraw-Hill, second edition, 1955, Section 17.)

11. Show that if $V(\mathbf{r})$ changes sign as $\mathbf{r}$ varies, then the appropriate modification of $\rho(\mathbf{r})$ in the weight-function method is to write $d\rho(\mathbf{r}) = |V(\mathbf{r})| d\mathbf{r}$. Obtain an estimate on the norm of the Lippmann-Schwinger integral operator using this weight function.

12. a) Making use of the definition $\psi(x) = e^{ikx}\phi(x)$ in the one-dimensional Lippmann-Schwinger equation, show that $\phi(x)$ satisfies the integral equation

$$\phi(x) = 1 - \frac{im}{h^2 k} \int_{-\infty}^{x} V(x')\phi(x') \, dx' - \frac{im}{h^2 k} e^{-ikx} \int_{x}^{\infty} e^{2ikx'} V(x')\phi(x') \, dx' .$$

   b) Make some plausible arguments to suggest that the last term on the right-hand side of the above equation is negligible if k is large (i.e., if the energy of the incident particle is large).

   c) Neglecting this term, show that the resulting $\phi(x)$, which we will call $\phi_E(x)$, satisfies the differential equation

$$\frac{d\phi_E(x)}{dx} = -\frac{im}{h^2 k} V(x)\phi_E(x) ,$$

   with the boundary condition $\phi_E(-\infty) = 1$. Hence show that

$$\phi_E(x) = \exp\left\{ -\frac{im}{h^2 k} \int_{-\infty}^{x} V(x') \, dx' \right\} .$$

This approximation is referred to as the *eikonal* approximation; its generalization to three dimensions has proved very useful in the analysis of certain high-energy scattering problems.

d) Returning to parts (a) and (b), show that for the case $V(x) = V_0$ for $x \in [-a/2, a/2]$, $V(x) = 0$ otherwise, the last term of the equation in part (a) really is small as $k \to \infty$. Do this by replacing $\phi(x)$ in the integral by the approximate $\phi_E(x)$ given by part (c). The resulting integral is simple; show that this term is less in magnitude than

$$\frac{1}{2}\left|\frac{E}{V_0} - \frac{1}{4}\right|^{-1},$$

so that for $E \gg V_0$ the term is small.

13. Consider the differential equation

$$\frac{d^2 x(t)}{dt^2} + 2\gamma \frac{dx(t)}{dt} + \omega_0^2 x(t) = 0$$

for a damped harmonic oscillator.

a) Show that if $x(0) = x_0$ and $\dot{x}(0) = 0$, then $x(t)$ satisfies the integral equation

$$x(t) = x_0 \cos \omega_0 t + \frac{2x_0\gamma}{\omega_0} \sin \omega_0 t - 2\gamma \int_0^t \cos \omega_0(t - t')x(t')\, dt'.$$

b) Iterate this equation a few times and show that your result agrees with the exact result expanded to the appropriate order.

14. Show that $x_1(t)$ as given by Eq. (8.49) satisfies the requirement that energy be conserved *through order* δ where $\delta = \epsilon x_0/\omega_0^2 \equiv ax_0/k$. That is, show that

$$\tfrac{1}{2}m\dot{x}_1^2 + \tfrac{1}{2}kx_1^2 + \tfrac{1}{3}ax_1^3 = \tfrac{1}{2}kx_0^2 + \tfrac{1}{3}ax_0^3 + \mathcal{O}(\delta^2),$$

where $\mathcal{O}(\delta^2)$ denotes terms of order δ^2 and higher.

15. In solving the equation for the anharmonic oscillator in Section 8.4, we used the notation $x_0(t)$, $x_1(t)$, $x_2(t)$, etc., to denote the zeroth iterate, first iterate, second iterate, and so forth. Similarly, let us denote by $\bar{x}_0(t)$, $\bar{x}_1(t)$, $\bar{x}_2(t)$, etc., that part of the iterative solution containing all terms through order δ^0, order δ^1, order δ^2, and so forth. Clearly, $\bar{x}_0(t) = x_0(t)$ and $\bar{x}_1(t) = x_1(t)$, but $\bar{x}_2(t)$ contains only part of $x_2(t)$. Find $\bar{x}_3(t)$ [this will involve computing only a few of the terms in $x_3(t)$] and show that all terms in $\bar{x}_3(t)$ which are *linear* in t may be removed, *through order* δ^3, by replacing ω_0 by ω_1 in all the trigonometric functions. Write ω_1 as

$$\omega_1 = \omega_0 [1 + a\delta + b\delta^2 + c\delta^3]^{1/2}.$$

Find the values of a, b, and c which remove the terms linear in t. Using physical arguments, determine how large x_0 could be before the above expansion for ω_1 would diverge (we are imagining that the above redefinition of the frequency is carried out to all orders in δ).

16. a) Obtain an integral equation equivalent to the differential equation for the anharmonic oscillator whose motion is governed by

$$\ddot{x}(t) + \omega_0^2 x(t) = -ax^3(t),$$

by making use of the Green's function for the operator $d^2/dt^2 + \omega_0^2$. Assume $x(0) = x_0$, $\dot{x}(0) = 0$.

b) Iterate this equation once to obtain the first correction to the lowest-order solution, $x_0(t) = x_0 \cos \omega_0 t$.

17. For the system of Problem 8.16, find $\bar{x}_2(t)$ (we use the notation introduced in Problem 8.15). Show that if we write

$$\omega_1 = \omega_0 \left[1 + a\bar{\delta} + b\bar{\delta}^2 \right]^{1/2},$$

then by appropriate choice of a and b, we can eliminate *through order* $\bar{\delta}^2$ all terms in $\bar{x}_2(t)$ proportional to t and t^2 by replacing ω_0 by ω_1 in all the trigonometric functions.

18. Solve the equations

a) $f(x) = x + \lambda \int_0^\infty e^{-(x+y)} f(y) \, dy$,   b) $f(x) = x + \dfrac{\lambda}{\pi} \int_0^{\pi/2} \cos(x+y) f(y) \, dy$.

19. Find the unique bound-state solution to Schrödinger's integral equation for a separable potential of the form $-g^2 v(r) v(r')$ with $v(r) = e^{-\mu r}/r$. Show that a bound-state solution exists if and only if $g^2 > \hbar^2 \mu^3/(4\pi m)$, where m is the mass of the bound particle. Show also that the energy of the bound state is

$$E_B = -\frac{\hbar^2}{2m} \left[\left(\frac{4\pi m g^2}{\mu \hbar^2} \right)^{1/2} - \mu \right]^2 .$$

What is the bound-state wave function?

20. Consider the quantity

$$f^S(E) = \frac{2\tau}{(q_i^2 + \mu^2)^2 + \dfrac{\tau}{\mu}(q_i - i\mu)^2} ,$$

where $\tau = 4\pi m g^2/\hbar^2$ and $q_i = (2mE/\hbar^2)^{1/2}$ [see Eq. (8.73)]. Show that if we consider E to be a complex variable, that is, if we do not restrict E to take on just physical real values, then $f^S(E)$ is a single-valued function of E on a two-sheeted Riemann surface cut along the positive real axis. Show that, as a function of E, $f^S(E)$ is analytic everywhere except for a pole of second order at $E = -\hbar^2 \mu^2/2m$ on the first sheet, a simple pole at $E = -\hbar^2(\mu + \sqrt{\tau/\mu})^2/2m$ on the second sheet, and a so-called bound-state pole which may be either on the first or second sheet. If $\mu > \sqrt{\tau/\mu}$, then this pole is on the second sheet at $E = -\hbar^2(\sqrt{\tau/\mu} - \mu)^2/2m$; if $\sqrt{\tau/\mu} > \mu$, the pole is on the first sheet at $E = -\hbar^2(\sqrt{\tau/\mu} - \mu)^2/2m$. This value of E is precisely the energy of the bound state determined in the previous problem. We see, therefore, that as g^2 drops below the critical value necessary to produce a bound state, the effect of the bound state does not magically vanish from the scattering amplitude; the pole corresponding to the bound state merely moves from the first ("physical") sheet to the second sheet.

21. At the beginning of Section 8.6 in discussing kernels of finite rank, we introduced briefly the notion of a linear functional. The purpose of this problem and the two that follow it is to introduce some of the simpler aspects of linear functionals on a Banach space. We make the following *definition*. A *functional* F, on a Banach space B, is an operation which assigns to every $g \in B$ a complex number (assuming that B is defined over the field of complex numbers). The action of F on g is denoted by $F(g)$. F is said to be *linear* if $F(\alpha g_1 + \beta g_2) = \alpha F(g_1) + \beta F(g_2)$ for all complex numbers, α and β, and all $g_1, g_2 \in B$. F is said to be *bounded* if there exists a real number M, such that $|F(g)| \leq M \|g\|$ for all $g \in B$, M being independent of g. Let us now consider two aspects of this.

a) Let F be a bounded, linear functional on B. Suppose that we have in B a sequence $\{f_n\}$ which tends in norm to $f \in B$. Show that $F(f_n) \to F(f)$, that is, that F is continuous.

b) Show that if $f \in L_p$, then the functional F defined on L_q ($1/p + 1/q = 1$) by

$$F(g) \equiv (f, g) \equiv \int f^*(x)g(x) \, dx \, ,$$

where $g \in L_q$, is a bounded, linear functional. [*Hint:* Look back at Problem 8.2]. It can be shown that every bounded, linear functional on L_q can be written in this form, i. e., can be generated by an element of L_p.

22. Just as for a bounded, linear operator on B, we define the norm of a bounded, linear functional on B as the least uppper bound of the set of all M satisfying $|F(g)| \le M||g||$ for all $g \in B$. As usual, we denote the norm of F by $||F||$.

a) Show that for the functional F, defined on L_q by

$$F(g) = (f, g) \, ,$$

where $f \in L_p$ and $1/p + 1/q = 1$ (see the preceding problem), we have $||F|| \le ||f||$. Here the norm of f is the norm appropriate to L_p, namely,

$$||f|| = \left[\int |f(x)|^p \, dx \right]^{1/p}.$$

b) Show that the function

$$g = \frac{|f|^{(p/q)+1}}{f^*}$$

belongs to L_q if $f \in L_p$ ($1/p + 1/q = 1$) and therefore that $||F|| \ge ||f||$. Do this by showing that

i) $|F(g)| = |(f, g)| = ||f||^p$,   ii) $||f|| \, ||g|| = ||f||^p$.

Hence $|F(g)| = ||f|| \cdot ||g||$, so $||F|| \ge ||f||$. Combining parts (a) and (b), we see that actually $||F|| = ||f||$.

23. Show that, by an obvious definition of addition and scalar multiplication, the bounded linear *functionals* on B form a Banach space in their own right. This space is called the *dual space* of B and is denoted by B^*. Since every linear functional on L_q is generated by an element of L_p ($1/p + 1/q = 1$), we can identify L_q^* with L_p and say that L_p is the *dual space* of L_q. Note that the space L_2 of square-integrable functions is its own dual space.

There are three parts to this problem. First, you must show that your definition of addition and scalar multiplication is such that it gives rise to a linear vector space. Second, you must show that the definition of norm given in the previous problem really is a norm (as we did in Section 8.2 in discussing norms of operators). These two parts are easy. Not so easy is the problem of showing that the normed, linear vector space which you have constructed is *complete*.

[*Hint:* You must show that any Cauchy sequence of functionals $\{F_n\}$ has a limit which is also a bounded linear functional. Note that for any $f \in B$, $\{F_n(f)\}$ is a Cauchy sequence of complex numbers. Since the complex numbers are complete, you can define the limit of $\{F_n\}$ acting on any $f \in B$ in terms of the limit of $\{F_n(f)\}$, which is guaranteed to exist. Denote this limit by $F(f)$. It is then not difficult to show that F so defined is linear and bounded and that $||F_n - F|| \to 0$ as $n \to \infty$. The basic idea for all these proofs is contained in the following identity which would be relevant for the proof of the linearity of F:

$$F(\alpha g_1 + \beta g_2) - [\alpha F(g_1) + \beta F(g_2)] \equiv [F(\alpha g_1 + \beta g_2) - F_n(\alpha g_1 + \beta g_2)]$$
$$- [\alpha F(g_1) - \alpha F_n(g_1)] - [\beta F(g_2) - \beta F_n(g_2)] .$$

Here we make use of the *known* linearity of F_n.]

24. Show that by defining addition and scalar multiplication in the obvious way, we can construct a Banach space out of the set of all bounded, linear *operators* on *B*. This proof can be patterned directly on the proof given in the previous problem for bounded linear functionals. Again, the completeness of the underlying space *B*, is the key ingredient in the proof.

25. Using Eqs. (8.75) and (8.88), show explicitly that

$$(I - \lambda K_F)(I + \lambda R_{K_F}) = I .$$

26. Show that if K_N is defined by Eq. (8.93) and P_N by Eq. (8.94), then $K_N = P_N K P_N$.

FURTHER READINGS

BLATT, J. M., and V. F. WEISSKOPF, *Theoretical Nuclear Physics*. New York: Wiley, 1952.

GOLDBERGER, M. L., and K. M. WATSON, *Collision Theory*. New York: Wiley, 1964.

LOVITT, W. V., *Linear Integral Equations*. New York: Dover, 1950.

MUSHELISHVILI, N. I., *Singular Integral Equations*. Groningen: P. Noordhoff, Ltd., 1953. This book gives a very useful and interesting account of integral equations with singular kernels.

NEWTON, R. G., *Scattering Theory of Waves and Particles*. New York: McGraw-Hill, 1966.

RIESZ, F., and B. SZ. NAGY, *Functional Analysis*. New York: Ungar, 1955.

CHAPTER 9

INTEGRAL EQUATIONS IN HILBERT SPACE

INTRODUCTION

In the last chapter we developed two of the basic techniques for the solution of integral equations, iteration and finite-rank approximation, and in this chapter we wish to exploit these methods to obtain some results which facilitate greatly the solution of practical problems. We shall begin by looking at the properties of completely continuous Hermitian operators in some detail; in particular, we shall obtain a completeness relation for the eigenfunctions of such operators and use these eigenfunctions to discuss perturbation theory and the solution of linear equations.

With the insights obtained from this special case, we will move on to consider general completely continuous operators and see how to solve linear equations by the method of finite-rank approximation. Finally, we will close the chapter by looking at the Fourier transform in the context of the theory of unitary operators on Hilbert space. This is one of the most important tools in mathematical physics, and the ease with which it can be handled in the context of infinite-dimensional vector spaces is a beautiful illustration of the power of the theory of linear operators.

9.1 COMPLETELY CONTINUOUS HERMITIAN OPERATORS

Before we attempt to deal with the most general type of completely continuous operators, we will investigate an important special case: the completely continuous, self-adjoint operators. This kind of operator is interesting in its own right; for example, the bound-state Schrödinger integral equations can be handled very deftly using the techniques we shall develop here. But in addition, this special case will give us some important clues as to how we can proceed to treat the general theory of completely continuous operators.

Just as in the finite-dimensional case, a completely continuous self-adjoint operator A satisfies

$$(x, Ay) = (Ax, y) \tag{9.1}$$

for all x, y in the vector space. Since A is completely continuous, it is also bounded, and therefore is defined on every element of the space. If A is an integral operator with kernel $a(t, t')$, then the Hermiticity requirement is equivalent to

$$a(t, t') = a^*(t', t) , \tag{9.2}$$

since

$$(x, Ay) = \int dt \int dt' \, x^*(t) a(t, t') y(t') \, ,$$

$$(Ax, y) = \int dt' \int dt \, a^*(t, t') x^*(t') y(t) = \int dt' \int dt \, x^*(t) a^*(t', t) y(t') \, .$$

Evidently Eq. (9.1) holds if Eq. (9.2) is obeyed. It should be said at this point that our change in notation, with the operator written as A and the vectors as x and y, is not capricious. We shall see in the next two sections that the theory of completely continuous, Hermitian operators is virtually identical to the finite-dimensional theory we discussed in Chapter 4. To emphasize this similarity, we shall observe the notational conventions of Chapter 4 in this section and the next. However, the reader should remember that the vectors x and y may be functions in this chapter, in which case we will write them as $x(t)$ and $y(t)$ if it is necessary to display their functional dependence.

We begin by recalling the definition of norm which we gave in Section 8.2, namely, $||A||$ is the smallest constant such that

$$||Ax|| \leq ||A|| \cdot ||x||$$

for all $x \in B$, where B is any normed vector space and A is a bounded operator. Now it is interesting to inquire whether or not there is actually some vector in the space for which one has

$$Ay = \pm ||A|| y \, . \tag{9.3}$$

Let H_1 be a Hilbert space, and let A be an operator with the property that there is always some vector in the space which satisfies Eq. (9.3). Suppose that we have found some vector x which satisfies

$$Ax_1 = \pm ||A||_1 x_1 \, ,$$

where $||A||_1$ is the norm of A when it acts on the whole Hilbert space, H_1. The space of all vectors orthogonal to x_1, say, H_2, is also a Hilbert space; if A were bounded on H_1, then A would be necessarily bounded on H_2. Thus

$$||Ax|| \leq ||A||_2 \cdot ||x||$$

for all $x \in H_2$. Clearly, $||A||_2 \leq ||A||_1$. Now if A still has the property assumed above, then there is some $x_2 \in H_2$ such that

$$Ax_2 = \pm ||A||_2 x_2 \, ,$$

where $(x_1, x_2) = 0$. We can continue this process indefinitely, generating H_1, H_2, H_3, $\cdots$ and x_1, x_2, x_3, $\cdots$.

Several possibilities may now arise. It might be that $||A||_1 = ||A||_2 = ||A||_3 = \cdots$. This would be the case, for instance, if A were the identity operator. However, if A is completely continuous and $A \neq 0$, then this cannot happen, i.e., we cannot obtain some nonzero eigenvalue an infinite number of times. For if we did, we would have an infinite orthonormal sequence $\{x_n\}$, and $\{Ax_n\}$ would need a convergent subsequence since A is completely continuous. But if $Ax_n = ax_n$ for all the vectors of the sequence, then $\{ax_n\}$ must contain a convergent subsequence. However, $||x_m - x_n|| = \sqrt{2}$ for all m, n, so there can be no convergent subsequence, unless, of course, $a = 0$. Hence we can obtain a given, nonzero eigenvalue only a finite number of times.

However, it is possible to obtain a zero eigenvalue an infinite number of times. This, for example, would be true for an operator of finite rank on a Hilbert space. In any case, however, the eigenvalues λ_n must tend toward zero, because if they did not, x_n/λ_n would be a bounded sequence. But $Ax_n = \lambda_n x_n$, so $\{x_n\}$ must contain a convergent subsequence, which it cannot as noted above. This behavior of the eigenvalues could arise either because all but a finite number of eigenvalues are zero, or because there is an infinite collection of nonzero eigenvalues, λ_n, all of finite multiplicity, which become arbitrarily small for n sufficiently large. In this latter case, we might also have some zero eigenvalues (perhaps even an infinite number of them). Corresponding to these eigenvalues, we have an infinite number of eigenvectors, x_n, and we may hope that they will form a complete set, although the fact that there is an infinite number of x_n is only necessary for completeness, not sufficient.

In finite-dimensional spaces, the completeness property held for the eigenfunctions of self-adjoint, isometric, and normal transformations. In the case of completely continuous self-adjoint transformations, we shall now show that this same result still holds. Of course, basic properties such as reality of eigenvalues will be the same since the proofs of these properties given in Chapter 4 were in no way restricted to the finite-dimensional case. However, by way of emphasizing the difference between the finite-dimensional case and the completely continuous case, we mention that there are *no* completely continuous *isometric* transformations of an infinite-dimensional Hilbert space. Clearly, every isometry is *bounded* since

$$||Uy||^2 = (Uy, Uy) = (y, y) = ||y||^2$$

for any $y \in H$. Thus, $||U|| = 1$. However, consider any sequence $\{y_n\}$, which does not contain a convergent subsequence, and the related sequence $\{Uy_n\}$:

$$||Uy_n - Uy_m|| = ||U(y_n - y_m)|| = ||y_n - y_m|| ,$$

so U does not change the convergence properties of $\{y_n\}$ in any way. In particular, if $\{y_n\}$ does not contain a convergent subsequence, neither will $\{Uy_n\}$. Thus isometric transformations are not completely continuous.

The most important property of self-adjoint transformations is that they have *real* expectation values. This fact leads us to the following important result.

Theorem 9.1. Let A be a bounded, self-adjoint linear operator on the Hilbert space, H. Then if $||y|| = 1$,

$$\sup_{y \in H} |(y, Ay)| = ||A|| ,$$

where sup denotes the least upper bound.

Proof. By the Schwartz inequality, for all $y \in H$,

$$|(y, Ay)| \leq ||y|| \cdot ||Ay|| \leq ||A|| \cdot ||y||^2 . \qquad (9.4)$$

Now, in analogy with our definition of the norm of A, we define the quantity $|A|$ as the smallest constant for which

$$|(y, Ay)| \leq |A| \cdot ||y||^2 , \qquad (9.5)$$

for all $y \in H$. According to Eq. (9.4), $|A| \leq ||A||$. We now show that $|A| \geq ||A||$. To do this, we utilize the identity

$$||Ay||^2 = (Ay, Ay) \equiv \frac{1}{4} \left\{ \left(\lambda y + \frac{1}{\lambda} Ay, A \left[\lambda y + \frac{1}{\lambda} Ay \right] \right) \right.$$
$$\left. - \left(\lambda y - \frac{1}{\lambda} Ay, A \left[\lambda y - \frac{1}{\lambda} Ay \right] \right) \right\} ,$$

which holds for all real λ. Thus, using Eq. (9.5), we get

$$||Ay||^2 \leq \frac{1}{4} |A| \cdot \left[||\lambda y + \frac{1}{\lambda} Ay ||^2 + ||\lambda y - \frac{1}{\lambda} Ay||^2 \right] ,$$

so that

$$||Ay||^2 \leq \frac{1}{2} |A| \cdot \left(\lambda^2 \cdot ||y||^2 + \frac{1}{\lambda^2} ||Ay||^2 \right) .$$

In particular, the inequality holds if $\lambda^2 = ||Ay||/||y||$. From this value, we find that

$$||Ay||^2 \leq |A| \cdot ||Ay|| \cdot ||y|| , \qquad \text{or} \qquad ||Ay|| \leq |A| \cdot ||y|| .$$

Thus $||A|| \leq |A|$. Since we have already shown that $||A|| \geq |A|$, we see that $||A|| = |A|$, as required. Note that this result holds for any bounded, self-adjoint operator, regardless of whether or not it is completely continuous. It might almost appear not to even depend on the Hermiticity of A. However, the reader can readily show that the identity in λ which is crucial to the proof is only true if A is self-adjoint.

With this result in hand, we can now carry out the program outlined at the beginning of this section.

Theorem 9.2. Let A be a completely continuous, self-adjoint transformation on a Hilbert space, H, and denote by C the set of all $y \in H$ such that $||y|| = 1$. The quantity $|(y, Ay)|$ attains a maximum value on this set, and the vector x, for which the maximum is attained is an eigenvector of A with eigenvalue $\lambda = \pm ||A||$.

Proof. Choose a sequence $\{y_n\}$, $y_n \in C$, such that (y_n, Ay_n) tends to λ_1, where $|\lambda_1| = ||A||$. The previous theorem tells us that this is always possible. Since we want to prove that λ_1 is an eigenvalue, let us consider

$$||Ay_n - \lambda_1 y_n||^2 = ||Ay_n||^2 - 2\lambda_1 (y_n, Ay_n) + \lambda_1^2 ||y_n||^2 .$$

Now $||Ay_n||^2 \leq ||A||^2 \cdot ||y_n||^2 = \lambda_1^2 ||y_n||^2$, so since $||y_n|| = 1$,

$$||Ay_n - \lambda_1 y_n||^2 \leq 2[\lambda_1^2 - \lambda_1(y_n, Ay_n)] \, .$$

But since $(y_n, Ay_n) \to \lambda_1$ by assumption,

$$||Ay_n - \lambda_1 y_n|| \to 0 \, . \tag{9.6}$$

Since A is completely continuous, the sequence $\{Ay_n\}$ contains a convergent subsequence, say, $\{A\eta_m\}$, where $\{\eta_m\}$ is a subset of $\{y_n\}$. For reasons which will soon be clear, we denote the vector to which $\{A\eta_m\}$ converges by $\lambda_1 x_1$:

$$||A\eta_m - \lambda_1 x_1|| \to 0 \, . \tag{9.7}$$

But

$$A\eta_m - \lambda_1 \eta_m \equiv A\eta_m - \lambda_1 x_1 + \lambda_1 x_1 - \lambda_1 \eta_m \, , \tag{9.8}$$

so

$$||\lambda_1 x_1 - \lambda_1 \eta_m|| \leq ||A\eta_m - \lambda_1 x_1|| + ||A\eta_m - \lambda_1 \eta_m|| \, .$$

Thus by Eqs. (9.6) and (9.7),

$$||\lambda_1 x_1 - \lambda_1 \eta_m|| \to 0; \tag{9.9}$$

in other words, the sequence $\{\eta_m\}$ converges to x_1 (assuming, of course, that $|\lambda_1| = ||A|| \neq 0$). By the triangle inequality,

$$||Ax_1 - \lambda_1 x_1|| \leq ||Ax_1 - A\eta_m|| + ||A\eta_m - \lambda_1 \eta_m|| + ||\lambda_1 \eta_m - \lambda_1 x_1||$$
$$\leq 2||A|| \cdot ||x_1 - \eta_m|| + ||A\eta_m - \lambda_1 \eta_m|| \, ,$$

so by Eqs. (9.6) and (9.9), we can make

$$||Ax_1 - \lambda_1 x_1|| < \epsilon$$

for any ϵ. Hence

$$Ax_1 = \lambda_1 x_1 \, ,$$

so that λ_1 is an eigenvalue of A corresponding to the eigenvector x_1. Also,

$$|(x_1, Ax_1)| = |(x_1, \lambda_1 x_1)| = |\lambda_1| = ||A|| \, .$$

This completes the proof of this theorem, which is the basic result on completely continuous, self-adjoint operators.

Now, let us consider again the Hilbert space H_2 of all vectors orthogonal to the vector x_1 found in the previous theorem. The operator A acting on this space is completely continuous and Hermitian. We write

$$||Ay|| \leq ||A||_2 \cdot ||y||$$

for all $y \in H_2$, where $||A||_2 \leq ||A||$. By repeating the procedure of the above theorem, we can find an x_2 such that

$$Ax_2 = \lambda_2 x_2 \, , \qquad |\lambda_2| = ||A||_2 \, .$$

We can continue the process indefinitely unless we arrive at a number, m, where the eigenvalue $\lambda_m = 0$ that is, $||A||_m = 0$. This means that after removing a number, m, of orthonormal vectors from our original space, H, we arrive at a space H_{m+1} such that A acting on this space produces only zero vectors. This means that H_{m+1} is the *null space* of A. This will clearly be the case for the operator of finite rank, A_F, defined by

$$A_F y \equiv \sum_{n=1}^{N} \alpha_n \phi_n (\phi_n, y) ,$$

where the ϕ_n form an orthonormal set. A_F has as eigenvectors the ϕ_n with corresponding eigenvalues, α_n. A_F also has as eigenvectors any vectors which are orthogonal to all the ϕ_n. Zero is the common eigenvalue for all these other eigenvectors. We may summarize the above discussion as follows:

Theorem 9.3. Let Y be the set of all vectors $y \in H$ such that $||y|| = 1$ and y is orthogonal to all the vectors $x_1, x_2, \cdots, x_n$ satisfying

$$A x_n = \lambda_n x_n .$$

Then $|(y, Ay)|$ can always be maximized on this set if A is a completely continuous, self-adjoint operator. Furthermore, the vector x_{n+1} obtained in this way is an eigenvector of A with eigenvalue λ_{n+1}, where $|\lambda_{n+1}| = ||A||_{n+1}$ and $||A||_{n+1}$ is the norm of A in the subspace of H consisting of all vectors orthogonal to $x_1, x_2, \cdots, x_n$. This process generates an infinite sequence of vectors $\{x_n\}$ and a set of eigenvalues $\{\lambda_n\}$. Each nonzero eigenvalue is of finite multiplicity and $\lambda_n \to 0$ as $n \to \infty$.

Now we are in a position to obtain a completeness theorem for completely continuous, self-adjoint operators on a Hilbert space.

Theorem 9.4. The eigenvectors of the completely continuous, self-adjoint operator A form a complete, orthonormal set of vectors in the Hilbert space, H, on which A acts.

Proof. Let us assume at first that A has only nonzero eigenvalues.* It is clear that at the very least there is always a subspace of H in which this is true. For any $y \in H$, we consider

$$y_N = y - \sum_{n=1}^{N} (x_n, y) x_n ,$$

where the set $\{x_n\}$ consists of the eigenvectors of A. To establish completeness, we must show that as $N \to \infty$, $||y_N|| \to 0$. But y_N is obviously orthogonal to all x_n with $n \le N$. Hence by our previous work

$$||A y_N|| \le |\lambda_{N+1}| \cdot ||y_N|| .$$

---

* We will also assume that A has an infinite number of eigenvectors belonging to nonzero eigenvalues. The case when A has only a finite number of nonzero eigenvalues is elementary and is left as a problem.

Since $||y_N|| \leq ||y||$, we have

$$||Ay_N|| \leq |\lambda_{N+1}| \cdot ||y|| .$$

But $\lambda_{N+1} \to 0$ as $N \to \infty$, so

$$||Ay_N|| \to 0$$

as $N \to \infty$. But it is easily shown that

$$Ay_N = Ay - \sum_{n=1}^{N} (x_n, y)Ax_n = Ay - \sum_{n=1}^{N} (x_n, Ay)x_n .$$

Thus we may say that

$$\sum_{n=1}^{N} (x_n, Ay)x_n$$

tends in norm to Ay as $N \to \infty$. We write this as

$$Ay \doteq \sum_{n=1}^{\infty} (x_n, Ay)x_n , \tag{9.10}$$

for any $y \in H$. Hence we have a completeness relation for all elements of the space of the form Ay.

If we knew that A were invertible, then we could immediately extend the completeness relation to all vectors in H, since then any vector in H could be written in the form Ay for some $y \in H$. However, more generally, we may argue as follows. Since H is a complete space,

$$\lim_{N \to \infty} \left[\sum_{n=1}^{N} (x_n, \eta)x_n \right]$$

converges in the mean to some vector, say $\tilde{\eta}$, because Bessel's inequality (Eq. 5.9) tells us that the sequence

$$\left\{ \eta_N = \sum_{n=1}^{N} (x_n, \eta)x_n \right\}$$

is a *Cauchy* sequence. We write

$$\tilde{\eta} \doteq \sum_{n=1}^{\infty} (x_n, \eta)x_n . \tag{9.11}$$

Since A is continuous,

$$A\tilde{\eta} \doteq \sum_{n=1}^{\infty} (x_n, \eta)Ax_n \doteq \sum_{n=1}^{\infty} (x_n, A\eta)x_n .$$

But by Eq. (9.10),

$$A\eta \doteq \sum_{n=1}^{\infty} (x_n, A\eta)x_n .$$

Hence

$$A\tilde{\eta} - A\eta = A(\tilde{\eta} - \eta) = 0 \, ,$$

except possibly on a set of measure zero. But we have assumed that A has no zero eigenvalues, so

$$\tilde{\eta} = \eta \, .$$

Thus Eq. (9.11) becomes

$$\eta \doteq \sum_{n=1}^{\infty} (x_n, \eta) x_n \qquad\qquad (9.12)$$

for any $\eta \in H$, which is the familiar completeness relation. It should be remembered that the convergence of the infinite sum in Eq. (9.12) is defined in the sense of *mean* convergence.

The case when $Ax = 0$ has solutions is easily handled. The set of all such solutions forms a Hilbert space, and we may pick an orthonormal basis $\{y_n\}$ for it. (Note that according to Theorem 4.18, every y_n is orthogonal to every x_m belonging to a non-zero eigenvalue.) Each element of the basis satisfies $Ay_n = 0$. Now given any x, form

$$\tilde{x} = x - \sum_{n=1}^{\nu} (y_n, x) y_n \, ,$$

where ν is the number of elements in the set $\{y_n\}$. Clearly, $\tilde{x}$ lies in the orthogonal complement of the space spanned by $\{y_n\}$, so we can apply the above result to it:

$$\tilde{x} \doteq \sum_{m=1}^{\infty} (x_m, \tilde{x}) x_m \doteq \sum_{m=1}^{\infty} (x_m, x) x_m \, ,$$

where the $\{x_m\}$ are the eigenvectors of A when A is restricted to act on the orthogonal complement of the space spanned by the y_n. Hence

$$x \doteq \sum_{n=1}^{\nu} (y_n, x) y_n + \sum_{m=1}^{\infty} (x_m, x) x_m$$

for any $x \in H$. Therefore the set $\{x_n, y_m\}$ is a complete orthonormal basis in H, and we are done.

As a simple example of some of the previous results consider the equation

$$\int_0^1 t_< (1 - t_>) x_n(t') \, dt' = \lambda_n x_n(t') \, , \qquad\qquad (9.13)$$

which was shown in Section 7.1 to be equivalent to the differential eigenvalue problem

$$\frac{d^2 x_n(t)}{dt^2} + \mu_n x_n(t) = 0 \, , \qquad x_n(0) = 0 = x_n(1) \, ,$$

where $\mu_n = 1/\lambda_n$. The eigenvectors of Eq. (9.13) are therefore just

$$x_n(t) = \sqrt{2} \sin (n\pi t) ,$$

with eigenvalues

$$\lambda_n = 1/n^2\pi^2 .$$

This may also be verified by direct substitution in Eq. (9.13). Theorem 9.4 tells us that the vectors $x_n(t) = \sqrt{2} \sin (n\pi t)$ are a complete set of orthonormal functions on the space of square-integrable functions on [0, 1] which vanish at $t = 0$ and $t = 1$. From our previous discussion, we know that the norm of the integral operator defined by Eq. (9.13) must be equal to the largest eigenvalue, $1/\pi^2$. We have also seen that the norm of an integral kernel is less than or equal to the square root of the integrated square of the kernel [see, for example, Eq. (8.47) et. seq.]. In this case, therefore, we must have

$$\lambda_1^2 \leq \int_0^1 dt \int_0^1 dt' \, t_<^2(1 - t_>)^2 = 1/90 \qquad \text{or} \qquad |\lambda_1| \leq 1/9.49 = 0.1054 .$$

The actual value of λ_1 is $1/\pi^2$, that is, $\lambda_1 = 0.1013$, so we see that by approximating the norm of A by the square root of the integrated square of its kernel, we get an excellent estimate of the lowest eigenvalue. We can also estimate the second eigenvalue in this way by calculating in this approximate manner the norm of the operator *restricted* to the space of all vectors orthogonal to x_1. This means calculating the norm of

$$(I - P_1)A(I - P_1) ,$$

where P_1 is the projection onto the subspace spanned by x_1. In terms of the kernel of A, $a(t, t') = t_<(1 - t_>)$; this means that

$$|\lambda_2| \leq \left[\int_0^1 dt \int_0^1 dt'[a(t, t') - \lambda_1 x_1(t')]^2 \right]^{1/2} .$$

Since x_1 is an eigenvector of A, this integral reduces immediately to

$$|\lambda_2| \leq \left[\int_0^1 dt \int_0^1 dt' (a(t, t')^2 - \lambda_1^2) \right]^{1/2} .$$

Both quantities in the bracket are known, and we find that

$$|\lambda_2| \leq 0.029 ,$$

which is quite close to the exact value, $\lambda_2 = 1/4\pi^2 = 0.025$. For λ_1, the approximation was good to 4%, while for λ_2 the result is accurate to only 16%. Applying the some method to λ_3 yields

$$|\lambda_3| \leq 0.015 ,$$

compared with the exact value, $\lambda_3 = 1/9\pi^2 = 0.011$, which tells us that the estimate continues to worsen as we go to higher eigenvalues. However, such estimates are often useful in practical problems in getting an idea of the size of the lowest eigenvalue. Clearly, the method cannot be used to estimate higher eigenvalues unless the lower eigenvalues are known *exactly*.

These estimates can be understood more easily if we consider the following corollary of the previous theorem.

Corollary. If A is a self-adjoint integral operator whose square-integrable kernel is $a(t, t')$, then

$$a(t, t') \doteq \sum_{n=1}^{\infty} \lambda_n x_n(t) x_n^*(t') , \qquad (9.14)$$

where $\{x_n\}$ and $\{\lambda_n\}$ are respectively the eigenvectors and eigenvalues of A, and the infinite sum is defined in the sense of mean convergence.

Proof. Denote the sum by

$$S(t, t') \doteq \sum_{n=1}^{\infty} \lambda_n x_n(t) x_n^*(t') .$$

We leave it for the reader to show that this sum is indeed convergent; this is just a matter of satisfying the Cauchy condition. Define the difference function

$$d(t, t') \equiv a(t, t') - S(t, t') ,$$

and consider the related integral operator, D:

$$Dy = \int d(t, t') y(t') \, dt' .$$

Let us assume that $||D||$ is *not* equal to zero. Now by Theorem 9.2, D has at least one nonzero eigenvalue, say λ, with associated eigenvector, $x(t)$. Let $x_n(t)$ $(n = 1, 2, \cdots)$ be any eigenvector of A [and hence of S, where S is the integral operator whose kernel is $S(t, t')$]. Consider

$$(x, x_n) \equiv \frac{1}{\lambda^*} (\lambda x, x_n) = \frac{1}{\lambda^*} (Dx, x_n) = \frac{1}{\lambda^*} (x, Dx_n) .$$

But

$$Dx_n = \int [a(t, t') - s(t, t')] x_n(t') \, dt' = (A - S)x_n = 0 .$$

Hence

$$(x, x_n) = 0 .$$

Thus, we have found a nonzero vector which cannot be expanded in terms of the supposedly complete set $\{x_n\}$, which contradicts the completeness theorem (Theorem 9.4). Hence our assumption that $||D|| \neq 0$ was incorrect, and therefore $||D|| = 0$. Thus, $d(t, t') = 0$, which proves the corollary.

This tells us that *every* symmetric, square-integrable function of two variables can be expanded in a series of the form of Eq. (9.14). We also have the result, which we leave to the reader to show, that

$$\int dt \int dt' \cdot |a(t, t')|^2 = \sum_{n=1}^{\infty} \lambda_n^2 , \qquad (9.15)$$

where $\{\lambda_n\}$ is the set of eigenvalues of the integral operator A whose kernel is given by the symmetric function $a(t, t')$. Equation (9.15) is the basis of our estimates of $\lambda_1, \lambda_2, \cdots$ given above. It tells us that if there are no eigenvalues "near" λ_1, that is, $\lambda_1^2 \gg \lambda_2^2 > \lambda_3^2 > \cdots$, then

$$\int dt \int dt' \, |a(t, t')|^2 \cong \lambda_1^2 .$$

Until now we have ordered the eigenvalues according to decreasing magnitude of $|\lambda_n|$, $|\lambda_1|$ being the maximum value of $|(y, Ay)|$ which is attained when $y = x_1$, where

$$Ax_1 = \lambda_1 \cdot x_1 .$$

λ_1 may be positive or negative. The previous theorem enables us to make a similar ordering for the positive and negative eigenvalues separately.

Theorem 9.5. Suppose that A is a completely continuous Hermitian operator. Let $\lambda_1^+, \lambda_2^+, \cdots$ be the positive eigenvalues of A ordered so that $\lambda_1^+ \geq \lambda_2^+ \geq \cdots$, with corresponding eigenvectors $x_1^+, x_2^+, \cdots$. Similarly, let $\lambda_1^-, \lambda_2^-, \cdots$ be the negative eigenvalues of A with $\lambda_1^- \leq \lambda_2^-, \leq \cdots$, and denote the corresponding eigenvectors by $x_1^-, x_2^-, \cdots$. Then λ_{n+1}^+ is the *maximum* value of (y, Ay) when y varies over the Hilbert space, H, subject to $||y|| = 1$ and $(y, x_i^+) = 0$ for $i = 1, 2, \cdots, n$. Similarly, λ_{n+1}^- is the *minimum* value of (y, Ay) when y varies over H subject to $||y|| = 1$ and $(y, x_i^-) = 0$ for $i = 1, 2, \cdots, n$.

Proof. By Theorem 9.4, we have for any $y \in H$

$$Ay \doteq \sum_{n=1}^{\infty} (x_n, Ay)x_n \doteq \sum_{n=1}^{\infty} \lambda_n (x_n, y)x_n .$$

Therefore

$$(y, Ay) = \sum_{n=1}^{\infty} \lambda_n |(x_n, y)|^2 .$$

Using the notation just introduced, we can write this as

$$(y, Ay) = \sum_{\nu=1}^{N} \lambda_\nu^+ |(x_\nu^+, y)|^2 + \sum_{\mu=1}^{M} \lambda_\mu^- |(x_\mu^-, y)|^2 ,$$

where N is the number of positive eigenvalues and M is the number of negative eigenvalues (either M or N or both may be infinite). Suppose that $(y, x_i^+) = 0$ for $i = 1, 2, \cdots, n$. Then

$$(y, Ay) = \sum_{\nu=n+1}^{N} \lambda_\nu^+ |(x_\nu^+, y)|^2 + \sum_{\mu=1}^{M} \lambda_\mu^- |(x_\mu^-, y)|^2 .$$

Clearly, if $y = x_{n+1}^+$, then $(y, Ay) = \lambda_{n+1}^+$. Now consider any y and expand it as

$$y = \sum_{i=n+1}^{N} c_i^+ x_i^+ + \sum_{j=1}^{M} c_j^- x_j^- ,$$

where

$$\sum_{i=n+1}^{N} |c_i^+|^2 + \sum_{j=1}^{M} |c_j^-|^2 = 1; \tag{9.16}$$

y is orthogonal to $x_1^+, x_2^+, \cdots, x_n^+$ and is normalized to 1. For this y,

$$(y, Ay) = \sum_{\nu=n+1}^{N} \lambda_\nu^+ |c_\nu^+|^2 + \sum_{\mu=1}^{M} \lambda_\mu^- |c_\mu^-|^2 .$$

Since all λ_ν^+ with $\nu \geq n + 1$ satisfy $\lambda_\nu^+ \leq \lambda_{n+1}^+$, and since $\lambda_\mu^- \leq \lambda_{n+1}^+$ for all μ,

$$(y, Ay) \leq \lambda_{n+1}^+ \left[\sum_{\nu=n+1}^{N} |c_\nu^+|^2 + \sum_{\mu=1}^{M} |c_\mu^-|^2 \right] .$$

Thus according to Eq. (9.16)

$$(y, Ay) \leq \lambda_{n+1}^+ ,$$

which proves the result for positive eigenvalues. A similar argument gives the result for negative eigenvalues. We have *not* shown that $(y, Ay) = \lambda_{n+1}^+$ *only* for $y = x_{n+1}^+$; this would not be true, since λ_{n+1}^+ may have multiplicity $\mu > 1$. In our ordering of eigenvalues, we always list an eigenvalue and its corresponding eigenvector as many times as its multiplicity, μ, requires.

This theorem generalizes to infinite-dimensional spaces the results of Section 4.8 which were derived for finite-dimensional spaces. Thus we see that for completely continuous Hermitian operators, the results of finite-dimensional theory can be taken over to infinite-dimensional spaces virtually without alteration. Since we have obtained a complete, orthonormal set of eigenfunctions for A, it is also a straightforward matter to construct the projection operators, $E(\lambda)$, discussed in Section 5.11 and thereby write for any self-adjoint, completely continuous operator,

$$A = \int_{\lambda_{\min}}^{\lambda_{\max}} \lambda \, dE(\lambda) ,$$

where $E(\lambda)$ is the resolution of the identity belonging to A. Thus, for this special class of self-adjoint operators on Hilbert space we have essentially proved the Spectral Theorem. However, by no means are all self-adjoint operators on Hilbert space completely continuous. Even in the class of *bounded*, self-adjoint operators problems arise which prevent us from using the above methods to obtain the Spectral Theorem. Let us indicate briefly what one of the difficulties is.

Consider the bounded, Hermitian operator X, defined by

$$Xf(x) \equiv xf(x) ,$$

for all $f \in L_2[0, 1]$, where $L_2[0, 1]$ is the Hilbert space of square-integrable functions defined in the interval $[0, 1]$. Clearly, since $x \in [0, 1]$, the operator X is bounded. However, X is not completely continuous. Furthermore, the operator X has no eigenfunctions, since the equation

$$xf(x) = \lambda f(x)$$

cannot be solved to give any sensible sort of function. Of course, it is possible to find a nonsensible "eigenfunction," namely $\delta(x - x_0)$; that is, we could write

$$x\delta(x - x_0) = x_0\delta(x - x_0)$$

and say that $\delta(x - x_0)$ is an eigenfunction of X with eigenvalue x_0. This is true for any $x_0 \in [0, 1]$. Unfortunately, $\delta(x - x_0)$ is not a function in the usual sense of the word, and furthermore

$$\int_0^1 |\delta(x - x_0)|^2 \, dx = \infty$$

if $x_0 \in [0, 1]$, so $\delta(x - x_0)$ is not even square-integrable. However, the δ-function does suggest the following possibility. Consider any point $x_0 \in [0, 1]$. We can construct a sequence of functions, which in the sense of Eq. (9.6) may be called "approximate" eigenfunctions, as follows. We define

$$\phi_{x_0}^{(N)}(x) = \begin{cases} \sqrt{\dfrac{N}{2}}, & \text{if } 0 \leq x_0 - \dfrac{1}{N} \leq x \leq x_0 + \dfrac{1}{N} \leq 1 , \\ 0 & \text{otherwise} ; \end{cases}$$

clearly $(\phi_{x_0}^{(N)}, \phi_{x_0}^{(N)}) = 1$. The *square* of $\phi_{x_0}^{(N)}$ looks like a δ-function when N is large. Now a simple calculation shows that

$$||X\phi_{x_0}^{(N)} - x_0\phi_{x_0}^{(N)}|| = ||(x - x_0)\phi_{x_0}^{(N)}|| = \frac{1}{3N^2} ,$$

so

$$||X\phi_{x_0}^{(N)} - x_0\phi_{x_0}^{(N)}|| \to 0$$

as $N \to \infty$. Thus the set $\{\phi_{x_0}^{(N)}\}$ provides us with an "approximate" eigenfunction whose eigenvalue is x_0, because given an ϵ, no matter how small, we can find an N such that $\phi_{x_0}^{(N)}$ satisfies

$$||X\phi_{x_0}^{(N)} - x_0\phi_{x_0}^{(N)}|| < \epsilon .$$

But unfortunately the sequence $\{\phi_{x_0}^{(N)}\}$ is not a Cauchy sequence, since

$$||\phi_{x_0}^{(N)} - \phi_{x_0}^{(M)}|| = 2(1 - \sqrt{M/N})$$

(where we suppose that $N \geq M$), and hence the sequence does not converge to an element of $L_2[0, 1]$. We may summarize by saying that for every $x_0 \in [0, 1]$ we have an "approximate" eigenfunction with eigenvalue x_0, but there are *no* true eigenfunctions. For some operators it may even happen that there are both true and "approximate" eigenfunctions. It is because of difficulties like this that the concept of eigenfunctions and eigenvalues must be abandoned in order to obtain the Spectral Theorem for the most general type of self-adjoint operator.

9.2   LINEAR EQUATIONS AND PERTURBATION THEORY

Now that we have a completeness relation and a maximum-minimum principle available for completely continuous, self-adjoint operators, we can proceed to the important problems of perturbation theory and linear equations. To begin, let us consider the fundamental problem of solving a linear equation of the form

$$x = y + \lambda A x \,, \tag{9.17}$$

where A is a completely continuous, self-adjoint operator. Let $\{x_i\}$ denote the complete set of eigenvectors of A, with associated eigenvalues λ_i. Taking the inner product of both sides of Eq. (9.17) with x_i, we get

$$(x_i, x) = (x_i, y) + \lambda(x_i, Ax)$$
$$= (x_i, y) + \lambda\lambda_i(x_i, x) \,,$$

and, therefore,

$$(1 - \lambda\lambda_i)(x_i, x) = (x_i, y) \,. \tag{9.18}$$

Thus if λ is not the reciprocal of any eigenvalue of A, then

$$(x_i, x) = \frac{(x_i, y)}{(1 - \lambda\lambda_i)} \,. \tag{9.19}$$

If $\lambda = \lambda_\nu^{-1}$, then Eq. (9.18) is well defined for $i = \nu$ only if $(x_\nu, y) = 0$, in which case the quantity (x_ν, x) is undetermined. If λ_ν has more than one associated eigenvector, a solution can exist only if y is orthogonal to all of them.

Now since

$$\phi \doteq \sum_{n=1}^{\infty} x_n(x_n, \phi)$$

in the sense of mean convergence, Eq. (9.19) tells us that

$$x \doteq \sum_{i=1}^{\infty} (1 - \lambda\lambda_i)^{-1}(x_i, y)x_i \,, \tag{9.20}$$

as long as λ is not the reciprocal of any λ_i. It is convenient to write this, using

$$(1 - \lambda\lambda_i)^{-1} = 1 + \lambda\lambda_i(1 - \lambda\lambda_i)^{-1} \,,$$

as

$$x \doteq \sum_{i=1}^{\infty} (x_i, y)x_i + \lambda \sum_{i=1}^{\infty} \frac{\lambda_i}{1 - \lambda\lambda_i} (x_i, y)x_i .$$

Hence

$$x \doteq y + \lambda R_A y , \tag{9.21}$$

where for any $\xi \in H$, R_A is defined by

$$R_A \xi \equiv \sum_{i=1}^{\infty} \frac{\lambda_i}{1 - \lambda\lambda_i} (x_i, \xi)x_i; \tag{9.22}$$

R_A is called the *resolvent* operator of A. Note that R_A is self-adjoint and that the infinite sum in Eq. (9.22) converges in the mean, since $\lambda_i/(1 - \lambda\lambda_i)$ is bounded ($\lambda_i \to 0$, $\lambda \neq 1/\lambda_i$ for any i), and the sequence of partial sums is therefore a Cauchy sequence. In fact, we can even say that the operator sequence of partial sums, $\{R_A^{(N)}\}$, where

$$R_A^{(N)} \xi \equiv \sum_{i=1}^{N} \frac{\lambda_i}{1 - \lambda\lambda_i} (x_i, \xi)x_i ,$$

converges in operator norm to R_A, since

$$||(R_A - R_A^{(N)})\xi|| = \left[\sum_{i=N+1}^{\infty} \frac{\lambda_i^2}{(1 - \lambda\lambda_i)^2} |(x_i, \xi)|^2 \right]^{1/2} \leq \frac{|\lambda_{N+1}|}{\Delta_{\min}} \left[\sum_{i=N+1}^{\infty} |(x_i, \xi)|^2 \right]^{1/2};$$

$\Delta_{\min}$ is the minimum value of $|1 - \lambda\lambda_i|$ on the set of all eigenvalues of A, and we are ordering eigenvalues by decreasing absolute magnitude. Now

$$\sum_{i=N+1}^{\infty} |(x_i, \xi)|^2 \leq ||\xi|| ,$$

so

$$||(R_A - R_A^{(N)})\xi|| \leq \frac{|\lambda_{N+1}|}{\Delta_{\min}} ||\xi|| .$$

But $\lambda_{N+1} \to 0$ as $N \to \infty$, $||R_A - R_A^{(N)}|| \to 0$ as $N \to \infty$. This means that since $R_A^{(N)}$ is an operator of finite rank, and hence completely continuous, then by Theorem 8.3, R_A is also completely continuous. We may summarize as follows:

Theorem 9.6. Let A be a completely continuous, self-adjoint operator on a Hilbert space, H. Then if λ is not equal to the inverse of any eigenvalue of A, $(I - \lambda A)^{-1}$ exists and is given by

$$(I - \lambda A)^{-1} = I + \lambda R_A , \tag{9.23}$$

where R_A is a completely continuous Hermitian operator defined for any $\xi \in H$ by

$$R_A \xi \equiv \sum_{i=1}^{\infty} \frac{\lambda_i}{1 - \lambda\lambda_i} (x_i, \xi)x_i . \tag{9.24}$$

The infinite sum converges in the mean; $\{x_i\}$ is the set of all eigenvectors of A.

Now suppose that $\lambda = 1/\lambda_\nu$. Then according to our previous work,

$$x = \bar{x} + \sum_{i=1}^{\infty}{}' \frac{\lambda_i}{1 - \lambda\lambda_i} (x_i, y)x_i$$

is a solution to $x = y + \lambda Ax$ if and only if y is orthogonal to every eigenvector belonging to λ_ν. The prime on the summation means that eigenvectors belonging to λ_ν are to be omitted, and $\bar{x}$ is *any* linear combination of eigenvectors belonging to λ_ν. Note that the statement that y be orthogonal to every eigenvector belonging to λ_ν is equivalent to the requirement that y be orthogonal to every linearly independent solution of the equation

$$A\xi = \lambda_\nu\xi \,,$$

or, since A is self-adjoint,

$$A^\dagger\xi = \lambda_\nu\xi \,.$$

As in the case of operators of finite rank, we may combine all our results as follows:

Theorem 9.7. The Fredholm alternative holds for any completely continuous Hermitian operator.

This may be compared to Theorem 8.1 and its two corollaries proved for *arbitrary* transformations of finite rank.

Theorem 9.6 also gives us an example of a situation in which the method sketched nonrigorously in Section 7.2 can be carried out to obtain the Green's function of an operator, A. In the terminology of the last chapter, the Green's function of the operator $(I - \lambda A)$ is $(I + \lambda R_A)$; this may be seen by looking at Eq. (9.23). It should also be emphasized that R_A, as defined by Eq. (9.24), is a meromorphic function of λ, with poles located at $\lambda = 1/\lambda_i$.

Now, in most circumstances, when confronted with a linear equation of the type of Eq. (9.17), one will not be fortunate enough to know all the eigenvectors and eigenvalues of A, so that Eqs. (9.21) and (9.22) are often impractical. However, the result of Theorem 8.4 suggests that it may be possible to split A into two parts, $A = A_0 + A_1$, where A_1 is a "small" operator in the sense that $||A_1|| \ll ||A_0||$. It may then happen that one can deal with A_0 in a reasonable fashion. However, before we plunge into actual calculations, it is very important to be certain that the addition of a "small" A_1 to A_0 does not have a severe effect on the spectrum of A_0, since clearly the spectrum of A_0 (and A) will play a very important role in all considerations. It is reassuring to see that if A, A_0, and A_1 are completely continuous, then as $||A_1|| \to 0$, the eigenvalues of A_0 tend toward those of A.

Theorem 9.8. If $A = A_0 + A_1$ and A, A_0, and A_1 are completely continuous Hermitian operators, then we always have

$$\lambda_n^{(0)} - ||A_1|| \leq \lambda_n \leq \lambda_n^{(0)} + ||A_1||,$$

where $\lambda_n^{(0)}$ and λ_n are, respectively, the nth eigenvalues of A_0 and A.

Proof. First, consider $\lambda_n^{(0)+}$. Let C be the set of all $y \in H$ such that $||y|| = 1$ and $(y, x_i^{(0)+}) = 0$ for $i = 1, 2, \cdots, n - 1$ where $x_i^{(0)+}$ denotes an eigenvector of A_0 with positive eigenvalue $\lambda_i^{(0)+}$. We have

$$\sup_{y \in C} (y, Ay) = \sup_{y \in C} [(y, A_0 y) + (y, A_1 y)]$$

$$\leq \sup_{y \in C} (y, A_0 y) + \sup_{y \in C} |(y, A_1 y)|.$$

But by Theorems 9.1 and 9.5

$$\sup_{y \in C} (y, A_0 y) = \lambda_n^{(0)+}, \qquad \sup_{y \in C} (y, A_1 y) \leq ||A_1||,$$

so

$$\sup_{y \in C} (y, Ay) \leq \lambda_n^{(0)+} + ||A_1||. \tag{9.25}$$

The term on the left of this equation looks very much like λ_n^+, but since y has to be orthogonal to $n - 1$ eigenvectors of A_0 rather than $n - 1$ eigenvectors of A, it is in fact *not* equal to λ_n^+. However, it is obviously greater than or equal to λ_n^+, since we can clearly find a normalized linear combination of the first n eigenvectors of A which lies in C (i.e., which is orthogonal to the first $n - 1$ eigenvectors of A_0). For this vector, η, we will obviously have $(\eta, A\eta) \geq \lambda_n^+$, so

$$\sup_{y \in C} (y, Ay) \geq \lambda_n^+.$$

Returning to Eq. (9.25), we have

$$\lambda_n^+ \leq \lambda_n^{(0)+} ||A_1||.$$

For the second half of the inequality, we consider the set D of all y such that $||y|| = 1$ and $(y, x_i^+) = 0$ for $i = 1, 2, \cdots, n - 1$. Then we have

$$\sup_{y \in D} (y, A_0 y) = \sup_{y \in D} [(y, Ay) - (y, A_1 y)]$$

$$\leq \sup_{y \in D} (y, Ay) + \sup_{y \in D} |(y, A_1 y)|.$$

Now by the definition of D,

$$\sup_{y \in D} (y, Ay) = \lambda_n^+, \qquad \text{so} \qquad \sup_{y \in D} (y, A_0 y) \leq \lambda_n^+ + ||A_1||.$$

But by our previous argument,

$$\sup_{y \in D} (y, A_0 y) \geq \lambda_n^{(0)+}.$$

Hence

$$\lambda_n^{(0)+} \leq \lambda_n^+ + ||A_1|| , \qquad \text{or} \qquad \lambda_n^{(0)+} - ||A_1|| \leq \lambda_n^+ ,$$

which completes the proof for λ_n^+. The case of λ_n^- is handled in an identical fashion.

Now that we have confirmed the stability of the spectrum of a completely continuous Hermitian operator under small perturbations, let us investigate a perturbation approach to the solution of linear equations. We break A into two parts:

$$A = A_0 + A_1 ,$$

such that $||A_1||$ is very small. Then we write Eq. (9.17) as

$$x = y + \lambda A_0 x + \lambda A_1 x ,$$

or more suggestively,

$$(I - \lambda A_0)x = y + \lambda A_1 x .$$

Thus, according to Eq. (9.21), if λ^{-1} is not an eigenvalue of A_0,

$$x = y + \lambda A_1 x + \lambda R_{A_0}(y + \lambda A_1 x) ,$$

or

$$x = y + \lambda R_{A_0} y + \lambda (A_1 + \lambda R_{A_0} A_1) x . \qquad (9.26)$$

This presents us with a new linear equation, but now the operator in question is one whose norm is small, since $||A_1||$ is assumed to be small. We have all the time assumed that λ^{-1} is not an eigenvalue of A_0. However, as $||A_1|| \to 0$, we know that the eigenvalues of A_0 get closer and closer to the eigenvalues of A. Thus, in this limit it is equivalent to assume that λ^{-1} is not an eigenvalue of A. As we make $||A_1||$ small, $||A_1 + \lambda R_{A_0} A_1||$ also becomes small; when $||A_1||$ becomes sufficiently small so that $|\lambda| \cdot ||A_1 + \lambda R_{A_0} A_1|| < 1$, then we can solve Eq. (9.26) by the Neumann series. Thus, in the limit $||A_1|| \to 0$,

$$x \to y + \lambda R_{A_0} y ,$$

if λ is not an eigenvalue of A. From Theorem 8.4, we know that it is always possible to approximate A in operator norm by a transformation of finite rank. Thus we can reduce the original problem to a matrix problem without knowing the eigenfunctions of A, by making use of the results of Section 8.6, in particular, Eq. (8.88). If A is an integral operator, the method of approximation will involve replacing the kernel by a series of step-functions, a method which we will discuss in more detail in the next section.

Now let us move on to the eigenvalue problem. For convenience, we write A in the form

$$A = A_0 + \epsilon A_1 ,$$

where we have put a constant, ϵ, in front of A_1 to emphasize the fact that this term will be small in norm. A, A_0, and A_1 are all completely continuous,

Hermitian operators. Consider the eigenvalue problem

$$Ax_n \equiv (A_0 + \epsilon A_1)x_n = \lambda_n x_n , \tag{9.27}$$

or, assuming that $\lambda_n \neq 0$,

$$\left(I - \frac{1}{\lambda_n} A_0\right) x_n = \frac{1}{\lambda_n} \epsilon A_1 x_n .$$

By our previous work, this linear equation with inhomogeneous term equal to $\epsilon A_1 x_n / \lambda_n$ can be solved by writing

$$x_n = \left(I - \frac{1}{\lambda_n} A_0\right)^{-1} \frac{1}{\lambda_n} \epsilon A_1 x_n .$$

By Eqs. (9.23) and (9.24), this is just

$$x_n = \sum_{m=1}^{\infty} \left(1 - \frac{\lambda_m^{(0)}}{\lambda_n}\right)^{-1} \frac{1}{\lambda_n} \epsilon (x_m^{(0)}, A_1 x_n) x_m^{(0)}$$

$$= \epsilon \sum_{m=1}^{\infty} (\lambda_n - \lambda_m^{(0)})^{-1} (x_m^{(0)}, A_1 x_n) x_m^{(0)} , \tag{9.28}$$

where the $x_m^{(0)}$ are the eigenvectors of A_0 and $\lambda_m^{(0)}$ are the corresponding eigenvalues. We assume that λ_n is not equal to any of the eigenvalues of A_0. When $\epsilon ||A_1||$ is sufficiently small, this certainly will be the case, *except* for the eigenvalue $\lambda_n^{(0)}$, which tends toward λ_n as $\epsilon \to 0$. We also assume for convenience that the spectrum of A_0 is nondegenerate. With the above difficulty in mind, let us isolate the possibly divergent denominator in Eq. (9.28) by writing

$$x_n = \frac{(x_n^{(0)}, \epsilon A_1 x_n)}{\lambda_n - \lambda_n^{(0)}} x_n^{(0)} + \epsilon \sum_{m=1}^{\infty}{}' \frac{(x_m^{(0)}, A_1 x_n)}{\lambda_n - \lambda_m^{(0)}} x_m^{(0)} , \tag{9.29}$$

where the prime on the summation means that the term with $m = n$ is omitted. Now Eq. (9.29) looks very much like an ordinary inhomogeneous linear equation. Before attempting to solve it by the methods we have developed, we should say something about the suspicious-looking constant multiplying $x_n^{(0)}$ in Eq. (9.29). Taking the inner product on both sides of Eq. (9.27) by $x_n^{(0)}$ and using the fact that

$$A_0 x_n^{(0)} = \lambda_n^{(0)} x_n^{(0)} ,$$

we get

$$(x_n^{(0)}, \epsilon A_1 x_n) = (\lambda_n - \lambda_n^{(0)})(x_n^{(0)}, x_n) . \tag{9.30}$$

This tells us that as $\lambda_n^{(0)} \to \lambda_n$, $(x_n^{(0)}, \epsilon A_1 x_n) \to 0$ in such a way that

$$\frac{(x_n^{(0)}, \epsilon A_1 x_n)}{\lambda_n - \lambda_n^{(0)}} = (x_n^{(0)}, x_n) < \infty .$$

This determines the constant, and allows us to write Eq. (9.29) as

$$x_n = (x_n^{(0)}, x_n) x_n^{(0)} + \epsilon \sum_{m=1}^{\infty}{}' \frac{(x_m^{(0)}, A_1 x_n)}{\lambda_n - \lambda_m^{(0)}} x_m^{(0)} . \tag{9.31}$$

Only under rather unusual circumstances would $(x_n^{(0)}, x_n) = 0$, and certainly not if ϵ is sufficiently small, for under this assumption we can generate a contradiction. Assuming that $(x_n^{(0)}, x_n) = 0$, Eq. (9.31) becomes

$$x_n = \epsilon \sum_{m=1}^{\infty}{}' \frac{(x_m^{(0)}, A_1 x_n)}{\lambda_n - \lambda_m^{(0)}} x_m^{(0)} \ .$$

It follows that

$$||x_n|| = \epsilon \left[\sum_{m=1}^{\infty}{}' \frac{|(x_m^{(0)}, A_1 x_n)|^2}{(\lambda_n - \lambda_m^{(0)})^2} \right]^{1/2} \le \frac{\epsilon}{\Delta_n} \left[\sum_{m=1}^{\infty}{}' |(x_m^{(0)}, A_1 x_n)|^2 \right]^{1/2} ,$$

where Δ_n is the minimum of $|\lambda_n - \lambda_m^{(0)}|$ taken over all eigenvalues of A_0 except $\lambda_n^{(0)}$. For ϵ sufficiently small, Δ_n tends toward a number which is independent of ϵ. Thus, by completeness, we have

$$||x_n|| \le \frac{\epsilon}{\Delta_n} (A_1 x_n, A_1 x_n)^{1/2} = \frac{\epsilon}{\Delta_n} ||A_1 x_n|| ,$$

so that

$$||x_n|| \le \frac{\epsilon ||A_1||}{\Delta_n} ||x_n|| \qquad \text{or} \qquad 1 \le \frac{\epsilon ||A_1||}{\Delta_n} \ .$$

For ϵ sufficiently small, we clearly have a contradiction.

Since the equation for x_n is homogeneous, x_n is arbitrary up to a multiplicative constant; setting $(x_n^{(0)}, x_n) = 1$ is a convenient way to fix that constant. With this choice, Eq. (9.31) takes the simple form

$$x_n = x_n^{(0)} + \epsilon \sum_{m=1}^{\infty}{}' \frac{(x_m^{(0)}, A_1 x_n)}{\lambda_n - \lambda_m^{(0)}} x_m^{(0)} \ . \tag{9.32}$$

Also, according to Eq. (9.30),

$$\lambda_n = \lambda_n^{(0)} + \epsilon (x_n^{(0)}, A_1 x_n) \ . \tag{9.33}$$

Equations. (9.32) and (9.33) are the starting points for studying perturbations in the spectra of completely continuous Hermitian operators.

Certainly the most promising attack on these equations for the case of $\epsilon ||A_1||$ small but finite would seem to be through iterative techniques. However, we shall have to proceed in a slightly different manner than in Sections 8.1 and 8.3, since the operator on the right-hand side of Eq. (9.32) contains an unknown quantity, λ_n. On the other hand, Eq. (9.33) is an equation for λ_n, but in terms of the unknown vector x_n. Thus we have a pair of coupled nonlinear equations for x_n and λ_n. Now we have seen that the norm of the operator on the right-hand side of Eq. (9.32) is equal to or less than $\epsilon ||A_1||/\Delta_n$. Therefore, if this quantity is less than 1, we can iterate Eq. (9.32) to obtain

$$x_n = x_n^{(0)} + \epsilon \sum_{m=1}^{\infty}{}' \frac{(x_m^{(0)}, A_1 x_n^{(0)})}{\lambda_n - \lambda_m^{(0)}} x_m^{(0)}$$

$$+ \epsilon^2 \sum_{l=1}^{\infty}{}' \sum_{m=1}^{\infty}{}' \frac{(x_m^{(0)}, A_1 x_l^{(0)})(x_l^{(0)}, A_1 x_n^{(0)})}{(\lambda_n - \lambda_m^{(0)})(\lambda_n - \lambda_l^{(0)})} x_m^{(0)} + \cdots . \tag{9.34}$$

When we have computed x_n to sufficient accuracy, we insert Eq. (9.34) into Eq. (9.33) and thus obtain a relation for λ_n. Of course, in general, this equation will be extremely complicated.

Another possibility would be to substitute Eq. (9.33) into Eq. (9.34) to obtain

$$
x_n = x_n^{(0)} + \epsilon \sum_{m=1}^{\infty}{}' \frac{(x_m^{(0)}, A_1 x_n^{(0)}) x_m^{(0)}}{\lambda_n^{(0)} - \lambda_m^{(0)} + \epsilon(x_n^{(0)}, A_1 x_n)}
$$

$$
+ \epsilon^2 \sum_{m=1}^{\infty}{}' \sum_{l=1}^{\infty}{}' \frac{(x_m^{(0)}, A_1 x_l^{(0)}) (x_l^{(0)}, A_1 x_n^{(0)})}{[\lambda_n^{(0)} - \lambda_m^{(0)} + \epsilon(x_n^{(0)}, A_1 x_n)][\lambda_n^{(0)} - \lambda_l^{(0)} + \epsilon(x_n^{(0)}, A_1 x_n)]} x_m^{(0)}
$$

$$
+ \cdots . \tag{9.35}
$$

If $\epsilon \lVert A_1 \rVert$ is small enough that

$$
\left| \frac{\epsilon(x_n^{(0)}, A_1 x_n)}{\lambda_n^{(0)} - \lambda_m^{(0)}} \right| < 1 , \tag{9.36}
$$

for all $m \neq n$, then we can expand each of the denominators occurring in Eq. (9.35) in a power series in ϵ:

$$
[\lambda_n^{(0)} - \lambda_m^{(0)} + \epsilon(x_n^{(0)}, A_1 x_n)]^{-1} = (\lambda_n^{(0)} - \lambda_m^{(0)})^{-1} \sum_{\mu=0}^{\infty} (-1)^{\mu} \epsilon^{\mu} \frac{(x_n^{(0)}, A_1 x_n)^{\mu}}{(\lambda_n^{(0)} - \lambda_m^{(0)})^{\mu}} . \tag{9.37}
$$

Putting this result into Eq. (9.35), we obtain for the first few terms of the combined iteration and denominator expansion

$$
x_n = x_n^{(0)} + \sum_{m=1}^{\infty}{}' \sum_{\mu=0}^{\infty} (-1)^{\mu} \epsilon^{\mu+1} \frac{(x_m^{(0)}, A_1 x_n^{(0)})}{[\lambda_n^{(0)} - \lambda_m^{(0)}]^{\mu+1}} (x_n^{(0)}, A_1 x_n)^{\mu} x_m^{(0)}
$$

$$
+ \sum_{m=1}^{\infty}{}' \sum_{l=1}^{\infty}{}' \sum_{\mu=0}^{\infty} \sum_{\nu=0}^{\infty} (-1)^{\mu+\nu} \epsilon^{\mu+\nu+2}
$$

$$
\times \frac{(x_m^{(0)}, A_1 x_l^{(0)}) (x_l^{(0)}, A_1 x_n^{(0)})}{[\lambda_n^{(0)} - \lambda_m^{(0)}]^{\mu+1}[\lambda_n^{(0)} - \lambda_l^{(0)}]^{\nu+1}} (x_n^{(0)}, A_1 x_n)^{\mu+\nu} x_m^{(0)}
$$

$$
+ \cdots . \tag{9.38}
$$

If ϵ is small enough, we obtain a convergent power series expansion for x_n. If we now write

$$
x_n = \sum_{l=0}^{\infty} \epsilon^l f_n^{(l)} \tag{9.39}
$$

and insert this expression into both sides of (9.38), we can calculate the vectors $f_n^{(l)}$ by equating the coefficients of equal powers of ϵ on either side of the equation. Doing this, we find for the first few $f_n^{(l)}$

$$
f_n^{(0)} = x_n^{(0)} ,
$$

$$
f_n^{(1)} = \sum_{m=1}^{\infty}{}' \frac{(x_m^{(0)}, A_1 x_n^{(0)})}{\lambda_n^{(0)} - \lambda_m^{(0)}} x_m^{(0)} ,
$$

and

$$f_n^{(2)} = \sum_{m=1}^{\infty}{}' \sum_{l=1}^{\infty}{}' \frac{(x_m^{(0)}, A_1 x_l^{(0)})(x_l^{(0)}, A_1 x_n^{(0)})}{(\lambda_n^{(0)} - \lambda_m^{(0)})(\lambda_n^{(0)} - \lambda_l^{(0)})} x_m^{(0)}$$

$$- (x_n^{(0)}, A_1 x_n^{(0)}) \sum_{m=1}^{\infty}{}' \frac{(x_m^{(0)}, A_1 x_n^{(0)})}{(\lambda_n^{(0)} - \lambda_m^{(0)})^2} x_m^{(0)} . \tag{9.40}$$

Putting these into Eq. (9.39), we obtain an expression for x_n through order ϵ^2. With this result, we then use Eq. (9.33) to calculate λ_n through third order in ϵ. The eigenvalue λ_n can also be written in a power series, the first term of which is $\lambda_n^{(0)}$. We have

$$\lambda_n = \sum_{l=0}^{\infty} \epsilon^l \lambda_n^{(l)} . \tag{9.41}$$

Using x_n as given by Eqs. (9.39) and (9.40), we find that

$$\lambda_n^{(1)} = (x_n^{(0)}, A_1 x_n^{(0)}), \qquad \lambda_n^{(2)} = \sum_{m=1}^{\infty}{}' \frac{|(x_m^{(0)}, A_1 x_n^{(0)})|^2}{\lambda_n^{(0)} - \lambda_m^{(0)}} \tag{9.42}$$

and similarly for higher-order terms.

These results agree exactly with those obtained in Rayleigh-Schrödinger perturbation theory (Section 4.11). Thus we have been able to give a derivation of Rayleigh-Schrödinger perturbation theory, at least in the nondegenerate case, and have shown that if ϵ is sufficiently small, the perturbation series for x_n will converge. It is difficult to give a more precise statement of convergence requirements, but it is fairly clear from the above discussion that if the difference between $\lambda_n^{(0)}$ and the nearest eigenvalue of A_0 is much greater in magnitude than $(\lambda_n - \lambda_n^{(0)})$, then the method has a good chance of converging. As a rule of thumb, this estimate is often helpful.

The results of Eqs. (9.39), (9.40), (9.41), and (9.42) suffer from the drawback that they require the knowlege of *all* the eigenvectors and eigenvalues of A_0. There are several ways to avoid this difficulty. One way is to make use of the proved *existence* of series expansions for λ_n and x_n and then obtain coupled equations for the vectors $f_n^{(l)}$ involving the $\lambda_n^{(l)}$ as was done in Section 4.11. In this way one obtains, for example,

$$(A_0 - \lambda_n^{(0)})f_n^{(1)} = -(A_1 - \lambda_n^{(1)})x_n^{(0)} ,$$

$$(A_0 - \lambda_n^{(0)})f_n^{(2)} = -(A_1 - \lambda_n^{(1)})f_n^{(1)} + \lambda_n^{(2)} x_n^{(0)} ,$$

$$(A_0 - \lambda_n^{(0)})f_n^{(3)} = -(A_1 - \lambda_n^{(1)})f_n^{(2)} + \lambda_n^{(2)} f_n^{(1)} + \lambda_n^{(3)} x_n^{(0)} , \tag{9.43}$$

and so forth, just as in Section 4.11. These equations involve only $x_n^{(0)}$ and $\lambda_n^{(0)}$ as their starting point, and one has just a system of inhomogeneous equations to solve. This system was discussed in some detail in Section 4.11.

Another approach is to make a direct attack on A itself, using the maximum and minimum principles of Theorem 9.5. Since we know that for any $y \in H$, $||y|| = 1$,

$$(y, Ay) \leq \lambda_1^+ ,$$

we can build "trial vectors," y_t, containing many variable parameters and then maximize (y, Ay) with respect to these parameters, subject to the constraint $||y_t|| = 1$. If the parameters occur linearly in y_t it can be shown (see Problem 5) that the problem reduces to a matrix problem, with the linear parameters in y_t being the unknowns. As we perform this process with more and more parameters, the successive values of (y_t, Ay_t) must increase toward, but never exceed, λ_1^+. If one chooses trial functions sensibly, this process can very quickly yield excellent approximations for λ_1^+ and x_1^+ (the function y_t which gives the good approximation to λ_1^+).

As an example of this method, we consider the equation

$$Ax = \int_0^1 t_<(1 - t_>)x(t')\,dt' = \lambda x(t) \,,$$

where A is defined on the space of square-integrable function on $[0, 1]$. We already know (see Section 7.1) that this equation has the eigenfunctions

$$x_n(t) = \sqrt{2} \sin (n\pi t)$$

and eigenvalues

$$\lambda_n = 1/n^2\pi^2$$

for the boundary conditions $x_n(0) = 0 = x_n(1)$. Now the simplest normalized trial function which vanishes at $t = 0$ and $t = 1$ is

$$y_t(t) = \sqrt{30}\, t(1 - t) \,.$$

If we calculate (y_t, Ay_t), we find that

$$(y_t, Ay_t) = 17/168 = 0.10119 \,,$$

which is less than $1/\pi^2 = 0.10132$, but not by much! Thus by making the most obvious choice, we get a result which is extremely close to the correct one. Needless to say, in most problems one is not quite so lucky. One can also calculate $||x_1^+ - y_t||$:

$$||x_1^+ - y_t|| = ||\sqrt{2} \sin (\pi t) - \sqrt{30}\, t(1 - t)||$$
$$= [2(1 - 4\sqrt{60}/\pi^3)]^{1/2} = 0.038 \,.$$

Thus y_t approximates x_1^+ very closely in norm. If one wanted still greater accuracy, one would choose a trial function with several parameters, for example,

$$y_t = at(1 - t) + bt^2(1 - t)^2 \,,$$

and then maximize (y_t, Ay_t) with respect to a and b subject to $||y_t|| = 1$. In practice, it is convenient to handle the constraint on the norm of y_t by using a Lagrange multiplier. Clearly, $\lambda_2^+, \lambda_3^+, \cdots$ can be computed in the same way by using more constraint equations to ensure that the proper orthogonality properties are satisfied.

9.3 FINITE-RANK TECHNIQUES FOR EIGENVALUE PROBLEMS

For most realistic physical problems, the chances of obtaining closed-form solutions are rather remote.   This perhaps comes as a shock to the student who has been exposed to the beautiful exact solutions which can be obtained for the harmonic oscillator and the $1/r$ potential in both classical and quantum mechanics. However, problems like these are the exception rather than the rule in physics (although very important exceptions, since they often provide the insight necessary for the understanding of more complicated problems). In the case of the Coulomb potential, for example, all one need do is to consider the potential as arising from a charge distribution of finite extent (a proton) rather than a point charge, and one is immediately forced to look beyond exact solutions to some sort of approximation procedure.

However, in the problem just mentioned, the effect of the finite proton size can be thought of as a small perturbation so that the techniques discussed in Section 9.2 can be successfully applied. The type of problem with which we shall be concerned in this section is one in which the idea of a small perturbation of a well-understood physical system is inadequate. For such problems, we will make use of a different sort of approximation, namely, the notion of approximation by an operator of finite rank, which was discussed in Section 8.7.

What we want to do is to consider the eigenvalue problem of Eq. (9.27) in the case when $\epsilon || A_1 ||$ tends to zero, i.e., when we approximate A extremely closely by A_0, and in principle, arbitrarily closely (see Theorem 8.4). In this case, according to our work in the last section

$$x_n^{(0)} \to x_n$$

and

$$\lambda_n^{(0)} \to \lambda_n .$$

Let us focus our attention on a Hermitian operator whose kernel is $a(t, t')$ with t and t' in an interval $[a, b]$. We have already encountered such problems in Chapter 7 when discussing Schrödinger's integral equation. The basic idea which we will use is to divide $[a, b]$ into N small segments, each of length $(b - a)/N$, and define the set of orthogonal functions

$$\phi_n^{(N)}(t) = \begin{cases} 1, & a + \dfrac{n - 1}{N} l \leq t \leq a + \dfrac{n}{N} l , \\ 0, & \text{otherwise} , \end{cases}$$

where $l = b - a$ and $n = 1, 2, \cdots, N$. If we wished, we could normalize $\phi_n^{(N)}(t)$ to 1 by multiplying it by $N^{1/2}$. Now we can approximate any kernel in L_2 arbitrarily closely by such functions; if the kernel is defined on an infinite range, then we truncate it by setting it equal to zero when t or t' is outside some large, but finite interval. It is usually possible to determine a sensible point of truncation by inspection of the kernel. With the $\phi_n^{(N)}$, we can approximate $a(t, t')$ arbitrarily closely by some $a_N(t, t')$, satisfying

$$|| a(t, t') - a_N(t, t') || < \epsilon$$

for any preassigned ϵ. If we call the operator associated with $a_N(t, t')$, A_N, then

$$\|A - A_N\| < \epsilon .$$

Thus according to Theorem 9.8 the eigenvalues of A_N tend toward those of A, and according to Eq. (9.32) the eigenvectors of A_N tend in norm toward those of A. Hence the problem reduces to solving the equation

$$A_N x_n^{(0)}(t) = \lambda_n^{(0)} x_n^{(0)}(t) , \tag{9.44}$$

for some sufficiently large N. In terms of the $\phi_n^{(N)}$, the kernel of A_N can be written as

$$a_N(t, t') = \sum_{\mu, \nu = 1}^{N} M_{\mu\nu} \phi_\mu^{(N)}(t) \phi_\nu^{(N)}(t') , \tag{9.45}$$

where

$$M_{\mu\nu} = (N/l)^2 \int dt \int dt' \ \phi_\mu^{(N)}(t) \phi_\nu^{(N)}(t') a(t, t') . \tag{9.46}$$

For convenience, we take $a(t, t')$ to be real. Note that $M_{\mu\nu}$ is simply the *average value* of the function $a(t, t')$ on the $\mu\nu$-square of the two-dimensional grid into which we have divided the tt'-plane. Using Eq. (9.45), we get for Eq. (9.44)

$$\sum_{\mu, \nu = 1}^{N} \phi_\mu^{(N)}(t) M_{\mu\nu} \int \phi_\nu^{(N)}(t') x_n^{(0)}(t') \ dt' = \lambda_n^{(0)} x_n^{(0)}(t) .$$

If we write

$$C_\nu^{(n)} \equiv (N/l) \int \phi_\nu^{(N)}(t') x_n^{(0)}(t') \ dt'$$

for the average value of $x_n^{(0)}$ on the νth subinterval of $[a, b]$, then our equation becomes

$$\sum_{\mu, \nu = 1}^{N} \phi_\mu^{(N)}(t) M_{\mu\nu} C_\nu^{(n)} \frac{l}{N} = \lambda_n^{(0)} x_n^{(0)}(t) . \tag{9.47}$$

Thus all we need to do is evaluate the scalars $C_\nu^{(n)}$ by using Eq. (9.47). Multiplying both sides by $\phi_{\nu'}^{(N)}(t)$ and integrating, we get

$$\frac{l}{N} \sum_{\nu = 1}^{N} M_{\nu'\nu} C_\nu^{(n)} = \lambda_n^{(0)} C_{\nu'}^{(n)} \tag{9.48}$$

for $\nu' = 1, 2, \cdots, N$. Equation (9.48) thus reduces our problem to one of finding the eigenvalues and eigenvectors of a finite-dimensional matrix, M. With Eq. (9.48) solved for $\lambda_n^{(0)}$ and $C_\nu^{(n)}$ ($\nu = 1, 2, \cdots, N$), then Eq. (9.47) tells us that

$$x_n^{(0)}(t) = \sum_{\nu = 1}^{N} C_\nu^{(n)} \phi_\nu^{(N)}(t) . \tag{9.49}$$

A simple way of looking at these results is to consider the equation

$$Ax_n = \lambda_n x_n = \int_a^b a(t, t') x_n(t') \, dt'$$

from the viewpoint of simple Riemann integration theory. If we subdivide the interval of integration into N parts, each of length l/N, where l is the length of the interval, then our equation can be written as

$$\sum_{\nu=1}^N a(t, t_\nu) x_n(t_\nu) \left(\frac{l}{N}\right) = \lambda_n x_n(t) \, ,$$

where t_ν is some point in the νth interval. If N is large enough this will approximate the original integral arbitrarily closely, as long as the functions involved are continuous. Thus

$$\sum_{\nu=1}^N a(t_{\nu'}, t_\nu) x_n(t_\nu) \left(\frac{l}{N}\right) = \lambda_n x_n(t_{\nu'}) \, .$$

Defining

$$\tilde{M}_{\nu'\nu} \equiv a(t_{\nu'}, t_\nu) \, , \qquad \tilde{C}_\nu^{(n)} \equiv x_n(t_\nu) \, ,$$

we get simply

$$\frac{l}{N} \sum_{\nu=1}^N \tilde{M}_{\nu'\nu} \tilde{C}_\nu^{(n)} = \lambda_n \tilde{C}_{\nu'}^{(n)} \, , \tag{9.50}$$

which obviously bears a very close relation to Eq. (9.48). We see that the basic idea behind the practical solution of integral equations is no more complicated than the basic idea involved in evaluating the Riemann integral.

For $||A_1|| \ll 1$, the approximate eigenvalues of A are given by Eq. (9.48) and the related eigenvectors by Eqs. (9.48) and Eq. (9.49). To estimate the size of the error involved in the approximation, we can make use of the perturbation theory results of Eqs. (9.39), (9.40), (9.41), and (9.42). A particularly important point in this connection is the fact that if $x_m^{(0)}$ and $x_n^{(0)}$ are any approximate solutions of the form

$$x_m^{(0)} = \sum_{\nu=1}^N C_\nu^{(m)} \phi_\nu^{(N)} \, , \qquad x_n^{(0)} = \sum_{\nu=1}^N C_\nu^{(n)} \phi_\nu^{(N)} \, , \tag{9.51}$$

then

$$(x_m^{(0)}, A_1 x_n^{(0)}) = (x_m^{(0)}, (A - A_N) x_n^{(0)}) = 0 \tag{9.52}$$

so that the perturbation theory results simplify considerably. Indeed, at first glance it might seem that they simplify too much, namely, to

$$\lambda_n = \lambda_n^{(0)} \qquad \text{and} \qquad x_n = x_n^{(0)} \, ,$$

since all the terms contributing to $f_n^{(1)}, f_n^{(2)}$, etc., in Eq. (9.40) and to $\lambda_n^{(1)}, \lambda_n^{(2)}$, etc., in Eq. (9.42) appear to vanish. However, this is not the case. Vectors of the form of Eq. (9.51) are *not* the only eigenvectors of A_N. *Any* vector which is orthogonal to all N of the $\phi_n^{(N)}$ is an eigenvector of A_N with eigenvalue zero. There is an infinite number of such vectors, and we have not determined any of them. If we agree to label these starting with index $N + 1$, that is, $x_{N+1}^{(0)}$, $x_{N+2}^{(0)}, \cdots$, then the corrections to x_n and λ_n can be put in the form

$$x_n = x_n^{(0)} + \frac{1}{\lambda_n^{(0)}} \sum_{\nu=N+1}^{\infty} (x_\nu^{(0)}, A_1 x_n^{(0)}) x_\nu^{(0)} + \cdots ,$$

$$\lambda_n = \lambda_n^{(0)} + \frac{1}{\lambda_n^{(0)}} \sum_{\nu=N+1}^{\infty} |(x_\nu^{(0)}, A_1 x_n^{(0)})|^2 + \cdots . \tag{9.53}$$

Since $A_0 x_\nu^{(0)} = 0$ for $\nu > N$, these can also be written as

$$x_n = x_n^{(0)} + \frac{1}{\lambda_n^{(0)}} \sum_{\nu=N+1}^{\infty} (x_\nu^{(0)}, A x_n^{(0)}) x_\nu^{(0)} + \cdots ,$$

$$\lambda_n = \lambda_n^{(0)} + \frac{1}{\lambda_n^{(0)}} \sum_{\nu=N+1}^{\infty} |(x_\nu^{(0)}, A x_n^{(0)})|^2 + \cdots . \tag{9.54}$$

In particular, note that the leading correction to $\lambda_n^{(0)}$, $(x_n^{(0)}, A_1 x_n^{(0)})$, vanishes. Equations (9.53) indicate that the first nonvanishing correction to $\lambda_n^{(0)}$ is always positive if $\lambda_n^{(0)}$ is positive, and that this correction is certainly less than or equal to $||A_1||^2/\lambda_n^{(0)}$. However, $||x_n - x_n^{(0)}|| \leq ||A_1||/\lambda_n^{(0)}$, so we have a better estimate on λ_n than on x_n. In either case, the corrections will grow steadily larger as we get to small eigenvalues.

As a typical example, we consider Schrödinger's integral equation for the bound states of a particle in a field given by the centrally symmetric potential $V(|\mathbf{r}|)$. From symmetry considerations we know that the angular part of the bound-state wave function is given by the spherical harmonic $Y_{lm}(\theta, \phi)$ where l is the angular momentum of the particle in question and m is the projection of the angular momentum on the z-axis. The radial wave functions satisfy Eq. (7.94) which we will reproduce here:

$$\phi_l(r) = \frac{2m\kappa}{\hbar^2} \int_0^\infty j_l(i\kappa r_<) h_l^{(1)}(i\kappa r_>) V(r') \phi_l(r') r'^2 \, dr' , \tag{9.55}$$

where κ is related to the binding energy of the particle by

$$\kappa = \sqrt{-2mE/\hbar^2}$$

and $r_>$ and $r_<$ are respectively the greater and lesser of r and r'. Now, as it stands, the kernel of Eq. (9.55) is not self-adjoint, because

$$k(r, r') \neq k^*(r', r) .$$

However, by using the symmetrization method discussed in Problem 8.5, we can easily bring it to this form. We define

$$\psi_l(r) \equiv r V^{1/2}(r) \phi_l(r) .$$

Then Eq. (9.55) becomes

$$\psi_l(r) = \frac{2m\kappa}{\hbar^2} \int_0^\infty r V^{1/2}(r) j_l(i\kappa r_<) h_l^{(1)}(i\kappa r_>) V^{1/2}(r') r' \psi_l(r') \, dr' \, . \tag{9.56}$$

The kernel is now the symmetric function

$$k_l(r, r') = \frac{2m\kappa}{\hbar^2} r V^{1/2}(r) j_l(i\kappa r_<) h_l^{(1)}(i\kappa r_>) V^{1/2}(r') r' \, .$$

This satisfies $k_l(r, r') = k_l^*(r', r)$ since, as the reader can easily show from Eqs. (7.86a) and (7.86c), the product $j_l(i\kappa r_<) h_l^{(1)}(i\kappa r_>)$ is always real.

As an illustration, we consider the familiar Coulomb potential,

$$V(r) = -Ze^2/r$$

with $l=0$ (although it is not difficult to work with other values of l). We choose the Coulomb potential in order to have exact results for comparison; actually, from the numerical point of view a potential like the Yukawa potential would be somewhat easier to handle because of its exponential cut-off.

Now, since by Eqs. (7.86a) and (7.86c),

$$j_0(i\kappa r_<) = \frac{\sinh(\kappa r_<)}{\kappa r_<} \, , \qquad h_0^{(1)}(i\kappa r_>) = -\frac{e^{-\kappa r_>}}{\kappa r_>} \, ,$$

we have

$$k_0(r, r') = \frac{2me^2Z}{\hbar^2\kappa} \left[\frac{\sinh(\kappa r_<) e^{-\kappa r_>}}{r_>^{1/2} r_<^{1/2}} \right] \, , \tag{9.57}$$

and the integral equation becomes

$$\psi_0(r) = \frac{2Z}{\kappa a_0} \int_0^\infty \frac{1}{r_>^{1/2} r_<^{1/2}} e^{-\kappa r_>} \sinh(\kappa r_<) \psi(r') \, dr' \, .$$

The quantity $a_0 \equiv \hbar^2/me^2$ has the dimensions of length and is called the *Bohr radius*.

It is convenient to make the problem dimensionless by defining

$$\rho \equiv r/a_0 \, , \qquad q \equiv \kappa a_0 \equiv [-E/(\tfrac{1}{2}mc^2\alpha^2)]^{1/2} \, , \tag{9.58}$$

where $\alpha \equiv e^2/\hbar c$ is the dimensionless "fine structure" constant. In these units,

$$\psi_0(\rho) = \frac{2Z}{q} \int_0^\infty \frac{1}{\rho_>^{1/2} \rho_<^{1/2}} e^{-q\rho_>} \sinh(q\rho_<) \psi_0(\rho') \, d\rho' \, . \tag{9.59}$$

Before trying to solve this equation by finite-rank approximation, we should make certain that it is completely continuous by showing that the kernel is square-integrable. We have

$$I = \int_0^\infty d\rho \int_0^\infty d\rho' |k_0(\rho, \rho')|^2 = \frac{4Z^2}{q^2} \int_0^\infty d\rho \int_0^\infty d\rho' \frac{e^{-2q\rho_>}[\sinh(q\rho_<)]^2}{\rho_> \rho_<} \, .$$

Assuming that q is positive, the integrations yield

$$I = \frac{\pi^2 Z^2}{6q^2} , \tag{9.60}$$

so that the kernel is indeed square-integrable.

Now the problem posed by Eq. (9.59) is to find the eigenvalues (binding energies), q, for a given Z. However, the kernel appears to have a rather complicated, nonlinear dependence on q. Actually in the present case, this dependence is illusory, since the change of variables

$$x = q\rho , \qquad x' = q\rho' , \tag{9.61}$$

leads to the eigenvalue equation

$$2Z \int_0^\infty \frac{e^{-x_>} \sinh (x_<)}{x_>^{1/2} x_<^{1/2}} \, \psi_0(x') \, dx' = q\psi_0(x) . \tag{9.62}$$

Note that the change of variable of Eq. (9.61) supposes that q is positive, as we have already assumed in showing that the kernel of Eq. (9.59) is square-integrable. However, in most cases—for example, if $V(r) = g^2 e^{-\mu r}/r$—it will be impossible to remove the q-dependence in this way; under these circumstances it is often desirable to regard q as fixed and Z as the quantity to be determined. In other words, we ask what potential "strength" will produce a given binding energy.

We can illustrate the problem of obtaining solutions of an integral equation by solving Eq. (9.62) for the hydrogen atom, where $Z = 1$. If we truncate the kernel for $x > 7$, $x' > 7$, and divide the interval $[0, 7]$ into thirty-five equal parts, then the procedure discussed above in obtaining Eqs. (9.47) and (9.48) leads to the problem of calculating the eigenvalues of a 35×35 matrix. With modern computing machines this is an elementary problem. For the first few eigenvalues, we find that

$$q_1 = 0.994 , \qquad q_2 = 0.495 , \qquad q_3 = 0.326 , \qquad q_4 = 0.233 .$$

The exact values may be obtained by using the formula for the bound-state energies of hydrogen

$$E_n = -\tfrac{1}{2} mc^2 \alpha^2/n^2 .$$

According to Eq. (9.58), this means that

$$q_1 = 1 = 1.000 , \qquad q_2 = \tfrac{1}{2} = 0.500 , \qquad q_3 = \tfrac{1}{3} = 0.333 , \qquad q_4 = \tfrac{1}{4} = 0.250 .$$

As suggested by Eq. (9.53), the approximate values are always below the exact values. As the eigenvalues get smaller, the agreement worsens, which is also in accord with Eq. (9.53). Note that

$$\sum_{n=1}^\infty q_n^2 = \sum_{n=1}^\infty \frac{1}{n^2} = \frac{\pi^2}{6} ,$$

which is equal to the integrated square of the kernel of Eq. (9.62), as may be seen by looking at Eq. (9.60). This is in agreement with the general result of Eq. (9.15). Since the wave functions of hydrogen are known, we can write the exact solutions to Eq. (9.62). Taking into account the changes of variable of Eqs. (9.58) and (9.61), and the definition of ϕ_0 in terms of ϕ_0, we have for the first three eigenvectors (see, for example, L.I. Schiff, *Quantum Mechanics*. New York: McGraw-Hill, 1969)

$$\phi_{10} = 2\sqrt{x}\, e^{-x},$$

$$\phi_{20} = 2\sqrt{2x}(1-x)e^{-x},$$

$$\phi_{30} = 2\sqrt{3x}(1-2x+\tfrac{2}{3}x^2)e^{-x}.$$

These are all orthogonal and normalized to 1 for convenience.

Figure 9.1 shows the exact ϕ_{10} (solid curve) compared with the approximate ϕ_{10} (dashed curve). The agreement is very close. Since, strictly speaking, the approximate ϕ_{10} consists of a series of flat line segments in each subinterval, we have interpolated by replacing this by a point at the middle of the interval. This is an excellent approximation when the curve varies slowly, and is not so good where the curve varies more rapidly (for example, in Fig. 9.1, near the origin). In such regions of rapid variation, one should choose smaller sub-intervals to obtain higher accuracy. In the framework we have developed, this is easily done. Figures 9.2 and 9.3 show similar comparisons for the second and third eigenvectors. Note that the deviations from the exact result are a bit more noticeable in these cases, although the agreement is still good.

The calculation would have been simpler had we evaluated the matrix in the spirit of the Riemann integral scheme discussed above. There each matrix element is obtained simply by evaluating the kernel at a point in the xx'-plane. For the sake of comparison, we include in Fig. 9.3 the curve which was obtained by this method for ϕ_{30}. The corresponding eigenvalue was $q_3 = 0.353$. It is

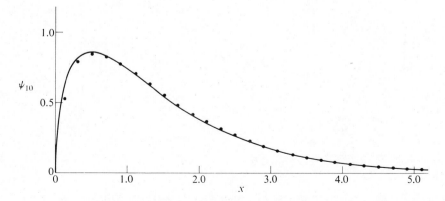

Fig. 9.1 The exact eigenvector, ϕ_{10}, solid curve, and the approximate ϕ_{10}, dotted curve.

Fig. 9.2 The exact eigenvector, ψ_{20}, solid curve, and the approximate ψ_{20}, dotted curve.

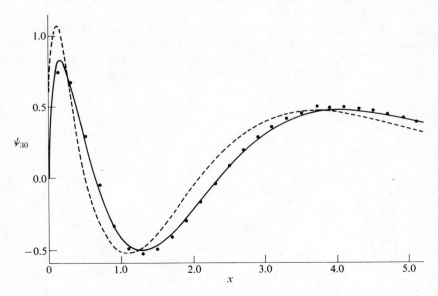

Fig. 9.3 The exact eigenvector, ψ_{30}, solid curve, compared with the approximate ψ_{30} as calculated from Eq. (9.48), dotted curve, and as calculated from Eq. (9.50), dashed curve.

clear that for a coarse subdivision such as the one employed here, the first method is more satisfactory; for sufficiently fine partitions of the interval of integration, the two approaches are equivalent.

9.4 THE FREDHOLM ALTERNATIVE FOR COMPLETELY CONTINUOUS OPERATORS

We now turn our attention to general completely continuous operators. We have less information to work with in this case than we did when considering Hermitian operators. For example, it is no longer possible to guarantee the existence of a complete set of eigenfunctions, and we have no maximum-minimum principles at our disposal. In dealing with non-Hermitian operators, however, we have already made some progress, because we know how to solve linear equations involving either operators with small norm or operators of finite rank. The link between these two types of operators is that any completely continuous transformation of Hilbert space can be written as

$$K = K_F + \Delta , \tag{9.63}$$

where K_F is an operator of finite rank and $||\Delta||$ can be made arbitrarily small. Using this basic decomposition, we will show in this section that the Fredholm alternative holds for an arbitrary completely continuous transformation. In doing so, we will also derive several useful results which will enable us to solve problems that arise in practice.

Suppose now that we want to solve

$$f = g + \lambda Kf , \tag{9.64}$$

or, using Eq. (9.63),

$$(I - \lambda K_F - \lambda\Delta)f = g .$$

The problem is to calculate the inverse of $I - \lambda K_F - \lambda\Delta$. We already know how to calculate $(I - \lambda\Delta)^{-1}$ if $||\Delta|| < 1/\lambda$, and how to calculate $(I - \lambda K_F)^{-1}$ when K_F is any kernel of finite rank and λ is not a singular value of K_F. Therefore we would like to write $(I - \lambda K_F - \lambda\Delta)^{-1}$, assuming that it exists, in terms of these known inverses. To do this, we make use of the operator identity (see Problem 3.26)

$$(A - B)^{-1} \equiv A^{-1} + A^{-1}B(A - B)^{-1} , \tag{9.65}$$

which is valid if $(A - B)^{-1}$ and A^{-1} both exist. Now for this problem, we identify $(I - \lambda\Delta)$ with A and λK_F with B. Assuming that $||\Delta|| < 1/\lambda$, we know that $(I - \lambda\Delta)^{-1}$ exists and can be calculated by the Neumann series

$$(I - \lambda\Delta)^{-1} = I + \lambda\Delta + \lambda^2\Delta^2 + \lambda^3\Delta^3 + \cdots . \tag{9.66}$$

Thus if $(I - \lambda K_F - \lambda\Delta)^{-1}$ exists,

$$(I - \lambda K_F - \lambda\Delta)^{-1} = (I - \lambda\Delta)^{-1} + \lambda(I - \lambda\Delta)^{-1}K_F(I - \lambda K_F - \lambda\Delta)^{-1} . \tag{9.67}$$

But if K_F is an operator of finite rank, then so is $(I - \lambda\Delta)^{-1}K_F$, since if K_F is defined for all $f \in H$ by

$$K_F f \equiv \sum_{i=1}^{N} \phi_i (\psi_i, f) \,,$$

then

$$(I - \lambda\Delta)^{-1} K_F f = \sum_{i=1}^{N} (I - \lambda\Delta)^{-1} \phi_i (\psi_i, f) \equiv \sum_{i=1}^{N} \phi_i^{(\Delta)} (\psi_i, f) \,. \qquad (9.68)$$

We have made the definition

$$\phi_i^{(\Delta)} \equiv (I - \lambda\Delta)^{-1} \phi_i = \phi_i + \lambda\Delta\phi_i + \lambda^2\Delta^2\phi_i + \cdots \qquad (9.69)$$

Let us define a new operator of finite rank, which depends explicitly on λ:

$$\tilde{K}_F (\lambda) \equiv (I - \lambda\Delta)^{-1} K_F \,. \qquad (9.70)$$

Since $||\Delta|| < 1/\lambda$, the λ-dependence will be of the form of a convergent power series in λ. Thus, adopting the definitions,

$$G_K (\lambda) \equiv (I - \lambda K)^{-1} \,, \qquad G_\Delta (\lambda) \equiv (I - \lambda\Delta)^{-1} \,, \qquad (9.71)$$

Eq. (9.67) can be rewritten as

$$G_K (\lambda) = G_\Delta (\lambda) + \lambda\tilde{K}_F (\lambda) G_K (\lambda) \,. \qquad (9.72)$$

In this notation, Eq. (9.70) becomes

$$\tilde{K}_F (\lambda) = G_\Delta (\lambda) K_F \,. \qquad (9.73)$$

Equation (9.72) can be written in the familiar form

$$[I - \lambda\tilde{K}_F (\lambda)] G_K (\lambda) = G_\Delta (\lambda)$$

so all that remains to be done is to calculate the inverse of $[I - \lambda\tilde{K}_F (\lambda)]$, where $\tilde{K}_F$ is a transformation of finite rank. If the inverse exists, then

$$G_K (\lambda) = [I - \lambda\tilde{K}_F (\lambda)]^{-1} G_\Delta (\lambda) \qquad (9.74)$$

and our original equation [Eq. (9.64)] is solved by

$$f = G_K (\lambda) g \,.$$

Equation (9.74) tells us that if $|\lambda| \cdot ||\Delta|| < 1$ (so that $G_\Delta (\lambda)$ exists), then $G_K (\lambda)$ exists if and only if $[I - \lambda\tilde{K}_F (\lambda)]^{-1}$ exists. From a practical point of view, the crucial fact is that Eq. (9.74) enables us to write $G_K (\lambda)$ as the product of two operators, each of which can, in principle, be computed by techniques already discussed: $G_\Delta (\lambda)$ is given by the straightforward iteration of Eq. (9.66), while $[I - \lambda\tilde{K}_F (\lambda)]^{-1}$ can be obtained by the methods of Section 8.6. According to Eqs. (9.68) and (9.70),

$$\tilde{K}_F (\lambda) f = \sum_{i=1}^{N} \phi_i^{(\Delta)} (\psi_i, f)$$

for any $f \in H$, where $\phi_i^{(\Delta)}$ may be written in terms of the original elements of the approximating kernel, K, as

$$\phi_i^{(\Delta)} = G_\Delta(\lambda)\phi_i \ .$$

Thus we can use Eqs. (8.87) and (8.88) to write

$$[I - \lambda \bar{K}_F(\lambda)]^{-1} = I + \lambda R_{\bar{K}_F}(\lambda) \ , \tag{9.75}$$

where

$$R_{\bar{K}_F}(\lambda)f \equiv \sum_{m=1}^{N} \sum_{n=1}^{N} [(I - \lambda A)^{-1}]_{mn} \phi_m^{(\Delta)}(\psi_n, f) \ . \tag{9.76}$$

A is very simple; it is just an $N \times N$ matrix, the mn-element of which is given by

$$A_{mn} = (\psi_m, \phi_n^{(\Delta)}) = (\psi_m, G_\Delta \phi_n) \ . \tag{9.77}$$

According to Eq. (9.69), each element of A can be expressed as a power series in λ, which is convergent if $|\lambda| < ||\Delta||^{-1}$. Thus the original problem can be reduced to one of inverting a finite-dimensional matrix, so in principle we have solved the problem.

It is often possible to use a finite-rank transformation with only a few terms and thereby obtain a Δ whose norm is fairly small. Even with a simple separable kernel of the form

$$k_s(x, y) = \alpha(x)\beta(y) \ ,$$

it is possible in many problems to get a Δ whose norm is much smaller than that of the original K. In specific cases this reduction may be very useful. However, it should be emphasized that no matter how small we make $||\Delta||$, for $|\lambda|$ sufficiently large $|\lambda| \cdot ||\Delta|| \geq 1$, and we can no longer be certain that $(I - \lambda\Delta)^{-1}$ exists.

However, if λ is an arbitrary complex number, then in any circle about the origin the complex λ-plane, there can be only a finite number of points for which $(I - \lambda K)^{-1}$ fails to exist. This is most apparent if we write everything in terms of resolvent operators:

$$G_K(\lambda) \equiv (I - \lambda K)^{-1} \equiv I + \lambda R_K(\lambda) \ ,$$

$$G_\Delta(\lambda) \equiv (I - \lambda \Delta)^{-1} \equiv I + \lambda R_\Delta(\lambda) \ .$$

Using these relations along with Eq. (9.75) in Eq. (9.74), we obtain

$$I + \lambda R_K(\lambda) = (I + \lambda R_{\bar{K}_F}(\lambda))(I + \lambda R_\Delta(\lambda)) \ ,$$

so

$$R_K(\lambda) = R_\Delta(\lambda) + R_{\bar{K}_F}(\lambda) \cdot (I + \lambda R_\Delta(\lambda)) \ . \tag{9.78}$$

Note that because of Eqs. (9.69) and (9.77), det $(I - \lambda A)$ is an analytic function of λ which is *not* identically zero (for example, det $(I - \lambda A) = 1$ when $\lambda = 0$). Therefore, if λ_0 is any point in the complex λ-plane for which det

$(I - \lambda_0 A) = 0$, it must be possible to find a neighborhood of λ_0 in which det $(I - \lambda A) \neq 0$ except at λ_0. Otherwise, all the derivatives of det $(I - \lambda A)$ would vanish at $\lambda = \lambda_0$, so the Taylor series about λ_0 would vanish identically. This means, according to the Bolzanno-Weierstrass theorem, that any finite circle in the complex λ-plane contains only a finite number of poles of $R_K(\lambda)$, since according to Eqs. (9.76) and (9.78) zeroes of det $(I - \lambda A)$ correspond to poles of $R_K(\lambda)$. Thus, $R_K(\lambda)$ is a *meromorphic* function of λ.

Another important by-product of breaking K into a transformation of finite rank, K_F, and a transformation with small norm, Δ, is the following result.

Theorem 9.9. The Fredholm alternative holds for any completely continuous transformation of Hilbert space.

Proof. The demonstration of this result is not difficult, but it is a bit long. We shall divide it into a series of lemmas.

Lemma 1. The equations

$$f = g + \lambda K f \tag{9.79}$$

and

$$\bar{f} = \bar{g} + \lambda^* K^\dagger \bar{f}, \tag{9.80}$$

are equivalent, respectively, to the equations

$$f = g_\Delta + \lambda(I + \lambda R_\Delta) K_F f, \tag{9.81}$$

$$\bar{f} = \bar{g}_\Delta + \lambda^*(I + \lambda^* R_\Delta^\dagger) K_F^\dagger \bar{f}, \tag{9.82}$$

where

$$g_\Delta = (I + \lambda R_\Delta)g, \qquad \bar{g}_\Delta = (I + \lambda^* R_\Delta)\bar{g},$$

and R_Δ is the resolvent defined above. Δ is an operator which satisfies $||\Delta|| < 1/|\lambda|$, and K_F is an operator of finite rank.

Proof. The result follows immediately from our previous work. We write

$$f = g + \lambda K f = g + \lambda K_F f + \lambda \Delta f,$$

where Δ is such that $||\Delta|| < 1/|\lambda|$. By Theorem 8.4, there is always a K_F for which this will be true. Hence

$$(I - \lambda \Delta) f = g + \lambda K_F f,$$

or, since $(I - \lambda \Delta)^{-1}$ exists and since by definition

$$(I - \lambda \Delta)^{-1} \equiv I + \lambda R_\Delta,$$

we have

$$f = g_\Delta + \lambda(I + \lambda R_\Delta) K_F f$$

with

$$g_\Delta = (I + \lambda R_\Delta)g.$$

An identical argument applied to

$$\tilde{f} = \tilde{g} + \lambda^* K^\dagger \tilde{f}$$

leads to

$$\tilde{f} = \tilde{g}_\Delta + \lambda^*(I + \lambda^* R_\Delta^\dagger) K_F^\dagger \tilde{f},$$

as required. By reversing the steps, we immediately see that Eqs. (9.81) and (9.82) imply Eqs. (9,79) and (9.80), respectively, which completes the proof of equivalence.

Lemma 2. Every value of λ is either a regular value or a singular value of the operator K. If it is a regular value, then the equation

$$f = g + \lambda K f \qquad (9.83)$$

has a unique solution given by

$$f = (I - \lambda K)^{-1} g,$$

where $(I - \lambda K)^{-1}$ exists. If λ is a singular value, then Eq. (9.83) has a solution if and only if g is orthogonal to every solution of

$$\lambda^* K^\dagger \tilde{h} = \tilde{h}.$$

Proof. This result follows from Lemma 1 and Theorem 8.1. According to Lemma 1, Eq. (9.83) is equivalent to

$$f = g_\Delta + \lambda(I + \lambda R_\Delta) K_F f \qquad (9.84)$$

for some appropriate Δ and K_F. But we have already shown

$$(I + \lambda R_\Delta) K_F$$

to be a transformation of finite rank, since K_F is a transformation of finite rank. Thus, by Theorem 8.1, Eq. (9.84) has a solution if and only if g_Δ is orthogonal to every solution of the homogeneous adjoint equation

$$\lambda^*[(I + \lambda R_\Delta) K_F]^\dagger \tilde{\phi} = \lambda^* K_F^\dagger (I + \lambda R_\Delta)^\dagger \tilde{\phi} = \tilde{\phi}. \qquad (9.85)$$

If we call

$$\tilde{h} \equiv (I + \lambda R_\Delta)^\dagger \tilde{\phi} = (I + \lambda^* R_\Delta^\dagger) \tilde{\phi},$$

then the requirement that Eq. (9.84) have a solution becomes

$$(g_\Delta, \phi) = 0 = (g_\Delta, [I + \lambda^* R_\Delta^\dagger]^{-1} \tilde{h}). \qquad (9.86)$$

Since $g_\Delta = (I + \lambda R_\Delta) g$, this simply requires that

$$(g, \tilde{h}) = 0.$$

Now $(I + \lambda^* R_\Delta^\dagger)^{-1}$ exists, and is by definition equal to $(I - \lambda^* \Delta^\dagger)$ (see Lemma 1). Moreover, $K^\dagger = K_F^\dagger + \Delta^\dagger$. Thus, according to Eq. (9.85), $\tilde{h}$ must obey the following equations:

$$\lambda^* K_F^\dagger \tilde{h} = \tilde{\phi} = (I + \lambda^* R_\Delta^\dagger)^{-1} \tilde{h} = (I - \lambda^* \Delta^\dagger) \tilde{h} = \tilde{h} + \lambda^* K_F^\dagger \tilde{h} - \lambda^* K^\dagger \tilde{h},$$

or

$$\lambda^* K^\dagger \tilde{h} = \tilde{h}.$$

Hence Eq. (9.84) has a solution if and only if g is orthogonal to all solutions of

$$\lambda^* K^\dagger \bar{h} = \bar{h} .$$

By Lemma 1, the same is true for Eq. (9.83), which completes the proof of this lemma.

Corollary. Every value of λ^* is either a regular value or a singular value of the operator $K^\dagger$. If it is a regular value, then the equation

$$\bar{f} = \bar{g} + \lambda^* K^\dagger \bar{f} \tag{9.87}$$

has a unique solution given by

$$\bar{f} = (I - \lambda^* K^\dagger)^{-1} \bar{g} ,$$

where $(I - \lambda^* K^\dagger)^{-1}$ exists. If λ is a singular value, then Eq. (9.87) has a solution if and only if $\bar{g}$ is orthogonal to every solution of $\lambda K h = h$.

Finally, we have

Lemma 3. The equations

$$\lambda K h_i = h_i , \qquad \lambda^* K^\dagger \bar{h}_i = \bar{h}_i$$

have the same number of linearly independent solutions.

Proof. According to Lemma 1, these two equations are equivalent respectively to

$$\lambda (I + \lambda R_\Delta) K_F h_i = h_i \tag{9.88}$$

and

$$\lambda^* (I + \lambda^* R_\Delta^\dagger) K_F^\dagger \bar{h}_i = \bar{h}_i \tag{9.89}$$

for some Δ and K_F. The last equation can be written as

$$\lambda^* K_F^\dagger (I + \lambda^* R_\Delta^\dagger) [(I + \lambda^* R_\Delta^\dagger)^{-1} \bar{h}_i] = [(I + \lambda^* R_\Delta^\dagger)^{-1} \bar{h}_i] , \tag{9.90}$$

since the inverse exists. If we define, as before,

$$\tilde{\phi}_i = (I + \lambda^* R_\Delta^\dagger)^{-1} \bar{h}_i ,$$

then Eq. (9.90) becomes

$$\lambda^* K_F^\dagger (I + \lambda^* R_\Delta^\dagger) \tilde{\phi}_i = \tilde{\phi}_i ,$$

and Eq. (9.89) becomes

$$\lambda^* [(I + \lambda R_\Delta) K_F]^\dagger \tilde{\phi}_i = \tilde{\phi}_i . \tag{9.91}$$

Now according to the second corollary to Theorem 8.1, Eq. (9.88) and Eq. (9.91) have the same number of linearly independent solutions, $\bar{h}_i$ and $\tilde{\phi}_i$. But $\bar{h}_i$ is related to $\tilde{\phi}_i$ by

$$\bar{h}_i = (I + \lambda^* R_\Delta^\dagger) \tilde{\phi}_i .$$

Since $(I + \lambda^* R_\Delta^\dagger)^{-1}$ exists, the $\bar{h}_i$ will be linearly independent if the $\tilde{\phi}_i$ are.

Thus Eqs. (9.88) and (9.89) have the same number of linearly independent solutions, and hence the same is true of the equations

$$\lambda K h_i = h_i \qquad \text{and} \qquad \lambda^* K^\dagger \bar{h}_i = \bar{h}_i \,.$$

This completes the proof of Lemma 3 and also of Theorem 9.9.

Note that the Fredholm alternative is exactly the same for completely continuous transformations as for transformations of finite rank. We have tried to emphasize this by retaining the same notation in discussing the two cases (see Section 8.6).

9.5   THE NUMERICAL SOLUTION OF INTEGRAL EQUATIONS

Having assured ourselves that solutions to linear equations with completely continuous kernels exist, it is worthwhile to indicate how one can actually proceed to solve such equations. It is rare that a closed-form solution can be found, so we will concentrate in this section on an approximation scheme which can be refined in principle to arbitrary precision. To do this we will make use of the technique discussed in Section 9.3. However, before applying this method, we must be sure that the eigenvalues of the operators in question behave in a sensible way, i.e., that eigenvalues of approximate kernels come arbitrarily close to the eigenvalues of the kernel which they approximate as the approximation is made arbitrarily fine. For this purpose, let us write

$$(I - \lambda K)^{-1} \equiv (I - \lambda K_F - \lambda \Delta)^{-1}$$

as

$$(I - \lambda K)^{-1} = (I - \lambda K_F)^{-1} + \lambda (I - \lambda K_F)^{-1} \Delta (I - \lambda K)^{-1} \,. \tag{9.92}$$

When we have computed $(I - \lambda K)^{-1}$, the solution to

$$f = g + \lambda K f \tag{9.93}$$

is just

$$f = (I - \lambda K)^{-1} g \,. \tag{9.94}$$

Now we want to approximate K so closely by K_F that the first term in the iterative solution of Eq. (9.92) will provide [via Eq. (9.94)] a satisfactory solution to Eq. (9.93). First, we remark that Eq. (9.92) is valid if and only if $(I - \lambda K)^{-1}$ and $(I - \lambda K_F)^{-1}$ both exist. What we want to show is that if we make $\|\Delta\|$ sufficiently small, then the values of λ for which $(I - \lambda K)^{-1}$ fails to exist and the values of λ for which $(I - \lambda K_F)^{-1}$ fails to exist get close to each other. (For *Hermitian* operators we have Theorem 9.8 which gives us the desired result in a very precise form.)

For general completely continuous operators, we suppose first that λ is a singular value of K, but that no matter how small $\|\Delta\|$ becomes $(I - \lambda K_F)^{-1}$ remains bounded, say

$$\|(I - \lambda K_F)^{-1}\| < B$$

for *all* Δ. But this assumption leads to a contradiction. For consider the equation

$$X = (I - \lambda K_F)^{-1} + \lambda(I - \lambda K_F)^{-1}\Delta X . \tag{9.95}$$

By familiar arguments, if $|\lambda| \cdot ||(I - \lambda K_F)^{-1}|| \cdot ||\Delta|| < 1$, this equation can be solved by iteration:

$$X = (I - \lambda K_F)^{-1} + \lambda(I - \lambda K_F)^{-1}\Delta(I - \lambda K_F)^{-1} + \cdots . \tag{9.96}$$

But $|\lambda| \cdot ||(I - \lambda K_F)^{-1}|| \cdot ||\Delta|| < 1$ means, by assumption, that $|\lambda| \cdot ||\Delta|| \cdot B < 1$. or

$$||\Delta|| < 1/(|\lambda| \cdot B) .$$

By Theorem 8.4, it is possible to obtain a Δ which satisfies this relation. The operator X is seen to have finite norm; in fact,

$$||X|| \leq \frac{B}{1 - \lambda B||\Delta||} < \infty .$$

But by multiplying the series of Eq. (9.96) on both sides by $(I - \lambda K)$, we find that

$$(I - \lambda K)X = X(I - \lambda K) = I .$$

Thus X is the bounded inverse of $I - \lambda K$. But this is impossible, since λ is assumed to be a singular value of K. Hence as $||\Delta|| \to 0$, $||(I - \lambda K_F)^{-1}|| \to \infty$, that is, λ comes closer and closer to being a singular value of K_F.

Since we know that any given singular value of K will come arbitrarily close to a singular value of K_F for $||\Delta||$ sufficiently small, it remains only to investigate the converse problem: Suppose that λ is *not* a singular value of K; can λ still be a singular value of K_F? The answer is that if $||\Delta||$ is sufficiently small, then λ is also not a singular value of K_F. Of course, for some finite value of $||\Delta||$ it might happen that λ is a singular value of K_F, but if we keep refining our approximation ($||\Delta|| \to 0$), eventually we can be certain that λ is not a singular value of K_F. To see that this is true, note that Eq. (9.92) implies that if $(I - \lambda K)^{-1}$ exists, then $(I - \lambda K_F)^{-1}$ exists if

$$[I + \lambda\Delta(I - \lambda K)^{-1}]^{-1}$$

exists. In this case,

$$(I - \lambda K_F)^{-1} = (I - \lambda K)^{-1}[I + \lambda\Delta(I - \lambda K)^{-1}]^{-1} .$$

But if $||(I - \lambda K)^{-1}|| < C$, then when $||\Delta|| < 1/|\lambda| \cdot C$ the quantity $[I + \lambda\Delta \cdot (I - \lambda K)^{-1}]^{-1}$ can be computed by iteration. Thus if λ is not a singular value of K for $||\Delta||$ sufficiently small, it must also not be a singular value of K_F. We know, therefore, that if $||\Delta||$ is small enough, and if λ is not a singular value of K, then Eq. (9.92) is well defined and can be solved by iteration:

$$(I - \lambda K)^{-1} = (I - \lambda K_F)^{-1} + \lambda(I - \lambda K_F)^{-1}\Delta(I - \lambda K_F)^{-1} + \cdots . \tag{9.97}$$

For $||\Delta||$ very small compared to $[|\lambda| \cdot ||(I - \lambda K_F)^{-1}||]^{-1}$, we may neglect all but the first term in Eq. (9.97) and write

$$(I - \lambda K)^{-1} \cong (I - \lambda K_F)^{-1}$$

in the sense of operator norm. Then Eq. (9.94) can be written as

$$f = (I - \lambda K_F)^{-1} g + O(\Delta) \; ,$$

where $O(\Delta)$ refers to terms which become small in norm as $||\Delta|| \to 0$. Of course, what one means by $||\Delta||$ sufficiently small is clearly, according to Eq. (9.97), dependent on $||(I - \lambda K_F)^{-1}||$. If one is near a singular value of K, and hence of K_F, then $||(I - \lambda K)^{-1}||$ and $||(I - \lambda K_F)^{-1}||$ are large, and $||\Delta||$ must be correspondingly small.

We are now ready to solve linear equations in the same manner employed in the solution of eigenvalue problems involving self-adjoint transformations. Assuming that K is an integral operator, we truncate the kernel $k(x, y)$ in such a way as to ensure the accuracy we desire, and then divide the resulting region on the x(or y)-axis into small subregions. Defining the unnormalized functions $\phi_n^{(N)}(x)$ as in Section 9.3, we obtain a kernel of finite rank, $k_N(x, y)$, which approximates $k(x, y)$ as closely as we please. Proceeding in this way, we find that

$$f = \sum_{n=1}^{N} a_n \phi_n^{(N)} \; , \tag{9.98}$$

where a_n is given by

$$a_n = \frac{N}{l} \sum_{m=1}^{N} [(I - \lambda A)^{-1}]_{nm} b_m \tag{9.99}$$

and b_m is just

$$b_m = (\phi_m^{(N)}, g) \; . \tag{9.100}$$

The matrix A is given by

$$A_{\mu\nu} = \frac{N}{l} \int dx \int dy \, k(x, y) \phi_\mu^{(N)}(x) \phi_\nu^{(N)}(y) \; . \tag{9.101}$$

In these equations l is the length of the interval outside of which we truncate the kernel, and N is the number of subintervals into which we divide the main interval. In obtaining Eq. (9.101), we have assumed that the quantity

$$\left[||g||^2 - \frac{N}{l} \sum_{m=1}^{N} |b_m|^2 \right]^{1/2}$$

is small compared to $||f||$; if the $\phi_n^{(N)}$ formed a complete set, then this quantity would be exactly zero. The reader should derive these results using the method by which we obtained Eqs. (9.48) and (9.49); an expression for f can also be obtained using the Riemann integral approach that led to Eq. (9.50) (see Problem 9.25). With Eqs. (9.98) through (9.101) at our disposal, the problem of solving an integral equation with completely continuous kernel is reduced to a matter of matrix inversion.

As an example of a linear equation with completely continuous kernel, let us consider the Lippmann-Schwinger equation discussed in Chapter 7. Dropping the subscript ($\pm$) of Eq. (7.68), we write the equation as

$$\psi(\mathbf{r}) = \frac{A}{(2\pi)^{3/2}} e^{i\mathbf{q}_i \cdot \mathbf{r}} - \frac{m}{2\pi\hbar^2} \int \frac{e^{iq_i|\mathbf{r}-\mathbf{r}'|}}{|\mathbf{r} - \mathbf{r}'|} V(\mathbf{r}')\psi(\mathbf{r}')d^3\mathbf{r}' . \tag{9.102}$$

This is related to the scattering amplitude, $f(\theta, \phi)$, by

$$f^s(\mathbf{q}_f) = -\frac{(2\pi)^{1/2} m}{\hbar^2 A} \int e^{-i\mathbf{q}_f \cdot \mathbf{r}} V(\mathbf{r})\psi(\mathbf{r}) \, d^3\mathbf{r} , \tag{9.103}$$

where $\mathbf{q}_f$ is a vector in the direction (θ, ϕ) which is equal in magnitude to $|\mathbf{q}_i|$. As remarked in Section 7.4, f^s is the quantity of real physical interest. Choosing the direction of the incident wave to be the z-direction and using $A = (2\pi)^{3/2}$ for convenience (f^s is clearly independent of A), we get

$$\psi(\mathbf{r}) = e^{iq_i z} - \frac{m}{2\pi\hbar^2} \int \frac{e^{iq_i|\mathbf{r}-\mathbf{r}'|}}{|\mathbf{r} - \mathbf{r}'|} V(\mathbf{r}')\psi(\mathbf{r}') \, d^3\mathbf{r}' ,$$

$$f^s(\mathbf{q}_f) = -\frac{m}{2\pi\hbar^2} \int e^{-i\mathbf{q}_f \cdot \mathbf{r}} V(\mathbf{r})\psi(\mathbf{r}) \, d^3\mathbf{r} .$$

Just as in Section 7.5, we expand everything in terms of Legendre polynomials. We write

$$\psi(\mathbf{r}) = \sum_{l=0}^{\infty} (2l + 1)\phi_l(r) P_l(\cos \theta) ,$$

$$f^s(\mathbf{q}_f) = \sum_{l=0}^{\infty} (2l + 1)f_l^s(q_i) P_l(\cos \theta_f) ,$$

where we have used the fact that $|\mathbf{q}_f| = q_i$ and have written the scattering angle as θ_f. In this way, we readily obtain a set of equations for the ϕ_l and the f_l^s. We will use the case $l = 0$ as an example. In this case,

$$\phi_0(r) = \frac{\sin (q_i r)}{q_i r} - \frac{2m}{\hbar^2 q_i} \int_0^\infty \frac{\sin (q_i r_<)e^{iq_i r_>}}{r_< r_>} V(r')\phi_0(r')r'^2 \, dr' \tag{9.104}$$

$$f_0^s(q_i) = -\frac{2m}{\hbar^2 q_i} \int_0^\infty \sin (q_i r) V(r)\phi_0(r)r \, dr . \tag{9.105}$$

In Eq. (9.104), $r_<$ and $r_>$ denote respectively the smaller of r and r' and the greater of r and r'.

To be specific, let us look at the case of an exponential potential,

$$V(r) = V_0 e^{-\mu r} .$$

Then Eqs. (9.104) and (9.105) become

$$\phi_0(r) = \frac{\sin (q_i r)}{q_i r} - \frac{2mV_0}{\hbar^2 q_i} \int_0^\infty \frac{1}{r} \sin (q_i r_<)e^{iq_i r_>}e^{-\mu r'}r'\phi_0(r') \, dr' , \tag{9.106}$$

$$f_0^s(q_i) = -\frac{2mV_0}{\hbar^2 q_i} \int_0^\infty \sin (q_i r)e^{-\mu r}r\phi_0(r) \, dr . \tag{9.107}$$

As it stands, neither the inhomogeneous term nor the kernel of Eq. (9.106) is square-integrable. However, the symmetrization process which we used in Section 9.3 will bring the equations to the desired form. We define

$$\xi_0(r) \equiv re^{-\mu r/2}\phi_0(r) \ .$$

Then our equations take the form

$$\xi_0(r) = \frac{1}{q_i} e^{-\mu r/2} \sin (q_i r) - \frac{2mV_0}{\hbar^2 q_i} \int_0^\infty e^{-\mu r/2} \sin (q_i r_<) e^{iq_i r_>} e^{-\mu r'/2} \xi_0(r') \ dr' \ ,$$

$$(9.108)$$

$$f_0^s(q_i) = -\frac{2mV_0}{\hbar^2 q_i} \int_0^\infty \sin (q_i r) e^{-\mu r/2} \xi_0(r) \ dr \ . \tag{9.109}$$

It is easily verified that the inhomogeneous term of Eq. (9.108) is square-integrable. What about the kernel

$$k_0(r, r') = - \frac{2mV_0}{\hbar^2 q_i} e^{-\mu (r+r')/2} \sin (q_i r_<) e^{iq_i r_>} \ ?$$

We find that

$$I(q_i) = \int_0^\infty dr \int_0^\infty dr' |k_0(r, r')|^2 = \frac{2m^2 V_0^2}{\hbar^4 \mu^2 (\mu^2 + q_i^2)} \ .$$

Then the norm of the operator, K_0, whose kernel is $k_0(r, r')$, satisfies

$$||K_0|| \leq \sqrt{2} \frac{mV_0}{\mu\hbar^2} (\mu^2 + q_i^2)^{-1/2} \ . \tag{9.110}$$

Thus the operator is completely continuous, and its norm tends toward zero as $q_i \to \infty$. Hence for q_i sufficiently large, we can always solve Eq. (9.108) by iteration. One might even hope that it will *always* be possible to solve Eq. (9.108) by iteration. However, for typical situations where an exponential potential is relevant (in nuclear physics, for example), the values of m, μ, and V_0 are such that the estimate on $||K_0||$ reads

$$||K_0|| \leq 2 \ , \tag{9.111}$$

when $q_i \ll \mu$. We have used

$$1/\mu = 1.4 \times 10^{-13} \text{ cm} \ ,$$
$$m = 1.66 \times 10^{-24} \text{ g} \ ,$$
$$V_0 = 30 \text{ MeV} = 4.8 \times 10^{-5} \text{ erg} \ ,$$

where $1/\mu$ is approximately equal to the range of nuclear forces, m is the mass of the proton (or neutron), V_0 is a reasonable estimate of the strength of nuclear forces, and $\hbar$ is Planck's constant. For $q_i \cong 2\mu$, $||K_0||$ becomes less than 1, but nevertheless for an important range of values of q_i, $||K_0||$ is by no means negligible compared with 1. Of course, Eq. (9.111) is only an *inequality*; $||K_0||$

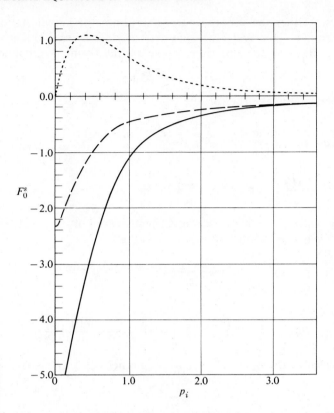

Fig. 9.4 The real part of F_0^s (dashed curve) and the imaginary part of F_0^s (dotted curve) for $l = 0$ scattering by an exponential potential. Included for comparison is the first iterative approximation, F_{0B}^s, which is purely real (solid curve). All the amplitudes are measured in units of the range of the potential $(1/\mu)$, and are plotted as functions of the dimensionless variable p_i, which is essentially the momentum of the scattered particle, $p_i = (2mE/\mu^2\hbar^2)^{1/2}$. The strength of the potential is such that the dimensionless parameter $(mV_0/\mu^2\hbar^2)$ appearing in Eqs. (9.112) and (9.113) is equal to 1.4, as discussed in the text.

might be less than 1, even for $q_i = 0$; however, for the iterative method to be of *practical* use, $||K_0||$ should be *much* less than 1, and the estimate provided by Eq. (9.111) makes that seem unlikely.

Thus we are left with the method which we used in the last section for solving the eigenvalue problem for a Hermitian operator. It is again convenient to scale the distances into appropriate units by defining

$$x \equiv \mu r , \qquad p_i = q_i/\mu = (2mE/\mu^2\hbar^2)^{1/2} ,$$
$$\eta_0 = \mu\xi_0 , \qquad F_0^s = \mu f_0^s .$$

With these changes, Eqs. (9.108) and (9.109) are transformed to

$$\eta_0(x) = \frac{1}{p_i} e^{-x/2} \sin(p_i x) - \frac{2mV_0}{\mu^2 \hbar^2 p_i} \int_0^\infty e^{-x/2} \sin(p_i x_<) e^{ip_i x_>} e^{-x'/2} \eta_0(x') \, dx' \, ,$$

(9.112)

$$F_0^s(p_i) = -\frac{2mV_0}{\mu^2 \hbar^2 p_i} \int_0^\infty \sin(p_i x) e^{-x/2} \eta_0(x) \, dx \, .$$

(9.113)

To solve Eq. (9.112) numerically, we truncate the kernel when x or x' is greater than 7, and then divide the interval [0, 7] into 35 equal parts. Defining $\phi_n^{(N)}$ as usual, we can use Eqs. (9.98) through (9.101) to reduce the problem to one of matrix inversion. Figure 9.4 shows the results for both the real and imaginary parts of F_0^s as a function of p_i for $(mV_0/\mu^2\hbar^2) = 1.4$. This value is obtained from the physically relevant estimates of m, V_0, and μ listed above. For comparison, we also show in Fig. 9.4 the first iterative approximation (Born approximation) to F_0^s, obtained by writing

$$\eta_0^B(x) = \frac{1}{p_i} e^{-x/2} \sin(p_i x) \, ,$$

$$F_0^{sB} = -2\left(\frac{mV_0}{\mu^2\hbar^2}\right)\frac{1}{p_i} \int_0^\infty \sin(p_i x) \, e^{-x/2} \eta_0^B(x) \, dx = -4\left(\frac{mV_0}{\mu^2\hbar^2}\right)\frac{1}{4p_i^2 + 1} \, .$$

Just as we expect from Eq. (9.110), for $q_i \leq \mu$ and $p_i \leq 1$ the first iterative approximation to the amplitude differs considerably from the correct

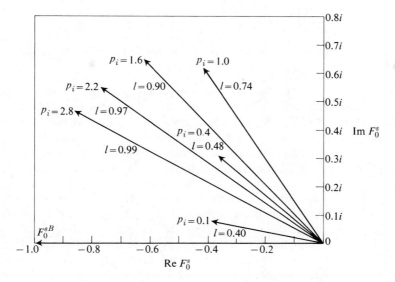

Fig. 9.5 Convergence of F_0^s to the first iterative approximation, as viewed in the complex plane.

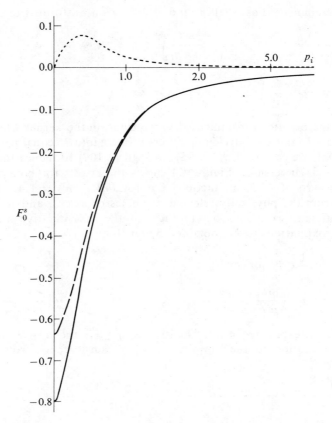

Fig. 9.6 Same as in Figure 9.4, but $(mV_0/\mu^2\hbar^2) = 0.2$.

amplitude. For $p_i = 1$, the real and imaginary parts of F_0^s are of the same order of magnitude, while F_0^{sB} is purely real. However, as p_i becomes larger, the imaginary part of F_0^s drops off more rapidly than the real part, and Fig. 9.4 shows that the real part of F_0^s tends toward F_0^{sB}. However, even for $p_i \cong 3$, the discrepancy is still striking if viewed from the vantage point of Fig. 9.5. In this figure we have divided all amplitudes by $|F_0^{sB}|$ to obtain a reasonable scale and have plotted F_0^s as a "vector" in the complex plane. The "vector" F_0^{sB} is now equal to -1 for all p_i, and we show it as a reference vector along the negative real axis. The tip of each vector is marked by the value of p_i to which it corresponds. We see that the vectors $F_0^s(p_i)$ are tending toward F_0^{sB} as p_i increases, but for $p_i = 2.8$ there is still much improvement to be desired. This is not surprising, for even at $p_i = 2.8$, Eq. (9.110) gives $||K_0|| = 0.66$, so although the relevant norm is less than unity, it is still not particularly small. Along each vector, we have written its length, l, and one is struck by the fact that the length of the complex "vectors" representing $F_0^s(p_i)$ tend very rapidly toward the length of F_0^{sB}, that is,

$$|F_0^s| \to |F_0^{sB}|$$

as $p_i \to \infty$, much faster than

$$|F_0^s - F_0^{sB}| \to 0 .$$

This means that the most important observable quantity, namely, the cross section, will be given deceptively well by the Born approximation, since it depends only on the *modulus* of F_0^s. However, quantities which depend on the phase of F_0^s will not be given so accurately by the Born approximation.

The iterative approach is much more successful for $(mV_0/\mu^2\hbar^2) = 0.2$. Figure 9.6 shows the real and imaginary part of F_0^s along with the first iterative approximation. Even when $p_i \le 1$, the imaginary part of F is much smaller than the real part, and by the time $p_i = 1$, F_0^{sB} differs by only three percent from the real part of F_0^s. At $p_i = 3$, the imaginary part of F_0^s is smaller than the real part by more than an order of magnitude, and F_0^{sB} and the real part of F_0^s are virtually identical. Thus, in this case, the iterative approach is simple and accurate. But unfortunately, this will not be the case in many problems of practical interest, and more powerful techniques involving some form of finite-rank approximation must be used.

*9.6 UNITARY TRANSFORMATIONS

Up to now, most of our detailed work has been on completely continuous transformations of Hilbert space, although we managed to put the discussion of iterative techniques in the more general setting of *bounded* transformations. In this section we want to touch on unitary transformations of Hilbert spaces, which are important in mathematical physics because of their connection with the theory of group representations and quantum mechanics, even though they are never completely continuous (see Section 9.1).

At the outset we must make a distinction between unitary and isometric transformations which did not arise in finite-dimensional vector spaces. An isometry is defined in vector spaces of any dimension as a linear transformation U satisfying

$$(Uf, Ug) = (f, g)$$

for all f, g in the vector space. This implies that $U^\dagger$ is a left inverse of U:

$$U^\dagger U = I .$$

Now in a finite-dimensional space, the existence of a left inverse guarantees the existence of a right inverse, but on an infinite-dimensional space this is not always the case. *If* a right inverse also exists, U is said to be unitary. This right inverse must of course be equal to the left inverse, since if $BA = I = AC$, then $BAC = C$, so $B = C$. Thus for *unitary* transformations, we write

$$U^\dagger = U^{-1} .$$

To show that not all isometries are unitary consider a complete orthonormal set in a Hilbert space, H, and define U acting on any $f \in H$ by

$$Uf = \sum_{i=1}^{\infty} \phi_{i+1}(\phi_i, f) .$$

The adjoint transformation $U^\dagger$ is given by

$$U^\dagger g = \sum_{i=1}^{\infty} \phi_i(\phi_{i+1}, g) ,$$

for any $g \in H$. The completeness of the $\{\phi_i\}$ guarantees that

$$(Uf, Ug) = (f, g)$$

for any $f, g \in H$. Thus $U^\dagger$ is a left inverse. Suppose that it were also a right inverse; then we must have

$$(U^\dagger f, U^\dagger g) = (f, UU^\dagger g) = (f, g) ,$$

for any $f, g \in H$, so $U^\dagger$ must be an isometry. But for our $U^\dagger$,

$$(U^\dagger f, U^\dagger g) = \sum_{i=1}^{\infty} (f, \phi_{i+1})(\phi_{i+1}, g) \neq (f, g) ,$$

so $U^\dagger$ is not an isometry and U is therefore *not* unitary. The reader should show that this construction does not produce a nonunitary isometry on a *finite-dimensional* space.

On the space of square-integrable functions, L_2, it is possible to obtain an explicit characterization of all unitary operators. This will lead us to a neater presentation of the Fourier transform, which we have already discussed in an intuitive fashion in Section 5.7. We use the method of Bochner as presented by Riesz and Nagy.

Theorem 9.10. Let U be a unitary transformation of the space of square-integrable functions, L_2. Then for any $f \in L_2$ such that $g = Uf$, there exist two functions $k(\xi, x)$ and $h(\xi, x)$ which satisfy the relations

$$\int_0^\xi g(x)\, dx = \int k^*(\xi, x) f(x)\, dx \qquad (9.114a)$$

and

$$\int_0^\xi f(x)\, dx = \int h^*(\xi, x) g(x)\, dx . \qquad (9.114b)$$

Proof. We define the function $e_\xi(x)$ which is equal to the sign of x when x lies between zero and ξ and vanishes otherwise. Now for any unitary transformation, let

$$h(\xi, x) \equiv Ue_\xi(x) , \qquad k(\xi, x) \equiv U^{-1}e_\xi(x) = U^\dagger e_\xi(x) .$$

Consider the equation $g = Uf$. We have

$$(e_\xi, g) \equiv (e_\xi, Uf) = (U^\dagger e_\xi, f) = (k(\xi, x), f(x)) .$$

Writing this out explicitly, we get

$$\int_0^\xi g(x)\,dx = \int k^*(\xi, x)f(x)\,dx \,,$$

making use of the fact that when $e_\xi(x) \neq 0$,

$$e_\xi(x) = \text{sgn}\ (x)$$

and *not* simply

$$e_\xi(x) = 1 \,.$$

Similarly,

$$(e_\xi, f) = (e_\xi, U^{-1}g) = (e_\xi, U^\dagger g) = (Ue_\xi, g) = (h(\xi, x), g(x)) \,,$$

so that

$$\int_0^\xi f(x)\,dx = \int h^*(\xi, x)g(x)\,dx \,.$$

This completes the proof of the theorem.

The functions k and h have certain special properties. Suppose that in Eq. (9.114b) we set $f = U^{-1}e_\eta = k(\eta, x)$, and hence $g = Uf = e_\eta$. Thus

$$\int_0^\xi k(\eta, x)\,dx = \int_0^\eta h^*(\xi, x)\,dx \,. \tag{9.115a}$$

Doing the same in Eq. (9.114a), we find that

$$\int k^*(\xi, x)k(\eta, x)\,dx = \int_0^\xi e_\eta(x)\,dx \,.$$

Clearly, if ξ and η are of opposite sign, this last integral is zero. If $\xi > 0$, $\eta > 0$, then

$$\int k^*(\xi, x)k(\eta, x)\,dx = \min\ (\xi, \eta) \,.$$

If $\xi < 0$, $\eta < 0$, then

$$\int k^*(\xi, x)k(\eta, x)\,dx = -\max\ (\xi, \eta) = \min\ (-\xi, -\eta) \,,$$

$$= \min\ (|\xi|, |\eta|) \,.$$

Hence we have

$$\int k^*(\xi, x)k(\eta, x)\,dx = \begin{cases} \min\ (|\xi|, |\eta|) & \text{if}\ \ \xi\eta > 0 \,, \\ 0 & \text{if}\ \ \xi\eta \leq 0 \,, \end{cases} \tag{9.115b}$$

and similarly

$$\int h^*(\xi, x)h(\eta, x)\,dx = \begin{cases} \min\ (|\xi|, |\eta|) & \text{if}\ \ \xi\eta > 0 \,, \\ 0 & \text{if}\ \ \xi\eta \leq 0 \,. \end{cases} \tag{9.115c}$$

The converse of Theorem 9.10 is extremely important from the practical point of view.

Theorem 9.11. Suppose that we are given two functions $k(\xi, x)$ and $h(\xi, x)$ which belong to L_2 for all ξ and which satisfy Eqs. (9.115a), (9.115b), and (9.115c). Then the equations

$$\int_0^\xi g(x)\, dx = \int k^*(\xi, x) f(x)\, dx\ ,$$

$$\int_0^\xi f(x)\, dx = \int h^*(\xi, x) g(x)\, dx\ ,$$

define a unitary transformation of L_2, U, and its inverse such that $g = Uf$, $f = U^{-1}g$.

Proof. The proof of this result involves a mathematical technique which we have not employed before. The idea is to use the functions k and h to define operators V and U which act on the functions $e_\xi(x)$ introduced in proving Theorem 9.10. We make the definitions

$$Ue_\xi(x) \equiv h(\xi, x)\ , \qquad Ve_\xi(x) \equiv k(\xi, x)\ .$$

For any functions e_ξ, e_η belonging to this class, we have, according to Eq. (9.115a),

$$(Ve_\xi, e_\eta) = (e_\xi, Ue_\eta)\ .$$

Also, Eq. (9.115b) tells us that

$$(Ue_\xi, Ue_\eta) = (e_\xi, e_\eta)\ ,$$

and Eq. (9.115c) yields

$$(Ve_\xi, Ve_\eta) = (e_\xi, e_\eta)\ .$$

We would now like to extend the definitions of U and V to a wider class of functions. The first obvious extension is to the class of all elements of L_2 which can be written as *linear combinations* of functions of the type $e_\xi(x)$. For example, we will have

$$U\left[\sum_{n=1}^N a_n e_{\xi_n}(x) \right] = \sum_{n=1}^N a_n h(\xi_n, x)\ ,$$

$$V\left[\sum_{n=1}^N a_n e_{\xi_n}(x) \right] = \sum_{n=1}^N a_n k(\xi_n, x)\ .$$

By the additivity of the inner product, we have for any ϕ, ψ which belong to this more general class,

$$(V\phi, \psi) = (\phi, U\psi)\ , \qquad (V\phi, V\psi) = (\phi, \psi)\ , \qquad (U\phi, U\psi) = (\phi, \psi)\ .$$

Among the functions in this extended class are the step functions, which take on the values C_n $(n = 1, 2, \cdots, N)$ on the intervals I_n $(n = 1, 2, \cdots, N)$ and are zero elsewhere. But any $f \in L_2$ can be approximated in the mean arbitrarily closely by step functions; that is, we can find a sequence of step functions $\{\phi_n\}$ such that for any $f \in L_2$,

$$||\phi_n - f|| \to 0$$

as $n \to \infty$. Since U is unitary, at least on the class of step functions,

$$\|U\phi_m - U\phi_n\| < \epsilon$$

when

$$\|\phi_m - \phi_n\| < \epsilon .$$

Therefore, if the ϕ_n converge to some element, f, of L_2, so must the set $\{U\phi_n\}$. We define the function to which this set converges to be Uf. Thus we extend U to the entire space by continuity. It only remains to show that if $f, g \in L_2$, then we still have

$$(Uf, Ug) = (f, g) , \qquad (Vf, Vg) = (f, g) , \qquad (Vf, g) = (f, Ug) .$$

We prove the first of these results and leave the others to the reader. Consider

$$\begin{aligned}
(Uf, Ug) - (f, g) &\equiv (Uf, Ug) - (U\phi_n, Ug) + (U\phi_n, Ug) \\
&\quad - (U\phi_n, U\psi_m) + (U\phi_n, U\psi_m) \\
&\quad - (\phi_n, g) + (\phi_n, g) - (f, g)
\end{aligned}$$

where $\phi_n \to f$, $\psi_m \to g$. For step functions,

$$(U\phi_n, U\psi_m) = (\phi_n, \psi_m) ,$$

so

$$\begin{aligned}
|(Uf, Ug) - (f, g)| &\leq |(Uf, Ug) - (U\phi_n, Ug)| \\
&\quad + |(U\phi_n, Ug) - (U\phi_n, U\psi_m)| \\
&\quad + |(\phi_n, \psi_m) - (\phi_n, g)| + |(\phi_n, g) - (f, g)| \\
&\leq |(Uf - U\phi_n, Ug)| + |(U\phi_n, Ug - U\psi_m)| \\
&\quad + |(\phi_n, \psi_m - g)| + |(\phi_n - f, g)| \\
&\leq \|Uf - U\phi_n\| \cdot \|Ug\| + \|Ug - U\psi_m\| \cdot \|U\phi_n\| \\
&\quad + \|\psi_m - g\| \cdot \|\phi_n\| \\
&\quad + \|\phi_n - f\| \cdot \|g\| .
\end{aligned}$$

But since $\phi_n \to f$ and $\psi_m \to g$, and by definition $U\phi_n \to Uf$ and $U\psi_m \to Ug$, we can make the right-hand side of this equation as small as we please. Therefore

$$(Uf, Ug) = (f, g) .$$

Similarly,

$$(Vf, Vg) = (f, g) , \qquad (Vf, g) = (f, Ug) ,$$

so that we may conclude that

$$U^\dagger U = I , \qquad V^\dagger V = I , \qquad V = U^\dagger .$$

Hence U has a right inverse and a left inverse:

$$U^{-1} = U^\dagger = V ,$$

that is, U is a unitary transformation whose inverse is given by V. According to the previous theorem, U and V are represented by

$$\int_0^\xi g(x)\, dx = \int k^*(\xi, x) f(x)\, dx\, ,$$

$$\int_0^\xi f(x)\, dx = \int h^*(\xi, x) g(x)\, dx\, ,$$

if $g = Uf$. This completes the proof of the theorem.

Note that Eqs. (9.114a) and (9.114b) can be written more conveniently as

$$g(x) = \frac{d}{dx} \int k^*(x, y) f(y)\, dy\, , \tag{9.116a}$$

$$f(x) = \frac{d}{dx} \int h^*(x, y) g(y)\, dy\, . \tag{9.116b}$$

An extremely useful special case of this theorem results when we consider the functions

$$k(x, y) = \frac{1}{\sqrt{2\pi}} \frac{e^{-ixy} - 1}{-iy}$$

$$h(x, y) = k^*(x, y)\, .$$

We want to show that these functions satisfy the conditions of Theorem 9.11. Consider first

$$\int k^*(\xi, x) k(\eta, x)\, dx = \frac{1}{2\pi} \int_{-\infty}^\infty \frac{(e^{i\xi x} - 1)(e^{-i\eta x} - 1)}{x^2}\, dx$$

$$= \frac{1}{2\pi} \int_{-\infty}^\infty \frac{1}{x^2} [e^{i(\xi - \eta)x} - e^{i\xi x} - e^{-i\eta x} + 1]\, dx$$

$$= \frac{1}{2\pi} \int_{-\infty}^\infty \frac{1}{x^2} [\cos(\xi - \eta)x - \cos \xi x - \cos \eta x + 1]\, dx$$

$$+ \frac{i}{2\pi} \int_{-\infty}^\infty \frac{1}{x^2} [\sin(\xi - \eta)x - \sin \xi x + \sin \eta x]\, dx\, .$$

The imaginary part vanishes since it is an odd function integrated over a symmetric domain. Note that the integral is well defined, because it converges at $x = \pm \infty$ and is *not* singular at $x = 0$. Thus

$$\int k^*(\xi, x) k(\eta, x)\, dx = \frac{1}{2\pi} \int_{-\infty}^\infty \frac{1}{x^2} [\cos(\xi - \eta)x - \cos \xi x - \cos \eta x + 1]\, dx$$

$$= \frac{1}{\pi} \int_{-\infty}^\infty [\sin^2 \tfrac{1}{2} |\xi| x + \sin^2 \tfrac{1}{2} |\eta| x - \sin^2 \tfrac{1}{2} |\xi - \eta| x] \frac{dx}{x^2}\, .$$

Making a change of variable in each term, we get

$$\int k^*(\xi, x) k(\eta, x)\, dx = \frac{1}{2\pi} [|\xi| + |\eta| - |\xi - \eta|] \int_{-\infty}^\infty \frac{\sin^2 z}{z^2}\, dz\, .$$

This integral can be readily evaluated by the complex variable methods of Chapter 6; it is equal to π. Thus

$$\int k^*(\xi, x)k(\eta, x)\,dx = \tfrac{1}{2}\left(|\xi| + |\eta| - |\xi - \eta|\right)$$

$$= \begin{cases} \min\left(|\xi|, |\eta|\right) & \text{if } \xi\eta > 0, \\ 0 & \text{if } \xi\eta \leq 0. \end{cases}$$

Likewise,

$$\int h^*(\xi, k)h(\eta, x)\,dx = \begin{cases} \min\left(|\xi|, |\eta|\right) & \text{if } \eta\xi > 0, \\ 0 & \text{if } \eta\xi \leq 0. \end{cases}$$

Finally

$$\int_0^\eta k(\xi, x)\,dx = \frac{1}{\sqrt{2\pi}}\int_0^\eta \frac{e^{-i\xi x} - 1}{-ix}\,dx = \frac{1}{\sqrt{2\pi}}\int_0^{\xi\eta} \frac{e^{-iz} - 1}{-iz}\,dz$$

and also

$$\int_0^\xi h^*(\eta, x)\,dx = \frac{1}{\sqrt{2\pi}}\int_0^\xi \frac{e^{-i\eta x} - 1}{-ix}\,dx = \frac{1}{\sqrt{2\pi}}\int_0^{\xi\eta} \frac{e^{-iz} - 1}{-iz}\,dz.$$

So

$$\int_0^\xi h^*(\eta, x)\,dx = \int_0^\eta k(\xi, x)\,dx.$$

Thus k and h fulfill all the hypotheses of Theorem 9.11, and we have the result:

Corollary. The formulas

$$g(x) = \frac{1}{\sqrt{2\pi}}\frac{d}{dx}\int_{-\infty}^{\infty} \frac{e^{ixy} - 1}{iy} f(y)\,dy \qquad (9.117a)$$

and

$$f(x) = \frac{1}{\sqrt{2\pi}}\frac{d}{dx}\int_{-\infty}^{\infty} \frac{e^{-ixy} - 1}{-iy} g(y)\,dy \qquad (9.117b)$$

define a unitary transform of L_2 and its inverse.

Note that if we interchange integration and differentiation, we obtain just the classical result of Fourier:

$$g(x) = \frac{1}{\sqrt{2\pi}}\int_{-\infty}^{\infty} e^{ixy}f(y)\,dy, \qquad (9.118a)$$

$$f(x) = \frac{1}{\sqrt{2\pi}}\int_{-\infty}^{\infty} e^{-ixy}g(y)\,dy. \qquad (9.118b)$$

Now we can easily justify this interchange if we interpret properly the infinite integration range. First note that any $f \in L_2$ can be approximated *in norm* arbitrarily closely by a function which vanishes outside a sufficiently large interval $[-L, L]$, namely, by the function f_L which equals $f(x)$ in $[-L, L]$ and is zero outside. Now let us consider the transform, g_L, of such an approximating function. We have

$$g_L(x) = \frac{1}{\sqrt{2\pi}} \frac{d}{dx} \int_{-L}^{L} \frac{e^{ixy} - 1}{iy} f(y)\, dy$$

$$= \frac{1}{\sqrt{2\pi}} \lim_{\epsilon \to 0} \int_{-L}^{L} \frac{e^{i(x+\epsilon)y} - e^{ixy}}{iy\epsilon} f(y)\, dy$$

$$= \frac{1}{\sqrt{2\pi}} \lim_{\epsilon \to 0} \int_{-L}^{L} \frac{\sin (\epsilon y/2)}{(\epsilon y/2)} e^{i\epsilon y/2} e^{ixy} f(y)\, dy \,. \qquad (9.119)$$

The function under the integral is less than $f(y)$ in absolute magnitude since

$$\left| \frac{\sin (\epsilon y/2)}{(\epsilon y/2)} e^{i\epsilon y/2} e^{ixy} \right| = \left| \frac{\sin (\epsilon y/2)}{(\epsilon y/2)} \right| \le 1$$

for all values of ϵy. But on any finite interval, $|f(y)|$ is clearly integrable, because

$$\int_{-L}^{L} |f(y)|\, dy = \int_{-\infty}^{\infty} [e_L(y) - e_{-L}(y)]^* \cdot |f(y)|\, dy$$

$$= (e_L, |f|) - (e_{-L}, |f|) < \infty \,,$$

since e_L, e_{-L}, and $|f|$ all belong to L_2. Therefore, the integrand of Eq. (9.119) is bounded by an integrable function for all values of ϵ, and we can interchange the limit and the integration sign to get

$$g_L(x) = \frac{1}{\sqrt{2\pi}} \int_{-L}^{L} e^{ixy} f(y)\, dy = \frac{1}{\sqrt{2\pi}} \frac{d}{dx} \int_{-\infty}^{\infty} \frac{e^{ixy} - 1}{iy} f_L(y)\, dy \,.$$

Since this last transformation is unitary, $Uf_L \to Uf = g$ as $f_L \to f$ in norm. Thus we may write

$$g(x) = \frac{1}{\sqrt{2\pi}} \int_{-\infty}^{\infty} e^{ixy} f(y)\, dy \,,$$

if we mean by the integral from $-\infty$ to $+\infty$ the limit in norm of the integral from $-L$ to $+L$ as L tends toward infinity. The integration in the inverse transform,

$$f(x) = \frac{1}{\sqrt{2\pi}} \int_{-\infty}^{\infty} e^{-ixy} g(y)\, dy \,,$$

is to be interpreted in the same way. Thus the Fourier integral gives rise to a unitary transformation of Hilbert space. The transform and its inverse are given by the familiar formulas of Eqs. (9.118a) and (9.118b).

PROBLEMS

1. If A is a completely continuous Hermitian operator with only a finite number of nonzero eigenvalues, show that the eigenvectors of A can be chosen to form a complete orthonormal set.

2. Show that if we modify $k(x, y)$ on a set of measure zero in the plane, then the resulting kernel, $\bar{k}(x, y)$ has essentially the same eigenvectors and eigenvalues as $k(x, y)$ and the solution to the equation

$$f(x) = g(x) + \lambda \int k(x, y) f(y) \, dy$$

is essentially the same as the solution to

$$\tilde{f}(x) = g(x) + \lambda \int \bar{k}(x, y) \, \tilde{f}(y) \, dy \, .$$

What is meant by "essentially" in the above statement?

3. Show that if $\{\lambda_n\}$ and $\{x_n(t)\}$ are respectively the eigenvalues and eigenvectors of a completely continuous Hermitian integral operator, then the sum

$$S(t, t') = \sum_{n=1}^{\infty} \lambda_n x_n(t) x_n^*(t')$$

converges in the sense of mean convergence.

4. Prove that if $\{\lambda_n\}$ and $\{x_n(t)\}$ are respectively the eigenvalues and eigenvectors of the Hermitian integral operator, A, with square integrable kernel $a(t, t')$, then

$$\int dt \int dt' \, |a(t, t')|^2 = \sum_{n=1}^{\infty} \lambda_n^2 \, .$$

5. Consider the Hermitian integral operator, A, whose square-integrable kernel is $a(t, t')$ and assume for convenience that all the eigenvalues of A are positive.

a) Show that if we write a "trial eigenvector" of A as

$$\phi^t = \sum_{n=1}^{N} a_n f_n(t) \, ,$$

where $\{f_n(t): n = 1, 2, \cdots, \nu\}$ is a given set of functions, then if we extremize $(\phi^t, A\phi^t)$ with respect to the coefficients a_n, subject to the constraint $(\phi^t, \phi^t) = 1$, the resulting equation for the a_n is

$$Mv = \lambda Nv \, . \tag{1}$$

In this equation λ is the Lagrange multiplier which is introduced to handle the constraint, and v is a column vector whose ith component is a_i. M and N are matrices whose ijth elements are

$$M_{ij} = \int f_i^*(t) a(t, t') f_j(t') \, dt \, dt' \, , \qquad i, j = 1, 2, \cdots, \nu \, ,$$

$$N_{ij} = \int f_i^*(t) f_j(t) \, dt \, , \qquad i, j = 1, 2, \cdots, \nu \, .$$

b) Show that M and N are Hermitian matrices.

c) Show that the values of λ which satisfy Eq. (1) must be real.

d) Will the eigenvectors corresponding to the various values of λ be orthogonal? Will they satisfy any relationship analogous to the orthogonality relationship?

e) What is the relationship between the largest λ which solves Eq. (1) and the largest eigenvalue of A? We may imagine that if we choose the set $\{f_n(t)\}$ intelligently, it will be possible to arrive at a very good approximation to this largest eigenvalue.

6. a) Let us denote the space of square-integrable functions on the interval $[0, 1]$ by $L_2[0, 1]$. Show that the operator P, defined on $L_2[0, 1]$ by

$$Pf(t) \equiv f(1 - t),$$

commutes with the integral operator A, acting on $L_2[0, 1]$, whose kernel is $a(t, t') = t_<(1 - t_>)$.

b) Show that P is self-adjoint and bounded. What is the norm of P?

c) What are the possible eigenvalues of P? Is P completely continuous? If so, why? If not, why not?

d) In accordance with Theorem 4.22 (assuming it to be applicable in this infinite-dimensional case), can you classify the eigenvectors of A [see part (a)] according to which eigenvalue of P they belong to?

7. a) Using the operator P of Problem 9.6, can you give an argument which suggests why the trial function

$$\psi_1^t = at(1 - t) + bt^2(1 - t)^2$$

would be a better function for obtaining a good value for the largest eigenvalue of A than the function

$$\psi_2^t = at(1 - t) + bt^2(1 - t).$$

Here A is the Hermitian integral operator on $L_2[0, 1]$ whose kernel is $a(t, t') = t_<(1 - t_>)$. Note that we have already shown in Section 9.2 that $\psi_0^t = at(1 - t)$ gives an excellent starting point.

b) Explain why both ψ_1^t and ψ_2^t must certainly give a value for the largest eigenvalue of A which is at least as close to the true value as the value (computed in Section 9.2) given by ψ_0^t.

c) Using the operator P, state directly, without further detailed computation (but making use of the computation in Section 9.2), what the function ψ_2^t of part (a) would give as an estimate of the largest eigenvalue of A.

8. a) Show that the function $\psi^t = at(1 - t)(1 - 2t)$ is orthogonal to $\sin \pi t$ on the interval $[0, 1]$ so it is an appropriate trial function to use in attempting to find the second largest eigenvalue (and corresponding eigenvector) of the operator A whose kernel is $a(t, t') = t_<(1 - t_>)$ on $L_2[0, 1]$.

[*Hint*: This can be done by brute force integration, but it is much simpler to use arguments involving the operator P of Problem 9.6.]

b) Using the function ψ^t given in part (a), obtain an estimate of the second largest eigenvalue of A and compare with the exact value, $\lambda_2 = 1/(4\pi^2)$.

9. Consider the hydrogen atom, consisting of an electron bound to a proton. Neglecting the fact that electrons and protons have spin, one can show on the basis of the nonrelativistic Schrödinger equation,

$$H_0\phi_n = \lambda_n^{(0)}\phi_n,$$

that there are an infinite number of bound states. Here H_0 is a Hermitian linear operator whose precise form is unimportant for our purpose. The state with lowest energy is a nondegenerate state with eigenvalue $\lambda_1^{(0)} = -13.6 \text{ eV}$ and eigenfunction ϕ_1. The next state with eigenvalue $\lambda_2^{(0)} = -3.4 \text{ eV}$ is fourfold degenerate. We can label the eigenvectors of these four states physically by $\phi_{2s}, \phi_{2p+}, \phi_{2po}$ and ϕ_{2p-}, where the 2 refers to $\lambda_2^{(0)}$, s and p refer to the fact that one state has angular momentum 0 (an "s-state") while the other has angular momentum h (a "p-state") and the subscripts $+$, 0, and $-$ refer to the components of angular momentum along the z-axis in the p-state, which can be either $\hbar$, 0 or $-\hbar$. In the first approximation these states are degenerate, but a closer look at the situation reveals that because of electromagnetic self-energy effects, the $2s$-state actually lies above the $2p$-state by an energy L whose value is roughly 4×10^{-6} eV. The states which lie nearest to this closely spaced $2s$-$2p$ cluster are the $3s$, $3p$, and $3d$ states (they are about 2 eV distant).

a) Imagine now that an electric field is applied to the hydrogen atom, so that the states of the system (the atom in the electric field) will be given by the eigenvectors which satisfy

$$H\psi_n = \lambda_n \psi_n \, ,$$

where $H = H_0 + H_1$, H_0 being the Hermitian linear operator mentioned above, and H_1 being given by $H_1 = eEz$. E is the magnitude of the electric field and e is the electronic charge. We will assume the electric field to be of such a magnitude as to shift the energies of the hydrogen atom by a number of the order of magnitude of L. Assuming the perturbation theory of Section 9.2 to be valid for this problem, explain why in calculating the effect of the field on the $2s$-state we can forget about all other states except the $2p$-states without making a significant error.

b) Show that if we use Eq. (9.34) to calculate the function ψ_{2s} (this is the function which would reduce to ϕ_{2s} if the electric field were turned off) in terms of ϕ_{2s} and ϕ_{2p}, then only the first two terms in Eq. (9.34) are nonvanishing. Show that this would not be the case if we used the analogous Rayleigh-Schrödinger expression of Eq. (9.40). You may use the fact that

$$(\phi_{2s}, H_1\phi_{2p+}) = (\phi_{2s}, H_1\phi_{2p-}) = (\phi_{2p}, H_1\phi_{2p+}) = (\phi_{2p}, H_1\phi_{2p-}) = 0 \, ,$$

and set the only significant nonvanishing inner product equal to M, that is

$$(\phi_{2s}, H_1\phi_{2po}) = M \, .$$

c) Using the result of part (b) and utilizing Eqs. (9.33) and (9.34), find ψ_{2s} and λ_{2s} in terms of ϕ_{2s}, ϕ_{2po}, L, and M.

d) Holding E (that is M) fixed, let L become very small. Explain the simple result which you obtain for ψ_{2s} and λ_{2s} in this limit.

10. Consider the quantity

$$\Phi = (f, (A_0 - \lambda_1^{(0)})f) + 2(f(A_1 - \lambda_1^{(1)})x_1^{(0)}) \, ,$$

where $\lambda_1^{(0)}$ is the *largest* eigenvalue of A_0 with corresponding eigenvector $x_1^{(0)}$. A_1 is a small perturbation on A_0, and $\lambda_1^{(1)} = (x_1^{(0)}, A_1x_1^{(0)})$. The spectrum of A_0 is assumed to be nondegenerate. A_0 and A_1 are both completely continuous Hermitian operators on a *real* Hilbert space, H. Show that for every $f \in H$,

$$\Phi \leq \lambda_1^{(2)} \, , \tag{1}$$

where $\lambda_1^{(2)}$ is given by Eq. (9.42). Show that the equality sign in Eq. (1) holds if and only if f is equal to $f_1^{(1)}$ as given by Eq. (9.40). Note that the assumption that $\lambda_1^{(0)}$ is the largest eigenvalue of A_0 is crucial, and that the assumption of a real Hilbert space is also important. How would one modify Φ if one wanted to extend this result to a complex Hilbert space?

Thus we have a maximum principle for $\lambda_1^{(2)}$ which will enable us to find $\lambda_1^{(2)}$ and $f_1^{(1)}$ by constructing trial functions in the manner indicated in Section 9.2.

Therefore the infinite summations in Eqs. (9.40) and (9.42) can be avoided, at least as far as $f_1^{(1)}$ and $\lambda_1^{(2)}$ are concerned. It can be shown that these sums can be avoided for all $f_i^{(n)}$ and $\lambda_i^{(n)}$ by the use of maximum principles.

11. a) By using Simpson's rule for the evaluation of real integrals, write a matrix expression to solve approximately the equation

$$f(x) = g(x) + \lambda \int_a^b k(x, y) f(y) \, dy ,$$

where $g(x)$ and $k(x, y)$ are continuous functions. (For a statement and derivation of Simpson's rule, see any book on differential calculus, for example, R. Courant, *Differential and Integral Calculus*.) In particular, show that if the interval $[a, b]$ is broken up by $2n + 1$ equally spaced points $(n > 1)$, $a = x_1$, $x_2, \cdots, x_{2n}$, $b = x_{2n+1}$, the integral equation reduces to

$$a = (I - \lambda MD)^{-1} b .$$

Here $a_i = f(x_i)$, $b_i = g(x_i)$, $M_{ij} = k(x_i, x_j)$ and D is a diagonal matrix whose elements are $D_{11} = \frac{1}{3}$, $D_{22} = \frac{4}{3}$, $D_{33} = \frac{2}{3}$, $\cdots$, $D_{2n-1, 2n-1} = \frac{2}{3}$, $D_{2n, 2n} = \frac{4}{3}$, $D_{2n+1, 2n+1} = \frac{1}{3}$.

b) Show how to use the same method to treat the homogeneous eigenvalue problem [that is, $g(x) \equiv 0$].

c) Show that if $k(x, y)$ is a real, symmetric kernel, then it is possible to convert the operator eigenvalue equation into a matrix eigenvalue equation involving a single real symmetric matrix.

12. Consider the integral equation

$$f(x) = 1 + 4 \int_0^{1/2} \sqrt{1 - xy} \, f(y) \, dy . \tag{1}$$

Compare the functions $f_1(x), f_2(x)$, and $f_3(x)$ obtained by making the successive finite-rank approximations:

a) $\sqrt{1 - xy} \cong 1$,   b) $\sqrt{1 - xy} \cong 1 - \frac{1}{2} xy$,

c) $\sqrt{1 - xy} \cong 1 - \frac{1}{2} xy - \frac{1}{8} x^2 y^2$,

for the kernel of Eq. (1). These are obtained in an obvious manner from the power series for the square root.

13. The purpose of this problem (and the three that follow) is to develop further the Fredholm method of solving a linear integral equation whose kernel is $k(x, y)$. We begin by defining the determinant Δ, a function of $2n$ variables, by

$$\Delta \begin{bmatrix} x_1, x_2, \cdots, x_n \\ y_1, y_2, \cdots, y_n \end{bmatrix} \equiv \begin{vmatrix} k(x_1, y_1) & k(x_1, y_2) & \cdots & k(x_1, y_n) \\ k(x_2, y_1) & k(x_2, y_2) & & k(x_2, y_n) \\ \vdots & & & \vdots \\ k(x_n, y_1) & k(x_n, y_2) & \cdots & k(x_n, y_n) \end{vmatrix} .$$

In what follows, we will assume that $k(x, y)$ is a continuous function for $a \le x \le b$ and $a \le y \le b$ with $|k(x, y)| \le M$. Generalizations from this special case to more general situations (e.g., square-integrable kernels on infinite intervals) is straightforward.

a) Consider the infinite series

$$D(\lambda) = 1 - \lambda \int_a^b \Delta \begin{bmatrix} x_1 \\ x_1 \end{bmatrix} dx_1 + \frac{\lambda^2}{2!} \int_a^b \int_a^b \Delta \begin{bmatrix} x_1, x_2 \\ x_1, x_2 \end{bmatrix} dx_1\,dx_2 + \cdots$$

$$+ (-1)^n \frac{\lambda^n}{n!} \int_a^b \int_a^b \cdots \int_a^b \Delta \begin{bmatrix} x_1, x_2, \cdots, x_n \\ x_1, x_2, \cdots, x_n \end{bmatrix} dx_1\,dx_2 \cdots dx_n + \cdots .$$

Using Hadamard's inequality (see Section 4.3), prove that the coefficient of $\lambda^n/n!$ is less in magnitude than $M^n n^{n/2}$, and hence show that the series $D(\lambda)$ converges for *all* λ. $D(\lambda)$ is called the *Fredholm determinant*.

b) Consider the infinite series

$$N(x, y, \lambda) = k(x, y) - \lambda \int_a^b \Delta \begin{bmatrix} x, x_1 \\ y, x_1 \end{bmatrix} dx_1 + \frac{\lambda^2}{2} \int_a^b \int_a^b \Delta \begin{bmatrix} x, x_1, x_2 \\ y, x_1, x_2 \end{bmatrix} dx_1\,dx_2 + \cdots$$

$$+ (-1)^n \frac{\lambda^n}{n!} \int_a^b \int_a^b \cdots \int_a^b \Delta \begin{bmatrix} x, x_1, x_2, \cdots, x_n \\ y, x_1, x_2, \cdots, x_n \end{bmatrix} dx_1\,dx_2 \cdots dx_n + \cdots .$$

Using the methods employed in part (a), prove that this series converges for all λ to a continuous function of x and y for $a \le x \le b$ and $a \le y \le b$. (For a discussion of what originally motivated the definition of N and D, see, for example, F. Smithies, *Integral Equations* (Chapter 5).

14. a) Expand the determinant

$$\Delta \begin{bmatrix} x, x_1, x_2, \cdots, x_n \\ y, x_1, x_2, \cdots, x_n \end{bmatrix}$$

by minors about its first row to show that

$$\Delta \begin{bmatrix} x, x_1, x_2, \cdots, x_n \\ y, x_1, x_2, \cdots, x_n \end{bmatrix} = k(x, y) \Delta \begin{bmatrix} x_1, x_2, \cdots, x_n \\ x_1, x_2, \cdots, x_n \end{bmatrix}$$

$$+ \sum_{i=1}^n k(x, x_i) \Delta \begin{bmatrix} x_i, x_1, x_2, \cdots, x_{i-1}, x_{i+1}, \cdots, x_n \\ y, x_1, x_2, \cdots, x_{i-1}, x_{i+1}, \cdots, x_n \end{bmatrix}$$

and therefore that

$$\int_a^b \int_a^b \cdots \int_a^b \Delta \begin{bmatrix} x, x_1, x_2, \cdots, x_n \\ y, x_1, x_2, \cdots, x_n \end{bmatrix} dx_1\,dx_2 \cdots dx_n$$

$$= k(x, y) \int_a^b \int_a^b \cdots \int_a^b \Delta \begin{bmatrix} x_1, x_2, \cdots, x_n \\ x_1, x_2, \cdots, x_n \end{bmatrix} dx_1\,dx_2 \cdots dx_n$$

$$- n \int_a^b \int_a^b \cdots \int_a^b k(x, z) \Delta \begin{bmatrix} z, x_1, x_2, \cdots, x_{n-1} \\ y, x_1, x_2, \cdots, x_{n-1} \end{bmatrix} dx_1\,dx_2 \cdots dx_{n-1}\,dz .$$

b) By expanding Δ about the first column, show in the manner of part (a) that

$$\int_a^b \int_a^b \cdots \int_a^b \Delta \begin{bmatrix} x, x_1, x_2, \cdots, x_n \\ y, x_1, x_2, \cdots, x_n \end{bmatrix} dx_1\,dx_2 \cdots dx_n$$

$$= k(x, y) \int_a^b \int_a^b \cdots \int_a^b \Delta \begin{bmatrix} x_1, x_2, \cdots, x_n \\ x_1, x_2, \cdots, x_n \end{bmatrix} dx_1\,dx_2 \cdots dx_n$$

$$- n \int_a^b \int_a^b \cdots \int_a^b \Delta \begin{bmatrix} x, x_1, x_2, \cdots x_{n-1} \\ z, x_1, x_2, \cdots x_{n-1} \end{bmatrix} k(z, y)\,dx_1\,dx_2 \cdots dx_{n-1}\,dz .$$

15. a) Using the result of Problem 9.14(a) in the expression of Problem 9.13(b) for $N(x, y, \lambda)$, show that

$$N(x, y, \lambda) = k(x, y) D(\lambda) + \lambda \int_a^b k(x, z) N(z, y, \lambda) \, dz \, .$$

Similarly, use the result of Problem 9.14(b) to show that

$$N(x, y, \lambda) = k(x, y) D(\lambda) + \lambda \int_a^b N(x, z, \lambda) k(z, y) \, dz \, .$$

b) Define

$$R(x, y, \lambda) \equiv \frac{N(x, y, \lambda)}{D(\lambda)} \, .$$

Show that the two equations of part (a) can be rewritten as

$$(I - \lambda K)(I + \lambda R(\lambda)) = I \, , \quad \text{and} \quad (I + \lambda R(\lambda))(I - \lambda K) = I \, ,$$

where $R(\lambda)$ is the integral operator whose kernel is $R(x, y, \lambda)$ and K is the integral operator whose kernel is $k(x, y)$. Thus we see that $I + \lambda R(\lambda)$ is the *inverse* of $I - \lambda K$, so that in the language of this chapter, $R(\lambda)$ is the *resolvent* of K. Therefore the equation

$$f = g + \lambda K f$$

can be solved for all values of λ for which $R(\lambda)$ exists by

$$f = g + \lambda R(\lambda) g \, .$$

In terms of the actual kernels, this may be written as

$$f(x) = g(x) + \lambda \int_a^b R(x, y, \lambda) g(y) \, dy = g(x) + \frac{\lambda}{D(\lambda)} \int_a^b N(x, y, \lambda) g(y) \, dy \, .$$

16. The only remaining question to settle is: What are the values of λ for which $R(\lambda)$ fails to exist? Clearly, since by Problem 9.13 $N(x, y, \lambda)$ and $D(\lambda)$ are analytic functions of λ, $R(\lambda)$ will fail to exist at any zero of $D(\lambda)$, unless that zero is canceled by a corresponding zero of $N(x, y, \lambda)$. In fact, such a cancellation cannot occur.

a) Using the results of Problem 9.13, show that

$$\frac{dD(\lambda)}{d\lambda} = - \int_a^b N(x, x, \lambda) \, dx \, .$$

b) Using the result of part (a), show that if $D(\lambda)$ has a zero at $\lambda = \lambda_0$, then $N(x, y, \lambda)$ *cannot* have a zero at this point. Prove this result by contradiction. First, write $D(\lambda) = (\lambda - \lambda_0) d(\lambda)$, where $d(\lambda)$ is analytic; next, assume that $N(x, y, \lambda)$ can also be written in this manner, i.e., as $N(x, y, \lambda) = (\lambda - \lambda_0) n(x, y, \lambda)$, where $n(x, y, \lambda)$ is an analytic function of λ; and finally show that under this assumption the equation of part (a) cannot be satisfied. Thus the zeroes of $D(\lambda)$ are precisely the values of λ for which $R(\lambda)$ does not exist. For these values, the homogeneous equation $f = \lambda K f$ will have a solution.

17. Let K be an integral operator with a continuous kernel and assume that the spectrum of K is nondegenerate. Using the results of Problems 9.15(a) and 9.16(a), show that the residue at a pole, λ_n, of $R(x, y, \lambda)$ is equal to

$$- \frac{\phi_n(x) \psi_n^*(y)}{\int \phi_n(x) \psi_n^*(x) \, dx} \, ,$$

where ϕ_n satisfies the equation $\lambda_n K\phi_n = \phi_n$, and ψ_n satisfies the adjoint equation $\lambda_n^* K^\dagger \psi_n = \psi_n$. Note that for Hermitian kernels this result is implicit in the eigen-function expansion of the resolvent given by Eq. (9.22).

18. Show that if $k(x, y) = \phi(x)\psi^*(y)$, then the Fredholm method reduces to

$$D(\lambda) = 1 - \lambda \int \phi(x)\psi^*(x)\, dx\,, \qquad N(x, y, \lambda) = k(x, y) = \phi(x)\psi^*(y)\,,$$

that is, all higher terms in the Fredholm series for $D(\lambda)$ and $N(x, y, \lambda)$ vanish. Show that this leads to a solution of $f = g + \lambda K f$ in agreement with Eq. (8.57).

19. Assuming that λ is sufficiently small, expand $[D(\lambda)]^{-1}$ in powers of λ and show that through order λ^2, $R(x, y, \lambda)$ is equal to the Neumann series expansion of the resolvent through order λ^2. It can be shown that this equality holds to *all* orders, as we would expect.

20. Suppose that one wished to extend the Fredholm method to square-integrable kernels. The most serious obstacle to doing this is the appearance of terms like

$$I = \int_a^b k(x, x)\, dx$$

in the treatment of Problems 9.13 through 9.16. Even if $k(x, y)$ is square integrable, I may not exist, and hence the method fails. This happens, for example, in the case of kernels of the form $k(\mathbf{r}, \mathbf{r}') = G(\mathbf{r}, \mathbf{r}')V(\mathbf{r})$, where $G(\mathbf{r}, \mathbf{r}')$ is given by Eq. (7.66), even if one makes the appropriate weight-function modification in the manner of Section 8.3.

a) Give an argument which suggests that we can *always* modify $k(x, y)$ in such a way that $k(x, x) = 0$ without altering in any essential way the solutions to

$$f(x) = g(x) + \lambda \int k(x, y)f(y)\, dy\,, \qquad (1)$$

where $k(x, y)$ is assumed to be square-integrable.
[*Hint*: See Problem 9.2.]

b) Part (a) seems to suggest that all difficulties with integrals like

$$\int_a^b k(x, x)\, dx$$

can be removed simply by defining

$$\tilde{D}(\lambda) = 1 - \lambda \int \tilde{\Delta}\begin{bmatrix} x_1 \\ x_1 \end{bmatrix} dx_1 + \frac{\lambda^2}{2!} \int\int \tilde{\Delta}\begin{bmatrix} x_1, x_2 \\ x_1, x_2 \end{bmatrix} dx_1, dx_2 + \cdots$$

$$\tilde{N}(x, y, \lambda) = k(x, y) - \lambda \int \tilde{\Delta}\begin{bmatrix} x, x_1 \\ y, x_1 \end{bmatrix} dx_1 + \frac{\lambda^2}{2!} \int\int \tilde{\Delta}\begin{bmatrix} x, x_1, x_2 \\ y, x_1, x_2 \end{bmatrix} dx_1\, dx_2 + \cdots$$

where $\tilde{\Delta}$ is the same determinant as Δ *except* that whenever an entry of the form $k(x_i, x_i)$ appears in Δ, we replace it by zero to get the equivalent entry in $\tilde{\Delta}$. Thus

$$\Delta\begin{bmatrix} x_1 \\ x_1 \end{bmatrix} = k(x_1, x_1)\,, \qquad \tilde{\Delta}\begin{bmatrix} x_1 \\ x_1 \end{bmatrix} = 0\,,$$

$$\Delta\begin{bmatrix} x_1, x_2 \\ x_1, x_2 \end{bmatrix} = k(x_1, x_1)k(x_2, x_2) - k(x_1, x_2)k(x_2, x_1)\,,$$

$$\tilde{\Delta}\begin{bmatrix} x_1, x_2 \\ x_1, x_2 \end{bmatrix} = -k(x_1, x_2)k(x_2, x_1)\,,$$

and so forth. Letting

$$\bar{R}(x, y, \lambda) \equiv \frac{\bar{N}(x, y, \lambda)}{\bar{D}(\lambda)},$$

and expanding $[\bar{D}(\lambda)]^{-1}$ (assuming λ is sufficiently small), show that through order λ^2, $\bar{R}(x, y, \lambda)$ is equal to the Neumann expansion of the resolvent of K. This equality can be shown to hold to all orders. In fact, the modification suggested by this problem is correct, namely, $\bar{N}(x, y, \lambda)$, $\bar{D}(\lambda)$, and $\bar{R}(x, y, \lambda)$ as defined above do indeed provide us with a solution to Eq. (1).

21. Obtain the function $\bar{D}(\lambda)$, defined in Problem 20, through order λ^2 for the kernel of the integral equation Eq. (9.102) if $V(\mathbf{r}) = g^2 e^{-\mu r}/r$. The variables s, t and u defined in Section 8.3 will be useful. Note that the integral which must be done is very similar to the one we encountered in the evaluation of the norm of this kernel in Section 8.3. Assuming q_i to be real, what is the difference between these two cases?

22. Using Eqs. (9.104) and (9.105), show that if we denote the second iterative approximation to the amplitude by $f_0^{s2B}(q_i)$, then for any real potential $V(r)$ we have

$$Im f_0^{s2B}(q_i) = q_i [f_0^{sB}(q_i)]^2 .$$

23. Calculate the second Born approximation to the s-wave scattering amplitude, $F_0^s(p_i)$, defined by Eqs. (9.112) and (9.113). Compare this result with the curves of Figs. 9.4, 9.5, and 9.6 and make any comments which seem appropriate.

24. It can be shown that the quantity $f_0^s(q_i)$ defined in Section 9.5 can be written as

$$f_0^s(q_i) = \frac{1}{q_i} e^{i\delta_0} \sin \delta_0 ,$$

where δ_0 is a function of q_i and is called the s-wave phase shift. Using Fig. 9.4, obtain a graph of $\delta_0(q_i)$ versus q_i. Are the results obtained for $\delta_0(q_i)$ from the two different curves in Fig. 9.4 consistent? To what extent is δ_0 determined uniquely?

25. a) Obtain Eqs. (9.98) through (9.101) using the methods employed in Section 9.3 to discuss the homogeneous problem.

   b) Derive an equation which "solves" the integral equation $f = g + Kf$ in the spirit of Riemann integration (see Eq. (9.50)). •

   c) If you have access to a computer make up a few integral equations and solve them numerically using the results of part (a) or (b). For example, you might consider Eqs. (9.112) and (9.113), but with a potential of the opposite sign (i.e., $mV/\mu^2\hbar^2 = -1.4$). You will find that the scattering amplitude looks rather different than it did in the case of positive V and that there is a striking change in the behavior of δ_0 (see Problem 9.24) as a function of p_i. This change is caused by the existence of an s-wave bound state in the attractive potential (negative V) which is not present in a repulsive potential.

26. Suppose that $\{\phi_n\}$ and $\{\psi_m\}$ are sequences of step functions and that $\phi_n \to f$ and $\psi_m \to g$. Show that if for any step functions ϕ and ψ we have

$$(V\phi, \psi) = (\phi, U\psi) ,$$
$$(V\phi, V\psi) = (\phi, \psi) ,$$

and

$$(U\phi, U\psi) = (\phi, \psi) ,$$

then the sequences $\{V\phi_n\}$ and $\{U\psi_m\}$ converge to some limit in Hilbert space and that if we denote these limits by Vf and Ug respectively, then

$$(Vf, g) = (f, Ug) \ .$$

This completes the proof of Theorem 9.11.

27. a) Show that if we define

$$\mathscr{H}_n(x) \equiv H_n(x)e^{-x^2/2} \ ,$$

where $H_n(x)$ is the nth Hermite polynomial which satisfies Eq. (5.105), then the Hermite function $\mathscr{H}_n(x)$ satisfies

$$\mathscr{H}_n''(x) - x^2 \mathscr{H}_n(x) + (2n + 1)\mathscr{H}_n(x) = 0 \ .$$

Note that according to Eq. (5.100), $\mathscr{H}_n(x)$ is orthogonal to $\mathscr{H}_m(x)$ on the interval $[-\infty, \infty]$.

   b) Denoting the unitary Fourier transformation by U_F, show that the functions $\mathscr{H}_n(x)$ are eigenfunctions of U_F. Do this by proving that the Fourier transform of $\mathscr{H}_n(x)$, say $\hat{\mathscr{H}}_n(x)$, satisfies the same differential equation as does $\mathscr{H}_n(x)$, so $\hat{\mathscr{H}}_n(x)$ must equal (to within a multiplicative constant) $\mathscr{H}_n(x)$. In operator language, this is just

$$U_F \mathscr{H}_n = \lambda_n \mathscr{H}_n \ ,$$

where λ_n has not yet been determined.
   [*Hint* $x^2 e^{ixy} = -(d^2/dy^2)e^{ixy}$; also, integration by parts will be useful.]

   c) Show that if $f(x)$ is any square-integrable function, then $U_F^2 f(x) = f(-x)$. Hence show that the only possible eigenvalues of U_F are 1, -1, i, and $-i$. There is an infinite number of Hermite functions which belong to each of these four eigenvalues. Give a simple characterization of those Hermite functions which will have real eigenvalues and those which will have imaginary eigenvalues.

FURTHER READINGS

Dettman, J. W., *Mathematical Methods in Physics and Engineering.* New York: McGraw-Hill, 1962.

Goldberger, M. L., and K. M. Watson, *Collision Theory.* New York: Wiley, 1964.

Newton, R. G., *Scattering Theory of Waves and Particles.* New York: McGraw-Hill, 1966.

Riesz, F., and B. Sz. Nagy, *Functional Analysis.* New York: Ungar, 1955.

Smithies, F., *Integral Equations.* New York: Cambridge University Press, 1958.

CHAPTER 10

INTRODUCTION TO GROUP THEORY

INTRODUCTION

Thus far in this book we have discussed objects (vectors) which combine in a way that is essentially *additive*, i.e., they combine commutatively. In investigating the properties of these objects we were led in a natural way to consider *transformations* which changed one vector into another. We observed that these transformations themselves could be considered as constituting a vector space. However, since the transformations took one vector into another, they could also be combined in a way which was essentially *multiplicative* in nature; i.e., the commutative law did not in general hold. In this concluding chapter we want to introduce some of the techniques by which one can study collections of objects which are characterized in terms of their multiplicative properties. Such a collection is called a *group*.

10.1 AN INDUCTIVE APPROACH

Let us first recall the definition of a group given previously in Chapter 3:

Definition 10.1. A *group*, G, is a collection of objects which can be combined via a closed operation, which we will denote by a dot. By a closed operation we mean one such that if $a, b \in G$, then $a \cdot b \in G$. The operation must furthermore satisfy the following three axioms:

1) $a \cdot (b \cdot c) = (a \cdot b) \cdot c$ (associative law)
2) there exists an identity element, e, such that $a \cdot e = a$ for all $a \in G$.
3) for every $a \in G$, there exists an inverse element, a^{-1}, such that $a \cdot a^{-1} = e$.

Note that in this definition we have required that the identity be only a *right* identity and that the inverse be only a *right* inverse. However, because of the other group properties, it follows that e is also a *left* identity ($e \cdot a = a$) and a^{-1} is also a *left* inverse ($a^{-1} \cdot a = e$).

To show this we note that since $a^{-1} \in G$, it must have an inverse, which we denote by $(a^{-1})^{-1}$. According to axiom (3),

$$(a^{-1}) \cdot (a^{-1})^{-1} = e . \tag{10.1}$$

But by Axioms (1), (2), and (3) we may write Eq. (10.1) as

$$e = a^{-1} \cdot (a^{-1})^{-1} = (a^{-1} \cdot e) \cdot (a^{-1})^{-1} = [a^{-1} \cdot (a \cdot a^{-1})] \cdot (a^{-1})^{-1}$$
$$= [(a^{-1} \cdot a) \cdot a^{-1}] \cdot (a^{-1})^{-1} = (a^{-1} \cdot a) \cdot [a^{-1} \cdot (a^{-1})^{-1}] .$$

Using Eq. (10.1) again, we have

$$e = (a^{-1} \cdot a) \cdot e = a^{-1} \cdot (a \cdot e) \ .$$

By Axiom (2), $a \cdot e = a$, so finally we obtain

$$e = a^{-1} \cdot a \ . \tag{10.2}$$

Hence a^{-1} is a left inverse as well as a right inverse. This result contrasts with the situation for general linear operators, where the existence of a right inverse does not necessarily imply the existence of a left inverse.

Using this result, we can immediately see that e must be a left identity. By Axiom (2), e is a right identity, that is,

$$a \cdot e = a \ ,$$

but according to Eq. (10.2), this is equivalent to

$$a \cdot (a^{-1} \cdot a) = a \ .$$

Using Axioms (1) and (3), we find that

$$a = a \cdot (a^{-1} \cdot a) = (a \cdot a^{-1}) \cdot a = e \cdot a \ ,$$

that is, we have

$$a = e \cdot a \ ,$$

so e is also a left identity.

Definition 10.2. A group, G is said to be *abelian* if $a \cdot b = b \cdot a$ for any $a, b \in G$.

Definition 10.3. A group with n elements is called a group of *order n*.

In the first three sections of this chapter, we shall consider only finite groups $(n < \infty)$ in order to fix our thinking on the most basic aspects of group theory. In subsequent sections, we shall have some occasion to mention infinite groups; when we do, we shall always state explicitly that this is the case.

Let us now introduce a few groups, starting with the simplest ones.

Example 10.1. The most uncomplicated group which one can imagine is the one element group: $\{e\}$. It obviously satisfies all the requirements of Definition 10.1. It is not a particularly interesting group.

Example 10.2. Next we have the group with two distinct elements: $\{e, a\}$. Now $a \cdot a$ must belong to this group according to Definition 10.1. Thus we must have either $a \cdot a = a$ or $a \cdot a = e$. The former is immediately ruled out by the fact that since a has an inverse, $a \cdot a = a$ implies that $a = e$. This contradicts the assumption that the group has two distinct elements. Thus $a \cdot a = e$. The integers $\{1, -1\}$ form a group with this structure if they combine via ordinary arithmetical multiplication ($e = 1$, $a = -1$). Also, the integers $\{0, 1\}$ form a group with addition modulo two as the rule of combination: $0 + 0 = 0$, $0 + 1 = 1$, $1 + 0 = 1$, $1 + 1 = 0$. In this case, $e = 0$, $a = 1$. Another structure of this type is the group of permutations of two objects; e is the permutation which leaves the order of the objects unchanged, and a is the permutation which interchanges them.

This last example leads naturally to the following definition.

> **Definition 10.4.** Two groups are said to be *isomorphic* if there exists a one-to-one operation-preserving correspondence between them. That is, suppose that G has elements $a, b, c, \cdots$, and G' has elements $a', b', c', \cdots$ If $(a \cdot b)' = (a' \times b')$ for all $a, b \in G$ and $a', b' \in G$, then the groups $\{G, \cdot\}$ and $\{G', \times\}$ are said to be isomorphic.

Evidently the three groups mentioned in Example 10.2 are isomorphic to each other: once we know everything about any *one* of them, we know everything about *all* of them.

Example 10.3. Let us now move on to groups with three distinct elements, which we denote by $\{e, a, b\}$. From the axioms we see immediately that $a \cdot b = e$, for if $a \cdot b = a$ or $a \cdot b = b$, then the existence of an inverse would imply $b = e$ in the first case and $a = e$ in the second case, which is contrary to our assumption that this group has three *distinct* elements. What about the product $a \cdot a$? Clearly, $a \cdot a = a$ implies that $a = e$, so either $a \cdot a = e$ or $a \cdot a = b$. But

$$a \cdot a = e \Longrightarrow a \cdot (a \cdot b) = b \Longrightarrow a = b,$$

since $a \cdot b = e$. But this, too, is impossible because we have assumed three distinct elements. Thus $a \cdot a = b$. Similarly $b \cdot b = a$. Adopting the obvious notation for quantities like $a \cdot a$, we may write our three element group as $\{e, a, a^2\}$, with $a^3 = e$. This is the *only* possibility for the three-element group. The postulates of Definition 10.1 restrict us to just one form. A simple example of this group is the set of three cube roots of unity, under ordinary multiplication of complex numbers.

Clearly, it is always possible to construct a group of the form $\{e, a, a^2, a^3, \cdots, a^{n-1}\}$ for any n; the basic model of such a group is the set of n nth roots of unity. In general, consider an arbitrary group, $\{G, \cdot\}$ and let $a \in G$. Form the sequence $a^0 = e, a, a^2, \cdots, a^i, \cdots$, and let n be the smallest *nonzero* integer such that $a^n = e$. Then the element a is said to be of *order n* (if n is infinite, we say that a is of infinite order). In this case, all the elements $a^0, a^1, a^2, \cdots, a^{n-1}$ are distinct, for if $a^i = a^j$ ($i < n, j < n$), then $a^{|i-j|} = e$. But since $0 \le i < n$ and $0 \le j < n$, $|i - j| < n$, which contradicts our assumption that n was the *smallest* nonzero integer for which $a^n = e$.

> **Definition 10.5.** A group whose elements can be written as $\{e, a, a^2, \cdots, a^{n-1}\}$ is called a *cyclic* group (of order n).

Thus far, all our groups have been of the cyclic type, so it is natural to ask: Are all groups cyclic? The answer is provided by the following example.

Example 10.4. We apply the methods already used to the possible groups of order four, which we denote by $\{e, a, b, c\}$. Let us begin by assuming $a^2 = b$;

then we can write the corresponding group as $\{e, a, a^2, c\}$. By an argument used before, $a \cdot c$ must equal either e or a^2. If $a \cdot c = a^2$, we conclude that $a = c$, which contradicts the assumption of four distinct elements. Thus $a \cdot c = e$, so it begins to look like we are obtaining a cyclic group. We therefore look at a^3. Suppose that $a^3 = e$; then $a^3 = a \cdot c$, so $a^2 = c$, which is impossible. If $a^3 = a$, then $a^2 = e$, which again is impossible. Similarly, if $a^3 = a^2$, $a = e$, which is impossible. Thus $a^3 = c$, and we indeed have found a cyclic group of order four: $\{e, a, a^2, a^3\}$, with $a^4 = e$.

The same result is obtained if we assume that $a^2 = c$, except that it then follows by the same reasoning as above that $b = a^3$. As mentioned above, $a^2 = a$ is not permissible. However, there remains the possibility that $a^2 = e$. Clearly, either $a \cdot b = e$ or $a \cdot b = c$. If $a \cdot b = e$, then $a^2 \cdot b = a$; since $a^2 = e$, we have $a = b$, which is impossible. Thus $a \cdot b = c$. By the same process of elimination, we find that $b \cdot a = c$, $a \cdot c = b$ and $c \cdot a = b$. Since $a \cdot b = c$ and $b \cdot a = c$, we have

$$(b \cdot a) \cdot (a \cdot b) = c \cdot c \Longrightarrow b \cdot a^2 \cdot b = c^2 \,.$$

But $a^2 = e$, so we have immediately $b^2 = c^2$, which means that c^2 cannot equal b or c. Thus either $c^2 = e$ or $c^2 = a$. We first examine the case $c^2 = a$. Then $a \cdot c^2 = a^2 = e$, but $a \cdot c = b$ so we have $b \cdot c = e$, which gives us explicit expressions for the products of all elements of the group. We summarize by writing

$$a^2 = e \,, \qquad b^2 = c^2 = a \,,$$
$$b \cdot c = c \cdot b = e \,,$$
$$a \cdot b = b \cdot a = c \,, \qquad a \cdot c = c \cdot a = b \,. \tag{10.3}$$

We now want to know if this group of order four is different from the cyclic group of order four which we have already found several times. A very convenient way of analyzing simple finite groups is by means of a *multiplication table*. We illustrate it by using the *cyclic group* of order four:

	e	a	b	c
e	e	a	b	c
a	a	b	c	e
b	b	c	e	a
c	c	e	a	b

$$(10.4)$$

The meaning of this table is simple: in the ij-box one writes the product of the ith element of the group times the jth element. The reader can check for himself that this table represents accurately the fourth-order cyclic group first discussed in Example 10.4. Now what about the group whose multiplicative properties are given by Eqs. (10.3)? We have for the multiplication table

	e	a	b	c
e	e	a	b	c
a	a	e	c	b
b	b	c	a	e
c	c	b	e	a

$$(10.5)$$

This looks completely different from the table for the fourth-order cyclic group. However, it may nevertheless be *isomorphic* to the fourth-order cyclic group. This will be the case if we can relabel the elements in such a way that the multiplication table is the same as that of the fourth-order cyclic group. If in Table (10.5) we redefine the elements according to

$$e \to e' , \qquad a \to b' ,$$
$$b \to a' , \qquad c \to c' ,$$

then Table (10.5) becomes

	e'	a'	b'	c'
e'	e'	a'	b'	c'
a'	a'	b'	c'	e'
b'	b'	c'	e'	a'
c'	c'	e'	a'	b'

$$(10.6)$$

Since Table (10.6) is the same as Table (10.4), we still have not found a group with a multiplicative structure different from that of the cyclic group of order four.

However, in the class of four-element groups, one possibility remains. We have been forced to conclude that $a^2 = e$, $a \cdot b = c$, $b \cdot a = c$, $a \cdot c = b$, $c \cdot a = b$, and $b^2 = c^2$. When we let $b^2 = c^2 = a$, we were led back to the cyclic group. There remains, however, the choice $b^2 = c^2 = e$. Then

$$a \cdot b = c \Longrightarrow a \cdot b^2 = c \cdot b \Longrightarrow c \cdot b = a ,$$

and similarly

$$b \cdot a = c \Longrightarrow b^2 \cdot a = b \cdot c \Longrightarrow b \cdot c = a .$$

This completes the multiplication table:

	e	a	b	c
e	e	a	b	c
a	a	e	c	b
b	b	c	e	a
c	c	b	a	e

(10.7)

The reader can check that there is no rearrangement of these elements which will give the Table (10.4). Thus we have finally found a noncyclic group. Note, however, that it is an abelian group; this is reflected in the fact that the array in Table (10.7) is symmetric with respect to the diagonal. This group is called the four-group. A simple realization of the four-group is the set of all transformations of a rectangle which leave the rectangle's orientation in space unchanged (remember that in a rectangle the right and left sides are indistinguishable, as are the top and bottom sides). If the rectangle sits on an xy-plane with its center at the origin, there are four such transformations: (i) the identity transformation, (ii) rotation through 180° about an axis perpendicular to the rectangle and passing through its center, (iii) reflection through the x-axis, and (iv) reflection through the y-axis. Note that we omit rotations through 360°, 540°, etc., since they just duplicate the transformations (i) and (ii) above. Figure 10.1 illustrates the configuration. We leave it to the reader to show that this is indeed a group and that its multiplication table is the same as that given in Table (10.7).

From Table (10.7) it also appears that the elements $\{e, a\}$ of the four-group form a group by themselves ($e \cdot e = e$, $e \cdot a = a$, $a \cdot e = a$, $a \cdot a = e$), as do $\{e, b\}$ and $\{e, c\}$. This leads to the following definition.

Definition 10.6. A set of elements H, which is contained in G, is said to be a *subgroup* of G if

  i) the product of any pair of elements in H is in H,
  ii) if $a \in H$, then $a^{-1} \in H$.

Fig. 10.1

Any subgroup is also a group because its elements are already in G, and hence obey the associative law; moreover, $a, a^{-1} \in H$ implies that $a \cdot a^{-1} = e$ also belongs to H. Clearly any group is a subgroup of itself, and the identity element is a subgroup of any group. As mentioned above, the four-group has $\{e, a\}$ as a subgroup, as well as isomorphic subgroups $\{e, b\}$ and $\{e, c\}$. Clearly, in any group, G, the collection $\{e, a, a^2, \cdots, a^{n-1}\}$, where n is the order of a and $a \in G$, is an abelian subgroup of G.

Another interesting feature of Table (10.7), which it shares with all the other multiplication tables written above, is the fact that each row (or column) contains each element of the group once and only once. This is not accidental; we have in fact the following result.

Theorem 10.1. If G is a group of order n, with elements $e, a_2, a_3, \cdots, a_n$, then every element of G occurs once and only once in the sequence

$$ea_i, a_2a_i, \cdots, a_na_i,$$

for any i, and similarly for

$$a_ie, a_ia_2, \cdots, a_ia_n.$$

Note that in the statement of this theorem we have omitted the dot in denoting the product of group elements. We shall do this throughout the chapter, except when this omission might cause confusion.

Proof. If some element occurred twice, we would have $a_\mu a_i = a_\nu a_i$; this would imply $a_\mu = a_\nu$, contrary to our assumption of distinct group elements. Since there are n elements in the sequence and no element occurs twice, each element occurs once and only once. This explains the above mentioned structure of the group multiplication table. This very simple looking theorem is actually of central importance in the proof of most of the results of this chapter.

One could continue inductively, in the manner of this section, developing the groups of order five, order six, etc., but this would not be very instructive. We may remark, however, that not all groups are abelian like the ones which we have discussed so far; at order six one finds the first nonabelian group, the group of permutations of three objects. It should also be emphasized that not all groups have a finite number of elements. For example, the integers under addition ($e = 0, n^{-1} = -n$) form an (abelian) group of infinite order; the set of all unitary $n \times n$ matrices is an infinite nonabelian group.

10.2 THE SYMMETRIC GROUPS

By way of further illustrating group structure, we now discuss one of the most important groups of mathematics and physics, the group of permutations on n objects, called the symmetric group, S_n. The structure of the groups S_n is extraordinarily rich, and in this section we will consider only the simplest aspects of these groups.

There are $n!$ permutations of n objects, so S_n is of order $n!$. A typical one of these $n!$ elements will be denoted by

$$p = \begin{pmatrix} 1 & 2 & 3 & \cdots & n \\ m_1 & m_2 & m_3 & \cdots & m_n \end{pmatrix},$$

where the set $\{m_1, m_2, m_3, \cdots, m_n\}$ is some arrangement of the first n integers. This symbol means that 1 is replaced by m_1, 2 by m_2, etc. For example, the permutation

$$p = \begin{pmatrix} 1 & 2 & 3 & 4 & 5 & 6 \\ 6 & 5 & 4 & 3 & 2 & 1 \end{pmatrix},$$

acting on the arrangement $\{1\ 2\ 3\ 4\ 5\ 6\}$ produces the arrangement $\{6\ 5\ 4\ 3\ 2\ 1\}$; p acting on $\{2\ 5\ 3\ 4\ 6\ 1\}$ produces $\{5\ 2\ 4\ 3\ 1\ 6\}$. In this example, 1 and 6 go into each other in a closed manner: 1 is replaced by 6, and 6 is replaced by 1. Such a structure is called a *cycle* and will be written simply as (16). Similarly, the above example contains the cycles (25) and (34). We can thus write

$$\begin{pmatrix} 1 & 2 & 3 & 4 & 5 & 6 \\ 6 & 5 & 4 & 3 & 2 & 1 \end{pmatrix} = (16)(25)(34).$$

When we perform such a factorization, we say that we factor the given permutation into *disjoint* cycles, or cycles having no elements in common.

Of course, not all cycles contain only two elements. A cycle containing l elements is called an *l-cycle*, or a cycle of length l. For example, the permutation

$$\begin{pmatrix} 1 & 2 & 3 & 4 & 5 & 6 \\ 6 & 4 & 1 & 2 & 5 & 3 \end{pmatrix}$$

can be written as a disjoint product of a three-cycle, a two-cycle, and a one-cycle:

$$\begin{pmatrix} 1 & 2 & 3 & 4 & 5 & 6 \\ 6 & 4 & 1 & 2 & 5 & 3 \end{pmatrix} = (163)(24)(5).$$

The three-cycle, (163), is to be read as "1 is replaced by 6, 6 is replaced by 3 and 3 is replaced by 1." This structure closes on itself just like a two-cycle. Note that

$$(163) = (316) = (631),$$

but

$$(163) \neq (136).$$

Thus as the name "cycle" suggests, if one writes the elements of a cycle clockwise around a circle, one can start performing the sequence of replacements at *any* element and proceed clockwise back to the starting point. However, if one proceeds in a counterclockwise direction, one gets a different permutation.

The two-cycles, usually referred to as transpositions, are especially important because any cycle (and hence any permutation) can be written as a product
of two-cycles (which are not, in general, disjoint). For example,

$$(163) = (13)(16) ,$$

since when (163) acts on say {136}, it produces {613}, and (16) acting on {136}
produces {631}, which in turn becomes {613} when acted on by (13). Here we
adopt the convention that when a string of cycles is written, the one on the right
acts first, and the one on the left acts last. If the cycles are disjoint, it clearly
makes no difference in which order they act, but if they are not disjoint, the
order is crucial. For example,

$$(163)\{136\} = (13)(16)\{136\} = \{613\} ,$$

whereas

$$(16)(13)\{136\} = \{361\} = (136)\{136\} .$$

Also, the decomposition into two-cycles is *not* unique. In the above case,

$$(163) = (13)(16)$$

and

$$(163) = (316) = (36)(31) .$$

In general, a decomposition of an *n*-cycle into transpositions can be written as

$$(1\ 2\ 3\ \cdots\ n) = (1n)(1\ \ n-1) \cdots (13)(12) ,$$

as may be readily verified. The parity of a permutation is defined to be $(-1)^N$,
where N is the number of transpositions in a given permutation. If N is odd, we
speak of an odd permutation; if N is even, we speak of an even permutation.

If now by a *product* of permutations, we mean simply the two permutations
carried out successively, then obviously the product of two permutations is
another permutation. All the other group axioms are trivially satisfied so the
collection of all permutations on n objects is a group, and this group will contain $n!$ elements. By our above discussion, it is easily seen that only S_1 and S_2
are abelian groups. S_n ($n \geq 3$) is nonabelian. For example, (12) and (13) belong to S_3, and $(12)(13) \neq (13)(12)$.

Note that in our convention for writing a permutation, we have quite a bit
of freedom in ordering; in the permutation symbol, only the vertical relationship matters, not the horizontal. Thus

$$\begin{pmatrix} 1 & 2 & 3 & 4 & 5 & 6 \\ 6 & 5 & 4 & 3 & 2 & 1 \end{pmatrix} = \begin{pmatrix} 6 & 5 & 4 & 3 & 2 & 1 \\ 1 & 2 & 3 & 4 & 5 & 6 \end{pmatrix} = \begin{pmatrix} 4 & 2 & 6 & 3 & 1 & 5 \\ 3 & 5 & 1 & 4 & 6 & 2 \end{pmatrix} .$$

Also, we have used numbers in our symbols merely for convenience (there is an
arbitrarily large number of them). One could equally well use apple, pear,
orange, $\cdots$, or Greek, Russian, French, $\cdots$, instead of one, two, three, $\cdots$

Example 10.5. The simplest symmetric groups are S_1, which contains the single element e, and S_2, which contains the elements e and (12). More interesting is S_3. Its six elements are

$$e, (12), (13), (23), (123), (321) .$$

As the reader can easily show, the multiplication table for S_3 is

	e	(12)	(13)	(23)	(123)	(321)
e	e	(12)	(13)	(23)	(123)	(321)
(12)	(12)	e	(321)	(123)	(23)	(13)
(13)	(13)	(123)	e	(321)	(12)	(23)
(23)	(23)	(321)	(123)	e	(13)	(12)
(123)	(123)	(13)	(23)	(12)	(321)	e
(321)	(321)	(23)	(12)	(13)	e	(123)

If we make the identifications $e = I$, $(12) = A$, $(13) = B$, $(23) = C$, $(123) = D$, $(321) = F$, then this table is identical to the one given in Table (3.4). Note that this group has quite a few subgroups. Clearly $\{e, (12)\}$ is a subgroup of order two, and $\{e, (13)\}$ and $\{e, (23)\}$ are isomorphic to it. $\{e, (123), (321)\}$ is a subgroup of order three, which is isomorphic to the cyclic group of order three discussed in Example 10.3. Inspection of the multiplication table shows that S_3 is a nonabelian group.

One of the most remarkable facts about S_n is embodied in the following theorem of Cayley.

Theorem 10.2. Every group G of order n is isomorphic to a subgroup of S_n.

Proof. The proof of this result is based on Theorem 10.1. Call the elements of G $a_1, a_2, a_3, \cdots, a_n$. Let a_i be any element of G. Then according to Theorem 10.1, the collection $\{a_ia_1, a_ia_2, \cdots, a_ia_n\}$ is a rearrangement of $\{a_1, a_2, \cdots, a_n\}$ in which every element occurs once and only once. Therefore, let us make the correspondence, which is clearly one-to-one,

$$a_i \rightarrow P_{a_i} = \begin{pmatrix} a_1 & a_2 & \cdots & a_n \\ a_ia_1 & a_ia_2 & \cdots & a_ia_n \end{pmatrix} .$$

Similarly, for $a_j \in G$,

$$a_j \rightarrow P_{a_j} = \begin{pmatrix} a_1 & a_2 & \cdots & a_n \\ a_ja_1 & a_ja_2 & \cdots & a_ja_n \end{pmatrix} .$$

For the element of G which is given by the product $a_i a_j$, we will have

$$a_i a_j \rightarrow P_{a_i a_j} = \begin{pmatrix} a_1 & a_2 & \cdots & a_n \\ a_i a_j a_1 & a_i a_j a_2 & \cdots & a_i a_j a_n \end{pmatrix} .$$

The crucial point in demonstrating that we have an isomorphism is to show that $P_{a_i} P_{a_j} = P_{a_i a_j}$. This result is easily obtained—it is merely an exercise in notation. The reader should keep this in mind as he plows through the manipulations which follow.

We have already remarked that the horizontal ordering of permutation symbols is unimportant. For example,

$$\begin{pmatrix} a_1 & a_2 & a_3 & \cdots & a_n \\ a_i a_1 & a_i a_2 & a_i a_3 & \cdots & a_i a_n \end{pmatrix} = \begin{pmatrix} a_3 & a_n & a_1 & \cdots & a_2 \\ a_i a_3 & a_i a_n & a_i a_1 & \cdots & a_i a_2 \end{pmatrix} .$$

In other words, we can rearrange the top row in any way we please provided we make a similar rearrangement of the bottom row. Therefore, since $\{a_j a_1, a_j a_2, \cdots, a_j a_n\}$ is a rearrangement of $\{a_1, a_2, \cdots, a_n\}$, we may write

$$P_{a_i} = \begin{pmatrix} a_1 & a_2 & \cdots & a_n \\ a_i a_1 & a_i a_2 & \cdots & a_i a_n \end{pmatrix} = \begin{pmatrix} a_j a_1 & a_j a_2 & \cdots & a_j a_n \\ a_i(a_j a_1) & a_i(a_j a_2) & \cdots & a_i(a_j a_n) \end{pmatrix}$$

$$= \begin{pmatrix} a_j a_1 & a_j a_2 & \cdots & a_j a_n \\ a_i a_j a_1 & a_i a_j a_2 & \cdots & a_i a_j a_n \end{pmatrix} .$$

Thus

$$P_{a_i} P_{a_j} = \begin{pmatrix} a_j a_1 & a_j a_2 & \cdots & a_j a_n \\ a_i a_j a_1 & a_i a_j a_2 & \cdots & a_i a_j a_n \end{pmatrix} \begin{pmatrix} a_1 & a_2 & \cdots & a_n \\ a_j a_1 & a_j a_2 & \cdots & a_j a_n \end{pmatrix}$$

$$= \begin{pmatrix} a_1 & a_2 & \cdots & a_n \\ a_i a_j a_1 & a_i a_j a_2 & \cdots & a_i a_j a_n \end{pmatrix} ,$$

since the multiplication can now be determined simply by inspection. Thus

$$P_{a_i} P_{a_j} = P_{a_i a_j} ,$$

and the proof of isomorphism is complete.

This result encompasses the remark made in Example 10.5, where it was noted that S_3 has a subgroup $\{e, (123), (321)\}$ which is isomorphic to the group of order three. Regarding the groups of order four, we take first the four-group. Using the multiplication table of Table (10.7), we find immediately the correspondence

$$P_e = \begin{pmatrix} e & a & b & c \\ e & a & b & c \end{pmatrix} , \qquad P_a = \begin{pmatrix} e & a & b & c \\ a & e & c & b \end{pmatrix} ,$$

$$P_b = \begin{pmatrix} e & a & b & c \\ b & c & e & a \end{pmatrix} , \qquad P_c = \begin{pmatrix} e & a & b & c \\ c & b & a & e \end{pmatrix} ,$$

by using the rule of correspondence of Cayley's theorem. In the compact cycle notation, these can be written as

$$P_e = e , \qquad P_a = (ea)(bc) , \qquad P_b = (eb)(ac) , \qquad P_c = (ec)(ab) .$$

It is a simple matter to check that the multiplication table of Table (10.7) is obeyed.

In the case of the cyclic group of order four, we find, using Table (10.4),

$$P_e = \begin{pmatrix} e & a & b & c \\ e & a & b & c \end{pmatrix}, \qquad P_a = \begin{pmatrix} e & a & b & c \\ a & b & c & e \end{pmatrix},$$

$$P_b = \begin{pmatrix} e & a & b & c \\ b & c & e & a \end{pmatrix}, \qquad P_c = \begin{pmatrix} e & a & b & c \\ c & e & a & b \end{pmatrix}.$$

As above, this can be written as

$$P_e = e, \qquad P_a = (eabc), \qquad P_b = (eb)(ac), \qquad P_c = (ecba).$$

This case gives us our first example of a four-cycle.

In looking at these two illustrations, one notes that except for the identity, all the permutations leave no symbol unchanged. A subgroup of S_n with this property is called a *regular subgroup* or a subgroup of regular permutations. It is clear from the construction used in proving Theorem 10.2 that every subgroup of S_n which is isomorphic to a group of order n is a regular subgroup.

We close this section with a few results about the regular subgroups of S_n.

Lemma. In a regular subgroup, no two elements take a given symbol into the same symbol.

Proof. Suppose that p_1 and p_2 ($p_1 \neq p_2$) belong to a regular subgroup and that both p_1 and p_2 take a into b. But then $p_1 p_2^{-1}$ ($\neq e$) leaves b unchanged. However, $p_1 p_2^{-1}$ also belongs to the regular subgroup (since the subgroup is closed), which contradicts the assumption that the subgroup is regular and hence that every element (except the identity) changes *all* the symbols.

Lemma. In a regular subgroup, if we decompose a given permutation into disjoint cycles, then each cycle must have the same length. For example, in S_5, (12) (345) could not belong to a regular subgroup.

Proof. Suppose that p is an element of a regular subgroup which can be decomposed into two cycles of length l_1 and l_2 with $l_1 < l_2$. Now since a cycle of length l must satisfy $(a_1 a_2 \cdots a_l)^l = e$, p^{l_1} leaves all the symbols contained in the first cycle unchanged. However, p^{l_1} must change some of the symbols contained in the second cycle (all of them, in fact), since if we have a cycle of length $\lambda > l'$, then $(a_1 a_2 \cdots a_\lambda)^{l''} \neq e$. Hence p^{l_1}, which is a permutation belonging to the subgroup containing p, changes some symbols, but not others. This contradicts our assumption that p belongs to a regular subgroup.

This lemma is illustrated by the results just obtained for the regular subgroups of S_4 corresponding to the four-group and to the cyclic group of order four. Using this lemma, we can also prove the following very powerful theorem.

Theorem 10.3. Every group $\{G, \cdot\}$ of order n is cyclic if n is a prime number.

Proof. By the previous lemma, the subgroup of S_n to which G is isomorphic must contain elements which are either a product of n one-cycles or just one n-cycle, since n is prime. The identity is a product of n one-cycles, so G consists of an identity, plus $n - 1$ elements which correspond isomorphically to n-cycles. Call these elements $a_2, a_3, \cdots, a_n$. Now since a_i corresponds to an n-cycle, each element of the sequence $\{a_i, a_i^2, a_i^3, \cdots, a_i^{n-1}\}$ is distinct (note that $a_i^n = e$), since if the elements were not all distinct, say $a_i^\mu = a_i^\nu$, then we would have $a_i^m = e$ for $m < n$, which is impossible because a_i corresponds to an n-cycle. Thus the distinct elements $\{e, a_i, a_i^2, \cdots, a_i^{n-1}\}$ exhaust all elements of the group. That is, we have a cyclic group of order n. Clearly this argument works for any element a_i.

For example, the group of order three is isomorphic to the subgroup $\{e, (123), (321)\}$ of S_3. It is easily checked that

$$(123)^1 = (123) , \qquad (123)^2 = (321) , \qquad (123)^3 = e ,$$

so we could write our group as

$$\{e, (123), (123)^2\} .$$

But also,

$$(321)^1 = (321) , \qquad (321)^2 = (123) , \qquad (321)^3 = e ,$$

so we could equally well reorder the group and write it as

$$\{e, (321), (321)^2\} .$$

Theorem 10.3 tells us, among other things, that although we might be tempted to imagine that for n large the number of groups of order n is also large, this is in fact not the case. There is only one group of order 97, namely, the cyclic group.

10.3 COSETS, CLASSES, AND INVARIANT SUBGROUPS

Having discussed in some detail a special category of finite groups, let us now look at some of the most important general properties which are common to all groups.

Definition 10.7. Let A be a subgroup of G, with elements $e, a_2, a_3, \cdots, a_m$ ($m \leq n$, where n is the order of G) and let $b \in G$, but $b \notin A$. Then the m distinct elements $be = b, ba_2, ba_3, \cdots, ba_m$ form a *left coset* of A, which we denote symbolically by bA. Similarly, $b, a_2b, a_3b, \cdots, a_mb$ form a *right coset*, Ab.

The notation bA is just a shorthand for the collection of objects formed by multiplying every element of A on the left by b. Note that a coset is *not* a subgroup, since it clearly cannot contain the identity element. If $ba_i = e$, then $b = a_i^{-1}$, which implies $b \in A$, contrary to the assumption in Definition 10.7. In fact, bA contains no elements of A at all, for if $ba_i = a_j$, then $b = a_j a_i^{-1}$, and hence $b \in A$, again contrary to assumption.

Lemma. Two left cosets of a subgroup A either contain all the same elements or else have no elements in common.

Proof. Let xA be one coset of A and yA be another. Suppose that $xa_i = ya_j$; then $y^{-1}x = a_j a_i^{-1}$, so $y^{-1}x \in A$. Thus $y^{-1}x$ applied to the group A must just be a rearrangement of A, according to Theorem 10.1. Hence A can be written as $\{y^{-1}xa_1, y^{-1}xa_2, \cdots, y^{-1}xa_m\}$, and the collection $\{y(y^{-1}xa_1), y(y^{-1}xa_2), \cdots, y(y^{-1}xa_m)\}$ must be identical with yA (the ordering of the elements of yA is immaterial). But this collection is just $\{xa_1, xa_2, \cdots, xa_m\}$, so it is equal to xA. Hence xA and yA are the same, and we conclude that if two cosets have one element in common, they have all elements in common. This is what we set out to prove.

Theorem 10.4 (Lagrange's theorem). The order, g, of the group G is an integral multiple of the order of any subgroup, A.

Proof. Consider all the distinct cosets of A, which we denote by $b_1A, b_2A, \cdots, b_{\mu-1}A$. (It is purely for convenience that we take the number of cosets to be $\mu - 1$.) Let h be the order of A; thus there are h elements in each coset. But every element of G must occur either in A or in one of its $\mu - 1$ distinct cosets, and no element can appear more than once. Hence $h + (\mu - 1)h = \mu h = g$, which is what was to be shown.

We call μ the *index* of the subgroup A. From this result it is apparent that the order of any element of a group must be an integral divisor of the order of the group, since each element, a, of order ν generates a subgroup $\{e, a, a^2, \cdots, a^{\nu-1}\}$ of order ν. This leads us to conclude again, as in Theorem 10.3, that the groups of prime order must be cyclic.

Example 10.6. Consider S_3, whose elements are e, (12), (13), (23), (123), and (321). The left cosets of the subgroup $\{e, (12)\} = A$ are:

$$(13)A = \{(13), (13)(12)\} \quad = \{(13), (123)\},$$
$$(23)A = \{(23), (23)(12)\} \quad = \{(23), (321)\},$$
$$(123)A = \{(123), (123)(12)\} = \{(123), (13)\},$$
$$(321)A = \{(321), (321)(12)\} = \{(321), (23)\}.$$

Thus there are two distinct left cosets of A:

$$(13)A = \{(13), (123)\}, \qquad (23)A = \{(23), (321)\}.$$

We may write symbolically

$$S_3 = A + (13)A + (23)A,$$

or equivalently,

$$S_3 = A + (123)A + (321)A.$$

Note that the right cosets of A are *not* the same as the left cosets:

$$A(13) = \{(13), (12)(13)\} = \{(13), (321)\},$$
$$A(23) = \{(23), (12)(23)\} = \{(23), (123)\},$$

and similarly for $A(123)$ and $A(321)$.

Another subgroup of S_3 is $B = \{e, (123), (321)\}$. Its left cosets are:

$$(12)B = \{(12), (12)(123), (12)(321)\}$$
$$= \{(12), (23), (13)\} \ ;$$

$(13)B$ and $(23)B$ must equal $(12)B$ according to the previous lemma. It also follows from that lemma that the right coset $B(12)$ is equal to $(12)B$. Thus there is only one distinct coset of B. In this case we may write symbolically

$$S_3 = B + (12)B \ .$$

An important relationship which can exist between group elements is that of conjugacy.

Definition 10.8. An element $b \in G$ is said to be *conjugate* to $a \in G$ if there exists some $x \in G$ such that

$$b = xax^{-1} \ .$$

This relationship of two group elements is analogous to that of similarity between matrices, which was discussed in Chapter 3. According to this definition, a is clearly conjugate to itself and if a is conjugate to b, then b is conjugate to a. We also have the following simple result.

Lemma. If a is conjugate to b and b is conjugate to c, then a is conjugate to c.

Proof. Since a is conjugate to b, there exists $x \in G$ such that $a = xbx^{-1}$; similarly, there exists $y \in G$ such that $b = ycy^{-1}$. Combining these two results, we find that

$$a = x(ycy^{-1})x^{-1} = xycy^{-1}x^{-1} = (xy)c(xy)^{-1} \ ,$$

since $(xy)^{-1} = y^{-1}x^{-1}$ as may be checked by direct multiplication. But $xy \in G$, so a is conjugate to c, as required.

Thus the relation of conjugacy is reflexive, symmetric, and transitive. This suggests the following definition.

Definition 10.9. All the elements of a group which are conjugate to each other form an *equivalence class*, referred to hereafter simply as a *class*.

According to this definition any two elements of a class must be of the same order. For suppose that a is of order n $(a^n = e)$ and that b is conjugate to a $(b = xax^{-1}$ for some $x \in G)$. Then $b^n = (xax^{-1})^n = xax^{-1} xax^{-1} \cdots xax^{-1} = xa^n x^{-1} = xex^{-1} = e$. We also have $b^m = xa^m x^{-1}$ for any $m < n$. Now if $b^m = e$, it follows that $a^m = e$, which is impossible since a is of order n and $m < n$. Thus n is the smallest integer for which $b^n = e$; that is, b is also of order n. Obviously, the identity forms a class by itself. For any other group element, a, we form the sequence

$$eae^{-1} = a, a_2 a a_2^{-1}, a_3 a a_3^{-1}, \cdots, a_n a a_n^{-1} \ .$$

The elements of this sequence are all conjugate to each other (of course some elements may occur more than once), and hence form a class. In this manner, the elements of any group can be divided into classes. For abelian groups, this procedure is very simple: every element constitutes a class by itself, since all the elements commute.

Example 10.7. Consider once again the group S_3: $\{e, (12), (13), (23), (123), (321)\}$. The respective inverses are e, (12), (13), (23), (321) and (123). Of course, e constitutes a class by itself. Now let us conjugate (12) by all the elements of S_3:

i) $\quad e(12)e^{-1} = (12)$,

ii) $\quad (12)(12)(12)^{-1} = (12)$,

iii) $\quad (13)(12)(13)^{-1} = (13)(12)(13) = (13)(132) = (13)(321)$
$\qquad\qquad = (13)(31)(32) = (23)$,

iv) $\quad (23)(12)(23)^{-1} = (23)(12)(23) = (23)(21)(23) = (23)(231)$
$\qquad\qquad = (23)(312) = (23)(32)(31) = (13)$,

v) $\quad (123)(12)(123)^{-1} = (123)(12)(321) = (13)(12)(12)(321)$
$\qquad\qquad = (13)(321) = (13)(31)(32) = (23)$,

vi) $\quad (321)(12)(321)^{-1} = (321)(12)(123) = (321)(12)(231)$
$\qquad\qquad = (321)(12)(21)(23) = (321)(23) = (31)(32)(23)$
$\qquad\qquad = (13)$.

The above calculations illustrate some of the techniques that are useful in the manipulation of cycles. In particular, we have repeatedly made use of two important properties of cycles: (1) that the square of any two-cycle gives the identity element; and (2) that one can order a three-cycle (or generally, an n-cycle) in more ways than one to suit a given situation. Thus we conclude that (12), (13), and (23) form a class. This leaves only (123) and (321) to place in classes. We have

$$e(123)e^{-1} = (123)$$
$$(12)(123)(12)^{-1} = (12)(13)(12)(12) = (12)(13) = (132) = (321) .$$

We need go no further, since we see that (123) and (321) are conjugate to each other. They are therefore in the same class. Since this exhausts the elements of the group, we have determined all the classes of S_3. We summarize as follows:

$$\mathscr{C}_1 = e ,$$
$$\mathscr{C}_2 = \{(12), (13), (23)\} ,$$
$$\mathscr{C}_3 = \{(123), (321)\} .$$

We remark here without proof that in the case of the permutation groups, the division into classes corresponds always to the division according to cycle structure, just as in the above case. That means, for example, that in the case of

S_4 the $4! = 24$ elements fall into the classes:

$\mathscr{C}_1 = e$,

$\mathscr{C}_2 = \{(12), (13), (14), (23), (24), (34)\}$,

$\mathscr{C}_3 = \{(123), (321), (124), (421), (134), (431), (234), (432)\}$,

$\mathscr{C}_4 = \{(12)(34), (13)(24), (14)(23)\}$,

$\mathscr{C}_5 = \{(1234), (1243), (1324), (1342), (1423), (1432)\}$.

Now let H be a subgroup of G. The set $H' = aHa^{-1}$, where $a \in G$, is also a subgroup of G For if $x \in H$ and $y \in H$, axa^{-1} and aya^{-1} are two elements of H'. But

$$(axa^{-1})(aya^{-1}) = a(xy)a^{-1} ,$$

and since $xy \in H$, $a(xy)a^{-1} \in H'$. This proves that H' is closed; the other group properties of H' may readily be verified. Evidently, if $a \in H$, then H' is just a one-to-one mapping of H onto itself. $H' = aHa^{-1}$ is said to be a *conjugate subgroup* of H in G.

Definition 10.10. If for all $a \in G$, $aHa^{-1} = H$, H is said to be an *invariant* subgroup.

Under these circumstances, $aH = Ha$, so we arrive at an alternative formulation: H is an invariant subgroup if the left and right cosets formed with any $a \in G$ are the same. Thus the subgroup B of S_3 discussed in Example 10.6 is an invariant subgroup. The subgroup A of S_3 is not invariant. Clearly, in any group, the identity is an invariant subgroup, as is the whole group itself.

Definition 10.11. A group which has no invariant subgroups save the whole group and the identity is a *simple* group.

Lemma. If H is a subgroup of G, H is invariant if and only if it contains the elements of G in complete classes; that is, if H contains one element of a class, then it must contain them all.

Proof. Assume first that H is invariant; then for any $x \in H$ and $a \in G$, $axa^{-1} \in H$. Hence if $\mathscr{C}$ is a class which contains x, all members of $\mathscr{C}$ are also in H, by Definition 10.9. By the same argument, if $y \in \mathscr{C}'$ ($\mathscr{C}' \neq \mathscr{C}$), all members of $\mathscr{C}'$ must also be in H. Thus H contains only complete classes and may contain more than one class. In fact, since e always constitutes a class by itself, only the most trivial invariant subgroup (the group consisting of the identity alone) will contain just one class. Conversely, suppose that H contains only complete classes. Then every $x \in H$ belongs to some class $\mathscr{C}$; furthermore, every element of $\mathscr{C}$ is contained in H. This means that for *any* $a \in G$, $axa^{-1} \in H$. Since this argument holds for any x, H is invariant.

One of the most interesting results of group theory is that the *cosets* of an invariant subgroup themselves constitute a group!

Theorem 10.5. The collection consisting of an invariant subgroup H and all its distinct cosets is itself a group, called the factor group of G, usually denoted by G/H. (Remember that the left and right cosets of an *invariant* subgroup are identical.) Multiplication of two cosets aH and bH is defined as the set of all distinct products $z = xy$, with $x \in aH$ and $y \in bH$; the identity element of the factor group is the subgroup H itself.

Proof. Consider any coset aH. Then since $HH = H$,

$$(aH)H = aHH = aH\,; \qquad H(aH) = HaH = aHH = aH\,,$$

so H is indeed the identity. Here we have used $aH = Ha$, which follows from the fact that H is invariant. Now take any two cosets aH and bH. We have

$$(aH)(bH) = aHbH = abHH = abH\,,$$

so the product of two cosets yields another coset. Finally, the inverse of aH is clearly $a^{-1}H$, since H is the identity and

$$(aH)(a^{-1}H) = aa^{-1}HH = HH = H\,.$$

This completes the proof that G/H is indeed a group.

A simple illustration of this theorem is provided by S_3. We have already noted that $B = \{e, (123), (321)\}$ is an invariant subgroup. Its coset can be written as $(12)B$. Thus the factor group S_3/B consists of two elements:

$$E = B = \{e, (123), (321)\}\,, \qquad A = (12)B = \{(12), (13), (23)\}\,,$$

with $A^2 = E$. In discussing the factor group we will use capital letters to denote factor group elements. When multiplying two such elements we will denote group multiplication by a dot to avoid possible confusion with matrix multiplication.

From another point of view, the factor group is a mapping of one group G onto another group G'. This mapping preserves group products, but is not necessarily one to one. Such a map is called a homomorphism; it is to be contrasted with the isomorphism, which is a product-preserving, one-to-one map. We say that G is homomorphic to G'. In the example under discussion we can consider e, (123) and (321) as being mapped onto E, the identity; and (12), (13) and (23) as being mapped onto A ($A^2 = E$). According to the proof of Theorem 10.5, this mapping must preserve products. For example, (13)(12) is an element of the product of A by A. Since (13)(12) = (123), this product belongs to E, as it should since $A \cdot A = E$. Similarly, (123)(12) $\in E \cdot A$, which is again as it should be since (123)(12) = (13), which belongs to A. The reader can check that all the multiplications work out as they are supposed to according to Theorem 10.5. We also leave it to the reader to show that in *any* homomorphic mapping of G onto G', the elements of G which are mapped onto the identity of G' must form an invariant subgroup of G. The other elements of G' then must be the images of the cosets of the invariant subgroup.

Example 10.8. To illustrate further some of the ideas of this section and also to look at a slightly more complicated group than we have examined so far, let us analyze the group S_4. As mentioned earlier, S_4 can be divided into five classes according to cycle structure:

$$\mathscr{C}_1 = e \,,$$
$$\mathscr{C}_2 = (12), (13), (14), (23), (24), (34) \,,$$
$$\mathscr{C}_3 = (123), (124), (134), (234), (321), (421), (431), (432) \,,$$
$$\mathscr{C}_4 = (12)(34), (13)(24), (14)(23) \,,$$
$$\mathscr{C}_5 = (1234), (1243), (1324), (1342), (1423), (1432) \,.$$

We would like to determine whether there are any nontrivial invariant subgroups of S_4. Since we know that such an invariant subgroup can contain only complete classes and since furthermore the order of the subgroup must be an integral divisor of the order (4! = 24) of S_4, there are, according to the previous lemma only two possibilities:

$$H = \mathscr{C}_1 + \mathscr{C}_4 \,, \qquad H' = \mathscr{C}_1 + \mathscr{C}_3 + \mathscr{C}_4 \,.$$

H is of order four and H' is of order twelve. Both these orders are integral divisors of 24; $H'' = \mathscr{C}_1 + \mathscr{C}_2$, for example, is excluded since $24/7 \neq$ integer. In addition, H'' is not even a subgroup. Now H' is just the subgroup of even permutations. Since any coset must have as many elements as the related subgroup, H' can have only one coset, the set $\mathscr{C}$ of all odd permutations (note that this is *not* a subgroup). In particular, the left and right cosets must be identical, so H' is indeed an invariant subgroup. The factor group S_4/H' (consisting of the two sets H' and $\mathscr{C}$) is isomorphic to the two-element cyclic group. It is obvious that the two-element cyclic group is a factor group of any S_n, since half the elements of S_n are even permutations and half are odd permutations.

That H is also a group is seen by noting that according to the discussion following the proof of Theorem 10.2, this collection of four elements is isomorphic to the four-group. Now what are the cosets of H? The computation is tedious but straightforward. We have

$$(12)H = \{(12), (34), (1324), (1423)\} \,,$$
$$(13)H = \{(13), (24), (1234), (1432)\} \,,$$
$$(23)H = \{(23), (14), (1243), (1342)\} \,.$$

According to the first lemma of this section, we must also have

$$(12)H = (34)H = (1324)H = (1423)H \,,$$
$$(13)H = (24)H = (1234)H = (1432)H \,,$$
$$(23)H = (14)H = (1243)H = (1342)H \,.$$

Now consider $(123)H$. We find that

$$(123)H = \{(123), (134), (432), (421)\} \,.$$

This contains half of $\mathscr{C}_3$, so we know (why?) that $(321)H$ must be the only remaining coset of H. In fact,

$$(321)H = \{(321), (234), (124), (431)\} \, .$$

This collection of six objects, $\{H, (12)H, (13)H, (23)H, (123)H, (321)H\}$, is isomorphic to S_3, and by inspection we may make the identifications:

$$H \to e \, , \qquad (12)H \to (12) \, , \qquad (13)H \to (13) \, ,$$
$$(23)H \to (23) \, , \qquad (123)H \to (123) \, , \qquad (321)H \to (321) \, .$$

For example, $(1324) \in (12)H$ and $(1234) \in (13)H$. A simple calculation gives

$$(1324)(1234) = (4132)(1234) = (42)(43)(41)(14)(13)(12)$$
$$= (42)(43)(13)(12) = (432)(123) = (324)(312)$$
$$= (34)(32)(32)(31) = (34)(31) = (314) = (431) \, ,$$

which belongs to $(321)H$. Since $(12)(13) = (132) = (321)$, we see that the isomorphism holds:

$$[(12)H][(13)H] = (321)H \qquad \text{and} \qquad (12)(13) = (321) \, .$$

10.4 SYMMETRY AND GROUP REPRESENTATIONS

The role of group theory in physics is intimately related to the symmetries of the world around us. The importance of such symmetries as translational and rotational invariance in giving rise to conservation of linear and angular momentum has long been known and is familiar to the student from classical mechanics. With the development of quantum mechanics, in which the physical world is separated from us by the intermediary of the "wave function," group theory became particularly significant. To see why this is the case, we must first say precisely what is meant by such phrases as "translational invariance" and "rotational invariance."

Suppose that we have a group, G, of operators, $U_1, U_2, U_3, \cdots$, which can act on elements, x, of a vector space, V. By a group of operators we simply mean a collection of operators on V which obeys the group axioms of Definition 10.1. The results of $U_1, U_2, U_3, \cdots$ acting on x will, as usual, be denoted by $U_1x, U_2x, U_3x, \cdots$ In three-dimensional space an example of such a group is the collection $\{T_a\}$, where a is any three-dimensional vector, and T_a acts on vectors according to the rule

$$T_a \mathbf{r} = \mathbf{r} - \mathbf{a} \, . \tag{10.8}$$

Thus T_a is a translation operator. Note that there is an infinitude of such operators, since a can be *any* vector. The entire collection is clearly a group; closure follows because the product of any two translations is again a translation. In fact, from the defining equation, we see that this group is abelian since

$$T_a T_b = T_{a+b} = T_b T_a \, .$$

Obviously, such operators can be generalized to any number of dimensions. Now we suppose further that on this vector space we have defined functions, $f, g, \cdots$, which assign to each vector some complex number. In three-dimensional Euclidean space, $f(\mathbf{r}) = x^4 + y^4 + z^4$ is an example of such a function.

In general, we denote the action of a function f on a vector x in V by $f(x)$. Let U_i be any element of the group of transformations written above. What can we say about the action of f on the transformed vector $U_i^{-1}x$? Let us define an operator $\mathscr{U}_i$ which acts on functions of x in such a manner that for all f

$$\mathscr{U}_i f(x) = f(U_i^{-1}x) \ .$$

Now consider the quantity $\mathscr{U}_i \mathscr{U}_j f(x)$. We have from the above equation

$$\mathscr{U}_i \mathscr{U}_j f(x) = \mathscr{U}_i f(U_j^{-1}x) = f(U_j^{-1}U_i^{-1}x) = f([U_iU_j]^{-1}x) \ .$$

Thus, if $U_iU_j = U_k$, then $\mathscr{U}_i \mathscr{U}_j = \mathscr{U}_k$, so that the elements $\mathscr{U}_1, \mathscr{U}_2, \cdots$ form a group, $\mathscr{G}$, which is isomorphic to G.

To illustrate what we have in mind, let us extend the example of the $\{T_a\}$, defined in Eq. (10.8), a bit further. We ask: Is it possible to find an operator $\mathscr{T}_a$ such that

$$\mathscr{T}_a f(\mathbf{r}) = f(T_a^{-1}\mathbf{r}) = f(\mathbf{r} + \mathbf{a}) \ ?$$

In general, it will be necessary to say something about the functions $f(x)$, $g(x)$, $\cdots$ before we can obtain an explicit expression for $\mathscr{T}_a$. For the sake of simplicity, suppose that we take our functions to be analytic. Then we can write a Taylor series for $f(\mathbf{r} + \mathbf{a})$:

$$f(\mathbf{r} + \mathbf{a}) = \sum_{n=0}^{\infty} \frac{1}{n!}[\mathbf{a} \cdot \nabla]^n f(\mathbf{r}) \ .$$

Symbolically, this can be written as

$$f(\mathbf{r} + \mathbf{a}) = e^{\mathbf{a} \cdot \nabla} f(\mathbf{r}) \ ,$$

so we see that

$$\mathscr{T}_a = e^{\mathbf{a} \cdot \nabla} \ . \tag{10.9}$$

If one were quantum-mechanically minded, one would write this as

$$\mathscr{T}_a = e^{i\mathbf{a} \cdot \mathbf{p}/\hbar} \ , \tag{10.10}$$

where $\mathbf{p} = -i\hbar\nabla$ is the quantum-mechanical momentum operator.

Similarly, if one consider rotations, R_α^z, of a coordinate system about the z-axis, so that $(r, \theta, \phi) \to (r, \theta, \phi - \alpha)$, then the corresponding operator would be

$$\mathscr{R}_\alpha^z = e^{\alpha (\partial/\partial\phi)} = e^{i\alpha L_z/\hbar} \ , \tag{10.11}$$

where $L_z = -i\hbar\partial/\partial\phi$ is the quantum-mechanical operator for the z-component of angular momentum. For rotation through angles β and γ about the y-axis and x-axis respectively, one has

$$\mathscr{R}_{\beta}^{y} = e^{i\beta L_y/\hbar}, \qquad \mathscr{R}_{\gamma}^{x} = e^{i\gamma L_x/\hbar} . \tag{10.12}$$

Groups of the type characterized by the collection $\{\mathscr{T}_{\mathbf{a}}\}$ or $\{\mathscr{R}_{\alpha}^{z}\}$ are called transformation groups. Both of these examples involve infinite groups. We have been able to parametrize the translation group by $\mathbf{a}$ ($= a_x, a_y, a_z$), and the group of rotations about the z-axis by α. The parameters in question vary continuously, and the groups are therefore called *continuous* groups.

Now we make contact with our work in earlier chapters. Suppose that the functions which we have been discussing above belong to a vector space, H, and that acting on H we have some linear operator, A_x. Acting on any $f(x) \in H$, A_x gives another vector $g(x) \in H$:

$$A_x f(x) = g(x) . \tag{10.13}$$

The subscript x on A serves to remind us that A_x is an operator on a space of functions whose action depends on the point at which the function is evaluated. For example, we might have

$$A_{\mathbf{r}} = \nabla^2 = \frac{\partial^2}{\partial x^2} + \frac{\partial^2}{\partial y^2} + \frac{\partial^2}{\partial z^2} .$$

Let $\mathscr{U} \in \mathscr{G}$ act on Eq. (10.13). Then we find that

$$\mathscr{U} A_x f(x) = \mathscr{U} g(x) = g(U^{-1}x) .$$

Since $\mathscr{U}^{-1} \mathscr{U} = I$, we have equivalently,

$$\mathscr{U} A_x \mathscr{U}^{-1} \mathscr{U} f(x) = g(U^{-1}x) ,$$

or

$$\mathscr{U} A_x \mathscr{U}^{-1} f(U^{-1}x) = g(U^{-1}x) .$$

But since $A_x f(x) = g(x)$, we have also

$$A_{U^{-1}x} f(U^{-1}x) = g(U^{-1}x) ,$$

so we conclude that

$$\mathscr{U} A_x \mathscr{U}^{-1} f(U^{-1}x) = A_{U^{-1}x} f(U^{-1}x) ,$$

for any $f \in H$, or

$$\mathscr{U} A_x \mathscr{U}^{-1} = A_{U^{-1}x} .$$

$\mathscr{U} A_x \mathscr{U}^{-1}$ is called the *transformed* operator; the above equation tells us that the transformed operator at the point x is equal to the untransformed operator at the point $U^{-1}x$. It is often simpler to find the transformed operator by evaluating $A_{x'}$, where $x' = U^{-1}x$, rather than $\mathscr{U} A_x \mathscr{U}^{-1}$. Now if it happens that the transformed operator at the point x equals the untransformed operator at the point x, that is, if

$$\mathscr{U} A_x \mathscr{U}^{-1} = A_x$$

for all $\mathscr{U} \in \mathscr{G}$, then we say that A_x is invariant under the action of the group $\mathscr{G}$. Similarly, if for all $\mathscr{U} \in \mathscr{G}$, $\mathscr{U} f(x) = f(x)$, then we say that f is invariant under $\mathscr{G}$. Note that the criterion for the invariance of A_x can also be written as

$$A_x \mathscr{U} = \mathscr{U} A_x .$$

In other words, if all $\mathscr{U} \in \mathscr{G}$ commute with A_x, then A_x is invariant under $\mathscr{G}$.

It is easily seen that the operator

$$A_{\mathbf{r}} = \nabla^2 = \frac{\partial^2}{\partial x^2} + \frac{\partial^2}{\partial y^2} + \frac{\partial^2}{\partial z^2}$$

is invariant under $\mathscr{T}_a$ for all $\mathbf{a}$, where $\mathscr{T}_a$ is defined by Eq. (10.9). This follows simply from the fact that the partial derivatives with respect to x, y and z commute with each other, and hence $\exp(\mathbf{a} \cdot \nabla)$ commutes with ∇^2. Thus we may say that the Laplacian is translation invariant. A similar situation prevails for the rotation operators $\mathscr{R}_\alpha^z$, $\mathscr{R}_\beta^y$ and $\mathscr{R}_\gamma^x$ as defined by Eqs. (10.11) and (10.12). According to Eq. (5.89) ∇^2 is simply related to $L^2 = L_x^2 + L_y^2 + L_z^2$, and since L_x, L_y and L_z all commute with L^2 (why?), we see that the rotation operators will also commute with L^2 and hence with ∇^2. Thus, ∇^2 is rotationally invariant.

As an example of a function which is rotationally invariant we mention $f(\mathbf{r}) = g(r)$, where g is any function and r is the magnitude of $\mathbf{r}$. This follows immediately from the fact that L_x, L_y and L_z depend only on the angles θ and ϕ which specify the orientation of $\mathbf{r}$ and not on the magnitude of $\mathbf{r}$ [see Eqs. (5.87)].

To get a feeling for how the above formalism works, it is useful to examine an operator which is *not* invariant under some group. For example, let us consider the operator X_x defined by $X_x f(x) \equiv x f(x)$. We shall investigate how this operator transforms under the x-translation operators $T_a (T_a x = x - a$, for all $x)$. We can compute the transform of X_x in two ways. The simplest method is to make use of the relation

$$\mathscr{T}_a X_x \mathscr{T}_a^{-1} = X_{T_a^{-1} x} .$$

Since $T_a^{-1} x = x + a$, we see immediately that

$$\mathscr{T}_a X_x \mathscr{T}_a^{-1} = X_x + a .$$

We can also proceed by letting $\mathscr{T}_a X_x \mathscr{T}_a^{-1}$ act on an arbitrary function:

$$\begin{aligned}
\mathscr{T}_a X_x \mathscr{T}_a^{-1} f(x) &= \mathscr{T}_a X_x f(T_a x) = \mathscr{T}_a X_x f(x - a) \\
&= \mathscr{T}_a x f(x - a) = (x + a) f(x) \\
&= (X_x + a) f(x) .
\end{aligned}$$

This is exactly the result obtained above; clearly the operator X_x is not invariant under the group of translations. For a slightly more complicated example of the transformation of operators, the reader should look at Problem 10.10.

Now let us look at the eigenvalue problem

$$A_x f(x) = \lambda f(x) . \tag{10.14}$$

We assume that we have a physical problem in mind, so that A_x is self-adjoint, and we also assume that A_x is invariant under some group of operators $\mathscr{G}$, a typical element of which we denote by $\mathscr{U}$. The question now arises: If the operator A_x is invariant under $\mathscr{G}$, are its eigenvectors invariant under $\mathscr{G}$? To answer this question we let $\mathscr{U}$ operate on both sides of the above equation to obtain

$$\mathscr{U} A_x f(x) = \lambda \, \mathscr{U} f(x) \, .$$

Since $\mathscr{U} A_x = A_x \mathscr{U}$,

$$A_x \, \mathscr{U} f(x) = \lambda \, \mathscr{U} f(x) \, .$$

This equation tells us that if $f(x)$ is an eigenfunction of A_x belonging to λ, then so is $\mathscr{U} f(x)$. This does *not* mean that $f(x) = \mathscr{U} f(x)$. However, if λ is a non-degenerate eigenvalue, then we conclude that $\mathscr{U} f(x)$ is just a simple multiple of $f(x)$:

$$\mathscr{U} f(x) = D(U) f(x) \, ,$$

where we write $D(U)$ to emphasize that the value of D may depend on which element of the group G is being used.

If, however, λ has multiplicity μ, then we must write

$$A_x f_i(x) = \lambda f_i(x) \, , \qquad i = 1, 2, \cdots, \mu \, ,$$
$$A_x \, \mathscr{U} f_i(x) = \lambda \, \mathscr{U} f_i(x) \, , \qquad i = 1, 2, \cdots, \mu \, .$$

In this case, we must conclude that $\mathscr{U} f_i(x)$ is a linear combination of the elements of the set $\{f_j(x)\}$:

$$\mathscr{U} f_i(x) = \sum_{j=1}^{\mu} D_{ji}(U) f_j(x) \, . \tag{10.15}$$

Now let us consider $\mathscr{U}_1 \, \mathscr{U}_2 f_i(x)$, where $\mathscr{U}_1, \, \mathscr{U}_2 \in \mathscr{G}$. By the previous equation we have

$$\mathscr{U}_1 \, \mathscr{U}_2 f_i(x) = \mathscr{U}_1 \sum_{j=1}^{\mu} D_{ji}(U_2) \, f_j(x) = \sum_{j=1}^{\mu} D_{ji}(U_2) \, \mathscr{U}_1 f_j(x) \, .$$

Since

$$\mathscr{U}_1 f_j(x) = \sum_{k=1}^{\mu} D_{kj}(U_1) \, f_k(x) \, ,$$

we have

$$\mathscr{U}_1 \, \mathscr{U}_2 f_i(x) = \sum_{j=1}^{\mu} \sum_{k=1}^{\mu} D_{kj}(U_1) D_{ji}(U_2) f_k(x) \, .$$

But also,

$$\mathscr{U}_1 \, \mathscr{U}_2 f_i(x) = \sum_{k=1}^{\mu} D_{ki}(U_1 U_2) \, f_k(x) \, .$$

Combining these last two equations gives the result

$$\sum_{k=1}^{\mu} \left[D_{ki}(U_1 U_2) - \sum_{j=1}^{\mu} D_{kj}(U_1) D_{ji}(U_2) \right] f_k(x) = 0 \, .$$

But the set $\{f_k(x): k = 1, 2, \cdots, \mu\}$ is linearly independent, so

$$D_{ki}(U_1 U_2) = \sum_{j=1}^{\mu} D_{kj}(U_1) D_{ji}(U_2)$$

for all $i, k = 1, 2, \cdots, \mu$. Thus the matrices $D(U_1), D(U_2), \cdots$ form a group which is homomorphic to the group G and the group $\mathscr{G}$. Such a collection of matrices is called a *representation* of the group G. A representation of a group G is just a homomorphic mapping of G onto a collection of finite-dimensional matrices.

Thus we see that there is a very close relationship between symmetries and degeneracy in physical eigenvalue problems. For example, in quantum mechanics it is often the case that the Hamiltonian which describes some physical system is rotationally invariant. We would then expect the eigenfunctions corresponding to some degenerate energy level to transform among themselves under rotations and thus give rise to a representation of the rotation group. Since degeneracy tends to be the rule rather than the exception in the eigenvalue problems of physics, it is not surprising that the study of group representations has come to play a very important role in physics. It is to the study and classification of such representations that we now turn our attention.

10.5 IRREDUCIBLE REPRESENTATIONS

Let us begin with a few general inferences about the possibility of finding representations of groups. Clearly, for any group there is always one available homomorphism, namely, the mapping which assigns the one-dimensional matrix, 1, to every element of the group. All group properties are trivially satisfied, but this representation is not very useful. However, it is *always* a possible representation and cannot be neglected when we classify representations. Also, if we can find some n-dimensional representation, then a related one-dimensional representation may always be obtained by mapping each element of G into the determinant of its representative matrix. This follows immediately from the relation

$$\det (AB) = (\det A)(\det B) .$$

Another possibility arises when the group, G, has an invariant subgroup, H, whose associated factor group, G/H, has known representations. Since the factor group is homomorphic to G, we can find representations of G by assigning to each element $U \in G$ the matrix representative of that element of G/H onto which U is mapped.

A third interesting representation can be obtained from the group table itself. This is called the *regular* representation and we will make use of it later in this chapter. The basic idea is contained in Theorem 10.1: If we take some element of G, say U_ν, and multiply every group element by U_ν, we rearrange the group elements. Symbolically,

$$U_\nu U_j = U_i , \tag{10.16}$$

where i and j run through all the group elements. We translate this ordering into matrix form by saying that U_ν will be represented by a $g \times g$ matrix, $D_{ij}(U_\nu)$, where g is the order of the group. Each column will contain all zeroes except for one "1," the position of the "1" being determined from Eq. (10.16) as follows: If $U_\nu U_j = U_i$, then the ij-element of $D(U_\nu)$ is 1 and all other elements of the ith row and jth column are zero. This rule is consistent since if $U_\nu U_j = U_i$ we cannot also have $U_\nu U_k = U_i$ unless $j = k$ and, similarly, if $U_\nu U_j = U_i$ we cannot also have $U_\nu U_j = U_k$ unless $i = k$. In this representation the identity is given by the $g \times g$ unit matrix, and all the other elements of G are represented by matrices which have only zeroes on the diagonal.

We now show that this is indeed a product-preserving mapping. Consider the matrix equation

$$M = D(U_\nu)D(U_\mu) .$$

In components this is

$$M_{ij} = \sum_{k=1}^{g} D_{ik}(U_\nu)D_{kj}(U_\mu) , \qquad i, j = 1, 2, \cdots, g .$$

It follows directly from the nature of matrix multiplication that M must be the same type of matrix as $D(U_\nu)$ and $D(U_\mu)$; that is, each row and column of M can have only one nonzero element, which must equal 1. Therefore, we need only check that this one nonzero element is in the proper place. Hence suppose that $M_{ij} = 1$. Therefore, for some unique k,

$$D_{ik}(U_\nu) = 1, \qquad D_{kj}(U_\mu) = 1 .$$

These equations, in turn, mean that

$$U_\nu U_k = U_i , \qquad U_\mu U_j = U_k .$$

Hence

$$U_\nu U_\mu U_j = U_i ,$$

which says that the ij-element of $D(U_\nu U_\mu)$ is unity. Thus we can identify M_{ij} with $D_{ij}(U_\nu U_\mu)$, for *all* i and j. Hence

$$D(U_\nu U_\mu) = D(U_\nu)D(U_\mu) ,$$

so we have a representation, as claimed above.

As an example, we consider the cyclic group of order four, whose multiplication table is given in Table (10.4). We find that if we call $a_1 = e, a_2 = a$, $a_3 = b = a^2, a_4 = c = a^3$, then, for example,

$$aa_1 = ae = a = a_2 ,$$
$$aa_2 = aa = b = a_3 ,$$
$$aa_3 = aa^2 = c = a_4 ,$$
$$aa_4 = aa^3 = e = a_1 ,$$

so that the 21-, 32-, 43- and 14-elements of $D(a)$ are equal to 1, and all the other elements vanish. A similar calculation gives $D(b)$ and $D(c)$. $D(e)$ is, of course, just the unit matrix. We list the results below:

$$D(e) = \begin{bmatrix} 1 & 0 & 0 & 0 \\ 0 & 1 & 0 & 0 \\ 0 & 0 & 1 & 0 \\ 0 & 0 & 0 & 1 \end{bmatrix}, \qquad D(a) = \begin{bmatrix} 0 & 0 & 0 & 1 \\ 1 & 0 & 0 & 0 \\ 0 & 1 & 0 & 0 \\ 0 & 0 & 1 & 0 \end{bmatrix},$$

$$D(b = a^2) = \begin{bmatrix} 0 & 0 & 1 & 0 \\ 0 & 0 & 0 & 1 \\ 1 & 0 & 0 & 0 \\ 0 & 1 & 0 & 0 \end{bmatrix}, \qquad D(c = a^3) = \begin{bmatrix} 0 & 1 & 0 & 0 \\ 0 & 0 & 1 & 0 \\ 0 & 0 & 0 & 1 \\ 1 & 0 & 0 & 0 \end{bmatrix}. \quad (10.17)$$

This demonstrates the existence of a representation which is not one-dimensional; the reader can easily prove that these four matrices satisfy Table (10.4). Moreover, since each matrix is distinct, the mapping from the cyclic group is an isomorphism; such a representation is said to be *faithful*. Unfortunately, several problems seem to arise from this example. For one thing, we can use this regular representation to generate many more representations by using similarity transformations, or by using the Kronecker (or direct) product introduced in Section 3.11.

The situation regarding similarity transforms is as follows: If $D(U_i)$ is a representation of G, then for any nonsingular matrix, S, of the same dimensionality as $D(U_i)$, we define

$$\tilde{D}(U_i) \equiv S^{-1}D(U_i)S ,$$

where the tilde does not indicate the transpose of a matrix, but is merely a label. We then have

$$\tilde{D}(U_i)\tilde{D}(U_j) = S^{-1}D(U_i)SS^{-1}D(U_j)S = S^{-1}D(U_i)D(U_j)S = S^{-1}D(U_iU_j)S ,$$

since $D(U_i)$ is a representation. Thus

$$\tilde{D}(U_i)\tilde{D}(U_j) = \tilde{D}(U_iU_j) ,$$

so $\tilde{D}(U_i)$ is also a representation.

In Section 3.11, we showed that if we denote the direct product of A and B by $A \otimes B$, then

$$(A_1 \otimes B_1)(A_2 \otimes B_2) = (A_1A_2) \otimes (B_1B_2) , \quad (10.18)$$

if A_1 and A_2 (and B_1 and B_2) are of the same dimensionality. This suggests that given any two representations of a group G, say $D(U_i)$ and $D'(U_i)$, another representation can be obtained by the identification

$$U_i \longrightarrow D(U_i) \otimes D'(U_i) .$$

This preserves products, since by Eq. (10.18)

$$[D(U_i) \otimes D'(U_i)][D(U_j) \otimes D'(U_j)] = [D(U_i)D(U_j)] \otimes [D'(U_i)D'(U_j)]$$
$$= D(U_iU_j) \otimes D'(U_iU_j) .$$

Thus we have indeed constructed another representation whose dimension will be the product of the dimensions of D and D'. Since we have already found one specific multidimensional representation, the regular representation, we can use direct products to generate an arbitrarily large number of other representations. Hence the problem of classifying representations would appear to be hopeless.

Before we accept such a pessimistic conclusion, however, it is a good idea to look at the problem from a different point of view. Let us start with some simple representations and then try to work up to more complicated ones. First, we must decide how to go about finding representations. In the previous section we have already seen that one way of constructing them is to find a collection of linearly independent functions which transform among themselves under the action of the group, that is, a collection of functions $\{f_i(x)\}$ which satisfy

$$\mathcal{U}f_i(x) = \sum_j D_{ji}(U) f_j(x)$$

for all $\mathcal{U} \in \mathcal{G}$.

Now the only problem is to decide how to find a set of functions which has this nice property of transforming into itself under the action of a group of operators. One possible way would be just to pick an arbitrary function $f(x)$ and operate on it with all the $\mathcal{U}_i \in \mathcal{G}$. In this way we find a set $\{f_i(x)\}$, where

$$f_i(x) \equiv \mathcal{U}_i f(x) .$$

By the group property, this set satisfies the basic requirement of closure:

$$\mathcal{U}_\nu f_j(x) = \mathcal{U}_\nu \mathcal{U}_j f(x) = \mathcal{U}_i f(x) = f_i(x) ,$$

where i is determined by the multiplication table. If all elements of the set $\{f_i(x)\}$ are linearly independent, then we have succeeded in our aims. In this case,

$$\mathcal{U}_\nu f_j(x) = \sum_k D_{kj}(U_\nu) f_k(x) ,$$

where

$$D_{kj}(U_\nu) = \delta_{ik} ,$$

i being determined by $\mathcal{U}_\nu \mathcal{U}_j = \mathcal{U}_i$. Looking back a few paragraphs, we find that this is just the regular representation. However, this is by no means the only possibility. It might well happen that the $f_i(x)$ are not linearly independent. Then we must pick out a linearly independent subset which will, of course, also be invariant under the group operations (Why?). Carrying out the above process, we obtain in this case a representation of smaller dimension than the regular representation. Of course, it is often not necessary to do this, for one may well be able to spot a set of functions which transform among themselves without recourse to this unintuitive formalism.

Example 10.9. A particularly straightforward example is the group of rotations about the z-axis. This is an infinite, continuous group, but that is no reason to be daunted. It is, in fact, very easy to analyze this group.

Now when one talks about angles and rotations, the functions which come to mind are sines and cosines. Denoting a rotation through α by R_α ($R_\alpha \phi = \phi - \alpha$), we consider $f_1(\phi) = \cos \phi$ and $f_2(\phi) = \sin \phi$. Then

$$f_1(R_\alpha^{-1}\phi) = \cos(\phi + \alpha) = \cos \alpha f_1(\phi) - \sin \alpha f_2(\phi) ,$$
$$f_2(R_\alpha^{-1}\phi) = \sin(\phi + \alpha) = \sin \alpha f_1(\phi) + \cos \alpha f_2(\phi) .$$

From this we conclude, using Eq. (10.15), that

$$D^{(1)}(R_\alpha) = \begin{pmatrix} \cos \alpha & \sin \alpha \\ -\sin \alpha & \cos \alpha \end{pmatrix} .$$

(We use the superscript to distinguish between various representations of this group.) A simple multiplication of matrices shows that

$$D^{(1)}(R_\alpha)D^{(1)}(R_\beta) = D^{(1)}(R_{\alpha+\beta}) = D^{(1)}(R_\beta)D^{(1)}(R_\alpha) = D^{(1)}(R_\alpha R_\beta) ,$$

so we have found a two-dimensional representation.

Of course, $\cos \phi$ and $\sin \phi$ are not the only choice of functions we could have made. For instance, $e^{i\phi} = f(\phi)$ is such that

$$f(R_\alpha^{-1}\phi) = e^{i(\phi+\alpha)} = e^{i\alpha}e^{i\phi} = e^{i\alpha}f(\phi) .$$

Thus we obtain a one-dimensional representation:

$$D^{(2)}(R_\alpha) = e^{i\alpha} .$$

Similarly, if we choose $g(\phi) = e^{-i\phi}$, we find that

$$D^{(3)}(R_\alpha) = e^{-i\alpha} .$$

In fact it is clear that the function $f(\phi) = e^{im\phi}$ leads directly to a representation $D(R_\alpha) = e^{im\alpha}$. We choose m to be a positive or negative integer (or zero) so that $D(R_0) = D(R_{2\pi})$. Now since the functions $f_1(\phi) = e^{i\phi}$ and $f_2(\phi) = e^{-i\phi}$ are linearly independent we can use them together to form a set $\{f_i\}$. This leads to the two-dimensional representation

$$D^{(4)}(R_\alpha) = \begin{pmatrix} e^{i\alpha} & 0 \\ 0 & e^{-i\alpha} \end{pmatrix} .$$

This example brings us to the heart of the basic problem of representation theory. The two-dimensional representation $D^{(4)}(R_\alpha)$ is clearly just two one-dimensional representations joined together. In some sense, we would not want to call this a *basic* representation since it is compounded out of representations of lower dimensionality. The situation is complicated further if we look back at $D^{(1)}(R_\alpha)$. This does not, on the surface of things, look much like $D^{(4)}(R_\alpha)$, but if we diagonalize $D^{(1)}$, we find that

$$S^{-1}D^{(1)}(R_\alpha)S = \begin{pmatrix} e^{i\alpha} & 0 \\ 0 & e^{-i\alpha} \end{pmatrix} = D^{(4)}(R_\alpha) ,$$

where

$$S = \frac{1}{\sqrt{2}}\begin{pmatrix} 1 & i \\ i & 1 \end{pmatrix}$$

is a matrix independent of α. Thus we have a similarity transformation which will bring $D^{(1)}(R_\alpha)$ to exactly the form of $D^{(4)}(R_\alpha)$, and this can be done simultaneously for *all* R_α. Thus, even $D^{(1)}(R_\alpha)$ is essentially a sum of the two one-dimensional representations, $D^{(2)}$ and $D^{(3)}$.

This can also be the case for more complicated situations. For example, the four matrices composing the regular representation of the four-element cyclic group [Eq. (10.17)] can be diagonalized simultaneously by the matrix

$$
S' = \begin{bmatrix} 1 & 1 & 1 & 1 \\ -1 & 1 & i & -i \\ 1 & 1 & -1 & -1 \\ -1 & 1 & -i & i \end{bmatrix}.
$$

Therefore $D(e)$, $D(a)$, $D(b)$, and $D(c)$ are each sums of four one-dimensional representations.

We can generalize this as follows: If we find a representation $D(U_i)$ which can be brought to the form

$$
\bar{D}(U_i) \equiv SD(U_i)S^{-1} = \begin{bmatrix} D^{(1)}(U_i) & & \mathbf{O} \\ & U^{(2)}(D_i) & \\ \mathbf{O} & & D^{(3)}(U_i) \end{bmatrix}, \qquad (10.19)
$$

where S is the same for all U_i, then we will not consider it as a basic representation, but rather as a sum of representations.

In terms of the functions $f_i(x)$, this means that although we have found a linearly independent set $\{f_i\}$, the elements of which transform among themselves, there are actually smaller subsets which also transform into themselves under the group in question.

Representations of the type of Eq. (10.19) are called *reducible* representations; those which cannot be reduced in this manner are called *irreducible* representations. It is clearly the irreducible representations of groups that we should study, since other representations are simply built up out of them. However, even among irreducible representations we do not want to count the similarity transformation of a representation as a separate representation. Two representations which are related by a similarity transform are said to be *equivalent*. Thus, in Eq. (10.19), assuming $D^{(1)}$, $D^{(2)}$, and $D^{(3)}$ to be irreducible and inequivalent, we would write symbolically

$$
D(U_i) = D^{(1)}(U_i) \oplus D^{(2)}(U_i) \oplus D^{(3)}(U_i)
$$

for all $U_i \in G$. In practice, when we reduce a representation to this form, a given irreducible representation may occur more than once. Thus we would write generally

$$
D(U_i) = a^{(1)}D^{(1)}(U_i) \oplus a^{(2)}D^{(2)}(U_i) \oplus \cdots \oplus a^{(N)}D^{(N)}(U_i) , \qquad (10.20)
$$

where $a^{(\nu)}$ is the number of times the irreducible representation $D^{(\nu)}(U_i)$, or any representation equivalent to it, appears in the decomposition.

A very useful characterization of a representation which is the same for all equivalent representations, is given by the *trace* of the representative matrices. The trace of $D(U)$ is denoted by $\chi(U)$ and is called the *character* of U in the representation in question. Since

$$\text{tr}\,[C^{-1}D(U)C] = \text{tr}\,[D(U)] \equiv \chi(U)\ ,$$

the character of U is the same for all equivalent representations. When we are dealing with an irreducible representation, $D^{(\nu)}(U)$, we will write for the corresponding character $\chi^{(\nu)}(U)$. Now within a given representation, many of the characters will be the same. In fact, consider a class, $\mathscr{C}_i$, of conjugate elements of the group G. Then if U_ν, $U_\mu \in \mathscr{C}_i$, there exists some $U_\lambda \in G$ such that

$$U_\nu = U_\lambda U_\mu U_\lambda^{-1}\ .$$

This means that

$$D(U_\nu) = D(U_\lambda)D(U_\mu)D(U_\lambda^{-1})\ ,$$

and hence

$$\begin{aligned}\chi(U_\nu) &\equiv \text{tr}\,[D(U_\nu)] = \text{tr}\,[D(U_\lambda)D(U_\mu)D(U_\lambda^{-1})]\\ &= \text{tr}\,[D(U_\lambda^{-1})D(U_\lambda)D(U_\mu)] = \text{tr}\,[D(U_\mu)] \equiv \chi(U_\mu)\ ,\end{aligned}$$

that is, all elements of $\mathscr{C}_i$ have the same character. For this reason one can, with no ambiguity, refer to $\chi_i^{(\nu)}$ as the character of the ith class in the νth irreducible representation, thereby removing the necessity of referring explicitly to the group elements. Thus in a group with k classes, for a given representation, ν, there are k characteristic numbers,

$$\chi_1^{(\nu)},\ \chi_2^{(\nu)},\ \cdots,\ \chi_k^{(\nu)}$$

to be determined. These k constants, in fact, provide a surprisingly large amount of information about the group, as we will see in the following sections.

10.6 UNITARY REPRESENTATIONS, SCHUR'S LEMMAS, AND ORTHOGONALITY RELATIONS

In this section we will develop the main results of representation theory, which will enable us to determine irreducible representations. To begin, we prove a theorem which restricts tremendously the possible forms which a representation can take.

Theorem 10.6. Every representation of a finite group is equivalent to a unitary representation.

Proof. The first step is to construct an inner product in the n-dimensional vector space, V, of the representation and show that the representation is unitary with respect to this inner product. For $x, y \in V$, we denote the usual inner product of x and y by the familiar (x, y); in terms of this inner product, we define a new inner product as follows:

$$\{x, y\} = \sum_{U \in G} (D(U)x, D(U)y) , \qquad (10.21)$$

where D is any representation of G. It is easy to check that since $(\ ,\ )$ is an inner product and since $D^{-1}(U)$ exists for all $U \in G$, $\{\ ,\ \}$ will also satisfy all the inner-product axioms. Consider now any $D(U')$. We want to show that

$$\{D(U')x, D(U')y\} = \{x, y\} .$$

From Eq. (10.21), we have

$$\{D(U')x, D(U')y\} = \sum_{U \in G} (D(U)D(U')x, D(U)D(U')y)$$

$$= \sum_{U \in G} (D(UU')x, D(UU')y) . \qquad (10.22)$$

But as U runs through all the elements of G, so does UU', according to Theorem 10.1. Of course, the ordering may be different, but that is immaterial. Hence

$$\sum_{U \in G} (D(UU')x, D(UU')y) = \sum_{\tilde{U} \in G} (D(\tilde{U})x, D(\tilde{U})y) = \{x, y\} . \qquad (10.23)$$

Combining Eqs. (10.22) and (10.23), we get

$$\{D(U')x, D(U')y\} = \{x, y\}$$

for any $U' \in G$, as required.

But to say that $D(U')$ is unitary with respect to some special inner product is simply to say that we have written $D(U')$ in an inconvenient basis. By a similarity transformation we can easily correct this difficulty and make D unitary with respect to the original inner product. Let $\{\xi_i\}$ be a complete orthonormal basis with respect to the inner product $(\ ,\ )$ and let $\{\eta_i\}$ be a complete orthonormal basis with respect to the special inner product $\{\ ,\ \}$. We define a linear operator S on V by

$$\eta_i = S\xi_i , \qquad i = 1, 2, \cdots, n . \qquad (10.24)$$

Note that with this definition for any $x, y \in V$

$$\{Sx, Sy\} = (x, y) , \qquad (10.25a)$$

or

$$(S^{-1}x, S^{-1}y) = \{x, y\} . \qquad (10.25b)$$

This follows by expanding x and y in the $\{\xi_i\}$ basis:

$$x = \sum_{i=1}^{n} a_i \xi_i , \qquad y = \sum_{j=1}^{n} b_j \xi_j .$$

Then

$$\{Sx, Sy\} = \sum_{i,j=1}^{n} a_i^* b_j \{S\xi_i, S\xi_j\} = \sum_{i,j=1}^{n} a_i^* b_j \{\eta_i, \eta_j\} ,$$

by use of Eq. (10.24). Since the η_i form an orthonormal set with respect to $\{\ ,\ \}$, we have

$$\{Sx, Sy\} = \sum_{i,j=1}^{n} a_i^* b_j \delta_{ij} = \sum_{i=1}^{n} a_i^* b_i = (x, y)\ ,$$

which is just Eq. (10.25a). S is precisely the operator we need to transform the original representation.

For any $U \in G$, we define

$$\tilde{D}(U) \equiv S^{-1}D(U)S\ .$$

Consider

$$(\tilde{D}(U)x, \tilde{D}(U)y) = (S^{-1}D(U)Sx, S^{-1}D(U)Sy)\ .$$

By Eq. (10.25b), we have immediately

$$(\tilde{D}(U)x, \tilde{D}(U)y) = \{D(U)Sx, D(U)Sy\}\ .$$

But with respect to $\{\ ,\ \}$ $D(U)$ is unitary, so

$$(\tilde{D}(U)x, \tilde{D}(U)y) = \{Sx, Sy\}\ .$$

Finally, Eq. (10.25a) gives

$$(\tilde{D}(U)x, \tilde{D}(U)y) = (x, y)\ ,$$

so $\tilde{D}(U)$ is unitary with respect to the original inner product.

According to this theorem, we can restrict ourselves to unitary matrices in our search for irreducible representations. Note that although we have stated this theorem for finite groups, we have made very little use of the finite order of G, using it only in Eq. (10.21) to write the sum over all $U \in G$. This sum is finite since it contains only a finite number of terms. For many infinite groups, it is possible to make the transition from discrete sums to integrals over a continuous parameter; for example, in the case of continuous groups such a possibility is evident. However, even if it is possible to replace sums over group elements by integrals over group elements, it may be that the integral formulation of Eq. (10.21) will not be meaningful because the integrations run over an infinite range and are divergent. Nevertheless, there are many groups, such as the rotation groups, where this does not happen, and for them Theorem 10.6 is valid, the proof being identical to the one presented here, save for the presence of integrals instead of summations.

The fact that the matrices in a representation are equivalent to unitary representations is a very powerful result. From it follows the two main theorems of representation theory, the first and second lemmas of Schur. The proof of these two important group theoretical results hinges on the following lemma, which has nothing to do with group theory.

Lemma. If a matrix, M, commutes with a unitary matrix, U, and if we write $M = M_+ + iM_-$, where $M_+ = (M + M^\dagger)/2$ and $M_- = (M - M^\dagger)/2i$, then both M_+ and M_- commute with U.

Proof. If

$$UM = MU,\tag{10.26}$$

then

$$M^\dagger U^\dagger = U^\dagger M^\dagger .$$

Multiplying on the left by U, we get

$$UM^\dagger U^\dagger = UU^\dagger M^\dagger = M^\dagger ,$$

since U is unitary. Multiplying this last equation on the right by U, we find that

$$UM^\dagger U^\dagger U = M^\dagger U .$$

Thus, using the unitarity of U once more,

$$UM^\dagger = M^\dagger U .\tag{10.27}$$

Combining Eqs. (10.26) and (10.27), we readily obtain

$$U\left[\frac{M + M^\dagger}{2}\right] = \left[\frac{M + M^\dagger}{2}\right]U ,\tag{10.28a}$$

$$U\left[\frac{M - M^\dagger}{2i}\right] = \left[\frac{M - M^\dagger}{2i}\right]U ,\tag{10.28b}$$

or

$$UM_+ = M_+U , \qquad UM_- = M_-U ,$$

as required.

    With this lemma at our disposal, we now prove the main result of this section.

    Lemma (Schur). If $D(U)$ is an element of an irreducible representation of G and if $D(U)M = MD(U)$ for all $U \in G$, then M must be a multiple of the unit matrix.

Proof. According to the previous lemma, if $MD(U) = D(U)M$ for all $U \in G$ and if we write

$$M = M_+ + iM_- ,\tag{10.29}$$

then since the representation can be taken to be unitary,

$$M_+D(U) = D(U)M_+ \qquad \text{and} \qquad M_-D(U) = D(U)M_-$$

for all $U \in G$. $M_+ = (M + M^\dagger)/2$ and $M_- = (M - M^\dagger)/2i$ are both self-adjoint, so let us begin by considering the eigenvalue problem associated with M_+:

$$M_+x_n^{(i)} = \lambda_n x_n^{(i)} , \qquad i = 1, 2, \cdots, m_n ,$$

where m_n is the multiplicity of λ_n. Since M_+ is Hermitian, the set of all $x_n^{(i)}$ spans the N-dimensional space of the representation. For all $U \in G$, we have

$$D(U)M_+x_n^{(i)} = \lambda_n D(U)x_n^{(i)} .$$

But $[D(U), M_+] = 0$, so this is just

$$M_+[D(U)x_n^{(i)}] = \lambda_n[D(U)x_n^{(i)}] .$$

Since $D(U)x_n^{(i)}$ is an eigenvector of M_+ belonging to λ_n, it must be a linear combination of the $x_n^{(i)}$ ($i = 1, 2, \cdots, m_n$):

$$D(U)x_n^{(i)} = \sum_{j=1}^{m_n} a_{ij}(U)x_n^{(j)} \tag{10.30}$$

for all $U \in G$. Let us compute the matrix D in the space spanned by the eigenvectors of M_+. We take $n = 1$ first. Using Eq. (10.30), we find that

$$(x_1^{(l)}, D(U)x_1^{(i)}) = \sum_{j=1}^{m_1} a_{ij}(U)(x_1^{(l)}, x_1^{(j)}) = a_{il}(U) , \qquad i, l = 1, 2, \cdots, m_1 ,$$

$$\tag{10.31a}$$

for all $U \in G$. For any $n \neq 1$, Eq. (10.30) tells us directly that

$$(x_n^{(l)}, D(U)x_1^{(i)}) = 0 ; \qquad l = 1, 2, \cdots, m_n , \quad i = 1, 2, \cdots, m_1 , \tag{10.31b}$$

for all $U \in G$, since the eigenvectors belonging to different eigenvalues of an Hermitian operator are orthogonal. Similarly, for $n \neq 1$, we also have from Eq. (10.30)

$$(x_1^{(l)}, D(U)x_n^{(i)}) = 0; \qquad l = 1, 2, \cdots, m_1 , \quad i = 1, 2, \cdots, m_n . \tag{10.31c}$$

Equations (10.31a), (10.31b), and (10.31c) mean that the matrix $D(U)$ looks like

$$D(U) = \left(\begin{array}{c|c} m_1 \times m_1 & 0 \\ \hline 0 & (N - m_1) \times (N - m_1) \end{array} \right) ,$$

for all $U \in G$, where N is the dimension of the representation. The $m_1 \times m_1$ matrix in the upper left-hand corner has elements which are given by the $a_{ij}(U)$ defined in Eq. (10.30). But the representation is assumed to be irreducible, so this can only be the case if $m_1 = N$; that is, the multiplicity of λ_1 must be equal to N, the dimensionality of the representation. The only Hermitian matrix having an eigenvalue whose multiplicity equals the dimension of the matrix is a real constant times the unit matrix. Thus $M_+ = c_+I$. Similarly, $M_- = c_-I$, so we obtain from Eq. (10.29) $M = (c_+ + ic_-)I$, and the proof is complete.

As an immediate corollary (really no more than a restatement) of this lemma, we have:

Corollary. If there exists a matrix which commutes with every element of a representation and is *not* a multiple of the unit matrix, then the representation is necessarily reducible.

At this point it is perhaps a good idea to say a word about a more abstract way of looking at irreducible representations which may clarify the situation, as well as boil down the preceding pages into a few words.

As a careful reading of the previous section shows, we can characterize the irreducible representations of a group, G, of order g in a more abstract manner as follows. Let

$$\mathscr{G} = \{D(U_i), \quad i = 1, 2, \cdots, g\}$$

be a group of linear operators on an n-dimensional vector space, V, and let this group of operators be homomorphic to G, that is, $\mathscr{G}$ is a representation of G. $\mathscr{G}$ is said to be an *irreducible* representation of G if no *proper* subspace of V is left invariant (i.e., mapped into itself) under all $D \in \mathscr{G}$. (The proper subspaces of V are all subspaces of V *except* for V itself.) It may of course happen that some *subset* of $\mathscr{G}$ leaves invariant some proper subspace of V, but if we have an irreducible representation, then $\mathscr{G}$ in its entirety must leave only V invariant. Obviously, if we look just at one unitary $D(U) \in \mathscr{G}$, then it will have n invariant subspaces, defined by the n orthonormal eigenvectors of $D(U)$.

In light of this, Schur's first lemma has a very simple meaning: If there is a matrix which commutes with $D(U)$ for all $U \in G$, the linearly independent eigenvectors of this matrix define a collection of subspaces of V which are invariant under $D(U)$ for all $U \in G$. The only admissible invariant subspace is V itself, and the only matrix which has every vector in V as an eigenvector is the unit matrix or a multiple thereof.

A simple, but very useful, consequence of Schur's first lemma is the fact that an abelian group can have only one-dimensional irreducible representations! This follows immediately from the statement that if G is abelian, then for any $U \in G$, $D(U)$ commutes with all elements of the representation D. Thus, by Schur's first lemma, for all $U \in G$,

$$D(U) = C(U)I,$$

where $C(U)$ is a constant which can depend on U. The unit matrix is irreducible only when it is the one-dimensional unit matrix. Thus, for an abelian group, all irreducible representations must be one-dimensional.

Schur's second lemma gives an analogous result for two *different* representations.

Lemma. Let $D(U)$ and $D'(U)$ be irreducible representations. If for all $U \in G$, $D(U)M = MD'(U)$, then either D and D' are equivalent or else $M = 0$.

Proof. In general, D and D' will have different dimensions, so that M need not be a square matrix. If D is $n \times n$ and D' is $m \times m$, then M must be $n \times m$. The proof starts out in the same direction as that of the first lemma. As before

$$D(U)M = MD'(U) \tag{10.32}$$

for all $U \in G$ implies that

$$M^\dagger D^\dagger(U) = D'^\dagger(U)M^\dagger$$

for all $U \in G$, where $M^\dagger$ is an $m \times n$ matrix, $(M^\dagger)_{ij} = M_{ji}^*$. Taking $D(U)$ to be unitary, we find that

$$M^\dagger D(U^{-1}) = D'(U^{-1})M^\dagger. \tag{10.33}$$

Multiplying Eq. (10.33) from the left by M, we get

$$MM^\dagger D(U^{-1}) = MD'(U^{-1})M^\dagger. \tag{10.34}$$

But by Eq. (10.32),

$$MD'(U^{-1})M^\dagger = D(U^{-1})MM^\dagger,$$

so Eq. (10.34) becomes

$$MM^\dagger D(U^{-1}) = D(U^{-1})MM^\dagger$$

for all $U \in G$. The previous lemma (and the uniqueness of inverses) tells us straightaway that

$$MM^\dagger = cI.$$

We leave it to the reader to show in the same way that multiplying Eq. (10.33) on the right by M leads to

$$M^\dagger M = cI.$$

It should be observed that the matrices $MM^\dagger$ and $M^\dagger M$ have different dimensions, the former being $n \times n$, the latter $m \times m$.

We now consider three cases separately:

(i) $m = n$. Then if $c = 0$, we have $MM^\dagger = 0$, which means that for all i,

$$(MM^\dagger)_{ii} = 0 = \sum_{j=1}^{n} M_{ij}(M^\dagger)_{ji} = \sum_{j=1}^{n} |M_{ij}|^2.$$

Thus, for all i,

$$\sum_{j=1}^{n} |M_{ij}|^2 = 0,$$

so we conclude that $M_{ij} = 0$, for all i and j, and $M = 0$. (For a slightly stronger result see Problem 3.14) If, on the other hand, $c \neq 0$, then

$$\det(MM^\dagger) \neq 0,$$

so $\det M \neq 0$, and M is invertible. Thus according to Eq. (10.32),

$$D(U) = MD'(U)M^{-1}$$

for all $U \in G$, therefore D and D' are equivalent representations.

(ii) $n > m$. In this case, we make M into a square matrix by filling in $n - m$ columns of zeros. Calling the new matrix N, we have

$$N = \begin{pmatrix} \overset{\longleftarrow m \longrightarrow}{} & \overset{\leftarrow n-m \rightarrow}{} \\ M & 0 \end{pmatrix} \Big\updownarrow n \;, \qquad N^\dagger = \begin{pmatrix} \overset{\longleftarrow n \longrightarrow}{} \\ M^\dagger \\ \hline 0 \end{pmatrix} \begin{matrix} \updownarrow m \\ \updownarrow n-m \end{matrix}.$$

It is clear that $MM^\dagger = NN^\dagger$, so $MM^\dagger = cI$ implies that $NN^\dagger = cI$. Now

$$\det(NN^\dagger) = c^n = (\det N)(\det N^\dagger),$$

but from the form of N, we see that det $N = 0$, so the constant, c, must vanish. Thus

$$NN^\dagger = 0 = MM^\dagger$$

and, just as in case (i), we conclude that $M = 0$.

(iii) $m > n$. In this case, we must add $m - n$ rows of zeros to M to turn it into a square matrix. Again denoting the new matrix by N, we have

In this case, $NN^\dagger \neq MM^\dagger$, but we do have $N^\dagger N = M^\dagger M$. Thus, using the relation $M^\dagger M = cI$ instead of $MM^\dagger = cI$, we see that the new matrix N satisfies

$$N^\dagger N = cI ;$$

as in case (i), we conclude that $N = 0$. Hence $M = 0$ as well, and the proof of the lemma is complete.

Note that in proving these lemmas, we have not made direct reference to the number of elements in the group G. We have actually proved these results for any finite-dimensional *unitary* representation. Of course, Theorem 10.6 tells us that for a finite group the representations can always be chosen to be unitary. But Schur's two lemmas hold also for the important class of infinite groups which have finite-dimensional unitary representations.

The reason that these two lemmas are so important is that it turns out to be rather easy to find matrices, M, which satisfy the conditions of the lemmas. These matrices in turn provide us with a vast amount of information about the irreducible representations and their characters. One simple example of a matrix which satisfies the conditions of Schur's first lemma is defined by

$$M_i^{(\nu)} = \sum_{U \in \mathscr{C}_i} D^{(\nu)}(U) . \tag{10.35}$$

$M_i^{(\nu)}$ is just the sum of all representative matrices of the elements of the class $\mathscr{C}_i$ in the νth irreducible representation. Now let U' be any element of G and consider the quantity

$$D^{(\nu)}(U') M_i^{(\nu)} D^{(\nu)}(U')^{-1} .$$

We have

$$D^{(\nu)}(U') M_i^{(\nu)} D^{(\nu)}(U')^{-1} = \sum_{U \in \mathscr{C}_i} D^{(\nu)}(U') D^{(\nu)}(U) D^{(\nu)}(U'^{-1})$$

$$= \sum_{U \in \mathscr{C}_i} D^{(\nu)}(U' U U'^{-1}) .$$

But by the definition of a class, if $U \in \mathscr{C}_i$, then $U' U U'^{-1} \in \mathscr{C}_i$. Since a similarity transformation just rearranges the elements of $\mathcal{C}_i$, we have from the previous equation

$$D^{(\nu)}(U')M_i^{(\nu)}D^{(\nu)}(U')^{-1} = \sum_{\tilde{U} \in \mathcal{C}_i} D^{(\nu)}(\tilde{U}) = M_i^{(\nu)} \,.$$

Thus, for all $U' \in G$,

$$D^{(\nu)}(U')M_i^{(\nu)} = M_i^{(\nu)}D^{(\nu)}(U') \,,$$

so $M_i^{(\nu)}$ satisfies the requirements of Schur's first lemma. We conclude that

$$M_i^{(\nu)} = c_i^{(\nu)}I \,.$$

The constant $c_i^{(\nu)}$ can be readily evaluated. We have, calling the dimension of the νth representation n_ν,

$$\operatorname{tr} M_i^{(\nu)} = c_i^{(\nu)}n_\nu \,. \tag{10.36}$$

But

$$\operatorname{tr} M_i^{(\nu)} = \sum_{U \in \mathcal{C}_i} \operatorname{tr} D^{(\nu)}(U) = \sum_{U \in \mathcal{C}_i} \chi^{(\nu)}(U) \,.$$

The trace of all the representative matrices in a given class is the same, as was pointed out at the end of the last section. Hence using the notation established there, we have

$$\operatorname{tr} M_i^{(\nu)} = g_i \chi_i^{(\nu)} \,, \tag{10.37}$$

where g_i is the number of elements in the class $\mathcal{C}_i$. Combining Eqs. (10.36) and (10.37), we obtain

$$c_i^{(\nu)} = \frac{g_i}{n_\nu} \chi_i^{(\nu)} \,.$$

Therefore

$$M_i^{(\nu)} = \frac{g_i}{n_\nu} \chi_i^{(\nu)} I \,, \tag{10.38}$$

that is, the sum of all the representative matrices in a given class is a simple multiple of the unit matrix. We shall soon have occasion to make use of this result.

A more fruitful example of a matrix which fulfills all the requirements of Schur's lemmas is the following:

$$M = \sum_{U \in G} D^{(\nu)}(U)XD^{(\mu)}(U^{-1}) = \sum_{U \in G} D^{(\nu)}(U)XD^{(\mu)}(U)^{-1} \,,$$

where $D^{(\nu)}$ and $D^{(\mu)}$ are irreducible representations and X is an arbitrary matrix, although in order for this expression to have any meaning, X must have n_ν rows and n_μ columns. Multiplying on the left by $D^{(\nu)}(U')$ and on the right by $D^{(\mu)}(U')^{-1}$, we find that

$$D^{(\nu)}(U')MD^{(\mu)}(U')^{-1} = \sum_{U \in G} D^{(\nu)}(U')D^{(\nu)}(U)XD^{(\mu)}(U)^{-1}D^{(\mu)}(U')^{-1}$$

$$= \sum_{U \in G} D^{(\nu)}(U'U)XD^{(\mu)}(U^{-1}U'^{-1}) \,.$$

Calling $\tilde{U} = U'U$ and remembering that $\tilde{U}^{-1} = U^{-1}U'^{-1}$, we have

$$D^{(\nu)}(U')MD^{(\mu)}(U')^{-1} = \sum_{U \in G} D^{(\nu)}(\tilde{U})XD^{(\mu)}(\tilde{U})^{-1} . \qquad (10.39)$$

But as U runs through the entire group, so does $\tilde{U} = U'U$, although in a different order. Thus the right-hand side of Eq. (10.39) is just equal to M, and

$$D^{(\nu)}(U')M = MD^{(\mu)}(U') \qquad (10.40)$$

for all $U' \in G$. Assuming that $D^{(\nu)}$ is not equivalent to $D^{(\mu)}$ (in the case $n_\nu = n_\mu$), we have by Schur's lemmas

$$M = c(X)I\delta_{\nu\mu} .$$

In other words, $M = 0$ if the representations have different dimensionality (Schur's second lemma) and $M = cI$ if they have the same dimensionality (Schur's first lemma). The value of the constant depends, of course, on the choice of X. Thus we arrive at the result

$$\sum_{U \in G} D^{(\nu)}(U)XD^{(\mu)}(U)^{-1} = c(X)I\delta_{\mu\nu} . \qquad (10.41)$$

If $D^{(\nu)}$ and $D^{(\mu)}$ are chosen to be unitary, this can also be written as

$$\sum_{U \in G} D^{(\nu)}(U)XD^{(\mu)\dagger}(U) = c(X)I\delta_{\mu\nu} . \qquad (10.42)$$

To exploit this equation, let us write it in component form:

$$\sum_{U \in G} \sum_{i',l'} D^{(\nu)}_{ii'}(U) \, X_{i'l'} \, [D^{(\mu)\dagger}(U)]_{l'l} = c(X)\delta_{il}\delta_{\mu\nu} .$$

Now suppose that we choose the matrix X so that all its elements are zero except for the jk-element. Denoting the related $c(X)$ by c_{jk}, we have

$$\sum_{U \in G} D^{(\nu)}_{ij}(U)[D^{(\mu)\dagger}(U)]_{kl} = c_{jk}\delta_{il}\delta_{\mu\nu} . \qquad (10.43)$$

Since

$$(A^\dagger)_{kl} = A^*_{lk} ,$$

we obtain from Eq. (10.43)

$$\sum_{U \in G} D^{(\mu)*}_{lk}(U)D^{(\nu)}_{ij}(U) = c_{jk}\delta_{il}\delta_{\mu\nu} , \qquad (10.44)$$

for all i, j, k, l, μ, and ν.

All that remains is to determine c_{jk}. To do this, we set $\mu = \nu$, $l = i$ and sum on i. Thus

$$\sum_{U \in G} \sum_{i} D^{(\nu)*}_{ik}(U)D^{(\nu)}_{ij}(U) = c_{jk} \sum_{i} \delta_{ii} = c_{jk}n_\nu .$$

But since $D^{(\nu)}$ is unitary, the sum on i on the left-hand side of this equation is just equal to δ_{kj}. Hence

$$c_{jk}n_\nu = \sum_{U \in G} \delta_{jk} = g\delta_{jk} ,$$

where g is the order of the group. Therefore

$$c_{jk} = \frac{g}{n_\nu} \delta_{jk} ,$$

and we have finally from Eq. (10.44) the remarkable orthogonality theorem,

$$\sum_{U \in G} D_{lk}^{(\mu)*}(U) D_{ij}^{(\nu)}(U) = \frac{g}{n_\nu} \delta_{jk} \delta_{il} \delta_{\mu\nu} , \qquad (10.45)$$

for all i, j, k, l, μ, and ν.

Now let us see what this means in simple terms. The sum on the left-hand side of Eq. (10.45) looks very much like an inner product of two vectors, except that the sum is over the elements of a group rather than a conventional subscript. However, there is no law against indexing the components of a vector by using the elements of a group. We may say, therefore, that Eq. (10.45) is an ortho-gonality relationship for the inner product of two g-dimensional vectors, each vector being identified by three labels. Equation (10.45) says that if, from any irreducible representation we pick the ij-element of the representative matrices, then this gives us a g-dimensional vector which is orthogonal to the g-dimen-sional vector obtained from any other element, say the $i'j'$-element, and *also* to any vector obtained in this way from any *other* representation. Thus in the g-dimensional space we have $n_1^2 + n_2^2 + \cdots + n_N^2$ orthogonal vectors, where N is the number of inequivalent irreducible representations. Since the number of orthogonal vectors in a g-dimensional space cannot exceed g, we must have

$$\sum_{\nu=1}^{N} n_\nu^2 \le g . \qquad (10.46)$$

Thus we arrive at the important result that a finite group can have only a finite number of inequivalent irreducible representations, all of which must have di-mension less than $\sqrt{g}$.

From Eq. (10.45) it is a simple matter to obtain an orthogonality relation for the characters of a representation. In Eq. (10.45), if one sets $k = l$ and sums on l, one finds that

$$\sum_{U \in G} \sum_{l=1}^{n_\mu} D_{ll}^{(\mu)*}(U) D_{ij}^{(\nu)}(U) = \frac{g}{n_\nu} \delta_{\mu\nu} \sum_{l=1}^{n_\mu} \delta_{il} \delta_{lj} = \frac{g}{n_\nu} \delta_{\mu\nu} \delta_{ij} .$$

But

$$\sum_{l} D_{ll}^{(\mu)*}(U) = \mathrm{tr}\, D^{(\mu)*}(U) = \chi^{(\mu)*}(U) , \qquad (10.47)$$

so

$$\sum_{U \in G} \chi^{(\mu)*}(U) D_{ij}^{(\nu)}(U) = \frac{g}{n_\nu} \delta_{\mu\nu} \delta_{ij} .$$

Finally, setting $i = j$ and summing on j, we find that

$$\sum_{U \in G} \chi^{(\mu)*}(U) \sum_{j=1}^{n_\nu} D_{jj}^{(\nu)}(U) = \frac{g}{n_\nu} \delta_{\mu\nu} \sum_{j=1}^{n_\nu} \delta_{jj} = g \delta_{\mu\nu} .$$

Using Eq. (10.47) once more, we arrive at

$$\sum_{U \in G} \chi^{(\mu)*}(U)\chi^{(\nu)}(U) = g\delta_{\mu\nu} . \qquad (10.48)$$

Since all the members of a given class have the same character, we can convert the sum on $U \in G$ in Eq. (10.48) into a sum on the classes. If g_i equals the number of elements in $\mathscr{C}_i$, and if k denotes the number of classes, Eq. (10.48) becomes

$$\sum_{i=1}^{k} g_i \chi_i^{(\mu)*} \chi_i^{(\nu)} = g\delta_{\mu\nu} . \qquad (10.49)$$

Equation (10.49) tells us that the N nonequivalent irreducible representations provide us with N k-dimensional orthogonal vectors via the class characters. Since in a k-dimensional space there cannot be more than k orthogonal vectors, we conclude that

$$N \leq k . \qquad (10.50)$$

In the case of abelian groups, Eq. (10.50) has the same content as Eq. (10.46). Since abelian groups have only one-dimensional representations, we have

$$\sum_{\nu=1}^{N} n_\nu^2 = \sum_{\nu=1}^{N} 1 = N .$$

So Eq. (10.46) becomes

$$N \leq g .$$

On the other hand, for an abelian group every element forms a separate class. Thus $k = g$, and Eq. (10.50) becomes

$$N \leq g .$$

Hence both Eqs. (10.46) and (10.50) lead to the same inequality for an abelian group.

It is also worth noting that in deriving the orthogonality relations of Eqs. (10.45) and (10.49), we have been writing sums on group elements quite freely. However, there are, as mentioned before, cases involving infinite groups where the sum can be replaced by an integration. Furthermore, for certain groups, integrals over the entire group will be convergent, and the proofs of this section will hold virtually unchanged. As a simple example, we look briefly at the group of rotations about the z-axis. We have already found the one-dimensional representations

$$D^{(m)}(\alpha) = e^{im\alpha} . \qquad (10.51)$$

The logical candidate for integration variable for this group is clearly α, with infinitesimal element $d\alpha$. For this case, we expect $\sum_{U \in G}$ to be replaced by $\int_0^{2\pi} d\alpha$. In particular, since

$$g = \sum_{U \in G} 1 ,$$

we expect g to be replaced by

$$\int_0^{2\pi} 1 d\alpha = 2\pi$$

in this case. For groups of this type we refer to g as the volume of the group. According to the above speculations, we would expect Eq. (10.45) to read

$$\int_0^{2\pi} D^{(m)} {}^* (\alpha) D^{(n)} (\alpha) d\alpha = 2\pi \, \delta_{mn} \, , \tag{10.52}$$

since the dimension of all representations is 1. We see that if $D^{(m)} (\alpha)$ is given by Eq. (10.51), then Eq. (10.52) is obeyed. Similar considerations can be applied to other continuous groups, such as the rotation group and the unitary groups. However, there are exceptions to this simple-minded type of extension of the theory of finite groups, the most significant one being the Lorentz group.

10.7 THE DETERMINATION OF GROUP REPRESENTATIONS

In this section we want to apply the major theorems proved thus far to the problem of actually finding group representations. In doing so, we shall also be able to sharpen slightly the orthogonality relations obtained in the previous section so that they become completeness relations.

First, we note that the characters of a representation, D, which is *not* irreducible can be simply written in terms of those of the irreducible representations. If D is written in the form of Eq. (10.19)—as it always can be by use of a similarity transformation—then the character, χ_i, of a given class will have the form

$$\chi_i = a^{(1)} \chi_i^{(1)} + a^{(2)} \chi_i^{(2)} + \cdots + a^{(N)} \chi_i^{(N)} \equiv \sum_{\nu=1}^N a^{(\nu)} \chi_i^{(\nu)} \, . \tag{10.53}$$

This follows directly from the definition of the characters in terms of the trace of the representative matrices. $a^{(\nu)}$ is just the number of times the νth irreducible representation occurs in the decomposition of D given by Eq. (10.20). Multiplying Eq. (10.53) on both sides by $g_i \chi_i^{(\mu) *}$, summing on i, and using the orthogonality relation Eq. (10.49), we get

$$\sum_{i=1}^k g_i \chi_i^{(\mu) *} \chi_i = \sum_{\nu=1}^N a^{(\nu)} \sum_{i=1}^k g_i \chi_i^{(\mu) *} \chi_i^{(\nu)} = \sum_{\nu=1}^N g a^{(\nu)} \delta_{\mu\nu} = g a^{(\mu)} \, .$$

Hence

$$a^{(\mu)} = \frac{1}{g} \sum_{i=1}^k g_i \chi_i^{(\mu) *} \chi_i \, , \tag{10.54}$$

so the number of times a given irreducible representation occurs in an arbitrary representation is readily determined from the characters of that representation. Thus if two representations have the same characters they must be equivalent, since the $a^{(\mu)}$ will then be the same for all of them.

As an example, let us apply Eqs. (10.53) and (10.54) to the regular representation discussed in Section 10.5. This special case will lead to several useful results. The characters of the regular representation are easily determined. Since its dimensionality is g (the number of elements of G), the character χ_1 of the identity class will be equal to the trace of the g-dimensional unit matrix:

$$\chi_1 = g . \tag{10.55}$$

All other characters vanish, since all other representative matrices have only zeros on the diagonal, as was pointed out in Section 10.5. Hence

$$\chi_i = 0 , \qquad i \neq 1 . \tag{10.56}$$

Thus Eq. (10.53) becomes, for $i = 1$,

$$g = \sum_{\nu=1}^{N} a^{(\nu)} \chi_1^{(\nu)} .$$

But in any representation of dimension n_ν, the character of the identity class is just n_ν, the trace of the n_ν-dimensional unit matrix. Thus

$$g = \sum_{\nu=1}^{N} a^{(\nu)} n_\nu . \tag{10.57}$$

On the other hand, using Eqs. (10.55) and (10.56) together with the fact that $g_1 = 1$, we find from Eq. (10.54) that

$$a^{(\mu)} = \frac{1}{g} g_1 \chi_1^{(\mu)*} \chi_1 = \chi_1^{(\mu)*} = n_\mu , \tag{10.58}$$

so Eq. (10.57) becomes

$$g = \sum_{\nu=1}^{N} n_\nu^2 . \tag{10.59}$$

Equation (10.58) says that in the regular representation *every* irreducible representation occurs precisely as many times as its dimensionality. Equation (10.59) is a much stronger result than Eq. (10.46). It tells us that the $D_{ij}^{(\nu)}(U)$ provide us with exactly g orthogonal vectors (because $g = \sum n_\nu^2$) in the g-dimensional vector space generated by the g group elements via their irreducible representations. Thus the $D_{ij}^{(\nu)}(U)$ $(U \in G)$ are a *complete* set of vectors for this space. Normalizing in the manner required by Eq. (10.45), we may say that the "representation vectors" whose g components are

$$\sqrt{\frac{n_\nu}{g}} D_{ij}^{(\nu)}(U_1), \ \sqrt{\frac{n_\nu}{g}} D_{ij}^{(\nu)}(U_2), \ \cdots, \ \sqrt{\frac{n_\nu}{g}} D_{ij}^{(\nu)}(U_g) \tag{10.60}$$

for $\nu = 1, 2, \cdots, N$; $i, j = 1, 2, \cdots, n_\nu$ form a complete orthonormal set in the g-dimensional complex vector space. Using a cumbersome, but minimal notation we may express this completeness properly as

$$\sum_{\nu=1}^{N} \sum_{i=1}^{n_\nu} \sum_{j=1}^{n_\nu} \sqrt{\frac{n_\nu}{g}} D_{ij}^{(\nu)}(U) \sqrt{\frac{n_\nu}{g}} D_{ij}^{(\nu)*}(U') = \delta_{UU'} ,$$

where $\delta_{UU'}$ is a Kronecker δ-symbol which is equal to 1 if $U = U'$ and is zero otherwise. This may be written more simply as

$$\sum_{\nu=1}^{N} \sum_{i=1}^{n_\nu} \sum_{j=1}^{n_\nu} \frac{n_\nu}{g} D_{ij}^{(\nu)}(U) D_{ij}^{(\nu)*}(U') = \delta_{UU'} . \tag{10.61}$$

Having strengthened the orthogonality properties of the D's in this manner, we are led naturally to conjecture that a similar strengthening can be achieved for the characters. To see that this is indeed the case, let us sum both sides of Eq. (10.61) over all $U \in \mathscr{C}_l$ and all $U' \in \mathscr{C}_m$. We find that

$$\sum_{\nu=1}^{N} \sum_{i=1}^{n_\nu} \sum_{j=1}^{n_\nu} n_\nu \left(\sum_{U \in \mathscr{C}_l} D_{ij}^{(\nu)}(U) \right) \left(\sum_{U' \in \mathscr{C}_m} D_{ij}^{(\nu)*}(U') \right) = g \sum_{U \in \mathscr{C}_l} \sum_{U' \in \mathscr{C}_m} \delta_{UU'} . \tag{10.62}$$

The right-hand side of this equation vanishes unless $\mathscr{C}_l = \mathscr{C}_m$, for otherwise $U \neq U'$. If $\mathscr{C}_l = \mathscr{C}_m$, then each term with $U = U'$ will contribute 1 to the sum and all other terms will contribute zero. There are g_l contributing terms if g_l is the number of elements in $\mathscr{C}_l$, so in the case $\mathscr{C}_l = \mathscr{C}_m$, the right-hand side of Eq. (10.62) equals gg_l. But according to the definition of Eq. (10.35),

$$\sum_{U \in \mathscr{C}_l} D^{(\nu)}(U) = M_l^{(\nu)} .$$

Hence Eq. (10.62) becomes

$$\sum_{\nu=1}^{N} \sum_{i=1}^{n_\nu} \sum_{j=1}^{n_\nu} n_\nu [M_l^{(\nu)}]_{ij} [M_m^{(\nu)}]_{ij} = gg_l \delta_{lm} . \tag{10.63}$$

Now by Eq. (10.38),

$$[M_l^{(\nu)}]_{ij} = \frac{g_l}{n_\nu} \chi_l^{(\nu)} \delta_{ij} , \qquad [M_m^{(\nu)}]_{ij} = \frac{g_m}{n_\nu} \chi_m^{(\nu)} \delta_{ij} ,$$

so Eq. (10.63) reduces to

$$\sum_{\nu=1}^{N} \sum_{i=1}^{n_\nu} \sum_{j=1}^{n_\nu} \frac{1}{n_\nu} \chi_l^{(\nu)} \chi_m^{(\nu)*} \delta_{ij} = \frac{g}{g_m} \delta_{lm} ,$$

where we have made use of the fact that $\delta_{ij}^2 = \delta_{ij}$. Carrying out the sum on i and j, we obtain finally

$$\sum_{\nu=1}^{N} \chi_l^{(\nu)} \chi_m^{(\nu)*} = \frac{g}{g_m} \delta_{lm} . \tag{10.64}$$

Thus if we consider the N constants obtained from the characters of the lth class in each irreducible representation as components of a vector in N-dimensional space, then this vector is orthogonal to the vector obtained in a similar way by using the mth class. Therefore, we have k orthogonal vectors in an N-dimensional space, and we conclude that

$$k \leq N .$$

Combining this result with Eq. (10.50), we get

$$k = N .$$
(10.65)

Hence the number of irreducible representations is equal to the number of classes in the group! Combining Eqs. (10.49) and (10.64), we may say that the "character vectors" whose k elements are

$$\sqrt{\frac{g_1}{g}} \chi_1^{(\nu)}, \sqrt{\frac{g_2}{g}} \chi_2^{(\nu)}, \cdots, \sqrt{\frac{g_k}{g}} \chi_k^{(\nu)}$$
(10.66)

for $\nu = 1, 2, \cdots, N$ form a *complete* orthonormal set in k-dimensional space.

We now summarize all the basic results in their final form:

a) $\sum_{\nu=1}^{N} n_\nu^2 = g ,$ (10.59)

b) $k = N ,$ (10.65)

c) $\sum_{U \in G} \sqrt{\frac{n_\mu}{g}} D_{lk}^{(\mu)*}(U) \sqrt{\frac{n_\nu}{g}} D_{ij}^{(\nu)}(U) = \delta_{il}\delta_{kj}\delta_{\mu\nu} ,$ (10.45)

d) $\sum_{\nu=1}^{N} \sum_{i=1}^{n_\nu} \sum_{j=1}^{n_\nu} \sqrt{\frac{n_\nu}{g}} D_{ij}^{(\nu)}(U) \sqrt{\frac{n_\nu}{g}} D_{ij}^{(\nu)*}(U') = \delta_{UU'} ,$ (10.61)

e) $\sum_{i=1}^{N} \sqrt{\frac{g_i}{g}} \chi_i^{(\mu)*} \sqrt{\frac{g_i}{g}} \chi_i^{(\nu)} = \delta_{\mu\nu} ,$ (10.49)

f) $\sum_{\nu=1}^{N} \sqrt{\frac{g_i}{g}} \chi_i^{(\nu)} \sqrt{\frac{g_j}{g}} \chi_j^{(\nu)*} = \delta_{ij} .$ (10.64)

Here g is the order of the group, g_i is the number of elements in the ith class, k is the number of classes, N is the number of irreducible representations and n_ν is the dimensionality of the νth representation.

With this arsenal at our disposal, we can easily determine the characters and representations of some of the basic finite groups. We start with the simplest group, namely, the one-element group consisting of the identity. Since there is only one class, there is only one representation which is one-dimensional. Thus the problem is solved:

$$D^{(1)}(e) = 1 .$$

Consider now the two element group, $\{e, a\}$. The classes are

$$\mathscr{C}_1 = e , \qquad \mathscr{C}_2 = a ,$$

so there are two representations. Since the group is abelian, these must be one-dimensional. Thus we expect to find

$$\sum_{\nu=1}^{2} n_\nu^2 = 2 .$$

Since $n_\nu = 1$ for both $\nu = 1$ and $\nu = 2$, this relation is obeyed. For one-dimensional representations, the characters are the same as the representations, so we can concentrate on the characters. It is useful to make a table of the form

$$
\begin{array}{c|cc}
{}_\nu\!\diagdown^{\,i} & 1 & 2 \\
\hline
1 & 1 & \alpha \\
\hline
2 & 1 & \beta
\end{array}
\qquad (10.67)
$$

where i labels the class and ν labels the representation. The $i\nu$th element of the square array is just $\chi_i^{(\nu)}$. Since the character of the identity class is equal to the dimensionality of the representation, we have filled in the first column in Eq. (10.67) accordingly (in what follows we shall always label the identity class by $i = 1$). Since in the case of one-dimensional representations the characters are equal to the representation matrices, they must obey the multiplication table of the group. Since $a^2 = e$, we have in this case $\alpha^2 = 1$, $\beta^2 = 1$, $\alpha = \pm 1$, $\beta = \pm 1$. Thus the two distinct representations form the character table

$$
\begin{array}{c|cc}
{}_\nu\!\diagdown^{\,i} & 1 & 2 \\
\hline
1 & 1 & 1 \\
\hline
2 & 1 & -1
\end{array}
\qquad (10.68)
$$

Note that the "character vector" $(1, 1)$ is orthogonal to the "character vector" $(1, -1)$, as it should be according to Eq. (10.49).

The three element group, $\{e, a, a^2\}$ with $a^3 = e$, has three classes

$$
\mathscr{C}_1 = e, \qquad \mathscr{C}_2 = a, \qquad \mathscr{C}_3 = a^2,
$$

and therefore three one-dimensional representations. Note that Eq. (10.59) is satisfied in this case. Using the multiplication table for the group, which says that the square of element two is equal to element three, we can write immediately for the character table

$$
\begin{array}{c|ccc}
{}_\nu\!\diagdown^{\,i} & 1 & 2 & 3 \\
\hline
1 & 1 & \alpha & \alpha^2 \\
\hline
2 & 1 & \beta & \beta^2 \\
\hline
3 & 1 & \gamma & \gamma^2
\end{array}
$$

and $\alpha^3 = \beta^3 = \gamma^3 = 1$. Thus α, β, and γ can take on three possible values, 1, $e^{2\pi i/3}$ and $e^{4\pi i/3}$. The three distinct representations are therefore

ν \ i	1	2	3
1	1	1	1
2	1	ϵ	ϵ^2
3	1	ϵ^2	ϵ

$$(10.69)$$

with $\epsilon = {}^{2\pi i/3}$. The three resulting "character vectors," $(1, 1, 1)$, $(1, \epsilon, \epsilon^2)$ and $(1, \epsilon^2, \epsilon)$ are mutually orthogonal, as the reader may readily verify.

At the fourth order, we find two groups awaiting our attention, the cyclic group of order four and the four-group. For the cyclic group, we shall just remark that by our treatment of the previous three cyclic groups, it should be clear to the reader that the characters of the cyclic group of order n are generated in an obvious way by the n nth roots of unity. Thus the character table for the fourth-order cyclic group looks like

ν \ i	1	2	3	4
1	1	1	1	1
2	1	δ	δ^2	δ^3
3	1	δ^2	1	δ^2
4	1	δ^3	δ^2	δ

where $\delta = e^{2\pi i/4} = i$ and we have used the fact that $\delta^4 = 1$ to simplify the array. The generalization to the cyclic group of order n is obvious.

For the four-group, if we denote the elements as usual by $\{e, a, b, c\}$, then the discussion in Section 10.3 makes it clear that $\{e, a\}$ is an invariant subgroup. The factor group is

$$E = \{e, a\}, \qquad A = \{b, c\}.$$

Thus representations of $\{E, A\}$ [see Eq. (10.68)] can be transferred to the four-group by assigning the representative of E to both e and a and the representative of A to both b and c. The character assignment $\chi(E) = 1$, $\chi(A) = 1$ gives $\chi(e) = 1$, $\chi(a) = 1$, $\chi(b) = 1$ and $\chi(c) = 1$. The assignment $\chi(E) = 1$, $\chi(A) = -1$ gives $\chi(e) = 1$, $\chi(a) = 1$, $\chi(b) = -1$ and $\chi(c) = -1$. Similarly, the invariant subgroup $\{e, b\}$ gives rise to two assignments for the four-group. One of these is the trivial representation (all characters equal unity) which we have already obtained from $\{e, a\}$; the other is $\chi(e) = 1$, $\chi(a) = -1$, $\chi(b) = 1$ and $\chi(c) =$

-1. Finally, the invariant subgroup $\{e, c\}$ gives rise to one new set of characters, $\chi(e) = 1$, $\chi(a) = -1$, $\chi(b) = -1$, and $\chi(c) = 1$. Thus the character table of the four-group looks like

ν \ i	1	2	3	4
1	1	1	1	1
2	1	1	-1	-1
3	1	-1	1	-1
4	1	-1	-1	1

(10.70)

Once again, the orthogonality relations are all satisfied.

Since five is a prime number, the only group of order five is the cyclic group which is dealt with by extension of our discussion of the cyclic group of order four. The same remark applies to the cyclic group of order six, which brings us to S_3, the six-element group of permutations on three objects. This is the smallest nonabelian group. We know that it has three classes,

$$\mathscr{C}_1 = e, \qquad \mathscr{C}_2 = \{(12), (13), (23)\}, \qquad \mathscr{C}_3 = \{(123), (321)\},$$

with corresponding characters χ_1, χ_2, and χ_3. The number of elements in each class is $g_1 = 1$, $g_2 = 3$, and $g_3 = 2$. Since there are three classes, there must be three irreducible representations. Hence by Eq. (10.59)

$$\sum_{\nu=1}^{3} n_\nu^2 = 6.$$

The only way to add three squares to obtain the value six is if $n_1 = 1$, $n_2 = 1$, and $n_3 = 2$. Thus for the first time we will have a two-dimensional representation. Using the facts above, we can start our character table as follows:

ν \ i	1	2	3
1	1	1	1
2	1	a	b
3	2	c	d

We have put in the trivial representation directly and have used the fact that $\chi_1^{(\nu)} = n_\nu$. Now by Eq. (10.49)

$$\sum_{i=1}^{3} g_i \chi_i^{(1)*} \chi_i^{(2)} = 0,$$

that is

$$1 + 3a + 2b = 0 . \tag{10.71}$$

Similarly, from

$$\sum_{i=1}^{3} g_i \chi_i^{(1)*} \chi_i^{(3)} = 0 ,$$

we conclude that

$$3c + 2d + 2 = 0 . \tag{10.72}$$

Using Eqs. (10.71) and (10.72), we simplify the character table to

ν \ i	1	2	3
1	1	1	1
2	1	a	$-\dfrac{3a + 1}{2}$
3	2	c	$-\dfrac{3c + 2}{2}$

We can now use other orthogonality properties of the characters [Eq. (10.61)] to write

$$\sum_{\nu=1}^{3} \chi_1^{(\nu)*} \chi_2^{(\nu)} = 0 ,$$

$$\sum_{\nu=1}^{3} \chi_1^{(\nu)*} \chi_3^{(\nu)} = 0 .$$

These both lead directly to

$$a + 2c + 1 = 0 ,$$

so the character table now contains only one unknown:

ν \ i	1	2	3
1	1	1	1
2	1	$-1 - 2c$	$1 + 3c$
3	2	c	$-1 - \frac{3}{2}c$

A simple way of tying down the value of c is to note that $(123)^3 = e$ and $(123)^2 = (321)$. Therefore in the one-dimensional representation $\chi_3^3 = 1$ and also $\chi_3^2 = \chi_3$, since (123) and (321) both belong to the same class. Thus $\chi_3 = 1$, and this implies that $1 + 3c = 1$, or $c = 0$. The character table now takes its final form:

ν \ i	1	2	3
1	1	1	1
2	1	-1	1
3	2	0	-1

The second irreducible representation is the so-called antisymmetric representation, obtained by representing odd permutations by -1 and even ones by $+1$. It clearly exists for all S_n. The reader should check that the six normalization conditions implied by Eqs. (10.49) and (10.61),

$$\sum_{i=1}^{3} g_i \chi_i^{(\nu)*} \chi_i^{(\nu)} = 6 , \qquad \nu = 1, 2, 3 ,$$

and

$$\sum_{\nu=1}^{3} \chi_i^{(\nu)*} \chi_i^{(\nu)} = 6/g_i , \qquad i = 1, 2, 3 ,$$

are also satisfied. It should be emphasized that this is by no means the fastest way of obtaining the character table for S_3. For example, the fact that $\mathscr{C}_1$ and $\mathscr{C}_3$ combine to form an invariant subgroup whose factor group is isomorphic to $\{e, a\}$ enables one to write the two one-dimensional representations immediately from Eq. (10.68). Then the character vector of the two-dimensional representation is uniquely determined by orthogonality requirements, as the reader can show.

The characters of the two one-dimensional representations are, of course, exactly equal to the corresponding one-dimensional representation matrices:

$$D^{(1)}(U) = 1 ,$$

for all $U \in S_3$, and

$$D^{(2)}(e) = D^{(2)}(123) = D^{(2)}(321) = 1 ,$$
$$D^{(2)}(12) = D^{(2)}(13) = D^{(2)}(23) = -1 .$$

However, the two-dimensional representation requires some additional work to obtain the representative matrices. The identity element is no problem. We have

$$D^{(3)}(e) = \begin{pmatrix} 1 & 0 \\ 0 & 1 \end{pmatrix} . \tag{10.74}$$

As for the matrix $D^{(3)}(12)$, let us choose it to be diagonal, since one can always pick one element of a representation to be diagonal in addition to the unit matrix (why?). Thus

$$D^{(3)}(12) = \begin{pmatrix} a & 0 \\ 0 & b \end{pmatrix}.$$

But $(12) \in \mathscr{C}_2$, so by the character table, $\chi_2^{(3)} = 0$, that is, the trace of $D^{(3)}(12)$ is zero. Hence $b = -a$. Also, since $(12)^2 = e$, we must have $a^2 = 1$. Thus choosing $a = 1$,

$$D^{(3)}(12) = \begin{pmatrix} 1 & 0 \\ 0 & -1 \end{pmatrix}. \tag{10.75}$$

Note that if we had taken $a = -1$, we would have found a different matrix, but one which is related to the matrix of Eq. (10.75) by a similarity transformation. Now what about $D^{(3)}(13)$ and $D^{(3)}(23)$? Clearly, since $(13)^2 = e$,

$$D^{(3)}(13) = D^{(3)}(13)^{-1}. \tag{10.76}$$

But since we need consider only unitary representations,

$$D^{(3)}(13)^\dagger = D^{(3)}(13)^{-1},$$

and combining this with Eq. (10.76), we get

$$D^{(3)}(13) = D^{(3)}(13)^\dagger,$$

that is, $D^{(3)}(13)$ is Hermitian. Similarly, $D^{(3)}(23)$ is Hermitian. Thus, using the fact that the trace of both $D^{(3)}(13)$ and $D^{(3)}(23)$ is zero, we may write in complete generality

$$D^{(3)}(13) = \begin{pmatrix} \alpha & \beta \\ \beta^* & -\alpha \end{pmatrix}, \qquad D^{(3)}(23) = \begin{pmatrix} \gamma & \delta \\ \delta^* & -\gamma \end{pmatrix} \tag{10.77}$$

where α and γ are real. But by Eqs. (10.35) and (10.38),

$$M_2^{(3)} = D^{(3)}(12) + D^{(3)}(13) + D^{(3)}(23) = \frac{g_2}{n_3}\chi_2^{(3)}I = 0,$$

since $\chi_2^{(3)} = 0$. Thus using Eqs. (10.75) and (10.77), we have

$$\begin{pmatrix} 1 + \alpha + \gamma & \beta + \delta \\ \beta^* + \delta^* & -1 - \alpha - \gamma \end{pmatrix} = \begin{pmatrix} 0 & 0 \\ 0 & 0 \end{pmatrix},$$

so that the matrices $D^{(3)}(13)$ and $D^{(3)}(23)$ take the form

$$D^{(3)}(13) = \begin{pmatrix} \alpha & \beta \\ \beta^* & -\alpha \end{pmatrix}, \qquad D^{(3)}(23) = \begin{pmatrix} -(\alpha + 1) & -\beta \\ -\beta^* & (\alpha + 1) \end{pmatrix}.$$

Finally, we use the unitarity conditions:

$$D^{(3)}(13)^\dagger D^{(3)}(13) = \begin{pmatrix} \alpha^2 + |\beta|^2 & 0 \\ 0 & \alpha^2 + |\beta|^2 \end{pmatrix} = \begin{pmatrix} 1 & 0 \\ 0 & 1 \end{pmatrix},$$

$$D^{(3)}(23)^\dagger D^{(3)}(23) = \begin{pmatrix} (\alpha + 1)^2 + |\beta|^2 & 0 \\ 0 & (\alpha + 1)^2 + |\beta|^2 \end{pmatrix} = \begin{pmatrix} 1 & 0 \\ 0 & 1 \end{pmatrix}.$$

These yield the two equations

$$\alpha^2 + |\beta|^2 = 1 , \qquad (\alpha + 1)^2 + |\beta|^2 = 1 ,$$

which are readily solved to give $\alpha = -\frac{1}{2}$, $\beta = (\sqrt{3}/2)e^{i\phi}$, where ϕ is arbitrary. Thus

$$D^{(3)}(13) = \begin{pmatrix} -\frac{1}{2} & \frac{\sqrt{3}}{2}e^{i\phi} \\ \frac{\sqrt{3}}{2}e^{-i\phi} & \frac{1}{2} \end{pmatrix} , \tag{10.78}$$

$$D^{(3)}(23) = \begin{pmatrix} -\frac{1}{2} & -\frac{\sqrt{3}}{2}e^{i\phi} \\ -\frac{\sqrt{3}}{2}e^{-i\phi} & \frac{1}{2} \end{pmatrix} . \tag{10.79}$$

Now $(123) = (13)(12)$, so

$$D^{(3)}(123) = D^{(3)}(13)D^{(3)}(12) = \begin{pmatrix} -\frac{1}{2} & \frac{\sqrt{3}}{2}e^{i\phi} \\ \frac{\sqrt{3}}{2}e^{-i\phi} & \frac{1}{2} \end{pmatrix}\begin{pmatrix} 1 & 0 \\ 0 & -1 \end{pmatrix}$$

$$= \begin{pmatrix} -\frac{1}{2} & -\frac{\sqrt{3}}{2}e^{i\phi} \\ \frac{\sqrt{3}}{2}e^{-i\phi} & -\frac{1}{2} \end{pmatrix} . \tag{10.80}$$

Also, $(321) = (123)^{-1}$, so

$$D^{(3)}(321) = D^{(3)}(123)^{-1} = D^{(3)}(123)^{\dagger} = \begin{pmatrix} -\frac{1}{2} & \frac{\sqrt{3}}{2}e^{i\phi} \\ -\frac{\sqrt{3}}{2}e^{-i\phi} & -\frac{1}{2} \end{pmatrix} , \tag{10.81}$$

which completes the determination of the representative matrices except for ϕ. However, it is always possible, without loss of generality, to choose $\phi = 0$, since a simple multiplication shows that any matrix of the form

$$\begin{pmatrix} a & be^{i\phi} \\ ce^{-i\phi} & d \end{pmatrix}$$

is reduced to the form

$$\begin{pmatrix} a & b \\ c & d \end{pmatrix}$$

when similarity transformed by the unitary matrix

$$\begin{pmatrix} e^{i\phi} & 0 \\ 0 & 1 \end{pmatrix} .$$

This fact, along with Eqs. (10.74), (10.75), (10.78), (10.79), (10.80), and (10.81), enables us to write finally

$$D^{(3)}(e) = \begin{pmatrix} 1 & 0 \\ 0 & 1 \end{pmatrix} , \quad D^{(3)}(12) = \begin{pmatrix} 1 & 0 \\ 0 & -1 \end{pmatrix} , \quad D^{(3)}(13) = \begin{pmatrix} -\frac{1}{2} & \frac{\sqrt{3}}{2} \\ \frac{\sqrt{3}}{2} & \frac{1}{2} \end{pmatrix} ,$$

$$D^{(3)}(23) = \begin{pmatrix} -\frac{1}{2} & -\frac{\sqrt{3}}{2} \\ -\frac{\sqrt{3}}{2} & \frac{1}{2} \end{pmatrix} , \quad D^{(3)}(123) = \begin{pmatrix} -\frac{1}{2} & -\frac{\sqrt{3}}{2} \\ \frac{\sqrt{3}}{2} & -\frac{1}{2} \end{pmatrix} , \tag{10.82}$$

$$D^{(3)}(321) = \begin{pmatrix} -\frac{1}{2} & \frac{\sqrt{3}}{2} \\ -\frac{\sqrt{3}}{2} & -\frac{1}{2} \end{pmatrix} .$$

We have already written these matrices in Eq. (3.5), where we pointed out that they were isomorphic to the group of permutations of three objects. Here we have started with S_3 and relentlessly derived these isomorphic matrices.

It is interesting to note that in this case, when the representation matrices are not all equal to characters, Eq. (10.45) is not equivalent to Eq. (10.49) as it is for purely one-dimensional cases. For example, the $i = 1, j = 1$ element of all the matrices of the two-dimensional representation [see Eq. (10.82)] gives a "representation vector" which is, according to Eq. (10.60),

$$\frac{1}{\sqrt{3}}\left(1,\ 1,\ -\frac{1}{2},\ -\frac{1}{2},\ -\frac{1}{2},\ -\frac{1}{2}\right).$$

On the other hand, the $i = 1, j = 2$ element gives

$$\frac{1}{\sqrt{3}}\left(0,\ 0,\ \frac{\sqrt{3}}{2},\ -\frac{\sqrt{3}}{2},\ -\frac{\sqrt{3}}{2},\ \frac{\sqrt{3}}{2}\right).$$

These two vectors are normalized to unity and are mutually orthogonal, as they should be according to Eq. (10.45). The nontrivial one-dimensional representation gives the "representation vector"

$$\frac{1}{\sqrt{6}}\ (1,\ -1,\ -1,\ -1,\ 1,\ 1)\ ,$$

which is normalized correctly to unity and is orthogonal to each of the two "representation vectors" written above. The reader may want to check the remaining orthonormality relations implied by Eqs. (10.45) and (10.61).

10.8 GROUP THEORY IN PHYSICAL PROBLEMS

Now that we know how to obtain the characters and representations of groups, we can indicate some of the ways in which group theory can be used to increase our understanding of certain basic physical processes.

As a particularly simple illustration of what we have in mind, consider the problem of a quantum-mechanical system which has various eigenstates which are degenerate because of the existence of some symmetry of Schrödinger's equation. As we mentioned in Section 10.4, the collection of eigenfunctions belonging to some degenerate eigenvalue will transform into itself under any transformation belonging to the symmetry group in question. According to Eq. (10.15), if $\mathscr{U} \in \mathscr{G}$, and $U \in G$, then

$$\mathscr{U}\phi_m(\mathbf{r})\ =\ \sum_{m'} D_{m'm}(U)\phi_{m'}(\mathbf{r})\ ,$$

where $D(U)$ $(U \in G)$ is a representation of the group G. Now suppose that we apply to the system a weak perturbation having a smaller symmetry group than the original system. For example, we might have an atom, which in its natural environment in free space is a rotationally invariant system, but which when put in, say, the lattice of a cubic symmetric crystal feels a potential which has the symmetry of the cube. The symmetry of the cube is obviously much smaller than that of complete rotational invariance; in fact, the infinite-element symmetry group of all rotations in three dimensions is replaced by the 24-element symmetry group of the cube (this group is isomorphic to the group, S_4, of permutations on four objects).

When the atom finds itself in this new cubic potential, the energy levels will be modified in such a way that the degenerate eigenvectors belonging to the new energy levels will transform among themselves according to the representations of the group, $\mathcal{O}$, of symmetries of the cube. In other words, a μ-fold degenerate level of the rotationally invariant system must break up into M sets of degenerate levels belonging to $\mathcal{O}$, with multiplicities $\mu_1, \mu_2, \cdots, \mu_M$. Clearly, $\mu_1 + \mu_2 + \cdots + \mu_M = \mu$.

The proper framework for a discussion of these questions is provided by degenerate perturbation theory (Section 4.12). If the reader will look back at that section, he will see that the important objects in the discussion of perturbation theory are the so-called matrix elements of the perturbing operator between states of the unperturbed system. To be precise, let us suppose as in Section 4.12, that A_0 is the linear operator governing the unperturbed system:

$$A_0 \phi_{n,\nu,i} = \lambda_{n,\nu} \, \phi_{n,\nu,i} \, .$$

Here we have chosen the indices to conform to the group theoretical facts which we have learned in this chapter. ν labels the irreducible representation which tells us how the eigenfunction transforms under the symmetry group, G_0, of A_0, and i is the column of the representation to which $\phi_{n,\nu,i}$ belongs. That is, in standard terminology,

$$\mathcal{V} \phi_{n,\nu,i} = \sum_{j=1}^{n_\nu} D_{ji}^{(\nu)}(V) \phi_{n,\nu,j} \; ; \tag{10.83a}$$

V is any element of G_0 ($\mathcal{V}$ is the corresponding element of $\mathcal{G}_0$) and n denotes any additional labels which may be necessary to specify uniquely the eigenvalue under consideration. For example, the νth representation may be of relevance more than once as we run through the entire spectrum of A_0.

We now imagine that the perturbation A_1 is invariant under each element, U, of the symmetry group G_1 and that $\psi_{n,\nu,i}$ is a set of functions which transform according to the νth representation of G_1:

$$\mathcal{U} \psi_{n,\nu,i} = \sum_{j=1}^{n_\nu} D_{ji}^{(\nu)}(U) \psi_{n,\nu,j} \tag{10.83b}$$

where $\mathcal{U} \in \mathcal{G}_1$. We wish to consider matrix elements of the form

$$M_{n,\nu,i;n',\mu,j} \equiv (\psi_{n,\nu,i}, \, A_1 \psi_{n',\mu,j}) \, . \tag{10.84}$$

Since $\mathcal{U}^\dagger \mathcal{U} = \mathcal{U} \mathcal{U}^\dagger = I$, we may write Eq. (10.84) as

$$\begin{aligned}
M_{n,\nu,i;n',\mu,j} &= (\psi_{n,\nu,i}, \, \mathcal{U}^\dagger \mathcal{U} A_1 \mathcal{U}^\dagger \mathcal{U} \psi_{n',\mu,j}) \\
&= (\mathcal{U} \psi_{n,\nu,i}, \, \mathcal{U} A_1 \mathcal{U}^{-1} \mathcal{U} \psi_{n,\mu,j}) \, .
\end{aligned}$$

Using the transformation properties of the $\phi_{n,\nu,i}$ we may write this as

$$M_{n,\nu,i;n',\mu,j} = \left(\sum_{k=1}^{n_\nu} D_{ki}^{(\nu)}(U)\phi_{n,\nu,k}, [\mathcal{U}A_1\mathcal{U}^{-1}] \sum_{l=1}^{n_\mu} D_{lj}^{(\mu)}(U)\phi_{n',\mu,l} \right),$$

or

$$M_{n,\nu,i;\,n',\mu,j} = \sum_{k=1}^{n_\nu} \sum_{l=1}^{n_\mu} D_{ki}^{(\nu)*}(U)D_{lj}^{(\mu)}(U)(\phi_{n,\nu,k}, [\mathcal{U}A_1\mathcal{U}^{-1}]\phi_{n',\mu,l}) . \quad (10.85)$$

But since we have assumed A_1 to be invariant under G_1,

$$\mathcal{U}A_1\mathcal{U}^{-1} = A_1 ,$$

so Eq. (10.85) becomes

$$M_{n,\nu,i;\,n',\mu,j} = \sum_{k=1}^{n_\nu} \sum_{l=1}^{n_\mu} D_{ki}^{(\nu)*}(U)D_{lj}^{(\mu)}(U)(\phi_{n,\nu,k}, A_1\phi_{n',\mu,l}) . \quad (10.86)$$

Now the crucial step is to sum both sides of Eq. (10.86) over all $U \in G_1$, so we will be able to take advantage of the orthogonality relation of Eq. (10.45) on the right-hand side. On the left-hand side, since M does *not* depend on U [see Eq. (10.84)], we get just gM, where g is the order of G_1. Thus

$$gM_{n,\nu,i;\,n',\mu,j} = \sum_{k=1}^{n_\nu} \sum_{l=1}^{n_\mu} \sum_{U \in G_1} D_{ki}^{(\nu)*}(U)D_{lj}^{(\mu)}(U)M_{n,\nu,k;\,n',\mu,l} . \quad (10.87)$$

But the main part of this sum involving the representation elements can be evaluated immediately by using the orthogonality theorem [Eq. (10.45)] which tells us directly that

$$\sum_{U \in G_1} D_{ki}^{(\nu)*}(U)D_{lj}^{(\mu)}(U) = \frac{g}{n_\nu} \delta_{kl}\delta_{ij}\delta_{\mu\nu} .$$

Inserting this into Eq. (10.87), we obtain

$$M_{n,\nu,i;\,n',\mu,j} = \frac{1}{n_\nu} \delta_{\mu\nu}\delta_{ij} \sum_{l=1}^{n_\nu} M_{n,\nu,l;\,n',\nu,l} . \quad (10.88)$$

Thus we see that matrix elements of this type vanish unless the eigenfunctions belong to the same representation and, furthermore, to the same column of this representation. This result can often be helpful in perturbation calculations by severely limiting the number of eigenfunctions which can occur in the perturbation-theory sums [see, e.g., Eq. (4.60)].

On the most elementary level, Eq. (10.88) tells us that a perturbation, A_1, with the *same* symmetry group as the dominant operator, A_0, cannot split degeneracies in first order, since, in computing the matrix of A_1 between the degenerate states belonging to some eigenvalue of A_0, we will find only diagonal elements [$i = j$ in Eq. (10.88)], and all the diagonal elements are equal. Hence by Eq. (4.65b), all the first-order energies will be equal, and there is no splitting of the degeneracy. This is not surprising since if A_1 has the same symmetry as A_0, then the operator $A = A_0 + \epsilon A_1$ will also have the same symmetry as A_0.

Therefore, according to the general arguments of Section 10.4, the degenerate levels of A_0 belonging to some irreducible representation of G_0 can never split since these new levels of A would have a smaller multiplicity than the original level. This in turn would mean that there exist several linear combinations of eigenfunctions of the original degenerate level which transform among themselves under G_0. The original level must therefore give rise to a reducible representation of G_0, contrary to assumption. Thus no splitting can occur.

A more useful application of Eq. (10.88) is found by considering the case where A_1 has a symmetry lower than that of A_0 and where the group G_1, under which A_1 is invariant is a subgroup of the larger group G_0, under which A_0 is invariant. The key fact is that in such a case the representations $D^{(\nu)}(V)$ ($V \in G_0$) of G_0 will give rise to representations of G_1 by associating $D^{(\nu)}(V)$ with the $U \in G_1$ which corresponds to $V \in G_0$. In general, this representation will be reducible. For example, the group $\{e, (12)\}$ is a subgroup of $S_3 = \{e, (12), (13), (23), (123), (321)\}$. Now, in the two-dimensional representation of S_3, e is represented by the unit matrix while (12) is represented by

$$\begin{pmatrix} 1 & 0 \\ 0 & -1 \end{pmatrix}.$$

Thus for the group $\{e, (12)\}$ the representation

$$e \to \begin{pmatrix} 1 & 0 \\ 0 & 1 \end{pmatrix}, \qquad (12) \to \begin{pmatrix} 1 & 0 \\ 0 & -1 \end{pmatrix}$$

is perfectly acceptable, but it is obviously reducible into the sum of two one-dimensional representations. In a more complicated case, where the decomposition is not so obvious, the number of times an *irreducible* representation of G_1 is contained in a representation of G_1 *induced* by G_0 can be calculated simply by knowing the characters of the irreducible representations of G_1 and using Eq. (10.54).

With this point of view clearly in mind, it is easy to see what happens when we split a degeneracy by applying a perturbation A_1, which is invariant under G_1, to a system A_0, which is invariant under G_0. A given degenerate level of A_0 belongs to an *irreducible* representation $D^{(\nu)}$ of G_0, i.e., the eigenfunctions of this level transform among themselves *under the action of G_0* according to $D^{(\nu)}$. However, we can also consider this level as belonging to a *reducible* representation of G_1; that is, certain sets of linear combinations of wave-functions belonging to this level transform into themselves *under the action of G_1*.

We can see this as follows. Suppose $D(V)$ is some *irreducible* representation of G_0. If we restrict ourselves to the subset of V's which are also elements of G_1 and denote a typical element of this subset by U, then $D(U)$ is in general a *reducible* representation of G_1. Therefore there exists some matrix S (independent of U) such that for all $U \in G_1$,

$$S^{-1}D(U)S = D'(U) \qquad \text{or} \qquad D(U) = SD'(U)S^{-1}.$$

$D'(U)$ has the same form as the matrix shown in Eq. (10.19), that is, it has square matrices (*irreducible* representations of G_1) on its diagonal, with all other elements equal to zero. Suppose that $\{f_i\}$ is a set of functions which transform among themselves under G_0 according to the irreducible representation $D(V)$. Then if we restrict our attention to those elements, U, which also belong to G_1, we may write

$$\mathscr{U} f_i = \sum_j D_{ji}(U) f_j$$
$$= \sum_j [SD'(U)S^{-1}]_{ji} f_j$$
$$= \sum_{j,\,k,\,m} S_{jk} D'_{km}(U)[S^{-1}]_{mi} f_j.$$

This last relation can be written as

$$\mathscr{U} \sum_i S_{il} f_i = \sum_{j,\,k} S_{jk} D'_{kl}(U) f_j .$$

If we write

$$g_l = \sum_i S_{il} f_i \qquad \text{then} \qquad \mathscr{U} g_l = \sum_k D'_{kl}(U) g_k .$$

Looking at the form of $D'(U)$ [see Eq. (10.19)] we can pick out by inspection the sets of g's which transform among themselves according to the irreducible representations of G_1 on the diagonal of $D'(U)$.

If we now apply degenerate perturbation theory to the perturbing operator A_1, using the linear combinations of degenerate eigenfunctions appropriate to G_1, then according to Eq. (10.88) there will be no nonzero matrix elements of A_1 which connect different irreducible representations of G_1, and within an irreducible representation of G, the diagonal elements will give the only non-vanishing contributions. These diagonal elements are all equal within a given irreducible representation. Thus the matrix of A_1, calculated between appropriately chosen linear combinations of eigenfunctions belonging to a degenerate level of A_0, might appear as follows:

$$
\begin{pmatrix}
a & & & & & & & & & & & \\
& a & & & & & & & & & & \\
& & a & & & & & & & & & \\
& & & a & & & & \mathbf{O} & & & & \\
& & & & b & & & & & & & \\
& & & & & b & & & & & & \\
& & & & & & b & & & & & \\
& & & & & & & c & & & & \\
& & & & & & & & c & & & \\
& & \mathbf{O} & & & & & & & c & & \\
& & & & & & & & & & c & \\
& & & & & & & & & & & c \\
\end{pmatrix}
$$

In this case, a thirteenfold degenerate level of A_0, belonging to a thirteen-dimensional representation of G_0, has been split into three levels—fourfold, threefold, and sixfold degenerate—belonging to three different irreducible representations of G_1. (The reader should note that we are assuming that a given irreducible representation of G_1 occurs only once in the decomposition. What would the matrix of A_1 look like if some irreducible representation occurred twice?) Of course, one would not often know in advance the correct linear combination of wave-functions, so the above diagonal array would in practice look like a complicated 13×13 matrix, which would take the above form after being similarity transformed (diagonalized). The similarity transform would also give the correct linear combinations of the original wave-functions in the manner explained in Section 4.12.

To illustrate the ideas contained in the above discussion, we consider the example mentioned at the beginning of this section, namely, a rotationally invariant system (an atom in free space) placed in a weak, cubic-symmetric potential (in a crystal with cubic symmetry). Before we can solve the problem, we must first obtain the characters of the irreducible representations in question. Let us take the rotation group first. This is a continuous group, and therefore strictly speaking lies outside the framework developed in the preceding sections. However, if we are interested only in characters, we may proceed as follows. We know from elementary considerations (see Section 5.8) that the $(2l + 1)$ spherical harmonics $Y_{lm}(\theta, \phi)$ $(m = -l, -l+1, \cdots, l-1, l)$ are eigenfunctions of the rotationally invariant operator L^2 and all belong to the single eigenvalue $l(l + 1)$ $(l = 0, 1, 2, \cdots)$. These degenerate functions must therefore transform among themselves according to a representation of the rotation group (which can be shown to be irreducible).

We know that a general rotation can be brought by a unitary transformation to the form of a simple rotation about an axis. Let us call the angle of rotation about this axis Φ. Since all rotations through an angle Φ are unitarily equivalent, such rotations form a class which can be labeled by Φ. To obtain the character of such a class, we need consider only a simple rotation through Φ about the z-axis. Such a rotation takes $Y_{lm}(\theta, \phi)$ into $e^{im\Phi} Y_{lm}(\theta, \phi)$ (see Section 5.8). Thus the matrix representing this rotation will be

$$\begin{pmatrix} e^{-il\Phi} & & & & & & O \\ & e^{-i(l-1)\Phi} & & & & & \\ & & \cdot & & & & \\ & & & \cdot & & & \\ & & & & e^{i(l-1)\Phi} & & \\ O & & & & & e^{il\Phi} \end{pmatrix}$$

The trace is readily computed; we find that

$$\chi^{(l)}(\Phi) = \sum_{m=-l}^{l} e^{im\Phi} = \frac{\sin (l + \frac{1}{2})\Phi}{\sin (\frac{\Phi}{2})}, \qquad (10.89)$$

where we have evaluated the sum by using the formula for summing a geometric series. Note that the dimension, n_l, of the lth representation is

$$\lim_{\Phi \to 0} \frac{\sin\,(l + \frac{1}{2})\Phi}{\sin\,(\frac{\Phi}{2})} = 2l + 1 ,$$

as we should expect since $\Phi = 0$ corresponds to the identity transformation. When $l = 0$, we find the trivial one-dimensional transformation in which every rotation is represented by 1. When $l = 1$, we obtain the three-dimensional representation which should be familiar from classical mechanics; it is given, as a function of the Euler angles, by Eq. (1.25).

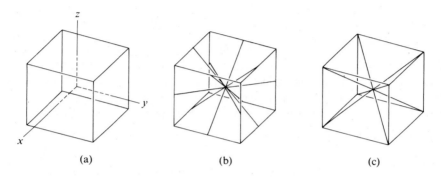

Fig. 10.2 The axes of symmetry of a cube.

Having found the class characters for all the representations of the group of three-dimensional rotations, let us now move to more familiar ground and find the representations and characters of the group $\mathscr{O}$ of symmetries of the cube. This group contains 24 elements in five classes, being isomorphic to S_4. The class $\mathscr{C}_1$ is the identity class. Figure 10.2(a) shows the axes of rotation which are relevant for the classes $\mathscr{C}_2$ and $\mathscr{C}_4$. $\mathscr{C}_2$ consists of the six rotations through $\pm\pi/2$ radians about each of the x, y, and z axes; the class $\mathscr{C}_4$ consists of the three elements corresponding to rotation through π radians about the x-, y-, and z-axes. Figure 10.2(b) shows the axes relevant to the class $\mathscr{C}_5$, which consists of rotations through π radians about each of these six axes. Finally, the class $\mathscr{C}_3$ consists of rotations through $\pm 2\pi/3$ radians about each of the four axes shown in Fig. 10.2(c). We have labeled these classes in this particular manner so they will correspond to the class assignments for S_4 given in Section 10.3. Just as with S_4, the classes $\mathscr{C}_1$ and $\mathscr{C}_4$ combine together to give an invariant subgroup V, the factor group of which is isomorphic to S_3. Thus, in the manner illustrated in the previous section, we can lift representations of S_3 onto S_4 (and hence onto $\mathscr{O}$). Since $\mathscr{O}$ has 24 elements and five classes, we must have

$$n_1^2 + n_2^2 + n_3^2 + n_4^2 + n_5^2 = 24 ,$$

where n_ν is the dimension of the νth representation. The only possible collection of n_ν which can satisfy this relation is $n_1 = 1$, $n_2 = 1$, $n_3 = 2$, $n_4 = 3$, and $n_5 = 3$.

According to our previous remarks, the first, second, and third representations (with $n_1 = 1$, $n_2 = 1$, and $n_3 = 2$) will correspond to those of $S_3 = S_4/V$. Thus, in usual manner, we can fill in a large part of the character table for $\mathscr{O}$:

ν \ i	1	2	3	4	5
1	1	1	1	1	1
2	1	-1	1	1	-1
3	2	0	-1	2	0
4	3	a	b	c	d
5	3	α	β	γ	δ

$$(10.90)$$

Since $g_1 = 1$, $g_2 = 6$, $g_3 = 8$, $g_4 = 3$, and $g_5 = 6$, we can use Eq. (10.49) to obtain

$$6a + 8b + 3c + 6d = -3,$$
$$-6a + 8b + 3c - 6d = -3,$$
$$-8b + 6c = -6.$$

The equations for α, β, γ, and δ are identical to the above three. These equations are readily solved to give $b = 0$, $c = -1$, $d = -a$; similarly $\beta = 0$, $\gamma = -1$, $\delta = -\alpha$. Thus Table (10.90) becomes

ν \ i	1	2	3	4	5
1	1	1	1	1	1
2	1	-1	1	1	-1
3	2	0	-1	2	0
4	3	a	0	-1	$-a$
5	3	α	0	-1	$-\alpha$

The normalization condition implied by Eq. (10.49) gives $a^2 = 1 = \alpha^2$, that is, $a = \pm 1$ and $\alpha = \pm 1$. The two distinct choices are $a = 1$, $\alpha = -1$ or $a =$

-1, $\alpha = 1$. These lead to the same character table except for an interchange of the last two rows. Thus the character table takes its final form:

ν \\ i	1	2	3	4	5
1	1	1	1	1	1
2	1	-1	1	1	-1
3	2	0	-1	2	0
4	3	1	0	-1	-1
5	3	-1	0	-1	1

$$(10.91)$$

In this case, the representation matrices can also be readily obtained. For the first three representations, the matrices are just those previously obtained for S_3. The three-dimensional representations are obtained in a simple manner from the three-dimensional representation of the rotation group. Since we will not need these matrices here, we will omit a detailed analysis of them.

With all the routine work out of the way, we can see what happens when a rotationally invariant atomic system is put into a weak cubic-symmetric environment. First, we note that the various representations of the rotation group induce representations of $\mathcal{O}$. Consider, for example, the $l = 1$ representation of the rotation group. The classes of the cubic group correspond to the following angles of rotations (in radians):

$$\mathscr{C}_1 \to 0, \quad \mathscr{C}_2 \to \pm\pi/2, \quad \mathscr{C}_3 \to \pm 2\pi/3, \quad \mathscr{C}_4 \to \pi, \quad \mathscr{C}_5 \to \pi.$$

The characters corresponding to these rotations are obtained from Eq. (10.89). We find that

$$\chi_1 = 3, \quad \chi_2 = 1, \quad \chi_3 = 0, \quad \chi_4 = -1, \quad \chi_5 = -1.$$

By looking at the character table of $\mathcal{O}$ [Table (10.91)], we see that this has given us an *irreducible* representation of $\mathcal{O}$, corresponding to the fourth row of the character table. Thus an eigenvalue of the rotationally invariant system belonging to the $l = 1$ representation of the rotation group will not be split when subjected to a perturbation of cubic symmetry.

Moving to the $l = 2$ representation and using Eq. (10.89), we find that

$$\chi_1 = 5, \quad \chi_2 = -1, \quad \chi_3 = -1, \quad \chi_4 = 1, \quad \chi_5 = 1$$

for the characters of the representation of $\mathcal{O}$ induced by the rotation group. Now, to determine the number of times a given *irreducible* representation of $\mathcal{O}$

is contained in this reducible representation, we use Eq. (10.54). We find that

$$a^{(1)} = \frac{1}{24} \sum_{i=1}^{5} g_i \chi_i^{(1)} \chi_i = \frac{1}{24}[5 - 6 - 8 + 3 + 6] = 0 ,$$

$$a^{(2)} = \frac{1}{24} \sum_{i=1}^{5} g_i \chi_i^{(2)} \chi_i = \frac{1}{24}[5 + 6 - 8 + 3 - 6] = 0 ,$$

$$a^{(3)} = \frac{1}{24} \sum_{i=1}^{5} g_i \chi_i^{(3)} \chi_i = \frac{1}{24}[10 + 0 + 8 + 6 + 0] = 1 ,$$

$$a^{(4)} = \frac{1}{24} \sum_{i=1}^{5} g_i \chi_i^{(4)} \chi_i = \frac{1}{24}[15 - 6 + 0 - 3 - 6] = 0 ,$$

$$a^{(5)} = \frac{1}{24} \sum_{i=1}^{5} g_i \chi_i^{(5)} \chi_i = \frac{1}{24}[15 + 6 + 0 - 3 + 6] = 1 .$$

Thus the third and fifth *irreducible* representations of $\mathcal{O}$ occur in the *reducible* representation induced by the $l = 2$ representation of the rotation group. Therefore the fivefold degenerate state corresponding to an $l = 2$ representation of the rotation group will split in a cubic symmetric field into a twofold degenerate state and a threefold degenerate state.

The lifting of degeneracy in the problem follows *completely* from the symmetry of the problem without any knowledge of the explicit form of the interactions! Such effects have been verified in innumerable experiments on the spectra of atoms in solids, providing one of the most beautiful examples of the power of group theoretical techniques in physics. In recent years, similar group theoretical methods have been used in elementary particle physics to obtain information about the relationship between the masses of various elementary particles, using only certain assumptions about the symmetry of the "unperturbed" elementary particle Hamiltonian and about the nature of the perturbation term which breaks the symmetry.

As a final illustration of the utility of group theoretical techniques in physics, we shall modify Eq. (10.85) slightly to obtain an interesting result concerning the transitions between quantum-mechanical states. We have already considered the case where A_1 is invariant under all $\mathcal{U} \in \mathcal{G}_1$. Suppose now that A_1 transforms under $\mathcal{G}_1$ according to some irreducible representation of $\mathcal{G}_1$. This would be the case if A_1 were one of a collection of operators, which we might write as $\{A_1^{(\lambda, m)}, m = 1, 2, \cdots, n_\lambda\}$, where λ indicates the irreducible representation under which the set of $A_1^{(\lambda, m)}$ transform; i.e.,

$$\mathcal{U} A_1^{(\lambda, m)} \mathcal{U}^{-1} = \sum_{m'=1}^{n_\lambda} D_{m'm}^{(\lambda)}(U) A_1^{(\lambda, m')} .$$

Thus we would rewrite Eq. (10.85) as

$$M_{n,\nu,i;\, n',\mu,j}^{(\lambda, m)} = \sum_{k=1}^{n_\nu} \sum_{l=1}^{n_\mu} \sum_{m'=1}^{n_\lambda} D_{ki}^{(\nu)*}(U) D_{lj}^{(\mu)}(U) D_{m'm}^{(\lambda)}(U) (\phi_{n,\nu,k}, A_1^{(\lambda, m')} \phi_{n',\mu,l}) , \quad (10.92)$$

where we have defined

$$M^{(\lambda,m)}_{n,\nu,i;\,n',\mu,j} \equiv (\phi_{n,\nu,i},\, A^{(\lambda,m)}_1 \phi_{n',\mu,j}) \; .$$

Thus Eq. (10.92) takes the form

$$M^{(\lambda,m)}_{n,\nu,i;\,n',\mu,j} = \sum_{k=1}^{n_\nu} \sum_{l=1}^{n_\mu} \sum_{m'=1}^{n_\lambda} D^{(\nu)}_{ki}{}^*(U) D^{(\mu)}_{lj}(U) D^{(\lambda)}_{m'm}(U) M^{(\lambda,m')}_{n,\nu,k;\,n',\mu,l} \; . \qquad (10.93)$$

What can we say about the product $D^{(\mu)}_{lj}(U) D^{(\lambda)}_{m'm}(U)$? According to Eq. (3.60) this is equal to the lm', jm-element of the direct product of $D^{(\mu)}$ and $D^{(\lambda)}$:

$$[D^{(\mu)}(U) \otimes D^{(\lambda)}(U)]_{lm',jm} = D^{(\mu)}_{lj}(U) D^{(\lambda)}_{m'm}(U) \; .$$

Thus Eq. (10.93) becomes

$$M^{(\lambda,m)}_{n,\nu,i;\,n',\mu,j} = \sum_{k=1}^{n_\nu} \sum_{l=1}^{n_\mu} \sum_{m'=1}^{n_\lambda} D^{(\nu)}_{ki}{}^*(U)[D^{(\mu)}(U) \otimes D^{(\lambda)}(U)]_{lm',jm} M^{(\lambda,m')}_{n,\nu,k;\,n',\mu,l} \; .$$

$$(10.94)$$

Now since the direct product of two representations is again a representation, the quantity in square brackets in Eq. (10.94) will be a representation matrix element, but even though $D^{(\lambda)}$ and $D^{(\mu)}$ are *irreducible*, their direct product will usually be *reducible*. The number of times that an irreducible representation of G occurs in the direct product is easily determined [by Eq. (10.54)] if we know the characters of the irreducible representations, since the character of U corresponding to $D^{(\mu)}(U) \otimes D^{(\lambda)}(U)$ is just $\chi(U) = \chi^{(\mu)}(U)\chi^{(\lambda)}(U)$, according to Eq. (3.61). Let us label the irreducible representations occurring in $D^{(\mu)} \otimes D^{(\lambda)}$ by the elements ρ, of a set $R_{\lambda\mu}$ of integers. Then we can write

$$[D^{(\mu)}(U) \otimes D^{(\lambda)}(U)]_{lm',jm} = \sum_{\rho \in R_{\lambda\mu}} \sum_{\sigma,\tau=1}^{n_\rho} a^{(\lambda\mu\rho)}_{lm',jm;\,\sigma\tau} D^{(\rho)}_{\sigma\tau}(U) \; . \qquad (10.95)$$

Putting Eq. (10.95) into Eq. (10.94) and, as before, summing both sides of Eq. (10.94) over all $U \in G$, we find that

$$M^{(\lambda,m)}_{n,\nu,i;\,n',\mu,j} = \frac{1}{n_\nu} \sum_{\rho \in R_{\mu\lambda}} \delta_{\nu\rho} \sum_{k,l,m'} a^{(\lambda\mu\nu)}_{lm',jm;\,ik} M^{(\lambda,m')}_{n,\nu,k;\,n',\mu,l} \; . \qquad (10.96)$$

Without any further work, we can see that unless $\nu \in R_{\lambda\mu}$ the expression in Eq. (10.96) vanishes. In other words, unless the direct product of $D^{(\lambda)}$ and $D^{(\mu)}$ contains the irreducible representation $D^{(\nu)}$, the quantity $M^{(\lambda,m)}_{n,\nu,i,n',\mu,j}$ must equal zero for any choice of i, j, and m.

The usefulness of this result can most easily be seen by considering the rate of transitions between two quantum-mechanical states of a system which is invariant under some symmetry group. Suppose the levels belong respectively to the νth and μth representations of the symmetry group. It is known from quantum mechanics that if A_1 is the operator which induces the transition, then the transition rate is proportional to

$$|(\phi_{n,\nu,i},\, A_1 \phi_{n',\mu,j})|^2 \; ,$$

where we label the wave functions in the usual manner. If A_1 transforms according to some representation λ of the symmetry group in question, we see that unless the νth representation is contained in the direct product of the μth representation times the λth representation, the transition cannot occur. This restriction follows purely from the symmetry of the problem.

The theory of selection rules of quantum mechanics follow from these considerations. For example, a rotationally invariant atomic (or nuclear) system has energy levels which, as we have seen, can be classified according to the irreducible representations of the rotation group. Now the operator which induces electric dipole transitions between atomic levels is proportional to the electronic position vector $\mathbf{r}$ which transforms according to the $l = 1$ representation of the rotation group, as we saw in Chapter 1. Thus for a transition to take place from a level labeled by l to a level labeled by l', the l' representation of the rotation group must occur in the direct product of the l-representation times the 1-representation. The study of the decomposition of the direct product of representations is thus very important for the applications of group theory to physics, since such a study leads to a direct determination of the selection rules which play a central role in atomic, nuclear, and elementary particle physics.

PROBLEMS

1. Consider the plane of Fig. 10.3, where the objects at A, B, and C are fixed to the circular loop. This figure is clearly invariant under rotation through 120° and 240° and under reflection through the lines a, b, and c. Show that these five operations plus the identity form a group. Write out the group multiplication table. What are the classes into which the various group elements fall?

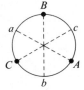

Fig. 10.3

2. Consider the group built up from the unit matrix and the Pauli spin matrices. The elements of this group are $\pm I$, $\pm i\sigma_x$, $\pm i\sigma_y$, and $\pm i\sigma_z$, where

$$\sigma_x = \begin{pmatrix} 0 & 1 \\ 1 & 0 \end{pmatrix}, \qquad \sigma_y = \begin{pmatrix} 0 & -i \\ i & 0 \end{pmatrix}, \qquad \sigma_z = \begin{pmatrix} 1 & 0 \\ 0 & -1 \end{pmatrix}.$$

What is the multiplication table? Find all subgroups and classes. Are there any invariant subgroups?

3. Find the symmetry group, including only rotations, of a square, rectangular parallelepiped (i.e., square on the top and bottom and rectangular on the sides). Show that this group is isomorphic to the symmetry group of the square which

includes both rotations and reflection. What are the classes? Show that there is an invariant subgroup. Find the factor group associated with this invariant subgroup.

4. Determine all the elements of the group of rotational symmetries of the regular tetrahedron (i.e., a tetrahedron whose sides are equilateral triangles). Put these elements into the classes to which they belong. Find all the subgroups. Are there any invariant subgroups?

5. Consider an arbitrary group, G, with a subgroup, H. Show that if H is of index two, then H is invariant. Remember that the index of a subgroup is the ratio of the order of the group to the order of the subgroup.

6. Find the subgroup of S_5 to which the cyclic group of order five is isomorphic. Demonstrate the isomorphism explicitly by performing all the relevant multiplications of the elements of S_5.

7. Let $(123\cdots l)$ be a cycle of length l. Prove that if $\lambda < l$ then $(123\cdots l)^\lambda \neq e$, while $(123\cdots l)^l = e$.

8. Let G and G' be two groups. Show that in a homomorphism of G onto G' the elements of G which are mapped into the identity of G' form an invariant subgroup, H, of G.

9. Show that the group G' of the previous problem is isomorphic to the factor group G/H, where H is as defined in the previous problem.

10. a) By direct calculation, show that

$$\nabla^2 = \frac{\partial^2}{\partial x^2} + \frac{\partial^2}{\partial y^2} + \frac{\partial^2}{\partial z^2}$$

is invariant under rotation through the Euler angles α, β and γ. To refresh your memory about Euler angles, see Section 1.4.

[*Hint*: Note that the most general rotation is built up from three simpler rotations.]

b) Determine how the three components of the quantum mechanical angular momentum [see Eqs. (5.86)] transform under the group of rotations about the z-axis.

11. Show that the set $P_n = [1, x, x^2, \cdots, x^{n-1}]$ transforms into itself under the action of the translation group in one dimension. Denoting a translation through a distance a by T_a (that is, $T_a x = x - a$) find the n-dimensional representation of the group of all one-dimensional translations which is provided by the set of functions P_n. Is this representation equivalent to a unitary representation? Show explicitly for the case of the three-dimensional representation that $T_a T_b = T_{a+b}$.

12. Show that the following three sets of functions, $[\cos 3\theta]$, $[\sin 3\theta]$ and $[\cos 4\theta, \sin 4\theta]$, transform among themselves under the elements of the group discussed in Problem 10.1. What are the representations and characters which are obtained from these three sets of functions? Are they irreducible representations? What can you say about the representation provided by $[\cos 5\theta, \sin 5\theta]$?

13. Show that if C_i is a class containing $S_1, S_2, \cdots, S_{g_i}$ and $C_{i'}$ is the collection of elements consisting of $S_1^{-1}, S_2^{-1}, \cdots, S_{g_i}^{-1}$, then $C_{i'}$ is also a class. Show that for a general irreducible representation, i.e., one which is not necessarily unitary,

$$\sum_i g_i \chi_i^{(\mu)} \chi_{i'}^{(\nu)} = g\delta_{\mu\nu}, \qquad a_\mu = \frac{1}{g}\sum_i g_i \chi_i \chi_i^{(\mu)},$$

where a_μ is the number of times the μth irreducible representation occurs in the representation (not necessarily irreducible) whose characters are χ_i.

14. Show that any 2×2 matrix which commutes with the three Pauli matrices given in Problem 10.2 must be a multiple of the unit matrix.

    [*Hint*: Show that any 2×2 matrix can be written as a linear combination of the unit matrix and the Pauli matrices.]

15. Show that the most general 2×2 unitary matrix whose eigenvalues are 1 and -1 can be written as

$$U = \begin{pmatrix} \cos \theta & \sin \theta e^{i\phi} \\ \sin \theta e^{-i\phi} & -\cos \theta \end{pmatrix}.$$

16. Find the characters and irreducible representations of the group discussed in Problem 10.3.

    [*Hint*: For the two-dimensional representation, the result of Problem 10.15 may be useful.]

17. Using the three-dimensional representation of the rotation group, given, for example, by Eq. (1.25), find the matrices for a three-dimensional representation of the symmetry group, $\mathcal{O}$, of the cube. We saw in Section 10.8 that there were *two* three-dimensional representations of $\mathcal{O}$. Give a simple prescription for finding the matrices belonging to the second three-dimensional representation (i.e., the one not given by the rotation group).

18. Using the results of Problem 10.4, find the characters and representations of the group of rotational symmetries of the regular tetrahedron.

19. Suppose that we have a linear operator with cubic symmetry, and we apply a small perturbation having the symmetry of a rectangular parallelepiped. Making use of the results of Problem 10.16 and the work of Section 10.8, find how the various possible degenerate states of cubic symmetry break up when this perturbation is applied.

20. Consider a linear operator, A_0, with rotational symmetry. Suppose that a small perturbation having the symmetry of a regular tetrahedron is applied. Using the results of Problem 10.18 and of Section 10.8, find how the four states of A_0 with the lowest degeneracies (onefold, threefold, fivefold, and sevenfold) break up when this perturbation is applied.

21. Consider all possible representations of the cubic group, $\mathcal{O}$, formed by taking the direct product of the various irreducible representations of $\mathcal{O}$. Find out how many times the irreducible representations of $\mathcal{O}$ occur in these product representations.

22. In quantum mechanics one defines an electron spin wave function using α for spin "up" and β for spin "down"; α and β are orthonormal. For a system of three electrons we can form product wave functions of the form $\alpha(1)\alpha(2)\alpha(3)$, $\alpha(1)\alpha(2)\beta(3)$, etc., there being $2^3 = 8$ such products. Clearly, these eight functions transform among themselves under the action of the elements of S_3, and they are mutually orthogonal. They therefore form a set of basis functions for a representation of S_3. Find how many times the various irreducible representations of S_3 occur in this representation. Is any representation missing? Why? Can you relate some of the objects you're dealing with to physics?

23. Suppose that all the eight product spin functions of the previous problem are degenerate eigenfunctions of some linear operator, A_0. Let A_0 be perturbed by an operator of the form $A_1 = AP_{12} + BP_{13} + CP_{23}$, where P_{ij} transforms coordinate i into coordinate j and vice versa. For example,

$$P_{12}\alpha(1)\beta(2)\alpha(3) = \alpha(2)\beta(1)\alpha(3) \;.$$

Show that the matrix which must be diagonalized to obtain the first-order corrections to the eigenvalue of A_0 to which the product functions belong can be written in the form

$$\begin{bmatrix} E & 0 & 0 & 0 & 0 & 0 & 0 & 0 \\ 0 & E & 0 & 0 & 0 & 0 & 0 & 0 \\ 0 & 0 & E & 0 & 0 & 0 & 0 & 0 \\ 0 & 0 & 0 & E & 0 & 0 & 0 & 0 \\ 0 & 0 & 0 & 0 & E_{11} & E_{12} & 0 & 0 \\ 0 & 0 & 0 & 0 & E_{12} & E_{22} & 0 & 0 \\ 0 & 0 & 0 & 0 & 0 & 0 & E_{11} & E_{12} \\ 0 & 0 & 0 & 0 & 0 & 0 & E_{12} & E_{22} \end{bmatrix} ,$$

where $E = A + B + C$, $E_{11} = A - (B + C)/2$, $E_{12} = \sqrt{3}(B - C)/2$ and $E_{22} = -E_{11}$, if we use the representation of S_3 given in Section 10.7.

24. If in the previous problem we had used a different (but unitarily equivalent) two-dimensional representation of S_3, we would have found different values for E_{11}, E_{12}, and E_{22}. Would the eigenvalues of the matrix of Problem 10.23 be different? Why?

FURTHER READINGS

Dixon, J. D., *Problems in Group Theory*. Waltham, Mass.: Blaisdell, 1967. Contains solutions.

Ledermann, W., *The Theory of Finite Groups*. New York: Interscience, 1964.

Hamermesh, M., *Group Theory*. Reading, Mass.: Addison-Wesley, 1962.

Tinkham, M., *Group Theory and Quantum Mechanics*. New York: McGraw-Hill, 1964.

Weyl, H., *Theory of Groups and Quantum Mechanics*. London: Methuen, 1931

Wigner, E. P., *Group Theory*. New York: Academic Press, 1959.

GENERAL BIBLIOGRAPHY

GENERAL BIBLIOGRAPHY

MATHEMATICAL METHODS OF PHYSICS

COURANT, R., and D. HILBERT, *Methods of Mathematical Physics* (2 Volumes). New York: Wiley-Interscience, 1961.

DETTMAN, J. W., *Mathematical Methods in Physics and Engineering*. New York: McGraw-Hill, 1962.

IRVING, J., and N. MULLINEUX, *Mathematics in Physics and Engineering*. New York: Academic Press, 1959.

MARGENAU, H., and G. M. MURPHY, *The Mathematics of Physics and Chemistry*. Princeton, N. J.: D. Van Nostrand, 1961.

MATHEWS, J., and R. L. WALKER, *Mathematical Methods of Physics*. New York: W. A. Benjamin, 1964.

MORSE, P. M., and H. FESHBACK, *Methods of Theoretical Physics* (2 Volumes). New York: McGraw-Hill, 1953.

SAGAN, H., *Boundary and Eigenvalue Problems in Mathematical Physics*. New York: Wiley, 1961.

SCHWARTZ, L., *Mathematics for the Physical Sciences*. Reading, Mass.: Addison-Wesley, 1966.

WHITTAKER, E. T., and G. N. WATSON, *A Course of Modern Analysis*. New York: Cambridge University Press, 1958.

WILF, H. S., *Mathematics for the Physical Sciences*. New York: Wiley, 1962.

WYLIE, C., *Advanced Engineering Mathematics*, Second edition. New York: McGraw-Hill, 1960.

MATHEMATICS BOOKS

APOSTOL, T. M., *Mathematical Analysis*. Reading, Mass.: Addison-Wesley, 1957.

BERBERIAN, S. K., *Introduction to Hilbert Space*. New York: Oxford University Press, 1961.

DUNFORD, N., and J. T. SCHWARTZ, *Linear Operators*, Part I, II. New York: Wiley-Interscience, 1966.

HALMOS, P. R., *Introduction to Hilbert Space*. New York: Chelsea, 1951.

KOLMOGOROV, A. N., and S. V. FOMIN, *Functional Analysis*, Volumes I, II. Groyloch, 1957.

RAINVILLE, E., *Special Functions*. New York: Macmillan, 1960.

RIESZ, F., and B. SZ. NAGY, *Functional Analysis*. New York: Ungar, 1955.

RUDIN, W., *Principles of Mathematical Analysis*, Second edition. New York: McGraw-Hill, 1964.

SAKS, S., and A. ZYGMUND, *Analytic Functions*. New York: Hafner, 1952.

SEELEY, R., *An Introduction to Fourier Series and Integrals*. New York: W. A. Benjamin, 1966.

SNEDDON, I. N., *Fourier Transforms*. New York: McGraw-Hill, 1951.

TITCHMARSH, E. C., *The Theory of Functions*. New York: Oxford University Press, 1939.

WATSON, G. N., *A Treatise on the Theory of Bessel Functions*, Second edition. New York: Cambridge University Press, 1944.

WIDDER, D. V., *Advanced Calculus*, Second edition. Englewood Cliffs, N. J.: Prentice Hall, 1961.

BOOKS OF SOLVED PROBLEMS IN MATHEMATICAL PHYSICS

CHOQUET-BRUHAT, Y., *Problems and Solutions in Mathematical Physics*. San Francisco: Holden-Day. 1967.

LEBEDEV, N. N., I. P. SKOLSKAYA, and Y. S. UFLYAND, *Problems of Mathematical Physics*. Englewood Cliffs, N. J.: Prentice Hall, 1965.

MISYURKEYEV, I. V., *Problems in Mathematical Physics with Solutions*. New York: McGraw-Hill, 1966.

USEFUL MATHEMATICAL TABLES

BATEMAN, H., *Higher Transcendental Functions* (3 Volumes), based in part on notes left by H. Bateman and compiled by the staff of the Bateman Manuscript Project. New York: McGraw-Hill, 1953–1955.

BIERENS DE HAAN, D., *Nouvelles Tables d'Integrales Definies*, Edition of 1867, corrected, with an English translation of the introduction by J. F. Ritt. New York: Hafner, 1957.

FLETCHER, A., J. C. P. MILLER, L. ROSENHEAD, and L. J. COMRIE, *An Index of Mathematical Tables* (2 Volumes). Reading, Mass.: Addison-Wesley, 1962.

JAHNKE-EMDE-LOSCH, *Tables of Higher Functions*. Sixth edition. New York: McGraw-Hill, 1960.

JOLLEY, L. B. W., *Summation of Series*, Second edition. New York: Dover Publications, 1961.

MAGNUS, W., and F. OBERHETTINGER, *Formulas and Theorems for the Special Functions of Mathematical Physics*, translated from the German by John Wermer. New York: Chelsea, 1949.

MARCUS, M., *Basic Theorems in Matrix Theory*, Applied Mathematics Series, Pamphlet No. 57, U. S. Department of Commerce.

INDEX

INDEX